Advances in

ORGANOMETALLIC CHEMISTRY

VOLUME 9

CONTRIBUTORS TO THIS VOLUME

G. E. Coates

R. S. P. Coutts

Henry Gysling

M. F. Lappert

G. L. Morgan

J. S. Poland

Eugene G. Rochow

Hubert Schmidbaur

Minoru Tsutsui

P. C. Wailes

J. J. Zuckerman

Advances in ORGANOMETALLIC CHEMISTRY

EDITED BY

F. G. A. STONE

DEPARTMENT OF INORGANIC CHEMISTRY
SCHOOL OF CHEMISTRY
THE UNIVERSITY
BRISTOL, ENGLAND

ROBERT WEST

DEPARTMENT OF CHEMISTRY
UNIVERSITY OF WISCONSIN
MADISON, WISCONSIN

VOLUME 9

1970

ACADEMIC PRESS New York · London

ACADEMIC PRESS, INC.
111 Fifth Avenue, New York, New York 10003

United Kingdom Edition published by
ACADEMIC PRESS, INC. (LONDON) LTD.
Berkeley Square House, London W1X 6BA

LIBRARY OF CONGRESS CATALOG CARD NUMBER: 64-16030

PRINTED IN THE UNITED STATES OF AMERICA

Contents

Of Time and Carbon–Metal Bonds

EUGENE G. ROCHOW

Applications of ^{119m}Sn Mössbauer Spectroscopy to the Study of Organotin Compounds

J. J. ZUCKERMAN

Organic Complexes of Lower-Valent Titanium

R. S. P. COUTTS and P. C. WAILES

Organoberyllium Compounds

G. E. COATES and G. L. MORGAN

Isoelectronic Species in the Organophosphorus, Organosilicon, and Organoaluminum Series

HUBERT SCHMIDBAUR

Organolanthanides and Organoactinides

HENRY GYSLING and MINORU TSUTSUI

α-Heterodiazoalkanes and the Reactions of Diazoalkanes with Derivatives of Metals and Metalloids

M. F. LAPPERT and J. S. POLAND

List of Contributors

Numbers in parentheses indicate the pages on which the authors' contributions begin.

G. E. Coates (195), *Chemistry Department, University of Wyoming, Laramie, Wyoming*

R. S. P. Coutts (135), *Division of Applied Chemistry, C.S.I.R.O., Melbourne, Australia*

Henry Gysling (361), *Department of Inorganic Chemistry, University of Newcastle upon Tyne, Newcastle, England*

M. F. Lappert (397), *School of Molecular Sciences, University of Sussex, Brighton, England*

G. L. Morgan (195), *Chemistry Department, University of Wyoming, Laramie, Wyoming*

J. S. Poland (397), *School of Molecular Sciences, University of Sussex, Brighton, England*

Eugene G. Rochow (1), *Harvard University, Cambridge, Massachusetts*

Hubert Schmidbaur (259), *Institut für Anorganische Chemie, Universität Würzburg, Würzburg, Germany*

Minoru Tsutsui (361), *Department of Chemistry, Texas A & M University, College Station, Texas*

P. C. Wailes (135), *Division of Applied Chemistry, C.S.I.R.O., Melbourne, Australia*

J. J. Zuckerman (21), *Department of Chemistry, State University of New York at Albany, Albany, New York*

Of Time and Carbon-Metal Bonds

EUGENE G. ROCHOW

Harvard University
Cambridge, Massachusetts

I

SALAD DAYS

Organometallic chemistry means many different things to different people. To the organic chemist it opens the door to many organic syntheses; indeed, to the artist in that field it provides the means (in infinite variation) for exquisite refinement of the art (*1*). To the physician it signals the advent of chemotherapy, and to the petroleum specialist it supplies the means to make high-octane gasoline and stereospecific catalysts. To the analytical chemist it is an annoying complication. But to the inorganic chemist, it means a golden opportunity to learn more about the chemical behavior of the metals and the metalloids.

Three-fourths of the chemical elements are metals, and they make up most of the mass of the earth. If we want to understand the chemical behavior of the metals, it does not do just to study their reactions with oxygen, sulfur, and the halogens; such a study could illuminate the ionic half of a metal's behavior, but the entire covalent half might be missed. Ever since Frankland prepared volatile, reactive dimethylzinc, it has been realized that metals have a certain side of their nature which is revealed only in association with organic groups and to one who knows how to look for it; and further, that this side can be very revealing about the chemical combining function of a metal. This was appreciated by Mendeleev in 1872 (*2*), when he used Frankland's unambiguous "chemical combining capacities" to assign metals to particular groups of his periodic table, and the same principle continues to help us as we seek to understand all of the subtleties of chemical combination. One might say that each time a new type of organometallic compound has been recognized, theoretical chemistry was enabled shortly thereafter to take a giant step forward (*3*).

It can be no surprise to learn that Louis Monroe Dennis turned very early to organometallic chemistry in his exploration of the little-known elements germanium, gallium, and indium. In so doing, he followed the lead of Clemens Winkler, who had made tetraethylgermanium as one means of establishing the discovery of germanium (Mendeleev had earlier predicted the formation and the boiling point of such a compound of ekasilicon). Throughout his long career as head of the chemistry department at Cornell, Dennis pursued the peculiarities of germanium (*4*) and especially its distinctions over silicon. He himself prepared many organic derivatives of germanium, in collaboration with the professor of organic chemistry, William Orndorff, and he encouraged all his graduate students to learn to make organometallic compounds, to analyze them, and to study their behavior, as an essential part of inorganic chemistry. His demonstration lectures in Systematic Inorganic Chemistry were sprinkled liberally with examples of organometallic chemistry, and I was spellbound as I sat there (in my junior year) hearing about a branch of chemistry that had never even been hinted at in high-school or freshman classes, and had only been mentioned in organic lectures the way a set of socket wrenches might be mentioned in a course on automotive design and construction.

Dennis was often thought to be hard of hearing after he sustained some injuries in a laboratory explosion involving azides, but there was nothing wrong with his eyesight. He could recognize a moonstruck student more readily than anyone, as he looked over the 40 or 50 Bachelor of Chemistry candidates taking his lectures. So it came about that a timid solitary undergraduate was allowed to sit in "the King's" seminar room the next year, and to hear the graduate students report on their experiments done during the previous week. I was impressed by (a) how little actually gets done, or really is learned about Nature, in any one week, (b) how much fun there is, nevertheless, in trying to outwit Nature, and (c) how important *numbers* were in convincing "the King" that something really had been learned from the experiments. These meetings were attended by the young assistant professor A. W. Laubengayer, who contributed much from his own wonderful bag of tricks in inorganic synthesis. Shortly afterward I was given a place in the laboratory to try out some little projects of my own, and I soon learned for myself how much laboratory effort it takes to make a substantial weekly report.

The following year I entered graduate school, and since that was the year that Alfred Stock was Baker Lecturer[1] at Cornell, I had an opportunity to learn much more about the nonmineral compounds of boron and silicon. Since I had made a little money on the side as a draftsman during those early depression years, I was given a chance to draw the diagrams for Professor Stock's book on the hydrides of boron and silicon (*5*), and this required so many forward and backward readings of the text that I soon had all of the "Stock and Somieski" work memorized.

The following year I had progressed far enough to earn a Heckscher Research Assistantship, which was a highly prized means of support at a time when there was very little support of any kind. In order to keep things on the proper democratic level, Heckscher assistants were not allowed to use for a thesis the results of their experiments done under the Heckscher grant, so in effect those of us under the grant carried on two parallel research projects, one under the grant and the other for a thesis. My thesis project was on fluorine chemistry, but my Heckscher project was on organometallic compounds. Under it I prepared germanium compounds for Hönigschmidt's determination of the atomic weight of Ge, I determined the physical and chemical properties of the colorless, beautifully refractive, volatile crystals of trimethylindium which Robert W. Work had first prepared (*6*), and then went on to investigate triethylthallium (*7*). It was a good introduction to practical organometallic chemistry, and it prepared me for what was to come.

II

CERAMICS AND SILICONES

Young chemists today can usually choose what field they want to work in, and in some instances they also can specify what organization will have the benefit of their services. This not always was so. In 1935 it very definitely was not so. Lucky was the chemist who was able to find *any* kind of job in chemistry, and not be forced to sell books from door to door. This explains

[1] At that time, the George Fisher Baker Non-Resident Lecturer stayed the entire year, and wrote a book embodying his lectures.

how I became a ceramics chemist. In the vain hope that the economic situation might improve in a year or two, I applied for an international exchange fellowship, and was happy to win one that would exchange me with a young man from Germany. Through the good offices of a friend from Cornell, Winton Patnode, I obtained a summer job (also rare!) at the General Electric Research Laboratory, and I boarded with a German family until it was time to depart for Berlin. That time never came. Instead, a telegram from the International Exchange Office in New York informed me that Hitler had suddenly decreed that there would be no young men or money leaving Germany until further notice, and so the exchange program had collapsed. The kind people at General Electric rescued me from deep gloom by offering a job in ceramic chemistry: a man was needed to study the electrical properties of refractory oxides, and to apply the findings to the high-temperature insulation used in Calrod units. This gave me a future and a chance to marry Professor Dennis' secretary; I have had kind feelings toward ceramic chemistry ever since. Inevitably I floundered about for some time, but through the patient guidance of Louis Navias I began to learn something about silicates. I learned how much information can be packed into one phase diagram, and how useful that Cornell course in chemical microscopy really could be. Our small group in ceramics made new glass compositions every day; I fused magnesium oxide in a homemade arc furnace, I grew single crystals, and I had the pleasure of measuring electrical conductivities with all the magnificent resources that such a laboratory has (*8*). It was a happy association, especially to one with a strong interest in electrical technology, and I never once felt deprived of an opportunity to do more in organometallics.

Fate intervened again, but very gradually this time. The organic chemistry group at GE was always on a search for better electrical insulation, seeking to supplant the common paper, pitch, and varnish (used in electrical motors, generators, and transformers since the days of Thomas Edison) with something of greater dielectric strength and durability. Phenolic resins and the newly invented alkyd polymers were an improvement, but these still were limited to moderate temperatures. From his training at Cornell with Dennis, Patnode was sure that silicon should figure in new chemical compositions for use at higher temperatures. In 1934 he had experimented with condensation products of silicon tetrachloride and ethylene glycol or glycerol, as a variation on the alkyd theme, and I knew about these experiments because he had written to Professor Dennis about his problems while I was still at Cornell. The proposal to use glass fibers in electrical insulation brought with it the necessity (and an invitation from Corning Glass Works) to develop a sympathetic polymer which would adhere well to glass and would bind the fibers into a compact, nonporous mass. I was asked to look into the matter on a part-time basis, and so in 1938 I began to combine ceramic chemistry and organometallic chemistry in an attempt to find a solution.

It seemed to me that carbon–silicon bonds provided the best key to a flexible organic–inorganic polymer, for alkoxy and aroxy groups could always be hydrolyzed from silicon, and R—N—Si linkages were even worse. In order to achieve the maximum differentiation over organic polymers, the material should contain a minimum of carbon and hydrogen and a maximum proportion of silicon and oxygen. It should preferably contain no carbon–carbon bonds at all, in order to minimize the possibility of charring if the material should become overheated. All these considerations led to a methyl siloxane as the preferred composition, a hypothetical polymer built upon a network of alternate silicon and oxygen atoms (as in glass and the natural silicates) in which the silicon atoms also bore one or more methyl groups. But such a methylpolysiloxane had never been made, and even the requisite methylchlorosilane intermediates had not been studied in bulk.[2] The Kipping investigations were not of much help, because they dealt only with phenyl, ethyl, and higher organosiloxanes, using intermediates which were prepared by the inappropriate and uneconomical Grignard synthesis. The first task, then, was to prepare CH_3SiCl_3, $(CH_3)_2SiCl_2$, and possibly $(CH_3)_3SiCl$, and to hydrolyze mixtures of these in a search for a promising polymer of methyl siloxane. This I did, and eventually at an average CH_3/Si ratio of 1.4, an attractive resinous polymer was obtained. The project did not proceed rapidly nor easily, for the separations were difficult and new analytical methods had to be developed. William F. Gilliam came from Cornell to help, and the analytical group helped to lead us out of the methylchlorosilane woods (*9*). The methyl silicones proved to have outstanding thermal stability, so the project gained more support and then began to generate some excitement.

It seemed necessary at this point to abandon all classical organometallic syntheses, since they depended on organometallic reagents, and to seek an

[2] Stock and Somieski had carried out a "micropreparation" of $(CH_3)_2SiH_2$, and had hydrolyzed a tiny amount. However, they obtained only a trace of dimethyl silicone, not enough for an investigation of its properties or even for a chemical analysis.

original and economic method for preparing the new polymers. I wasted a great deal of time trying to insert methyl groups into $SiCl_4$ without organometallic reagents before realizing (from simple stoichiometry) that $SiCl_4$ could *never* be a good starting material—it contained only 16% silicon. I then tried to bring about a reaction of ferrosilicon or calcium silicide with organic halides, but no organosilanes resulted. There was an old, partially oxidized sample of "copper silicide" in the stockroom, and since copper is helpful in the preparation of $SiHCl_3$ from HCl and silicon, it seemed worthwhile to try some experiments with a mixture of CH_3Cl and HCl in the hope of sneaking in a few methyl groups along with the hydrogen atoms, as they were seized by silicon atoms. The very first trial, using a mixture of 9 volumes of HCl and 1 volume of CH_3Cl, gave a positive result: hydrolysis of the high-boiling fraction from the product (after distilling off $SiHCl_3$ and $SiCl_4$) gave a sticky colorless resin! Subsequent trials showed that not so much hydrogen chloride was needed, but the idea that *some* HCl was necessary in order to take apart the silicon crystals (which was the original reason for trying the reaction this way) persisted for a long time, and it was weeks before I would even try CH_3Cl alone. Eventually, however, I found the conditions for bringing about reaction of pure CH_3Cl with the copper–silicon alloy, and both CH_3SiCl_3 and $(CH_3)_2SiCl_2$ were then isolated in quantity—ether-free, and without ever having seen magnesium. Needless to say, it was a great day.

The joy lasted exactly as long as the old 5 lb sample of copper–silicon alloy. When that was gone I ordered more, but the new batch was entirely inoperative. Lumps of it sullenly resisted reaction at any useful temperature. "Poisoning by traces of antagonistic elements" was the diagnosis; iron was the chief suspect, because ferrosilicon had failed to react with methyl chloride and iron was supposed to be a catalyst for the degradation of methyl groups to carbon. No definite culprit could be found, however. Instead it was found that the new alloy could be brought to the same appearance and activity as the old alloy just by aging it artificially: the alloy was roasted in air to the point where intergranular oxidation caused it to crumble, and then the loose material reacted satisfactorily. Winton Patnode, objecting quite properly to the long and costly processes of fusion and oxidation just to get a loose powder, set out to produce a porous and reactive "contact mass" from powdered metallurgical silicon and reduced copper dust. His first success came with sintering the lightly pressed powders in hydrogen at the eutectic temperature (*10*), and from there he went on to liberate us forever from expensive alloys and needless rigmarole. Working with Scheiber and Sprung and others recruited from other chemical projects, Patnode started on the long path toward engineering studies and pilot plants that led eventually to a commercial process. A young professor of chemical engineering who had been brought in from MIT, named Charles Reed, foresaw what form the plant might ultimately take, and with a former student of his, Jerome Coe, he set out happily to design a new industry.

On the chemical front, new discoveries came thick and fast. The director of chemical research, A. L. Marshall, encouraged men with experience in conventional polymer chemistry to enter the new and strange organosilicon field. Patnode and Wilcock devised a way of making end-blocked nonreactive silicone oils, Agens discovered how to make an elastomer of methyl silicone, Wright made the famous "bouncing putty," and Marsden made a very useful methyl silicone varnish. Gilliam and I worked long and hard on a direct synthesis of *phenyl*chlorosilanes from chlorobenzene,[3] which proved much more difficult than the synthesis of methylchlorosilanes but seemed essential because of the marked superiority of methyl phenyl silicone resins over pure methyl resins for electrical insulation. As more men became interested and new research groups formed spontaneously around new discoveries, results poured in rapidly. It was my task to relate all that had gone on before to each newcomer in the field, and to condense scores of reports to a semiannual survey of what had been done. This might not seem necessary in so small a group, but each new man who was initiated into organosilicon chemistry wanted to do all the same things that had already been done, and only an indexed summary could prevent endless repetition. Interest ran high in the chemical fraternity outside, also, and I prepared a long series of demonstration lectures in response to requests from local American Chemical Society sections. Out of the GE summaries and the ACS lectures there gradually developed a plan for a small book on the chemical aspects of the new polymers and their intermediates. I wrote it out at home and my wife typed it, and at last there came the day when I sallied forth with a packet of typescript under my arm. The reaction was immediate, direct, and not at all what I had expected. The publisher I

[3] Things were very different in the days of no automatic controls and no precision micropumps: Gilliam and I came in on weekends and holidays, Christmas and all, to fill the reservoirs, drain the condensed products, and regulate the temperatures of our beloved reaction tubes. Rarely did they go 8 hours without attention.

approached so timidly with what I thought was a too-small and too-specialized contribution was delighted; but the laboratory administration (which I had thought would be pleased at this account of its triumphs) took a different view. Since everything was documented and all the results had already been incorporated in patent applications, the liberal publication policy of the laboratory finally prevailed, and the book appeared (*11*). It was kindly received in many printings and languages, and did what I most had hoped: it established organosilicon chemistry as a unique new field of great potential.

The *mechanism* of the direct synthesis of organochlorosilanes next came in for considerable study. The peculiarities of the fused Cu–Si alloys, the variability of the sintered powders, and the differences in behavior between several samples of copper made a study of the role of copper seem imperative. Even before that, though, it seemed advisable to check *all* metals for catalytic behavior, either alone or in combination with copper. I had previously made a study of the common metals in this respect, but now a systematic survey of the periodic table was begun by Gilliam and Sprung, and was carried through patiently and exhaustively by Gilliam over a period that actually took 5 years. It turned out that copper is indeed the best catalyst for the reaction between methyl chloride and elementary silicon, by far; a few other metals help or hinder the action of copper, but most are indifferent. Silver is a somewhat better catalyst than copper for the reaction of chlorobenzene with silicon, but a fair job can also be done by copper in this reaction. Just *how* the copper or silver acts catalytically could not be determined by studying yields of organochlorosilanes vs. temperature and proportion of catalyst; such experiments only gave the most favorable conditions for the overall reaction. To find out what the copper actually *does*, it seemed necessary to observe individual grains of copper and silicon while they were reacting. I built a heated microreaction tube that would fit on the stage of a microscope, and with the aid of vertical-illumination objectives I could see what happened as the mixed powders were heated in a stream of methyl chloride at 320° C. The copper grains were consumed, but unequally; those in contact with silicon crystals disappeared faster. To prove this point further, I embedded some crystals of silicon in a block of soft copper and then ground and polished a flat surface on it. This surface I photomicrographed under vertical illumination, before and after heating in methyl chloride. There was no doubt that copper was a *reactant*; along the lines of contact, both copper and silicon were removed, leaving a V-shaped depression. But surely copper was regenerated, for it did not appear in the product, and only 1:10 wt. ratio (1:20 atom ratio) of Cu:Si was necessary for good results. Further experiments, this time with evaporated films of copper and silicon on microscope slides, showed that CuCl and a short-lived volatile compound of copper were formed, and that *both* of these reacted with adjacent silicon films to regenerate copper. Hence silicon atoms were dislodged from their diamond-lattice sites by being converted to volatile $(CH_3)_4Si$, $(CH_3)_3SiCl$, $(CH_3)_2SiCl_2$, CH_3SiCl_3, and $SiCl_4$. The ratios of these indicated that the capture of methyl groups and chlorine atoms was not random, however, so there must have been time for rearrangement of the products before they departed, favoring the formation of $(CH_3)_2SiCl_2$ (which is the product of highest stability). Furthermore, methyl groups and chlorine atoms did not appear in the product mixture in equal numbers; some methyl groups always were lost by pyrolysis (presumably in transition), giving rise to Si—CH_2—Si species, some $SiHCl_3$ and CH_3SiHCl_2, and some carbon and methane. The reduction of CuCl by silicon was a solid–solid reaction, of course, and this explained why the contact mass was so sensitive to differences in how the copper was laid down on the silicon. It also explained, later, why stirred beds and fluid beds of Cu–Si powder gave better results than static beds.[4]

All in all, the results gave a satisfactory working picture of how the direct synthesis took place, and this picture (if it cannot really be dignified by the name of mechanism) served us well in deciding how to build and operate large-scale reactors. Nevertheless, it came under much criticism by later investigators who favored views about Cu_3Si being the only reactive species, or *n*-type and *p*-type silicon being different, etc. The longest and by far the most thorough study of the mechanism later was made by Bažant and his group at the Institute for Chemical Process Fundamentals at Prague, and at the conclusion of this 6-year study, Bažant reported (*12*) substantial agreement with our original view. The Cu_3Si and semiconductor theories were found irrelevant; the reaction consists essentially of three steps: (1) adsorption of RCl on the surface of the Cu–Si agglomerates, in such a way that the chlorine is oriented toward copper, (2) reaction of the adsorbate with the substrate, involving labile compounds of copper and subsequent regeneration of Cu, and (3) desorption of the volatile products, accompanied by some side reactions. There the matter stands, summarized in a number of recent books (*13–15*).

[4] The reaction is also strongly exothermic, so that motion of the powder is desirable in order to transfer heat and maintain control of the temperature.

III

OTHER METALS AND METHODS OF RESEARCH

What holds for silicon has special meaning for germanium, so all the same tricks were tried on germanium powder reduced from the oxide, and later on massive germanium alloyed with 10 to 20% of copper. The direct synthesis of organogermanium halides turned out to be simpler than that of organosilicon halides, and the desired $(CH_3)_2GeCl_2$ in particular appeared in much higher yield than that of $(CH_3)_2SiCl_2$ because of the greater mobility of C—Ge bonds and Ge—Cl bonds at the reaction temperature. So it became possible to write a simple overall equation

$$2CH_3Cl + Ge \xrightarrow[Cu]{340°C} (CH_3)_2GeCl_2 \ (90\%)$$

without a further page of qualifying and explanatory equations indicating all of the side reactions and by-products (*16*). True to its greater maximum covalency and electronegativity, however, germanium did not form analogs of the silicone polymers, but rather a series of water-soluble, ephemeral, polymeric organogermanium oxides which were quite the opposite of the silicones.

The direct synthesis of dimethyltin dichloride

$$2CH_3Cl + Sn \xrightarrow[Cu]{350°C} (CH_3)_2SnCl_2 \ (98\%)$$

was still easier, because at last it was possible to conduct a gas–liquid reaction with continually renewed fresh surfaces of metal. Strangely enough, the preparation of ethyl and higher alkyl tin halides by this method turned out to be unsatisfactory because the reaction stopped after a few minutes. As for obtaining silicone-like polymers, the white $(CH_3)_2SnO$, obtained by precipitating $(CH_3)_2Sn(OH)_2$ from a water solution of $(CH_3)_2SnCl_2$ by adding NaOH,[5] was an infusible, insoluble, unworkable powder. The higher coordination number of tin encourages a degree of polymerization that gives a tight three-dimensional network of tin and oxygen atoms, rather than analogs of the familiar siloxane chains.

It was evident by this time that what began as a research project in organosilicon chemistry had branched out into a considerable area of all

[5] In marked contrast to $(CH_3)_2SiCl_2$, $(CH_3)_2SnCl_2$ is only 10% hydrolyzed in H_2O; and OH^- ions must be added to form an oxide or hydroxide.

organometallic chemistry, and that there would be many more interactions involving a variety of other metals. How to publish all this new work, or even how to find out what other people were doing, became a vexing question. At that time (1945–1950) there was no separate section of *Chemical Abstracts* devoted to organometallic chemistry, nor any divisional program at ACS meetings. In fact, there was no organization whatever. Papers on organometallic compounds were scattered all through the literature and the meeting programs, depending on whether the author's interest was synthesis, or structure, or reactions, or theoretical, or whatever. Readers simply had to hunt everywhere, as was made abundantly clear to me as I tried to catch up on the literature after a 2-year excursion into nuclear chemistry. It seemed that the science needed some standing, some organization of purpose and meaning, and some centralization of its rapidly growing literature. These aims were not to be achieved on a lasting basis by agitation or salesmanship, but rather through education and appreciation. The first requirement was a small book suitable for an introductory course in organometallic chemistry, and in our naive way Dallas Hurd, Dick Lewis, and I set out to write it (*17*). The timing was fortunate in that the organometallic chemistry of the transition metals had just begun to blossom forth, beginning with the discovery of ferrocene a few years before and continuing with the vigorous opening-up of the field especially by E. O. Fischer and by Geoffrey Wilkinson and their co-workers. Furthermore, the Ziegler catalysts for polymerization had just been discovered (see *17*, p. 306), bringing with them greatly increased industrial interest in organometallic chemistry. What we strove for was not a compendium of compounds, nor an exhaustive treatise, but a simple summary of principles and an organized description of the preparation and behavior of some exemplary compounds —in short, the book we might have hoped for as students. The approach was not imaginary; I had begun giving an introductory course in the subject at Harvard University, where I had joined the staff in 1948, and it was easy to find out what aspects of the subject interested graduate students most. Later on, improvements in secondary-school education made it possible to introduce organometallic chemistry at the freshman level (*18*), where the "yearn to learn" is greater and the reception was even more gratifying.

Each chemical element has its pronounced individuality, of course, but there are guiding principles about the carbon–metal bond which hold (to understandable degrees) for all the metals and metalloids. Insofar as these principles relate to the prediction of reactions or the explanation of previously observed chemical behavior, they are widely believed and quoted. When they relate to the physical and mechanical properties of substances, however, all is mystery. I hope that 17 years of work on intramolecular motion in various organometallic compounds (and especially on rotation about their carbon–metal bonds) will change this attitude a little bit, but that is by no means sure. I am resigned to the fact that most chemists regard mechanical properties as the domain of the engineer, forgetting that they arise from the fundamental structure of matter, and that chemists are supposed (by definition) to be devoted to the study of matter.

It all began with some reflections on the properties of the commonest silicones. The chemical properties (such as thermal stability, resistance to oxidation, indifference to acids and salts but sensitivity to HF and to strong alkalies) are readily understood and explained in terms of the Si—O and Si—C bonds which comprise the material, but the *physical properties* (low temperature coefficient of viscosity in silicone oils, very low glass-transition temperature in silicone rubber, high compressibility, and low intermolecular attraction in general) cannot be explained in terms of bond energies or bond polarities at all. Something else, something equally fundamental but not widely appreciated, must be involved here. The success of Herbert Gutowsky in explaining the transitions within the crystalline ammonium halides, in 1950, by what is now known as the technique of wide-line NMR,[6] led me to think of this as a potentially important tool for the study of all organometallic compounds, and especially as a probe into those mysterious physical properties of methyl silicone. It had been suggested by Roth and Harker (on the basis of an X-ray diffraction study of a crystalline dimethylsiloxane) that dimethylsilyl groups seemed to occupy more space than would be expected from the atomic radii of C, H, and Si, and that this expansion might be the result of motion. If the dimethylsilyl groups really were swinging around their Si—O bonds, as was suggested, the extent of this motion (and the temperature of its onset) could be determined by measuring the proton magnetic resonance of the material *in the solid state*. In a rigid lattice each neighboring proton contributes its fixed magnetic effect, so that the local field H at any given proton is not the external imposed field H_0, but rather

[6] Gutowsky worked under the direction of Professor Kistiakowsky; I merely served on his doctorate examination committee, but I was intrigued at once by the possibilities of the method.

$$H = H_0 \pm \frac{\mu}{r^3}(3\cos^2\theta - 1)$$

where μ is the nuclear magnetic moment of a proton, r is the interproton distance, and θ is the angle between the interproton line and the direction of H_0. Such local magnetic perturbations cancel out in pure liquids and in liquid solutions, but are very noticeable and useful in solids, for they provide an accurate measure of the degree of internal or intramolecular motion. A completely rigid lattice gives a very broad resonance line; a liquid gives a very narrow line; a solid in which the protons are moving about will give a resonance line intermediate in width, depending on the extent of motion. Measuring the line width of a solid or semisolid substance over a range of temperatures therefore tells us at what temperature the protons start moving, what the activation energy of the motion is, and when to expect a phase transition (before it happens). Hence if the methyl protons of a pure methylsiloxane or a pure methylchlorosilane actually were moving about more than those of an analogous organic compound, the method should tell us, unambiguously. And if there should be an unusual degree of internal motion, the moving groups would occupy more space than static ones, and this situation would give rise to greater compressibility and lower intermolecular attraction.[7] Abnormally low intermolecular attraction would explain all the odd physical properties of methyl silicone polymers, such as low activation energy of viscous flow, low heat of vaporization, and (in silicone rubber) low glass-transition temperature.

All we needed to settle the point was an NMR spectrometer in which we could examine our dozens of samples over wide ranges of temperature. In a year we should have the answer. Alas, there was no spectrometer; Gutowsky moved to Illinois with his equipment, and there was no commercial instrument to be had at that time (1951), nor even any funds for such a scheme. The Korean war was in progress, and government priority certificates were necessary to buy all electrical supplies, even a spool of copper wire. We had no priority number, no funds, no experience, nothing but a naive faith in the applicability of the method. Nevertheless, Hugh LeClair (a graduate student with extraordinary courage) succeeded in building a workable instrument in less than 2 years. George Kistiakowsky gave us some soft-iron forgings from which we had a yoke and two pole

[7] Moving groups necessarily sweep out more space than static ones, and larger volumes necessarily mean greater linear distance. Molecular attraction falls off with the inverse sixth power of the distance.

pieces machined for our magnet, and I begged 80 lb of Alnico from the General Electric Company, on loan. We found some discarded copper wire and wound enormous coils on top of the Alnico cylinders, using four strands of wire in parallel to carry the expected magnetizing current. Then we rolled the completed magnet over to the cyclotron building and let their DC generator build up current in the coils until the circuit breakers opened. The result was a permanent magnet of about 4000 gauss, with a decidedly inhomogeneous field but with a region good enough for a small sample. Then we set about building the oscillator, the phase-sensitive detector, the modulator, and the power supplies. We followed the Purcell-Pound-Pake-Watkins circuits, using components torn from my 20-meter amateur radio transmitter at home and from various government surplus electronic gear. The cash outlay for the entire instrument, magnet and all, was $800. It was amazing that it should work at all, but there came one magic day when LeClair finally located the proton resonance line. From there on it was a matter of improving the magnet and the detector until the signal was sharp enough to be used. It was a triumph of amateur nonexperts over copper, iron, pentodes, and random noise.

The very first investigation (*19*) showed that motion of the protons in methylchlorosilanes and methylsiloxanes is a physical reality, and that at 77° K it exceeds by far the motion in analogous organic compounds. Analysis of the line shape indicated that the motion was not that of the entire $(CH_3)_2Si$ assembly moving about the Si—O bond, but rather a C_3 rotation about the C—Si bond. This suggested that the abnormal motion might not be associated uniquely with C—Si bonds, but might be rather general for all carbon–metal bonds—that is, it might be a characteristic of organometallic substances in general. Experiments with $[(CH_3)_2GeO]_3$, $[(CH_3)_2GeO]_4$, $[(CH_3)_2GeS]_4$, and $[(CH_3)_2SnO]_x$ showed that the methyl groups of these also rotated freely, and to a comparative extent which did not depend solely on the covalent radii of Si, Ge, and Sn, nor on their C—M bond polarities, but rather in some more complicated way. Soon afterward E. O. Fischer loaned us some of the first *bis*-benzenechromium, and we found that this and ferrocene both showed rather free motion of the hydrocarbon rings, even at 300° C below their melting points. A subsequent study with substituted ferrocenes made it clear that the cyclopentadiene rings rotated (or oscillated) with respect to each other, and that the motion was not a simple tumbling of the entire molecule within its lattice space.

The motion in ferrocene and bis(benzene)chromium ceased shortly below 65° K, but that in methylsiloxanes disappeared only at 4° K, we found.

The work on intramolecular motion within organometallic compounds was spread over many years and appears in many reports and publications (*20*), but it represents only a small beginning. Such work requires unusual courage and talents on the part of a graduate student or a postdoctoral fellow, for he must understand practical electronics as well as chemistry, and must be a theoretician as well as a builder and repairman. Such men are rare. Through the years our homemade equipment has been modified over and over by the few courageous souls I could find, making it suitable for studying fluorosilanes (*21*) and fluorocarbons, organic polymers (*22*), and, of course, many types of silicone and silazane polymers (*20*). We feel proud that as mere chemists we have contributed to the techniques and equipment of wide-line NMR, and have shown what it can do. Perhaps the initial dream of forecasting all of the mechanical properties of a polymer by the wide-line NMR examination of a solid 5 gm sample has not come about, but we have been able to show that dimethylsilazanes are not low-temperature competitors of silicone rubber, and that the silica–silicone interaction in reinforced silicone rubber is a variety of chemical cross-linking. As for the *type* of motion that differentiates silicones from organic polymers, refinements of technique now indicate that it is a combination of C_3 rotation, double rotation, and chain translation. Silicones are not a mystery any more.

The contrast between germanium and silicon has already been mentioned, and a thorough study of the polymer system $(CH_3)_2GeO$ (*23*) showed that it is a system interesting for the mobility of its polymorphs but extremely different from the $(CH_3)_2SiO$ system. There can be some cross-breeding, of course (*23*), but germanium remains very different from silicon. The difference arises from the same aspects of atomic structure that make other fourth-period elements (such as Br and Ga) different from their congeners. For 82 years much has been made of the close parallel between Mendeleev's predictions about ekasilicon and Winkler's findings about germanium, but actually Winkler's findings themselves point out the difference. To quote a book on metalloids I wrote (*24*): "Mendeleev predicted that elementary eka-silicon would decompose steam with difficulty, whereas germanium does not decompose it at all. This is to say that germanium is less metallic than was predicted. Mendeleev also said that acids would have a slight action on the element, but they have none; again, it is a more negative element than was predicted. There are many more chemical facts[8] which point in the same direction: germanium is more electronegative than was expected by interpolation, and it actually behaves a great deal like arsenic." There also are many physical facts about Ge(IV) compounds coming out of thermochemistry and nuclear quadrupole moments, which lead to a lower electronegativity of Ge(IV) *in its compounds* than for Si(IV), and these were put forth very clearly by Allred, together with his own measurements (*25*). The findings proved hard to accept by those who learn (through too little instruction in inorganic chemistry) that "within any group in the Periodic System the elements increase in electropositive or metallic character as we descend the group." Such a view ignores the effects of transition-series contraction and lanthanide contraction, which result in reversals like Cu–Ag–Au, Ni–Pd–Pt, Zn–Cd–Hg, and the Group IV situation itself. Fortunately, neither theory nor opinion can blot out the facts of descriptive chemistry.

This narrative should report not only the Group IV triumphs and controversies, but should also mention the direct synthesis of organometallic derivatives of Group V elements (*26*), which led to generalizations about the reactions of *all* metals with hydrocarbon halides (*27*). Group V also came into the picture extensively in the person of nitrogen, involving 10 years of work with silylamines, silizanes, and many new silicon–nitrogen compounds. The initial aim was to make new polymers based on Si–N networks, but the preparative aspects soon ran away with the project and opened up so many inviting avenues of investigation that preparations began to absorb all the attention and support. A comprehensive account of the new synthetic methods, the new types of compound (a few of which refuted the age-old axiom that all silicon–nitrogen compounds hydrolyze), the silylamine and silazane and siloxazane polymers, and the coordination of these to metals cannot be encompassed here, but I salute the outstanding work in inorganic and organometallic syntheses by Ronn Minné, Carl Kruger, Dieter Kummer, Joachim Pump, Klaus Lienhard, and Peter Geymayer. There are a few summaries, some as long as this entire narrative, that tell the tale (*28*).

[8] The generation of pure GeH_4 in aqueous media by the action of aq. $NaBH_4$ on GeO_2, whereas SiH_4 is rapidly decomposed by water; the water solubility of GeO_2 and $(CH_3)_2GeO$, etc. See Allred and Rochow (*25*).

IV

AND NOW?

To a young chemist with an inquiring mind, who may be reading this and asking, "What does organometallic chemistry hold for me?" I would answer in this way: although some other areas of chemistry may seem to have been worked over extensively, organometallic chemistry is still comparatively new and untouched. Almost any tree in C—M land may be shaken, and the plums come raining down. Since the field is decidedly interdisciplinary, it is largely disregarded by the straight-line orthodox chemists, and hence the population density is small. Just because it *is* interdisciplinary, organometallic chemistry is all the more receptive to good ideas from outside of the traditional areas. When these ideas result in new and unorthodox materials, industry seems to welcome them eagerly. After all, industry has had ample opportunity to exploit the natural and conventional materials; in our age it yearns for something new. An idea which becomes a research project in organometallic chemistry can grow and mature more rapidly in an industrial research laboratory than in a university, because of the concentration of time and facilities, but on the other hand, campaigning for the broad advancement of organometallic chemistry goes on more rapidly at a university, especially if one has students like Allred, Frost, Seyferth, West, and White who multiply one's efforts by becoming university teachers themselves. I am fortunate in having lived in both worlds, and I can report that not only are they compatible, but mutually stimulating. I am happy also to have found enthusiastic, friendly, and helpful associates in both worlds—I wish it were possible in a memoir of this sort to list all of them, and to summarize all their triumphs and accomplishments. Fortunately, the more formal scientific literature contains the full record, and the scientific fraternity has been generous with praise.

Carbon–metal bonds take many forms: some old, some new, and some as yet undiscovered. Those of us who have worked with them have found them fascinating—not just interesting, but fascinating because they are so different. If I were starting over I would choose no other field, just work harder and better. And now I should like to thank the Editors for inviting me to tell of organometallic chemistry as I have known it, and I commend the reader to the authoritative articles which follow.

References

1. H. Gilman, *Advan. Organometal. Chem.* **7**, 1 (1968).
2. D. I. Mendeleev, *Ann. Chem. Pharm.* **8**, Suppl., 151 (1872).
3. See, for example, the tremendous consequences to coordination chemistry that followed discovery of the carbonyls [W. Hieber, *Advan. Organometal. Chem.* **8**, 1 (1970)], or note the great changes in the understanding of delocalized-electron bonds that followed the discovery of ferrocene.
4. L. M. Dennis, *Z. Anorg. Allgem. Chem.* **174**, 7 (1928).
5. A. Stock, "The Hydrides of Boron and Silicon." Cornell Univ. Press, Ithaca, New York, 1933.
6. L. M. Dennis, R. W. Work, and E. G. Rochow, *J. Am. Chem. Soc.* **56**, 1047 (1934).
7. E. G. Rochow and L. M. Dennis, *J. Am. Chem. Soc.* **57**, 486 (1935).
8. E. G. Rochow, *J. Appl. Phys.* **9**, 664 (1938).
9. E. G. Rochow, W. F. Gilliam, H. A. Liebhafsky, and A. F. Winslow, *J. Am. Chem. Soc.* **63**, 798 (1941).
10. W. Patnode, U.S. Patents 2,380,996 and 2,380,997 (1945).
11. E. G. Rochow, "An Introduction to the Chemistry of the Silicones," 1st ed. Wiley, New York, 1946 (2nd ed., 1951; xerox version of last printing distributed by University Microfilms, Inc., Ann Arbor, Michigan, after 1964).
12. V. Bažant, *Plenary Lecture, 2nd Intern. Symp. Organosilicon Chem., Bordeaux-Talence,* 1968.
13. V. Bažant, V. Chvalovský, and J. Rathousky, "Organosilicon Compounds," Vol. 1. Academic Press, New York, 1965.
14. W. Noll, "Chemie und Technologie der Silikone," 2nd ed. Verlag Chemie, Weinheim, 1968.
15. A. D. Petrov, V. F. Mironov, V. A. Ponomarenko, and E. A. Chernyshev, "Synthesis of Organosilicon Monomers." Consultants Bureau, New York, 1964.
16. E. G. Rochow, *J. Am. Chem. Soc.* **69**, 1729 (1947).
17. E. G. Rochow, D. T. Hurd, and R. N. Lewis, "The Chemistry of Organometallic Compounds." Wiley, New York, 1957.
18. E. G. Rochow, *in* "Selected Topics in Modern Chemistry." Reinhold, New York, 1964 (British and Japanese ed., 1965; Italian ed., 1966).
19. E. G. Rochow and H. G. LeClair, *J. Inorg. & Nucl. Chem.* **1**, 92–111 (1955).
20. L. N. Mulay, E. G. Rochow, and E. O. Fischer, *J. Inorg. & Nucl. Chem.* **4**, 232 (1957); L. N. Mulay, E. G. Rochow, E. O. Stejskal, and N. E. Weliky, *ibid.* **16**, 23 (1960); J. R. Barrante and E. G. Rochow, *J. Organometal. Chem.* (*Amsterdam*) **1**, 273 (1964); F. S. Model, G. Redl, and E. G. Rochow, *J. Polymer Sci., A*-1 **4**, 639 (1966); E. G. Rochow, *Allgem. Prakt. Chem.* **17**, 43 (1966).
21. E. Schnell and E. G. Rochow, *J. Am. Chem. Soc.* **78**, 4178 (1956); *J. Inorg. & Nucl. Chem.* **6**, 303 (1958).
22. R. Mattes and E. G. Rochow, *J. Polymer Sci., A*-2 **4**, 375 (1966).
23. D. Seyferth and E. G. Rochow, *J. Org. Chem.* **20**, 250 (1955); *J. Am. Chem. Soc.* **77**, 907 (1955); *J. Polymer Sci.* **18**, 543 (1955); M. P. Brown and E. G. Rochow, *J. Am. Chem. Soc.* **82**, 4166 (1960).
24. E. G. Rochow, "The Metalloids." Heath, Boston, Massachusetts, 1966.
25. A. L. Allred and E. G. Rochow, *J. Am. Chem. Soc.* **77**, 4489 (1955); *J. Inorg. & Nucl. Chem.* **5**, 264 and 269 (1958).

26. L. Maier, E. G. Rochow, and W. C. Fernelius, *J. Inorg. & Nucl. Chem.* **16**, 213 (1961); L. Maier, D. Seyferth, F. G. A. Stone, and E. G. Rochow, *Z. Naturforsch.* **12b**, 263 (1957); *J. Am. Chem. Soc.* **79**, 5884 (1957); see also subsequent publications of L. Maier on the direct synthesis of organophosphorus halides.
27. E. G. Rochow, *J. Chem. Educ.* **43**, 58 (1965).
28. 17*th I.U.P.A.C. Congr.*, 1959 Priestley Lectures, Penn. State Univ., 1960; *Chim. Ind. (Paris)* **85**, 897 (1961); *Bull. Soc. Chim. France* p. 1360 (1963); *Monatsh. Chem.* **95**, 750 (1964); *Chim. Pure Appl.* **13**, 247 (1966).

Applications of ^{119m}Sn Mössbauer Spectroscopy to the Study of Organotin Compounds

J. J. ZUCKERMAN

Department of Chemistry
State University of New York at Albany
Albany, New York

I

INTRODUCTION

Information useful for the characterization of compounds in the laboratory has multiplied enormously of late, thanks to the use of physical techniques. These techniques have for the most part been borrowed from experimental physics and modified suitably for use by the practicing chemist. The general ground rules are now apparent—if some physically measurable parameter varies with the chemical state of the system, then chemical information about the state of the system can be obtained from a physical technique based on the measurement of this parameter. Many such techniques have already found use in chemical laboratories, including the several forms of spectroscopy applied to the study of organometallic compounds. Mössbauer spectroscopy is now emerging as another such technique, and this article will attempt to review its application to tin.

Spectroscopic methods are inherently capable of yielding three general types of information: (i) to establish identity, (ii) to establish purity or the composition of a mixture, and (iii) to provide information concerning structure and bonding in molecules and the forces between molecules. The first of these represents an application of the generally accepted principle: "identical species behave identically," and the second operates on the assumption that physical mixing does not alter chemical nature. These two are analytical uses and are reasonably straightforward. It is the third type of information, however, which the chemist is often most anxious to have, and it is just this third type of information which is most difficult to obtain. In most cases it is impossible to derive exact theoretical predictions concerning the change in measurable quantities from first principles, and the practicing chemist must, therefore, rely on a body of analogy upon which to build his hypotheses. In the case of a technique only recently introduced, it is necessary first to test a wide variety of substances in order to find the empirical correlations which relate chemical behavior to changes in the physical parameters. This process has been seen to occur in infrared and nuclear magnetic resonance spectroscopy where the systematics of spectral changes are now known. In the case of what has been called the "Sporting Techniques" (spectroscopic techniques as operated by the synthetic chemist himself), the evidence provided is inevitably what a lawyer would call "circumstantial," and the practicing chemist must often decide between a number of apparently reasonable interpretations. It is especially here that additional data from other physical methods can be of great value.

There are now about 300 research papers and notes which comprise the literature of ^{119m}Sn Mössbauer spectroscopy. In preparation for this review I arranged the papers in the order in which they were received by their various editors, a procedure I can recommend. In this way the priority for discovery could be unequivocally established, often a difficult question in this fast-developing field. The bibliography is presented in alphabetical order in Appendix I.

II

THE MÖSSBAUER EFFECT

A. Nuclear Processes and Chemistry

Lately the old chestnut that nuclear processes are independent of the chemical environment of the nucleus has been quietly returned to the limbo of inexact scientific statements. There was a time when nuclear physicists thought that radioactive decay processes were entirely independent of chemical state. This view was based upon the fundamentally sound precept that the energies involved in nuclear processes are so much larger than the energies of chemical binding that the nucleus can almost always be thought of as being part of a free atom. On the other hand nuclear properties (apart from mass and electric charge) were thought to be of little interest to the chemist.

Today, however, a broad range of phenomena are known which arise from interactions of nuclei with their electron shells. These phenomena include the following:

(a) The small shift in optical spectra seen on isotopic substitution (said to result from the different dimensions of the nuclei).

(b) The even smaller isomer shift in optical spectra produced by an excited (isomeric) nucleus [arising from the same cause as in (a)].

(c) The chemical shift and the splitting of nuclear magnetic resonance lines (due to interactions between the nuclei, the valence electrons, and an applied magnetic field).

(d) The dependence of the observed molecular rotational, nuclear magnetic resonance, or nuclear quadrupole resonance spectra on the symmetry of the chemical bonds around the nucleus under study (due to interaction between the nuclear electric quadrupole moment and electric field gradients).

None of the phenomena so far mentioned relate to radioactive transformation of the nuclei in question. However, in the last few decades studies have also been made on the effect of the chemical environment on nuclear transformations. These include the following:

(a) Changes in the lifetimes of radioactive decay by electron-capture processes from one chemical situation to another (the probability of electron capture is proportional to the electron density at the nucleus; for example, the half-life of ^{7}Be for electron capture is 0.08% greater in BeF_2 then in beryllium metal).

(b) Changes in the rate of isomeric nuclear transitions accompanied by strong internal electron conversion (the rate depends on the electronic states; for example, the half-life for internal conversion in ^{99m}Tc is 0.27% greater in TcS than in $KTcO_3$).

(c) Dependence of the mean lifetime of positrons and their mode of annihilation upon the electron density in the stopping material.

(d) Dependence of the annihilation rate of the transient, bound species, $e^{+}e^{-}$, upon the oxidizing power of the medium, the presence of free radicals, etc.

(e) Dependence of the degree of anisotropy in cascade reactions on the medium—small for metals and ionic solids, large for liquids.

(f) Dependence of the depolarization of muons upon the chemical state of the medium.

The latest addition to this list is the observation that there are chemical effects on the energies of γ-rays emitted by nuclei in excited states. These energies are studied by the technique of resonance fluorescence.

B. *The Resonance Fluorescence of γ-Rays*

The phenomenon of resonance depends on having a pair of systems, the emitter of energy and the absorber, with nearly the same characteristic frequencies. The two frequencies need not be exactly equal, however; every resonance is characterized by a plot of response against frequency peaked at the resonant energy, E, with characteristic width, Γ. A sharply tuned system gives a narrower resonance line relative to the resonance frequency. Radio engineers speak of this sharpness of "tuned" electrical circuits as the quality, or Q factor. When the energy added is exactly E, the probability of excitation of the level will be unity. The excitation probability at any other energy E', will be something less. The same is true for the emitting nucleus.

Resonance absorption for optical processes in atomic systems was predicted by Lord Rayleigh and demonstrated by R. W. Wood in 1904 for sodium emission. Wood allowed the emitted yellow sodium radiation to pass into a sample of gaseous sodium at low pressure in a glass bulb. A yellow glow in the bulb was the result of the sodium atoms absorbing and reradiating (i.e., scattering) the incident yellow light. Other atoms not "tuned" to the incident radiation are transparent. Rayleigh's classical predictions may be understood in quantum terms. The emission of radiation arises from transitions between discrete electronic energy levels with both the emitting and the absorbing sodium atoms having the same level separation. For a typical atom the resonance energy is of the order of 1 eV, and the half-height width, Γ, about 10^{-8} eV so that the Q factor, E/Γ, is 10^8. The atom is thus a finely tuned oscillator and the lines in atomic spectra are very sharp. In an optical laser, where an ensemble of atoms emits in unison, the ratio of E to Γ is even higher ($\sim 10^{13}$).

The nuclear analog to the optical process is the resonant absorption of γ-rays. The search begun by W. Kuhn in the late twenties for this nuclear resonance, however, remained unsuccessful for two decades. The reasons for this can be readily understood. The energies involved in the nuclear transitions are much larger than those in atoms, but the natural widths of the spectral lines are about the same. Thus the E/Γ ratio can be 10^{15}, or even higher. The resonance between γ-rays and nuclei is one of the most sharply tuned systems in nature, and is thus sensitive to the smallest departures from resonant conditions. The part played by recoil effects now becomes very important. In accord with Newton's third law, some of the energy of the emitted γ-ray will be taken up in the recoil of the emitting nucleus. This energy dissipation destroys the sharply tuned resonance. Recoil processes are present in all such resonant systems by virtue of the law of conservation of momentum, but the higher energies involved in nuclear transitions make recoil a much more important consideration here.

The recoil energy, E_R, is proportional to the square of the transition energy, E, and for a free atom this is easily computed from momentum conservation to be $E^2/2Mc^2$, where M is the mass of the emitting nucleus and c is the speed of light. For tin the recoil energy, E_R, is only about 10^{-3} eV, tiny compared with the transition energy, E (23,800 eV in this case), but large compared with Γ (10^{-8} eV). The energy of a γ-ray emitted by a freely recoiling tin nucleus is thereby reduced by an amount E_R, and the energy carried by the γ-ray is less than that necessary for resonance. Thus most of the early experiments failed to detect nuclear resonance fluorescence. In optical transitions, on the other hand, the recoil energy, E_R, is much less than the natural linewidth; for example, in the case of yellow sodium radiation, E_R is only 10^{-10} eV, less than 1/100 of Γ, and so resonance is readily observed despite the fact that the emission line is displaced $2E_R$ from the energy required by the absorber.

TABLE I

TRANSITION CHARACTERISTICS

	Atomic: Sodium	Nuclear: Tin-119m
Transition energy, E (eV)	2.1	23,800
Natural linewidth of excited level, Γ (eV)	4.4×10^{-8}	2.4×10^{-8}
Resonance wavelength (cm)	5.89×10^{-5}	5.3×10^{-9}
Doppler width at room temperature (eV)	3.13×10^{-6}	1.6×10^{-2}
Recoil energy of a single nucleus, E_R (eV)	10^{-10}	2.5×10^{-3}
Ratio E/Γ	5×10^{7}	10^{12}

The linewidths for the γ-rays are actually broadened considerably by Doppler effects. An emitted γ-ray of energy E produced by a nucleus receding with velocity V appears to have energy $E - EV/c$ while the energy associated with a γ-ray produced by an approaching nucleus is $E + EV/c$. The definition or frequency spread of the γ-rays is thus made larger than the natural linewidth. The velocities of the nuclei, and hence the line broadening, are proportional to the square root of the temperature in degrees absolute. Since the Doppler width is also proportional to the transition energy, E, the broadening of nuclear transition energies, will be much greater than the broadening of optical quanta produced by sodium. Some of the transition characteristics for the atomic sodium line and an analogous nuclear transition in tin-119m are shown in Table I.

C. Mössbauer's Discovery

Rudolf L. Mössbauer simplified the whole problem considerably by demonstrating in 1958 that loss of energy by recoil for nuclei in solids could be avoided altogether. To understand Mössbauer's discovery it is necessary to distinguish three cases of the scattering of γ-rays by atoms bound in solids (see Fig. 1):

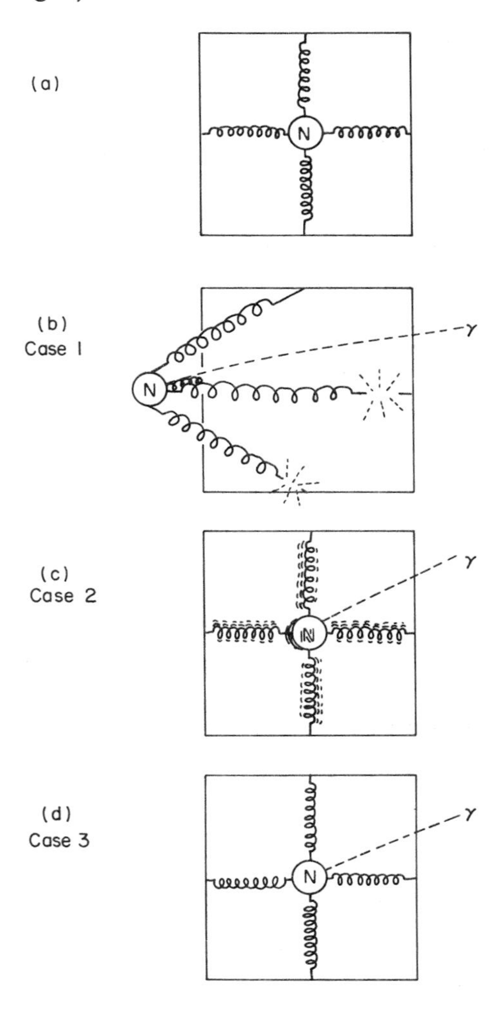

FIG. 1. Possible effects of recoil.

(a) If E_R is large compared with the strength of the chemical forces binding the atom in the solid, then the atom will be ripped out of its lattice site [Fig. 1(b)].

(b) If E_R is larger than the characteristic vibrational energy of the solid (the phonon energy), but not great enough to dislodge the atom completely from its site, then the atom will oscillate at its site, and the recoil energy will be dissipated as heat [Fig. 1(c)].

(c) If the recoil energy is less than the phonon energy, a new effect arises because the lattice is a quantized system which cannot be excited in an arbitrary manner. In this case it becomes possible for some fraction of the emission and absorption events to occur with no loss in recoil energy at all. For these events it is possible to consider that the effective recoiling mass is now the mass of the whole lattice rather than just the mass of the emitting nucleus. The recoil energy would then drop to a quite negligible value.

TABLE II

SPECTROSCOPIC ENERGIES

Spectroscopy	Typical energy of radiation (cm^{-1})	Typical energy difference detected (eV)
X-Ray: inner electronic states	10,000,000	10^3
Photoelectron: electronic states	—	10
Visible–ultraviolet: valence electronic states	10,000	1
Infarared–Raman: vibrational states	1,000	10^{-1}
Microwave: rotational states	10	10^{-1}
Electron spin resonance: electron spin states in a magnetic field	0.1	10^{-4}
Nuclear magnetic resonance: nuclear spin states in a magnetic field	0.001	10^{-7}
Mössbauer: nuclear states	100,000,000	10^{-8}

This production of monochromatic γ-rays is the Mössbauer effect. Conventional techniques of spectroscopy are hopelessly inadequate for resolving the tiny differences in energy in these Mössbauer effect γ-rays due to changes in chemical state. The nuclear transition energies themselves are quite apart from those encountered in other physical techniques useful to organometallic chemists, as shown in Table II. The γ-ray energies are huge, but the precise values are a measure of small changes in the atom. Mössbauer recognized that the converse of the recoil-free emission process, recoil-free resonant absorption, constitutes an ideal detector, one that is precisely tuned to the energy of the γ-ray. Recoil-free resonant absorption makes it possible to compare the nuclear transition energy in a source with that in an absorber with unprecedented precision. While the measurement of the energies of γ-rays could be carried out in pre-Mössbauer days at best with a precision of 0.1%, the discovery of the Mössbauer effect has raised the precision by a factor of 10^9.

D. Mössbauer Spectroscopy

In any resonance experiment the resonance condition is best observed by systematically perturbing the system and then noting the influence of the variation on the measurable parameters. In chemical applications of the Mössbauer effect the source and absorber nuclei are usually in different chemical states. The means to bring the system back into resonance is the method based on the Doppler effect used first by Mössbauer. The source and absorber are moved such that relative motion shifts the positions of their nuclear energy levels until resonance is achieved. Just how mismatched are the source and absorber is measured by the relative velocity required.

The experimental factors which enter into the design of a suitable spectrometer include the method chosen to modulate the energy of the ^{119m}Sn γ-ray by the Doppler effect, detection of the γ-ray of interest against the background of other radiation; collection, storage, and handling of the data; the geometry of the experiment; the need for cryostats; and the state of the sample and the host material for the tin-119*m* nuclei. A full discussion of these factors is beyond the scope of this review and can be found in several excellent books and articles.[1]

There follows a brief summary of the general principles as applied to the specific case of ^{119m}Sn Mössbauer spectroscopy.

1. *The Mover*

The Doppler velocities necessary to restore resonance between nuclear energy levels even in widely different tin systems can be conveniently

[1] See Appendix I,C and I,D.

achieved by a variety of means. The two most disparate tin species thus far measured, $SnCl_2$ and SnF_6^{2-}, are mismatched by an energy equivalent to $\backsim$5 mm/sec of Doppler shift. The "Rube Goldberg" lying in the heart of every American physical scientist (the "Heath Robinson" for a Briton, or unsung crackpot inventors of the other nationalities) now has a chance to come to the fore. Mechanical, electrodynamic, piezoelectric, hydrostatic, and even biological devices have been pressed into service. The experiment can even be reversed to obtain an unknown velocity. For example, movement in a group of Bulgarian worker ants (*Formica pratensis*, DeGeer) whose abdomens were coated with tin(IV) oxide has been investigated recently, as a function of temperature and oxygen availability (*40*). More prosaic experimental setups employ a constant acceleration mover which for tin would sweep through velocities from -6 to $+6$ mm/sec. Excellent movers based on electromechanical feedback systems using low-friction flexural suspensions (*361*, *387*) are commercially available. The choice of flyback or parabolic modes of motion is offered. Other systems which meet the requirements for drift-free and noise-free operation will no doubt be marketed in the future.

2. *The Detector*

The requirement for a low-noise, high-resolution detector for the 23.8 keV γ-rays of ^{119m}Sn can be met by three types of systems listed in the order of increasing expense: NaI(Tl) scintillation counters, proportional counters, and lithium-drifted germanium and silicon solid state detectors. NaI scintillation crystals integrally mounted on a photomultiplier tube are in most general use for tin because of both their low cost and higher resolution in the energy range of the tin-119*m* γ-ray. More recently "resonant counting" systems have been developed (*173*, *338*, *380*, *381*) in which an absorber tin compound is located inside a Geiger or proportional counter. Internal conversion electrons or X-rays emitted in the subsequent decay of the excited state trigger the counter and are recorded with virtual 100% efficiency since the secondary emitter is located inside the counter. Only recoil-free γ-rays are detected, whereas conventional methods give the Mössbauer γ-ray against a background of nonresonant radiation from which it must be distinguished. Fortunately, the K-absorption edge of palladium (24.36 keV) is very close to the energy (23.8 keV) of interest, and a thin foil of palladium metal which will absorb the 25.3 keV X-ray of tin-119*m* is usually used as a filter, combined with electronic energy discriminators.

3. *Data Handling*

The γ-ray counts in predetermined ranges of Doppler velocity are usually stored in the memory bank of a multichannel analyzer. The data are presented as a velocity (channel number) vs. number of counts per channel plot. The application of curve-fitting techniques is often desirable.

4. *The Geometry of the Experiment*

While up to now almost all Mössbauer spectra have been obtained in transmission (see Fig. 2), more recently the possibilities of using Mössbauer

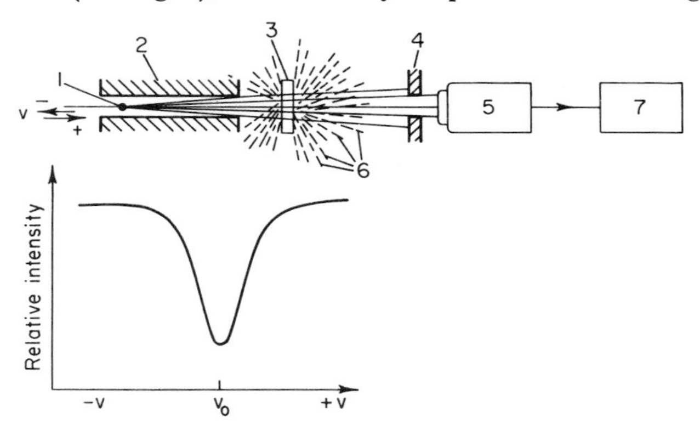

FIG. 2. Experimental arrangement for observing the resonance absorption of γ_1-quanta: (1) the source of γ-quanta, which moves with velocity ν_1 relative to a stationary absorber; (2) source collimator; (3) absorber under investigation; (4) collimator; (5) radiation detector; (6) γ-quanta scattered by the absorber; and (7) electronic pulse-handling and -storing devices.

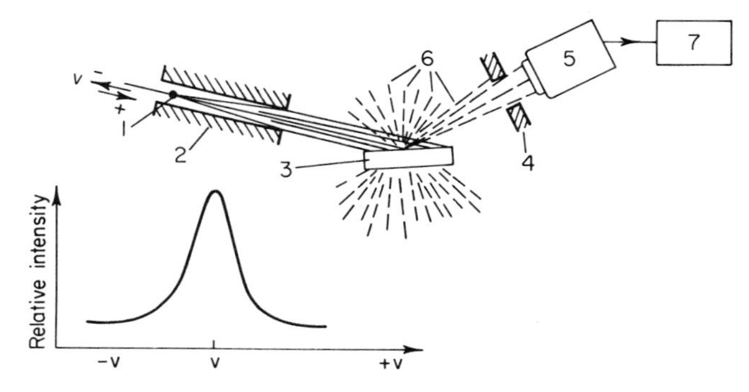

FIG. 3. Experimental arrangement for observing the resonance scattering of γ_1-quanta: (1), (2), (4–7) are the same as in Fig. 2; (3) scattering material under investigation.

spectroscopy to study surfaces by back-scattering have received attention (*355*). While the technical difficulties in such an arrangement as pictured in Fig. 3 are more severe, there are experimental situations in which transmission geometry is denied to the investigator. For example, a back-scattering Mössbauer spectrometer might ride in a Mars probe in order to detect tin-bearing minerals on the Martian surface. Other, more commonplace applications in tin chemistry and technology are sure to be developed.

5. *Cryostats* (*372*)

Most Mössbauer measurements on organotin compounds must be carried out at cryoscopic temperatures because of low recoil-free fractions at room temperature. Cooling with liquid nitrogen is always sufficient to produce a spectrum in reasonable time. The cryostat employed must incorporate thin transmission windows to avoid the absorption of low-energy ^{119m}Sn γ-rays. Glass dewars are thus of limited usefulness. Metal dewars with windows of Mylar or aluminum foil secured by O rings provide low-absorption transmission.

6. *The Sample*

Mössbauer spectroscopy is confined to the study of solids, but there is no requirement that the solids be crystalline. Polycrystalline powders, single crystals, or amorphous materials may be used. Spectra can also be measured in disks prepared by dissolving an organotin compound in poly(methylmethacrylate) or polyethylene polymers with a suitable organic solvent and then evaporating the solvent (*6*, *59*, *81*, *108*, *119*, *316*). More exciting is the possibility of recording the Mössbauer spectra of the same solutions used for IR, UV–visible, or NMR studies by very rapid freezing to produce organic glasses. An extension of this technique to the study of saline water as ice is also possible. Matrix isolation techniques can allow the tin compound to be examined just as it exists in the gas phase or in solution.

7. *The Calibration Problem*

The velocity calibration of Mössbauer spectrometers has proved to be an unexpected difficulty. Unfortunately, spectrometers are almost never calibrated against fundamental standards of length and time.[2] Since

[2] A He–Ne laser interferometer designed for this purpose is now available from Austin Science Associates of Austin, Texas.

checking of constant-acceleration movers with their sinusoidal or parabolic motion would be difficult in any case, and the nominally constant velocity would need to be known to a small fraction of a percent, most spectrometers are calibrated against a standard spectrum. In ^{57}Fe work, for example, the doublet spectrum of sodium nitroprusside (disodium pentacyanonitroso ferrate dihydrate) serves to calibrate the velocity scale of the mover in both an absolute as well as a relative way, and also serves as the reference standard to which all iron data are compared. It is of interest to examine some of the characteristics of a material which would recommend it as an appropriate choice for such a standard: (a) it must be readily available, inexpensive, stable with time and easily purified and handled; it must not deteriorate under laboratory conditions; (b) it must be well defined chemically and physically; (c) it must possess a large recoil-free fraction at room temperature, obviating the need for isotopic enrichment or cryostating; (d) the linewidth must be nearly theoretical; (e) the energy should fall in the same region as for other compounds and should have a low temperature coefficient; and (f) it should have a simple, well-resolved doublet spectrum which would provide a calibration of the linearity of the velocity of the mover. Sodium nitroprusside is now supplied as a Standard Reference Material by the U.S. National Bureau of Standards (SRM-725).

Unfortunately, at this writing no satisfactory standard reference material for tin is at hand. At present α- and β-tin, Mg_2Sn, Pd(Sn), and SnO_2 (or $BaSnO_3$) are all to be found in the literature as standards used by various laboratories. The lack of a single, certified, standard makes precise comparison of data from different laboratories impossible. Since the exact energy of any given source is somewhat dependent upon its particular prehistory, even data taken from different spectrometers equipped with sources of the same chemical composition cannot be compared with confidence. Because of these factors it is hazardous to draw chemical conclusions from small differences in data taken from more than one laboratory.

The search for a suitable standard reference material is being pursued. Since tin resonances are broad compared with those of ^{57}Fe, the splitting of the doublet in a tin standard should be greater than that in sodium nitroprusside (1.73 mm/sec). The possibility of using a mixture (or laminate) of two compounds, each producing a single sharp line, has been raised, but a standard of this type would violate criteria (a) and (b) above. Recently dimethyltin difluoride has been suggested as a possible choice (*361a*).

E. Parameters of Mössbauer Spectra

The parameters of the Mössbauer experiment are briefly summarized below with reference to the six parts of Fig. 4:

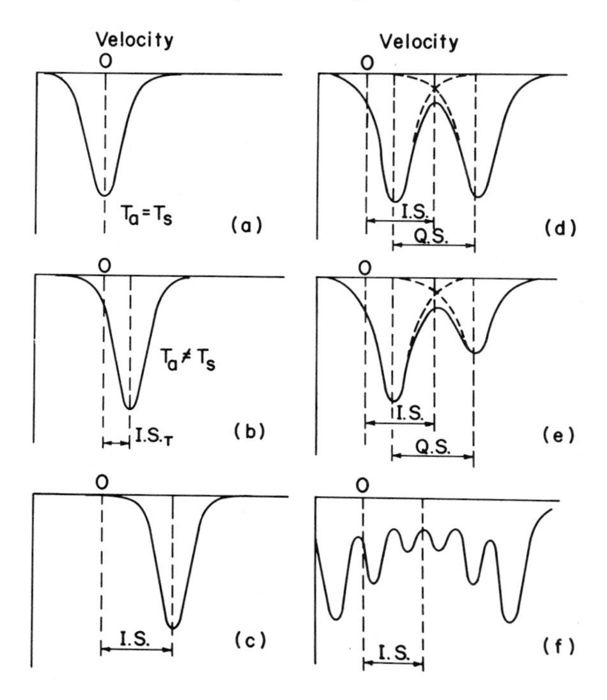

FIG. 4. Parameters of Mössbauer spectra.

(a) Source = absorber. The peak area is proportional to the recoil-free fraction, f', of the absorber where

$$f' = \exp - \frac{4\pi^2 \langle \bar{r}^2 \rangle}{\lambda^2} \tag{1}$$

and $\langle \bar{r}^2 \rangle$ is the mean square of the amplitude of atomic displacement.

(b) Source = absorber, but the temperatures of the two solids are different. The temperature shift of the resonance line, δ, is given by

$$\delta = \frac{E_R \langle \bar{v}^2 \rangle}{2c^2} \tag{2}$$

where $\langle \bar{v}^2 \rangle$ is the mean square velocity of the atom in vibrational motion.

(c) Source $\neq$ absorber. The isomer shift of the resonance line, I.S., is given by

$$\text{I.S.} = \frac{4\pi}{5} Ze^2 R^2 \frac{\Delta R}{R}[|\psi(0)|_a{}^2 - |\psi(0)|_s{}^2] \tag{3}$$

where the nucleus is of atomic number Z and radius R and ΔR is the change in nuclear radius in decay from the excited isomeric state.

(d) Source $\neq$ absorber, and the absorber nucleus experiences an electric field gradient, eq, the quadrupole splitting, Q.S., is given by

$$\text{Q.S.} = \frac{e^2 qQ}{4I(2I-1)}[3m^2 - I(I+1)]\left(1+\frac{\eta^2}{3}\right)^{1/2} \tag{4}$$

where I is the nuclear spin quantum number, m the magnetic quantum number, eQ the quadrupole moment of the nucleus, and η the asymmetry parameter. For tin nuclei this reduces to

$$\text{Q.S.} = \frac{e^2 qQ}{2}\left(1+\frac{\eta^2}{3}\right)^{1/2} \tag{5}$$

(e) Source $\neq$ absorber, the absorber nucleus experiences an electric field gradient and the anisotropy of the recoil-free fraction, f', gives rise to asymmetries in the line intensities of doublet spectra, even in polycrystalline samples [the Goldanskii-Karyagin effect].

(f) Source $\neq$ absorber, and the absorber nucleus experiences a magnetic field, H. The nuclear Zeeman splitting is given by

$$\Delta = -\frac{\mu H m}{I} \tag{6}$$

where μ is the magnetic moment of the nucleus and m and I are the magnetic and spin quantum numbers.

While a detailed discussion of all the parameters which can be derived from Mössbauer spectroscopy and their significance is beyond the scope of this review, there follows a brief exposition of each with particular relation to ^{119m}Sn Mössbauer spectroscopy.

1. *The Isomer Shift*

As in the more familiar NMR spectra, Mössbauer spectra show a shift, and frequently a splitting. The splittings in the Mössbauer case arise for totally different reasons than the NMR spin–spin couplings, and these will be discussed in the next section. Both shifts, however, arise from rather similar causes, but the physics of the Mössbauer shift is somewhat more straightforward. The term "isomer shift" (I.S.) has been almost universally adopted, although chemical shift or chemical isomer shift are preferred by some authors.

Experimentally, the I.S. is the displacement of the resonance from zero relative velocity as shown in Fig. 4c. The Mössbauer experiment always involves a pair of compounds, the emitter (source) and the absorber. When these are identical, the I.S. is zero. When two different chemical compounds are used, the I.S. represents the mismatch of the two sets of nuclear energy levels, expressed in Doppler shift energy units (mm/sec). The precise value of the energy level separation in each compound is never measured directly. Relative motion of the source–absorber pair toward one another (taken as positive velocity) adds energy to the emitted γ-ray to bring an absorber nucleus with a larger level spacing into resonance. Thus a series of absorbers can be compared with a single defined chemical state (the source), or by the use of data derived from a given source, with one another (but see Section II,D,7).

This mismatch of the two sets of nuclear levels arises from the interaction of the two nuclei with their electronic environments. This is an electric monopole interaction.

The relationship between the I.S. and the electric field density at the nucleus is given by

$$\text{I.S.} = \frac{4\pi}{5} Ze^2 R^2 \left(\frac{\Delta R}{R}\right)[\rho_a(0) - \rho_s(0)] \tag{7}$$

where the absorber and source nuclei are of atomic number Z and radius R and experience a total electric field density, ρ. The effect is called the isomer shift because it depends on the difference in the nuclear radii of the ground and excited isomeric states, ΔR. From this equation we see that the I.S. for any nuclide is the product of a constant term $[(4\pi/5)Ze^2 R^2]$, a nuclear term $[\Delta R/R]$, and an extranuclear, atomic electronic term $[\rho_a(0) - \rho_s(0)]$.

Chemists replace $\rho(0)$, the total electric field density at the nucleus, by $|\Psi(0)|^2$, the square of the total wave function for the atom evaluated at the nucleus

$$\text{I.S.} = \text{const.} \frac{\Delta R}{R}[|\Psi(0)|_a{}^2 - |\Psi(0)|_s{}^2] \tag{8}$$

Further, of the types of electrons in the atom, only the s-electron density does not vanish at the nucleus $[|\psi_{ns}(0)|^2 \neq 0]$ and we can further modify the expression to[3]

$$\text{I.S.} = \text{const.}\frac{\Delta R}{R}[|\psi_{ns}(0)|_a{}^2 - |\psi_{ns}(0)|_s{}^2] \quad (9)$$

Thus the I.S. is directly sensitive to changes in *s*-electron density and, thereby, indirectly dependent upon the other electrons in the atom. The I.S. is perhaps the most important parameter to the chemist. To relate the I.S. to $|\psi_{ns}(0)|^2$ requires knowledge of the sign and magnitude of the fractional change in the nuclear charge radius on excitation, $\Delta R/R$. The sign of the change in the charge radius of the ^{119}Sn nucleus on excitation has been the subject of recent theoretical controversy (*28*, *32*, *102*, *154*, *160*), now happily resolved as a result of elegant high-resolution internal conversion measurements of the electron lines from the 23.87 keV Ml transition in ^{119m}Sn which give the value $+3.3 \times 10^{-10}$ (*34*). While the exact magnitude of the $\Delta R/R$ term for tin is still at this writing a point of contention (*200*), our discussion remains valid so long as the value of this ratio remains invariant with chemical state. More serious at present for our purposes are the assumptions implicit in the usual practice of replacing $\rho(0)$ by the total electron density at the nucleus, $|\Psi(0)|^2$, and then by $|\psi_{ns}(0)|^2$, the total *s*-electron density at the nucleus, and further, by $|\psi_{5s}(0)|^2$, assuming that the changes in the field at the nucleus arise from changes in the valence (5*s* for tin) electrons alone.

This treatment neglects the influence of the *p*, *d*, and *f* electrons, and it ignores the indirect effects of screening by the inner *s* electrons and the resultant shrinkage of the tin atom on loss of electrons from the valence shell, both of which, for example, would tend to counteract the change in $|\Psi(0)|^2$ on oxidation.

Second-order effects could predominate in the relationship between the I.S. and the electron population, but it is generally true for the compounds thus far examined that ^{119m}Sn I.S. values seem to be related by

$$\text{I.S.} = \text{const.}\frac{\Delta R}{R}[|\psi_{5s}(0)|_a{}^2 - |\psi_{5s}(0)|_s{}^2] \quad (10)$$

[3] This is strictly true only for a point nucleus, while Eq. (7) is developed for nuclei of finite radii. Thus other types of electrons will be found within the nucleus as well, but their direct effect is expected to be small.

It is worth mentioning the investigations of the pressure dependence of the I.S., if only to illustrate the true complexity of the situation. Early work on metallic tin indicated that the I.S. became smaller with increasing pressure (*190*), contrary to the simple view that with decreasing volume the density of the electrons at the tin nucleus should increase. Apparently in this case the density of at least the *s* electrons decreases with the application of pressure. Later work with tin(IV) oxide at 150 kbar, however, showed an increase in the I.S. value (*121*). The latest experiment, and incidentally, the sole reference in the literature of ^{119m}Sn Mössbauer spectroscopy by Mössbauer himself, shows a sign reversal in the dependence of I.S. on pressure in Mg_2Sn at 60 kbar; $|\Psi(0)|^2$ first increases, then decreases with the application of pressure (*177*). Thus, while the simple relationship between the I.S. and $|\psi_{ns}(0)|^2$ generally holds, it is not altogether unreasonable to expect that inversions will be found.

The standard of isomer shift used in this article will be SnO_2. The vast majority of the available data were recorded with reference to $^{119m}SnO_2$ sources, and the best current source material, $BaSnO_3$, has the same I.S. as SnO_2 within experimental error. The relative energies of the various conventional source materials are as follows:

$$\beta\text{-Sn} > Mg_2Sn > \alpha\text{-Sn} > Pd(Sn) > BaSnO_3 = SnO_2.$$

2. *The Quadrupole Splitting*

We will consider three types of multipole interactions of a nucleus with its environment in an atom: the electric monopole arising from the electric charge on the nucleus, eZ; the magnetic dipole arising from the magnetic dipole moment of the nucleus, μ; and the electric quadrupole arising from the electric quadrupole moment of the nucleus, eQ. The isomer shift discussed in the last section arises from the electric monopole interaction. The magnetic dipole interaction or nuclear Zeeman effect will be discussed in the next section. In this section we will briefly describe the interaction of the nuclear quadrupole with gradients in the extranuclear electric field.

There is an old chestnut to the effect that a charge (pole) moves in a field toward the opposite pole; a dipole rotates in a field to achieve the lowest energy orientation ($+ \leftrightarrow -$). A dipole moves along a field gradient; a quadrupole rotates in a field gradient to achieve the lowest energy orientation.

Any nuclear state with a spin greater than $\frac{1}{2}$ has a quadrupole moment,

eQ, coulomb-cm^2, and this can align itself either with or across an electric field gradient, eq, volts/cm^2. In the case of tin-119 the situation is represented in Fig. 5. The excited spin $\frac{3}{2}$ state has a quadrupole moment and this state can be split into two by the interaction with a nonspherically symmetric electric field produced by the placement of the extranuclear charges. The presence of a non-zero field gradient at the nucleus is determined primarily by the symmetry of the distribution of electrons about the nucleus, which

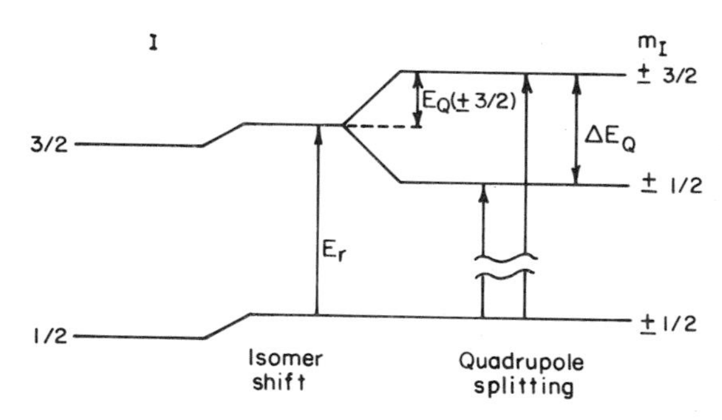

FIG. 5. The origin of quadrupole splitting.

is in turn determined by the symmetry of the bonding of the tin atom in question. Cubic symmetry (tetrahedral or octahedral arrangement of identical attached atoms) will result in a zero field gradient, whereas quadrupolar splitting of spectral lines will be expected for lower symmetries. The magnitude of E_Q is directly observed as the quadrupole splitting (Q.S.) which is given for the case of a tin-119 nucleus as

$$\Delta E_Q = E_{3/2} - E_{1/2} = \frac{e^2 qQ}{2}\left(1+\frac{\eta^2}{3}\right)^{1/2} \tag{11}$$

where $E_{3/2}$ and $E_{1/2}$ are the energies associated with those values of the magnetic quantum number m as in Fig. 5, e is the electronic charge, and η, called the asymmetry parameter, is related to the magnitudes of the three principal moments of the electrostatic field gradient which are the second derivatives of the potential with respect to each coordinate, $\partial^2 V/\partial z^2$, $\partial^2 V/\partial y^2$, and $\partial^2 V/\partial x^2$, and is given by

$$\eta = \frac{|(\partial^2 V/\partial y^2) - (\partial^2 V/\partial x^2)|}{\partial^2 V/\partial z^2} \tag{12}$$

When the tin atom is at a lattice site which experiences an axially symmetric field, i.e., one in which $\partial^2 V/\partial x^2 = \partial^2 V/\partial y^2$, $\eta = 0$, Eq. (12) reduces to

$$\Delta E_Q = \pm \frac{eQV_{zz}}{2} \tag{13}$$

where $V_{zz} = \partial^2 V/\partial z^2$ is the principal axis of the electric field gradient (e.f.g.). The product eQV_{zz} is the quadrupole coupling constant. In this manner the magnitude, but not the sign of the quantity QV_{zz} can be derived from a spectrum showing Q.S., even though in the case of tin-119 the nucleus has a quadrupole moment only in the excited state. Nuclear quadrupole resonance allows the determination of quadrupole interaction constants for nuclei which are quadrupolar in the ground state. Thus the two techniques complement one another.

The sign of ΔE_Q can be established by studying the relative intensities of the two lines of the doublet produced by a single-crystal absorber as a function of the angle of observation relative to known crystallographic axes or by the study of the relative intensities of the six lines of the spectrum produced in an applied magnetic field as discussed in Section III,C,3. Like the I.S., the Q.S. is produced as the product of a constant term $[e^2/2]$, a nuclear term (Q), and an extranuclear, atomic term $(q[1+(\eta^2/3)]^{1/2})$. The quadrupole moment of the ^{119m}Sn excited state, Q, is -0.08×10^{-24} cm^2.

Two important sources of the electric field gradient in other atoms—charges on distant ions, and the incompletely filled electron shells of the atom itself—will probably not concern us here. Distant ions can contribute if the symmetry of their array is lower than cubic. The e.f.g from the distant charges can distort the electrons of the atom so as to create an e.f.g. of their own which usually serves to amplify the e.f.g. arising from the distant charges, a phenomenon known as antishielding. Antishielding is more important in ionic lattices, and we shall ignore it in discussions of molecular organotin crystals. The even more important e.f.g. due to electrons in partially filled, nonspherical orbitals will not be a matter of concern in tin chemistry.

Our discussions will be simplified by the assumption that the e.f.g. at the tin nucleus is due only to the surrounding electrons and that the rôle played by the atoms directly bonded to the resonant tin atom is to distort this electronic environment from the spherical symmetry it otherwise has. Thus we expect no Q.S. when the tin atom occupies a site of tetrahedral or octahedral symmetry.

3. *The Magnetic Splitting*

In Fig. 5 both the $+m$ and $-m$ states occur at the same energy in an asymmetric electric field. This degeneracy can be removed in a magnetic field. Such a field is experienced by impurity tin atoms in a ferromagnetic material, or by a nonmagnetic tin compound in an applied magnetic field. Under these conditions a nuclear Zeeman effect is observed, as depicted in Fig. 6 where each nuclear energy level is split into $(2m+1)$ components.

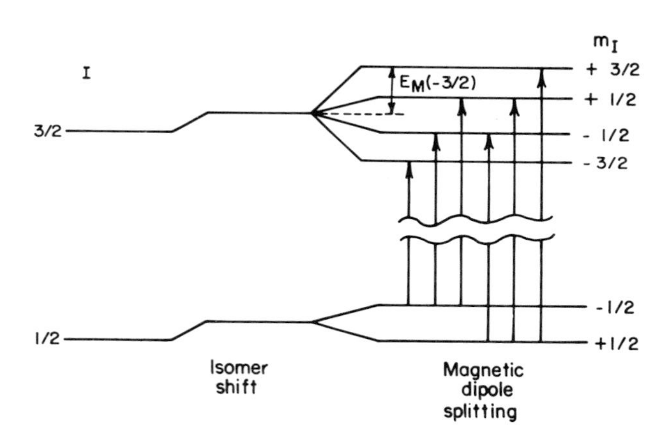

FIG. 6. The origin of magnetic splitting.

The selection rules which govern allowed transitions between these substates result in a six-line spectrum as in Fig. 4f. The energies of these levels are given by Eq. 6. As in the case of the I.S. and Q.S., the energy depends both upon a nuclear factor, μ, and an extranuclear factor H. It is worth comparing this situation to that found in NMR spectroscopy. In NMR, transitions are found to occur between adjacent sublevels of the ground state, while in Mössbauer spectroscopy of nuclei in a magnetic field ("Magbauer") the observed transitions are between sublevels of the ground and excited nuclear states. The two techniques differ in energy by a factor of 10^{10}, but the definition of the Mössbauer γ-ray allows these hyperfine interactions to be resolved.

The even spacing of the lines in Fig. 4f is modified if quadrupolar interactions are also present, and small quadrupolar perturbations can be detected in the magnetic experiment (*112a*).

4. *The Magnitude of the Resonance Effect*

The first three parameters considered above, I.S., Q.S., and nuclear Zeeman splitting, arise from the electromagnetic interaction of the nucleus with molecular and crystalline electric fields and internal and applied magnetic fields. The next parameters which will be considered depend upon the dynamics of motion of the emitting and absorbing nuclei.

The first of the dynamical parameters is obtainable directly from the usual Mössbauer spectrum. The magnitude of the resonance effect, ϵ, is commonly reported as a percentage

$$\epsilon = 100\left[\frac{R-R_0}{R}\right] \tag{14}$$

where R_0 is the counting rate at the resonance maximum and R the rate at a Doppler velocity well removed from the resonance maximum. The magnitude measured is not a fundamental quantity, but depends upon a number of experimental factors such as the fraction of counts included due to non-recoil-free events, velocity-dependent solid angle effects, pulse shape-dependent counter dead-time effects, and the number of absorber nuclei in the optical path.

5. *The Recoil-Free Fraction*

The magnitude of the effect, ϵ, can be related under certain conditions to the recoil-free fraction, f, but it should not be confused with it. The probability of the Mössbauer effect depends upon the amplitude of thermal motion of the Mössbauer nucleus. When this motion is unbounded, the probability of the effect is zero. The fraction of recoil-free, or Mössbauer, events is dependent on the ratio of the mean square vibrational amplitude, $\langle\bar{r}^2\rangle$, of the emitting or absorbing nucleus to the square of the wavelength, λ, of the scattered radiation. This dependence can be understood on the basis of a classical explanation. Movement of the emitting atom over distances comparable to a wavelength during the emission process will destroy the phase coherence of the emitted wave and parts of this wave will interfere destructively and be weakened at the natural frequency of the emitter.

The recoil-free fraction, f, is expressed as

$$f = \exp - \frac{4\pi^2\langle\bar{r}^2\rangle}{\lambda^2} \tag{15}$$

where $\langle \bar{r}^2 \rangle$ is the mean square amplitude of the vibration in the direction of emission of the γ-ray, averaged over the lifetime of the nuclear level involved in the γ-ray emission process. Thus unbounded motion as in a liquid or gas will cause the recoil-free fraction to vanish. It may be noted that Eq. (15) gives no indication that periodicity is required and it is thus not surprising that the Mössbauer effect is observed in amorphous solids and frozen solutions. If the binding of the atom is anisotropic then the mean square amplitude of its motion will be different in different directions along the crystallographic axes, and oriented single crystals will exhibit anisotropic recoil-free fractions.

A number of methods for evaluating the recoil-free fraction of a source, f, and of an absorber, f', are available. Evaluation generally requires knowledge of the natural linewidth, Γ, and of the experimental source and absorber linewidths, Γ_s and Γ_a. Unfortunately, the obtaining of reliable f' values is not simple or straightforward (*128*, *212*, *216*), and many of the values quoted in the early literature show discrepancies and are unreliable.

6. *Line Asymmetries in Doublet Spectra*

Asymmetries in the intensities of component lines of doublet spectra of polycrystalline material were observed for organotin halides early on (*5*, *59*, *99*, *103*, *104*, *107*, *152*, *203*) and have been interpreted by Karyagin as due to the lattice-dynamic anisotropy in the recoil-free fraction, f', of the absorber (*145*). The phenomenon has been referred to as the Goldanskii-Karyagin effect (*213*, *245*). That the anisotropy of the recoil-free fraction does not disappear even in a randomly oriented polycrystalline powder may seem at first surprising, but it comes about from the fact that the various hyperfine components themselves have intensities which are a function of the direction of emission relative to the crystallographic axes, and therefore, provide means of taking spatially weighted averages of the recoil-free fraction. While the early results for triphenyltin chloride (*5*, *59*) have been disputed (*203*), the Goldanskii-Karyagin effect has been observed in a number of linear polymeric organotin absorbers such as trimethyltin fluoride, cyanide, and hydroxide and triphenyltin hydroxide (*213*, *214*), and in the two-dimensional layer structure of dioctyltin oxide (*214a*), where the amplitude of motion of the tin atoms is anisotropic (*213*, *214*).

7. *The Linewidth*

In the ideal Mössbauer experiment the observed linewidth, Γ_{obs}, is simply twice the natural linewidth, Γ, as given by the Heisenberg uncertainty principle

$$\Gamma = \frac{h}{2\pi\tau} \tag{16}$$

where τ is the mean lifetime of the excited state ($=2.67 \times 10^{-8}$ second for ^{119m}Sn) which gives the natural linewidth of 2.4×10^{-8} eV quoted in Table I or 0.31 mm/sec in Doppler shift units. Thus the narrowest line observable would be 0.62 mm/sec. In practice Γ_{obs} is always larger than 2Γ. Several experimental factors responsible for line broadening are mentioned in Section II,F,3. Sections II,E,1,2, and 3 treated the electromagnetic effects on spectra giving rise to completely resolved hyperfine structure. However, in many experiments the hyperfine structure is not observed, and instead only broadened resonance lines are seen. In cases where tin atoms experience several different environments in the same material, the slightly shifted single lines will combine to produce an envelope with $\Gamma_{obs} > 2\Gamma$. Single line broadening may arise from several factors acting simultaneously; interpretation of its cause in any given case may be a very complicated and difficult problem.

8. *Dependence of the Parameters on Temperature*

It can be shown that the recoil-free fraction of a molecular crystal will always be smaller than that for a network polymeric lattice. In the former there are stronger bonds within the molecular unit than between units, while the unit itself has larger mass than in the latter case where the individual masses may be quite small, but where all the bonds are strong. It can be further shown that the dependence of the recoil-free fraction, f', on temperature is sharply increased in a molecular crystal where the f' value can be very low at higher temperatures. This fact underlies the need to cryostat organotin samples. At liquid nitrogen temperatures the f' value can be close to unity, even for molecular crystals. The f' value increases at any temperature if weak van der Waals interactions are replaced by hydrogen or donor–acceptor covalent bonds between discrete molecules in the crystal. The temperature dependence of the f' value diminishes at the same time.

The isomer shift is also temperature-dependent through a second-order

Doppler shift. The temperature shift, $E_R \bar{v}^2/2c^2$ [see Eq. (2)], appears as a higher order term in the treatment of resonance absorption. Since the temperature difference between the source and absorber in tin work is rarely greater than 225° K, and the total shift for this temperature difference is less than one linewidth, it is usual to ignore this correction. This discussion is based on the assumption that the *s*-electron density at the nucleus, $|\psi_{ns}(0)|^2$ is independent of temperature. In principle, variation of $|\psi_{ns}(0)|^2$ with temperature is possible if there are strong fields in the solid which vary with temperature.

For there to be a change of quadrupole splitting with temperature, it is necessary to have an electronic excited state which is close enough to the electronic ground state to be thermally populated at ambient temperatures. This effect is usually more serious in atoms heavier than tin.

The temperature dependence of the magnetic hyperfine interaction (Zeeman splitting) is, of course, closely related to the temperature dependence of the magnetism.

F. Tin as a Mössbauer Element

1. *General Considerations*

Tin is one of at least 32 elements for which the Mössbauer effect has been observed, and there are a further 17 for which a Mössbauer effect has been predicted. The considerations which make possible the use of any given nuclide include the following:

(a) *The lifetime of the excited state.* The width of the resonance line is inversely proportional to the lifetime of the excited state; a very long lifetime may produce a linewidth so narrow that observation will be difficult if not impossible. Suitable lifetimes are in the range of 10^{-6} to 10^{-12} second. The value for ^{119m}Sn is 2.67×10^{-8} second.

(b) *The energy of the transition.* Acceptable γ-ray energies are found in the 5–200 keV range. With high-energy γ-radiation the recoil effects are such that the recoil-free fraction will be low even at cryogenic temperatures, and observation of the Mössbauer event becomes unlikely. For very low energy γ-rays the problems of transmission through absorbers are aggravated. In addition it becomes a much more difficult matter to resolve the energy of interest from the general low-energy background. The energy of the ^{119m}Sn γ-ray is 23.8 keV.

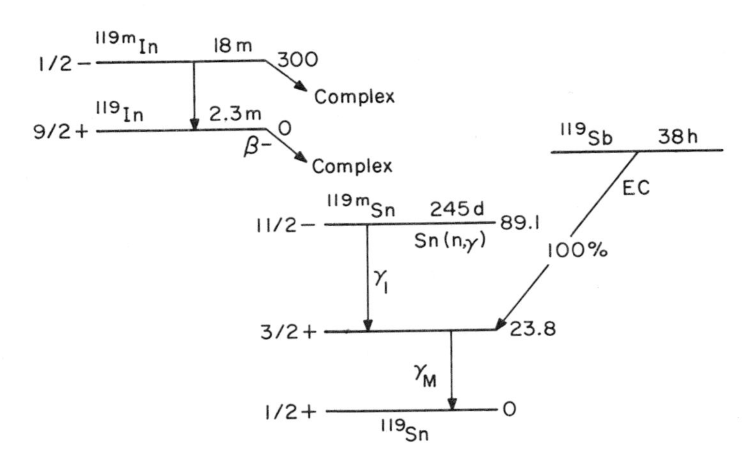

FIG. 7. Characteristics of ^{119}Sn.

TABLE III

CHARACTERISTICS OF ^{119}Sn[a]

Measured properties		
Half-life of the Mössbauer level	1.84×10^{-8} sec	
Total internal conversion coefficient of the Mössbauer transition	5.5	
Natural abundance of ^{119}Sn	8.58%	
Magnetic moment of Mössbauer level	+0.70 nm	
Magnetic moment of ground level	−1.046 nm	
Quadrupole moment of Mössbauer level	−0.97 BM	
Derived parameters		
Resonance cross section	1.321×10^{-18} cm^2	
Natural width, Γ	2.480×10^{-11} keV	
Minimum observable width	0.6227 mm/sec	
Recoil energy, E_R	2.572×10^{-3} eV	
Energies and intensities	E_γ	I
Mössbauer γ-ray	23.875 keV	(*100*)
Precursor γ-ray	65.66 keV	(*155*)
K X-ray	28.5 keV	

[a] Taken from "Mössbauer Effect Data Index 1958–1965" (A. H. Muir, Jr., K. J. Ando, and H. M. Coogan, eds.), p. 126. Wiley (Interscience), New York, 1966.

In connection with both (a) and (b) above, it is of interest to examine the energy definition Γ/E. Short-lifetime excited states will give rise to Γ/E values too large and resonance selectivity would be lost. An extremely small Γ/E ratio would reduce the probability of recoil-free emission and the possibility of observation would be slight. The most promising range for the Γ/E ratio is 10^{-10} to 10^{-14}. The Γ/E ratio for tin is 10^{-12}.

(c) *The natural abundance of the ground-state absorber nuclei.* To avoid the problems involved in isotopic enrichment, the natural abundance of the Mössbauer nuclide should be several percent. A high natural abundance of the precursor nuclide will also contribute to the ease of production of source material. Tin-118 and -119 are 23.84% and 8.58%, respectively, of naturally occurring tin.

(d) *The lifetime of the precursor state.* It is desirable to have a reasonably long-lived precursor nuclide which, once prepared, can be utilized in a series of Mössbauer experiments. In the case of tin, the 245-day tin-119*m* can be used for a few half-lives, giving over a year's service from each source.

(e) *The absence of interfering radiation.* Resolution of the Mössbauer γ-ray from other X- and γ-radiation will be more difficult the closer this interference is to the energy of interest. An example of this is the 25.27 keV X-ray emitted in ^{119m}Sn decay (the internal conversion process involving the 65 keV transition in ^{119m}Sn also produces X-rays at 25.04 and 28.49 keV). Fortunately, palladium metal which has a K-absorption edge of 24.36 keV can be used to filter this radiation.

2. *Tin*-119*m*

A schematic diagram showing the nuclear transitions leading to the ^{119}Sn ground state is presented in Fig. 7. Table III gives various measured and derived quantities.

3. *Tin Sources*

Since the strength of the Mössbauer effect, as measured by the fraction of events which are recoil-free as well as the width of the resonance line, varies a good deal with the host matrix for the tin-119*m*, a suitable solid-state environment is essential for strong sources with sharp resonance lines. The best results for each isotope have been found mainly by trial and error. An "ideal" tin source would have a recoil-free fraction of unity, and produce γ-rays of the natural linewidth. The source material should be easily prepared and handled, and should be chemically inert. The characteristics of the radiation emitted should not be sensitive to the method of preparation or prehistory of the particular source which would render difficult the comparison of data with other investigators using the same source material. The radiation, for example, apart from strength, should not change with time. The host material itself should not give rise to interfering X-rays, or photoelectric or Compton scattering. With a half-life of 245 days, the initial strength of a tin-119*m* source should be at least 1 mCi to allow for one or two half-lives of use. Tin sources of 5 and even 10 mCi are becoming commercially available, but it is necessary that the specific activity be high enough so that the source can be fabricated with a surface diameter consistent with a thickness providing low absorption of γ-rays within the source itself.

Broadening of the resonance lines comes about as a result of the finite thickness of the source and absorber, the presence of impurities, thermal noise, the velocity resolution of the mover as influenced by vibration, the presence of solid-state defects in the source and absorber, etc. The technology of Mössbauer spectroscopy has been devoted to the effort of minimization of these effects. The linewidth can never be less than 2Γ.

Tin-119*m* is produced by neutron irradiation of tin-118 in the thermal flux of a nuclear reactor. The target material in such irradiations is usually enriched beyond the 23.84% natural abundance of tin-118 and depleted in tin-119 to reduce self-absorption and line-broadening effects in the resultant 245-day nuclide. The first ^{119m}Sn Mössbauer experiments were carried out using ordinary white tin as the source matrix (*22*). This material apparently suffers from a small splitting of the resonance line (0.25 ± 0.02 mm/sec) (*172*) and a low recoil-free fraction at room temperature (*128*, *214*). Apart from α- and β-tin, four other host matrices have received wide use. Most of the data for the ~300 tin compounds examined thus far have been derived using $^{119m}SnO_2$ sources. The characteristics of each of the four sources currently employed are discussed below.

a. *$^{119m}SnO_2$*. Tin(IV) oxide has been the most popular host matrix for ^{119m}Sn. The reasons for this include a recoil-free fraction 12 to 18 times that of tin metal at room temperature and low cost derived because of ease of production from neutron irradiation of $^{118}SnO_2$ in high-flux reactors without the need for additional purification steps. Despite its advantages to earlier workers, tin(IV) oxide possesses characteristics which in the face of the availability of a wider range of host matrices now disqualify it from consideration. Chief among these is the noncubic symmetry of the tin sites in SnO_2 [which crystallizes in a rutile structure of point group symmetry D_{2h} (*347, 380, 391*)], which give rise to a small splitting (0.48 mm/sec) of the resonance line (*121, 172, 212, 215*). While precise values for the splitting are difficult to measure, the tin(IV) oxide source produces an inherently broad resonance line.

b. *$Mg_2{}^{119m}Sn$*. A detailed study of the characteristics of magnesium stannide as a host matrix has been carried out in the range 77°–290° K (*307*) and shows that such a source is capable of giving a resonance line of nearly natural width with a high recoil-free fraction at liquid nitrogen temperatures. To take advantage of these qualities, however, requires an experimental setup where the source can be cryostated. The recoil-free fraction of 0.77 ± 0.08 at 77° K drops to 0.28 ± 0.03 at 290° K (*50, 307*) (still 7 times greater than the recoil-free fraction of tin metal at room temperature). This, coupled with the air and moisture sensitivity of Mg_2Sn, impose limitations on the use of such sources. In addition it has been noted recently that nonstoichiometric melts of Mg_2Sn have shown considerable deviation in electrical and infrared absorption behavior (*212*). Such melts may contain two or more chemical environments giving rise to a broad line.

c. *$Pd(^{119m}Sn)$*. The possible usefulness of palladium–tin alloys emerged from the study of a wide variety of metal host matrices for ^{119m}Sn (*50, 51, 57*). Detailed study of the palladium–tin system (*122, 212*) has revealed that $Pd(^{119m}Sn)$ sources with up to 10–12% tin can be fabricated with large recoil-free fractions at room temperature (between 0.28 and 0.41 at 293° K) and very narrow linewidths (0.74 ± 0.06 mm/sec at 293° K). This source material is now commercially available and has received some use. However, since Pd(Sn) is a substitutional-type alloy there may exist different Pd_xSn_y compounds, depending upon the concentration of tin in palladium. The different tin environments may introduce line broadening (*212*). In addition, while the palladium metal acts as an internal filter of the unwanted higher energy X-ray flux accompanying the ^{119m}Sn decay, thereby obviating the need for the usual filters, the palladium photoelectric transitions give rise to lower energy X-rays (21.02, 21.18, and 23.82 keV) which are isotropically scattered.

d. *$Ba^{119m}SnO_3$*. At the present time the best source for ^{119m}Sn Mössbauer spectroscopy appears to be barium stannate, $BaSnO_3$, which can be readily prepared from reactor-irradiated SnO_2 by treatment with a stoichiometric quantity of BaO or $BaCO_3$ and heating in air to ∽1400° C for 1 hour. Alternatively, $BaSnO_3$ can be precipitated from aqueous solution. The recoil-free fraction of $Ba^{119m}SnO_3$ is the same at room temperature as the $Mg_2{}^{119m}Sn$ source at liquid nitrogen temperature ($f = 0.46$ at 693° K and 0.6 at 293° K), and the temperature dependence of f and of the γ-ray energy is small. The linewidth is measured to be 0.33 mm/sec or only 7% above the natural linewidth (*193*, *194*, *201*). Barium stannate sources are commercially available. Fortunately the energy of the $Ba^{119m}SnO_3$ γ-ray seems to be equal within experimental error (± 0.03 mm/sec) to that from $^{119m}SnO_2$. Thus the data from both sources are directly comparable without the necessity of conversion.

III

^{119m}Sn MÖSSBAUER SPECTROSCOPY

The sections which follow will treat the parameters of the Mössbauer effect of significance to ^{119m}Sn Mössbauer spectroscopy as applied to the study of organometallic compounds. The discussion will be limited to the isomer shift, the quadrupole splitting, the recoil-free fraction, and the line asymmetries in doublet spectra.

A. The ^{119m}Sn Mössbauer Isomer Shift

1. *The Relationship with* $|\psi_{ns}(0)|^2$

From the theory of the isomer shift,

$$\text{I.S.} = \frac{4\pi}{5} Ze^2 R^2 \left(\frac{\Delta R}{R}\right) [|\psi_{ns}(0)|_a{}^2 - |\psi_{ns}(0)|_s{}^2] \tag{17}$$

where it is assumed that the I.S. for a particular compound will depend on the s-electron density at the nucleus of the tin atom. The s-electron densities on the right-hand side of Eq. (17) can be rewritten as

$$|\psi_{ns}(0)|^2 = |\psi_{5s}(0)|^2 + 2 \sum_{n=1}^{4} |\psi_{ns}(0)|^2$$

taking account that it is only the valence electrons in the fifth quantum level which will take part in chemical bonding, leaving the electrons in the $n = 1$ to 4 shells chemically inert and spherically symmetric about the nucleus. Thus in this approximation the term $[|\psi_{ns}(0)|_a^2 - |\psi_{ns}(0)|_s^2]$ in Eq. (17) reduces to $[|\psi_{5s}(0)|_a^2 - |\psi_{5s}(0)|_s^2]$. The 5*s*-electron density is considered to be a parameter capable of continuous variation between 0 and 2. Calculating I.S. values theoretically would require independent evaluation of $|\psi_{5s}(0)|_a^2$, a difficult problem as tin is a 50-electron atom.

Recent attempts in this direction have utilized (a) the SCMO method of Pople, Santry, and Segal to obtain the 5*s*-orbital occupation numbers and the values of $|\psi_{5s}(0)|^2$ (*311*); (b) a Fermi-Segre-Goldsmit evaluation of $|\psi_{5s}(0)|^2$ using empirically determined values of the necessary shielding parameters (*105*); (c) Hartree-Fock self-consistent-field atomic wavefunctions (nonrelativistic) for different electronic configurations and charge states using an enhancement factor to correct $|\psi_{ns}(0)|^2$ for relativistic effects (*200*); (d) a Liberman-Waber-Cromer relativistic wavefunction for different electronic configurations and charge states (*160*); and (e) an LCAO-MO treatment approximating LCAO-MO-SCF wavefunctions for tin (*226*). Although calculations (a) through (d) were carried out in order to determine the value of $\Delta R/R$ by supplying $|\psi(0)|^2_a$ in combination with experimental I.S. values for tin compounds for which specific electronic configurations could be assigned, by using a reasonable value for $\Delta R/R$ [for example, $+3 \times 10^{-4}$ (*34*)], the results of the calculations can be used to establish the direct dependence of I.S. on $|\psi_{5s}(0)|_a^2$. A comparison of the various theoretical approaches is given in the discussion by Goldanskii and Makarov in Greenwood *et al.* (*311*).

In each of the treatments there emerges a linear relationship between the I.S. values and $|\psi_{5s}(0)|_a^2$, but the relationship is clearly too simple. This treatment neglects the influence of *p*, *d*, and *f* electrons and ignores other indirect effects such as the decrease in screening by the inner *s* electrons and resultant shrinkage of the tin atom on loss of electrons from the valence shell, both of which would tend to counteract changes in $|\psi_{5s}(0)|^2$ on oxidation. Also, the hypothesis that ^{119m}Sn isomer shifts can be correlated with the ionic character of tin bonds has been tested with reference to data for a number of series of simple homologous compounds of both tin(II) and tin(IV). No such reciprocal relation exists (*233*). The complexities of the real electronic situation at the tin atom are obviously very great.

Yet examination of I.S. data is reassuring. Not only do intuitive estimates of *s*-orbital occupancy seem a reliable guide to the rationalization of changes in I.S. values, but comparison with I.S. data for the analogous compounds of neighboring elements serves to test the correctness of the interpretation. For example, the correlation between the I.S. data for similar compounds of tin and antimony is very good. While ^{121}Sb Mössbauer spectroscopy is at this writing much less well developed, I.S. data tend to support the relationship with *s*-orbital population (*270*). Calculations using Hartree-Fock SCF nonrelativistic wave functions yield results for ^{121}Sb very much like those for tin (*200*).

In this connection it is important to mention the recent reports on the differential shifts of inner energy levels of tin in tin metal vs. SnO_2. The study of the K_α X-ray lines in tin shows that changes in the inner atomic levels with chemical bond formation can no longer be considered negligible. The values quoted for the Sn–SnO_2 shift are -0.152 ± 0.005 eV for the K level (*392*, *393*), and $+1.1 \pm 0.3$ eV for the L level (*384*) where the effect of oxidation is to decrease the binding of the K level and increase the binding of the L level. Detailed theoretical work on the problem of the effect of chemical bonding on inner shell electrons is necessary before satisfactory understanding of the relation between Mössbauer I.S. and chemical behavior can be achieved.

There are two common types of changes in the chemical state which are worthy of discussion in relation to the I.S. parameter: a change in oxidation or valence state, and a change in coordination number or hybridization on formation of a complex. These are discussed separately below.

2. *Isomer Shift and Valence State*

It is the practice of the chemist to distinguish the formal oxidation states of tin(II) and tin(IV), and further to write various electronic configurations for tin as shown in Table IV. The electron population in the 5*s*- subshell decreases from 2 to 0 as the list is descended, and the known I.S. values

TABLE IV

ELECTRONIC CONFIGURATIONS FOR TIN

Free tin atoms	Sn(Kr) $4d^{10}\,5s^2\,5p^2$
Sn^{2+}	$5s^2\,5p^0$
Covalent stannous	$5s^{2-n}\,5p^n$
Covalent stannic	$5sp^3$
Higher coordination stannic	$5sp^3\,d^n$
Sn^{4+}	$5s^0\,5p^0$

seem to follow the same order. The usual form of tin metal itself, called white tin or the β- or tetragonal form, reacts with hydrogen chloride gas to produce tin(II) compounds (*367*) and its I.S. value, commonly quoted as 2.65 mm/sec, can be taken as the dividing line between the two valencies: all compounds formally recognized as tin(IV) falling below and all as tin(II) above. There are no known exceptions to this rule. Interpretations of tin(II) data based only on covalent *s–p* hybridization correctly predict the order of I.S. values for all simple compounds but fluorides and oxides, where *s–p* mixing may arise from electrostatic crystal field effects absent in molecular solids (*85*).

3. *The Change in Isomer Shift on Complex Formation*

While the change in isomer shift on complex formation is usually not so striking as the change between valence states, nevertheless the I.S. is seen to move to smaller positive values with increasing coordination numbers in either tin(II) or tin(IV) species, and both complexes which arise through donor–acceptor interactions or ion formation follow this rule. Generally the donor–acceptor adducts of tin halides of both valence states are found at lower I.S. values than the analogous complex ions, but several exceptions are known.

a. *Formation of Neutral, Donor–Acceptor Adducts*. The I.S. of tin(II) halides moves to decreased positive values when complexation with nitrogen- and oxygen-containing organic ligands takes place (*87b*, *301*). Likewise, complexes of the tin(IV) halides with a variety of monodentate and chelating nitrogen- and oxygen-containing organic ligands show decreased positive I.S. values (*106*, *110*, *114*, *133*, *192*, *208*, *215*). In the tin(IV) series the thiourea, tetrahydrothiofuran (*106*, *192*), and tri-*n*-butylphosphine (*179*) adducts of $SnCl_4$ are exceptions. The effectiveness of the donor atom in reducing the I.S. value seems to follow the order $O > N > S > P$, but this begins to break down when organotin halides, R_nSnX_{4-n}, are used as the Lewis acid, and the breakdown becomes somewhat more serious with higher n. For example, while the I.S. values in the di-*n*-butyltin dihalide complexes with chelating aromatic amines are smaller than those for the organotin halide itself (*179*), the data for the trialkyltin chloride and bromide complexes with aromatic amines are mixed, and with the I.S. of complexes of trimethyltin bromide with all seven aromatic amines studied showing an increase in positive values (*181*).

b. *The Formation of Complex Ions*. In the tin(II) series ions of the SnX_3^- type (X = F, Cl) and $Sn_2F_5^-$ have been studied with a variety of gegenions. In all cases the values of the I.S. are lowered on complexation. In both groups of ions there is variation in I.S. with the polarizing power of the cation (*86*).

Data for all the tin(IV) halide ions of the SnX_6^{2-} type and some of the $SnX_4Y_2^{2-}$ type (*118c*, *294a*) are known, and the values are to lower positive I.S. from the SnX_4 species for all the gegen cations studied (*72*, *106*, *114*, *129*, *218*, *337*). It appears that the magnitude of the decrease in I.S. value for the change $SnX_4 \rightarrow SnX_6^{2-}$ decreases in the order $I > Br > Cl > F$.

The formation of the organotin(IV) anions $(CH_3)_2SnCl_3^-$ (*76*), $(C_6H_5)_2SnCl_3^-$ (*76*), n-$C_4H_9SnCl_5^{2-}$ (*76*), $C_6H_5SnCl_5^{2-}$ (*94a*), $(CH_3)_2SnCl_4^{2-}$ (*94*, *94a*), and $(CH_3)_3SnCl_2^-$ (*76*) of five- and six-coordination also leads to lower I.S. values. The organotin(IV) cations of five- and six-coordination also show decreased I.S. values as well, and, curiously enough, the species assigned formal anionic and cationic charge for any given organotin halide show the same I.S. values within experimental error despite their differences (*76*).

c. *Complex Formation and* $|\psi_{5s}(0)|^2$. The general situation is summarized in Table V. It is clear from these halides, as well as from the organotin(IV) anions and cations, that the decrease in I.S. value follows the coordination number at tin, and not, for example, the charge of the species produced.

TABLE V

THE CHANGE IN ISOMER SHIFT AS A FUNCTION OF HALOGEN TO TIN ATOM RATIO

Compound or ion	SnF_6^{2-}	—	SnF_4	SnF_3^-	$Sn_2F_5^-$	SnF_2
	$SnCl_6^{2-}$	$SnCl_5^-$	$SnCl_4$	$SnCl_3^-$	—	$SnCl_2$
	$SnBr_6^{2-}$	—	$SnBr_4$	—	—	$SnBr_3$
	SnI_6^{2-}	—	SnI_4	—	—	SnI_2
X/Sn ratio	6	5	4	3	2.5	2
Charge	−2	−1	0	−1	−1	0
Relative isomer shift	<	<	<	<	<	

A pair of electrons from a donor atom might raise the electron density of all the types of electrons at the tin nucleus, but this is contrary to the observations summarized above. On the other hand, the s-electron density can be redistributed on complexation and lower $|\psi_{ns}(0)|^2$. The complexity of the real situation can be better understood with reference to NMR data for the methyltin-substituted complexes where the spin–spin coupling $J(^{119}Sn—C—^{1}H)$ between the tin-119 atom and the methyl group proton can be measured. The I.S. change indicates a decrease in $|\psi_{ns}(0)|^2$ and it may be assumed that this represents an isotropic view of changes in *s*-electron density at the tin-119 nucleus. The NMR coupling constant, $J(^{119}Sn—C—^{1}H)$, however, based upon a predominant Fermi contact interaction mechanism, presumably represents a highly anisotropic view of *s*-electron density—namely, that directed along the axis of the tin bonding orbitals to carbon. $J(^{119}Sn—C—^{1}H)$ increases continuously with coordination numbers (*385*) and this can be interpreted as arising from increasing concentration of *s* character in the tin–carbon bond. This redistribution of *s* density in the bonding orbitals of tin is apparently accompanied by a decrease in *s* density at the nucleus (*76*). The redistribution of the *s* density in the tin bonding orbitals is in accord with the predictions of isovalent hybridization (*349*), while the decrease in the *s* density at the nucleus may be in accord with the dictates of the change in primary hybridization on complexation (see Table IV). The change in I.S. in going to higher coordination number species may then be thought to arise from the additional screening of the 5*s* electrons by the *p* and *d* electrons in the complexes. An alternative explanation is based upon the increased polarity of the tin–halogen bonds on complexation (*191a*).

Corroboratory information comes from preliminary studies of two other Mössbauer nuclei, ^{121}Sb where the $\Delta R/R$ value is negative and ^{125}Te where $\Delta R/R$ is positive. Comparison of the isoelectronic complexes SnX_6^{2-}, SbX_6^{-}, and TeX_6^{2-} for X = F, Cl, Br, and I show that the I.S. values decrease on formation of the tin and tellurium complexes and increase on formation of the antimony complexes. Similar arguments apparently hold for these neighboring atoms (*200*, *270*, *337*).

Before leaving this section it is necessary to add that the actual situation with regard to the changes wrought by complexation is very involved since the coordination numbers of the tin atoms in the so-called simple halide solids are probably already higher than their empirical formulas would indicate. Thus while the structures of SnX_4 (X = Cl, Br, I) have been determined by electron diffraction of the vapors, and all are tetrahedral (*377*, *378*), the tin atom in solid SnF_4 is at the center of a distorted octahedron with four fluorine atoms at 2.04 Å from each metal atom and equally shared, while two fluorines are at 1.879 Å and are bonded to only one tin atom (*371*). X-Ray diffraction studies show stannous oxide to have a layer structure (*383*), while the sulfide takes what is regarded as a very badly distorted NaCl lattice (*370*). Stannous fluoride has a complex structure in which the tin atoms have three possible distorted environments (*350*), and tin atoms in the anhydrous chloride are at the center of a distorted octahedron (*388*, *395*). More recently it has been recognized that certain organotin halides exist in the solid as pentacoordinated chain polymers (*385*). In addition it is likely that these species exist in solution as higher coordination aggregates, so that Mössbauer spectra of these solutions will not serve to produce the I.S. parameters of the simple species. Matrix isolation techniques have yet to be applied to the problem.

4. *Isomer Shift and the Nature of the Ligand Attached to Tin*

As has been pointed out in Section III,A,1, no simple reciprocal relation exists between the ^{119m}Sn isomer shift and percentage ionic character of the bonds exerted by the tin atom in the simple tin(II) and tin(IV) compounds (*233*). It is also true, however, that striking correlations of I.S. values and electronegativity have been observed.

These linear plots would seem to offer compelling evidence for the origin of I.S. value changes, but when the situation is examined in detail it is seen that the matter is much more complex (and interesting!) than these plots would indicate. For example, the I.S. value for a tin(II) compound will be higher than that for a tin(IV) compound regardless of the sum of the ligand electronegativities, and thus comparisons between compounds belonging to these two different valence states will be of no value in drawing a correlation.

One difficulty which arises for the tin(II) and tin(IV) halides is the result of the structural situation in the neat solids discussed in Section III,A,3. The poor fit of the I.S. value for SnF_4 is a reflection of the change of coordination number and bond hybridization which apparently occurs in the tetrahalide solids between $SnCl_4$ and SnF_4. For tetrahedral (sp^3) tin compounds, effects of *d*-electron shielding might be expected to contribute to the slope of plots of electronegativity vs. isomer shift in a monotonic way. When different hybridizations are considered, however, such *d*-electron shielding will make different contributions to the slope, and thus compounds in which tin atoms form sp^3, sp^3d, and sp^3d^2 hybrids cannot be correlated to obtain information concerning bond ionicity. In terms of coordination numbers in the solid, such correlations are invalid when any but strictly isomorphous series are being discussed. Since structural studies have shown that tin(IV) compounds exhibit various coordination numbers and hybridizations in a variety of systems, and that even the four compounds in the simple SnX_4 series fail to conform to a single pattern, it is necessary to have detailed structural information available with reference to the solid phase concerning any pair of compounds to be compared before conclusions about bond ionicity can be drawn.

Another facet of the problem with specific reference to tin bonding requires discussion. The role of low-lying empty *d* orbitals is well known in elements of the second row and lower, not only in enabling these atoms to exert expanded-octet hybridization and higher coordination numbers in certain compounds, but also in supposed contributions of higher bond order $(p \rightarrow d)$–π character to what are nominally single bonds. While much more evidence has been accumulated for silicon, effects of this type may be important for tin as well. The magnitude of overlap of *p*-orbital lone pairs with empty 5*d* orbitals of tin (delocalization of lone-pair electrons into tin *d* orbitals) would itself be expected to be a complicated function of the properties of the particular tin atom as affected by its other substituent groups. It is by no means clear that the amount of $(p \rightarrow d)$–π interaction in a given bond should change monotonically with the electronegativity coefficient of the bonded atom. Differences between observed bond lengths and covalent radii sums are of little help here since the general shortening observed can be interpreted as either the effect of ionic character or to partial double bonding.

Obviously, should linear correlations actually be derived, then they can be assumed to arise through extensive mutual cancellation of the various factors involved.

5. *Possible Chemical Consequences of Thermal Neutron Capture by* ^{118}*Sn or Decay of the Resulting* ^{119m}*Sn*

As discussed in Section II,F,3, ^{119m}Sn is produced from ^{118}Sn by a process involving the capture of a thermal neutron. The nuclear process converts one isotope of tin to another. It is seen in Fig. 7, however, that ^{119m}Sn can also be produced from the 38-hour half-life isotope ^{119}Sb. Here one begins with Group V nucleus in a typical Group V chemical environment, so that the tin atom produced by the transmutation finds itself initially in a very strange situation. Indeed iron Mössbauer γ-rays arise from ^{57}Co decay, iodine γ's from ^{127}Te and ^{129}Te decay, xenon γ's from ^{129}I decay, etc. In each case the consequences of the chemical changes necessary to accommodate the newly formed atoms are of interest. Antimony γ-rays arise from the decay of ^{121m}Sn, in turn produced from the thermal neutron irradiation of ^{121}Sn. In this case it is of interest to discover the final state of the resulting antimony atom in its Group IV environment.

In the case of ^{119m}Sn itself, the absorption of thermal neutrons by ^{118}Sn nuclei can also result in radiation damage in the target solid (*17c*, *17d*, *36b*, *118a*, *182*, *183*), but until recently studies with inorganic and organotin compounds failed to detect such effects (*118a*, *232a*, *313a*, *322*). However, using an ^{119m}Sn-labeled $K_6Sn_2(C_2O_4)_7 \cdot 4\ H_2O$ source some decomposition to tin(II) is observed (*201a*).

6. *The ^{119m}Sn Mössbauer Isomer Shift and the NMR $J(^{119}Sn\text{–}^{1}H)$ and $J(^{119}Sn\text{—}C\text{—}^{1}H)$*

Both of the above-named parameters are related to the electron density at the nucleus of bonding atoms. Equation (17) gives the relation of the isomer shift to the s-electron densities at the nucleus. The Fermi contact contribution to the spin–spin coupling J, can be expressed by

$$\begin{aligned} J(^{119}\text{Sn—L}) &= k(1+\alpha)\rho_{\text{Sn}}(0)\rho_{\text{L}}(0) \\ &= k(1+\alpha)\left[\sum_{n=1}^{5} |\psi_{ns}(0)|^2_{\text{Sn}} \sum_{n=1}^{i} |\psi_{ns}(0)|^2_{\text{L}}\right] \end{aligned} \tag{18}$$

where L is the attached ligand atom and k and α are constants.

For the organostannanes, R_nSnH_{4-n}, as a first approximation the total s-electron density at the tin nucleus can be partitioned as

$$\sum_{n=1}^{5} |\psi_{ns}(0)|^2 = n \sum_{n=1}^{5} |\psi_{ns}(0)|^2_{\text{Sn–C}} + (4-n) \sum_{n=1}^{4} |\psi_{ns}(0)|^2_{\text{Sn–H}} \tag{19}$$

where the s-electron densities of the Sn—C and Sn—H bonds are represented. Solving for the s-electron densities in Eq. (18), Eq. (19) becomes

$$\sum_{n=1}^{5} |\psi_{ns}(0)|^2 = n \frac{J(^{119}\text{Sn—C})}{k(1+\alpha)\rho_{\text{C}}(0)} + (4-n) \frac{J(^{119}\text{Sn—H})}{k(1+\alpha)\rho_{\text{H}}(0)} \tag{20}$$

Combining and solving for the *s*-electron density at the tin nucleus,

$$D_0 = \frac{\text{I.S.}}{1.075 \times 10^3} + \sum_{n=1}^{5} |\psi_{ns}(0)|^2{}_{\beta\text{-Sn}}$$

$$= n\frac{J(^{119}\text{Sn—C})}{k(1+\alpha)\rho_{\text{C}}(0)} + (4-n)\frac{J(^{119}\text{Sn—H})}{k(1+\alpha)\rho_{\text{H}}(0)} \qquad (21)$$

Now $J(^{119}\text{Sn—H})$ has been recorded for the four compounds $(CH_3)_n SnH_{4-n}$ where $n = 1$–4 (*379*) and $\rho_C(0)$ and $\rho_H(0)$ are available from the results of self-consistent field calculations (*356*). No data are available concerning magnitude of $J(^{119}\text{Sn—}^{13}\text{C})$, or how these values change in the series of alkyltin hydrides, but $J(^{119}\text{Sn—C—}^1\text{H})$ is available (*366*), and if it can be assumed that changes in $J(^{119}\text{Sn—C—}^1\text{H})$ are ascribable to changes in $J(^{119}\text{Sn—}^{13}\text{C})$ only, then these values can be used. With these assumptions the I.S. and the NMR J values are seen to correlate (*168*). A similar model has been examined for trimethyltin chloride adducts (*127a*).

B. The ^{119m}Sn Quadrupole Splitting

1. *The Origin of Resolvable Quadrupole Splitting*

The most puzzling phenomenon in ^{119m}Sn Mössbauer spectroscopy is the absence of resolvable quadrupole splitting in compounds possessing obvious chemical asymmetry at the tin atom. This was first noted in 1964 (*9*) and the relevant compounds have been listed in Tables VI and VII. In Table VI are listed 88 compounds which depart from T_d symmetry, and in Table VII, 73 compounds which depart from O_h symmetry at the tin atom. As discussed in Section II,E,2, a nonzero value of the electric field gradient (e.f.g.) at the tin nucleus is expected in any molecule which does not possess cubic symmetry at this site,[4] and since splitting of the resonance line arises from a nonzero e.f.g. at the tin nucleus, the problem is to explain the rather surprising lack of a Q.S. in these cases.

a. *Resolvable Quadrupole Splitting and the* $(p \rightarrow d)$–π *Bond.* The situation of surprise ellicits from the chemist a rather restricted set of responses. For example, surprise over the magnitudes of bond energies, internuclear distances, or heats of hydrogenation or combustion, produces a response of

[4] Not strictly true. An octahedral molecule A_3B_3Sn with the A's and B's in opposite octants would have zero e.f.g. at tin.

TABLE VI: Compounds Which Show Absence of Resolvable Quadrupole Splitting in Symmetries at Tin $< T_d$

$(CH_3)_3SnCH{=}CH_2$
$(CH_3)_3SnC_6H_5$
$(CH_3)_3SnC_6H_4CH{=}CH_2$
$[(CH_3)_3SnC_6H_4\overset{|}{C}H{-}CH_2{-}]_n{-}$
$(CH_3)_3SnCH_2O\overset{\overset{O}{\|}}{C}CH_3$
$(CH_3)_3SnCH_2F$
$(CH_3)_3SnCH_2Cl$
$(CH_3)_3SnCH_2OCH_3$
N-(Trimethylstannyl)aziridine
$(CH_3)_3SnC_6H_4$-*o*-F
$(CH_3)_3SnC_6H_4$-*o*-OCH_3
$(CH_3)_3SnC_6H_4$-*p*-$C(CH_3)_3$
$(CH_3)_3SnC_6H_4$-*p*-$N(CH_3)_2$
$(CH_3)_3SnC_6H_4$-*p*-OCH_3
$(CH_3)_3SnC_6H_4$-*p*-F
$(CH_3)_3SnC_6H_4$-*p*-Cl
$(CH_3)_3SnC_6H_4$-*p*-$Sn(CH_3)_3$
$(CH_2{=}CH)_3SnC_6H_5$
$(C_2H_5)_3SnCH_3$
$(C_2H_5)_3SnC_3H_7$-*n*
1-(Trimethylstannylmethyl)pyrrole
N-(Trimethylstannylmethyl)morpholine
N-methyl-*N*-(trimethylstannylmethyl)-morpholinium iodide
$(C_2H_5)_3SnCH_2Cl$
$(C_2H_5)_3SnCH_2C{\equiv}N$
$(C_2H_5)_3SnCH_2OCH_3$
$(C_2H_5)_3SnCH_2N(CH_3)_2$
N-(Triethylstannylmethyl)aziridine
1-(Triethylstannylmethyl)pyrrole
$[(C_2H_5)_3Sn\overset{|}{C}H{-}CH_2{-}]_n{-}$
$(C_2H_5)_3Sn(CH_2)_2\overset{\overset{O}{\|}}{C}CH_3$
$(C_2H_5)_3SnCH_2O\overset{\overset{O}{\|}}{C}CH_3$
1,1-Dimethyl-2,3,4,5-tetraphenylstannole
1,1-Divinyl-2,3,4,5-tetraphenylstannole
Hexaphenylstannole
9,9-Diphenyl-9-stannafluorene
CH_3SnH_3
iso-$C_3H_7SnH_3$
n-$C_4H_9SnH_3$
N-(Triethylstannylmethyl)morpholine
$(C_6H_5)_3SnCH_3$
$(C_6H_5)_3SnCH{=}CH_2$
$(C_6H_5)_3SnC_4H_9$-*n*
$(C_6H_5)_3SnC_6H_4$-*p*-CH_3
$(C_6H_5)_3SnC_6H_4$-*o*-CH_3
$(C_6H_5)_3SnC_6H_4$-*p*-$CH{=}CH_2$
$(C_6H_5)_3SnC_6H_4$-*p*-Cl
$(C_6H_5)_3C_6H_4$-*p*-Br
$(CH_3)_2Sn(CHCl)_2$
$(C_2H_5)_2Sn(CH{=}CH_2)_2$
$C_6H_5SnH_3$
$(CH_3)_2SnH_2$
$(n\text{-}C_3H_7)_2SnH_2$
$(n\text{-}C_4H_9)_2SnH_2$
$(C_6H_5)_2SnH_2$
$(CH_3)_3SnH$
$(C_2H_5)_3SnH$
$(n\text{-}C_3H_7)_3SnH$
$(n\text{-}C_4H_9)_3SnH$
$(\text{iso-}C_4H_9)_3SnH$
$(C_6H_5)_3SnH$
$[(CH_3)_3Sn]_2$
$[(C_2H_5)_3Sn]_2$
$[(C_6H_5)_3Sn]_2$
$[(p\text{-}FC_6H_4)_3Sn]_2$
$[(p\text{-}ClC_6H_4)_3Sn]_2$
$[(m\text{-}CF_3C_6H_4)_3Sn]_2$
$[(C_6H_5)_3Sn]_2Sn(C_6H_5)_2$
$[(C_6H_5)_3Sn]_4Sn$
$[(C_6H_5)_2Sn]_6$
$[(n\text{-}C_4H_9)_2Sn]_n$
$[(C_6H_5)_2Sn]_n$
$[(9\text{-Phenanthryl})_2Sn]_n$
$(CH_3)_3SnNa$
$(C_6H_5)_3SnLi$
$(p\text{-}FC_6H_4)_3SnH$
$C_6H_5Sn[Fe(CO)_2\pi\text{-}C_5H_5]_3$
$C_6H_5Sn[Re(CO)_5]_3$
$(CH_3)_2Sn[Fe(CO)_2\pi\text{-}C_5H_5]_2$
$(C_2H_5)_2Sn[Fe(CO)_2\pi\text{-}C_5H_5]_2$
$(C_6H_5)_2Sn[Fe(CO)_2\pi\text{-}C_5H_5]_2$
$(C_6H_5)_2Sn[Re(CO)_5]_2$
$(C_6H_5)_3SnFe(CO)_2\pi\text{-}C_5H_5$
$(C_6H_5)_3SnMn(CO)_5$
$(C_6H_5)_3SnRe(CO)$
$(C_6H_5)_3SnRe(CO)P(C_6H_5)_3$
$[(C_6H_5)_3Sn]_4Ge$
$[(C_6H_5)_3Sn]_4Pb$

TABLE VII: COMPOUNDS WHICH SHOW ABSENCE OF RESOLVABLE QUADRUPOLE SPLITTING IN SYMMETRIES AT TIN $< O_h$

$SnF_4 \cdot 2\ C_2H_5OH$
$SnF_4 \cdot 2$ DME
$SnF_4 \cdot 2$ py
$SnF_4 \cdot 2\ (C_2H_5)_2O$
$SnF_4 \cdot 2$ DMSO
$SnF_4 \cdot 3$ THF
$SnCl_4 \cdot 2\ C_4H_8S$
$SnCl_4 \cdot 2\ (C_6H_5)_3P$
$SnCl_4 \cdot 2\ (NH_2)_2C{=}S$
$SnCl_4 \cdot 2\ C_4H_8O$
$SnCl_4 \cdot CH_3S(CH_2)_2SCH_3$
$SnCl_4 \cdot 2$ py
$SnCl_4 \cdot 2\ H_2N(CH_2)_2NH_2$
$SnCl_4 \cdot (CH_3)_2N(CH_2)_2N(CH_3)_2$
$SnCl_4 \cdot 2\ C_6H_4(OH)CHO$-*p*
$SnCl_4 \cdot (C_5H_{10}N)_3P{=}S$
$SnCl_4 \cdot C_{10}H_8N_2$
$SnCl_4 \cdot 2$ 8-hydroxyquinoline
$SnCl_4 \cdot (C_4H_8N)_3P{=}S$
$SnCl_4 \cdot C_5H_5N \cdot CH_3\overset{\overset{O}{\|}}{C}OH$
$SnCl_4 \cdot$ 8-hydroxyquinoline
$SnCl_4 \cdot$ bipyridyl
$SnCl_4 \cdot [(C_6H_5)_2\overset{\overset{O}{\|}}{P}]_2NH$
$SnCl_4 \cdot 2\ CH_3CH(NH_2)\overset{\overset{O}{\|}}{C}OH$
$SnCl_4 \cdot 2$ DMSO
$SnCl_4 \cdot 2\ (CH_2)_5C{=}O$
$SnCl_4 \cdot 2$ *p*-phenylenediamine
$SnCl_4 \cdot C_5H_{11}N \cdot CH_3\overset{\overset{O}{\|}}{C}OH$
$SnCl_4 \cdot (CH_3)_2CHOH$
$SnCl_4 \cdot 2\ C_6H_5CH{=}CH_2OH$
$SnCl_4 \cdot 3\ H_2N(CH_2)_2NH_2$
$SnCl_4 \cdot 4\ H_2N(CH_2)_2NH_2$
$SnCl_4 \cdot 2\ H_2N(CH_2)_4NH_2$
$SnCl_4 \cdot 3\ H_2N(CH_2)_4NH_2$
$SnCl_4 \cdot 2\ (CH_3)_2(CH)_2NH_2\overset{\overset{O}{\|}}{C}OH$
$SnCl_4 \cdot 2\ C_5H_{11}N \cdot 2\ CH_3\overset{\overset{O}{\|}}{C}OH$
$SnCl_4 \cdot 2$ DMF
$SnCl_3(OC_2H_5) \cdot C_2H_5OH$
$SnCl_2 \cdot$ (8-hydroxyquinoline)$_2$
$SnCl_2 \cdot (acac)_2$
$SnCl_2 \cdot (C_6H_5\overset{\overset{O}{\|}}{C}CH\overset{\overset{O}{\|}}{C}CH_3)_2$
$SnCl_2 \cdot \{[(C_6H_5)_2\overset{\overset{O}{\|}}{P}]_2N\}_2$
$SnBr_4 \cdot 2\ C_4H_8S$
$SnBr_4 \cdot CH_3S(CH_2)_2SCH_3$
$SnBr_4 \cdot 2\ [(CH_3)_2N]_2C{=}S$
$SnBr_4 \cdot 2$ DME
$SnBr_4 \cdot 2\ (H_2N)_2C{=}S$
$SnBr_4 \cdot 2$ py
$SnBr_4 \cdot C_{10}H_8N_2$
$SnBr_4 \cdot$ DMSO
$SnBr_4 \cdot$ bipyridyl
$SnBr_4 \cdot [(C_6H_5)_2\overset{\overset{O}{\|}}{P}]_2NH$
$SnBr_4 \cdot (C_4H_8N)_3P{=}S$
$SnBr_4 \cdot 2\ H_2N(CH_2)_2\overset{\overset{O}{\|}}{C}OH$
$SnBr_4 \cdot 2\ H_2N(CH_2)_2NH_2$
$SnBr_4 \cdot 3\ H_2N(CH_2)_2NH_2$
$SnBr_4 \cdot 2\ H_2N(CH_2)_6NH_2$
$SnBr_4 \cdot 4\ H_2N(CH_2)_4NH_2$
$SnBr_4 \cdot 4\ H_2N(CH_2)_2NH_2$
$SnBr_4 \cdot 3\ H_2N(CH_2)_6NH_2$
$SnI_4 \cdot$ bipyridyl
$SnI_4 \cdot 2\ H_2N(CH_2)_2NH_2$
$SnI_4 \cdot 3\ H_2N(CH_2)_2NH_2$
$SnI_4 \cdot 4\ H_2N(CH_2)_2NH_2$
$SnBr_2 \cdot \{[(C_6H_5)_2\overset{\overset{O}{\|}}{P}]_2N\}_2$
$SnI_2 \cdot \{[(C_6H_5)_2\overset{\overset{O}{\|}}{P}]_2N\}_2$
$[SnCl_3 \cdot \text{terpyridyl}]_2{}^+[SnCl_6]^{2-}$
$SnBr_2\{[(C_6H_5)_2\overset{\overset{O}{\|}}{P}]_2N\}_2$
$SnI_2\{[(C_6H_5)_2\overset{\overset{O}{\|}}{P}]_2N\}_2$
$Sn[(OCH_2CH_2)_2NCH_3]_2$
$CH_3OSn(OCH_2CH_2)_3N$
$(CH_3)_2NH \cdot 2\ Sn(OCH_3)_4$
$(CH_3)_2NH \cdot 2\ Sn(OC_2H_5)_4$

"resonance" or "π-bonding." The more serious is the surprise, the more likely is the postulate of π-bonding to be made. π-Bonding is thus a function of surprise: the more surprise there is, the more π-bonding there is said to be. Departure from the predictions of first principles has led in the present case as well to a rationalization involving π-bonding.

It is known that a resolvable Q.S. is observed for certain compounds which as monomers should have T_d symmetry at the tin atom. Tin(IV) fluoride (see Section III,A,3,c) with D_{4h} symmetry in the solid is a good example here. Likewise, bis(ethanedithiolato)tin(IV) enjoys additional coordination in the solid and a resolvable Q.S. has been observed (*91*). With the exception of such systems as these, and discounting early work known to be in error, no Q.S. is found for compounds with cubic symmetry at the tin atom.

The 161 compounds found in Tables VI and VII depart from T_d or O_h symmetry by reason of differences in attached ligand atoms or groups. Although structural data are sparse, it can be assumed that the basic structures are tetrahedral and octahedral, respectively, about tin. All the known five-coordinated tin structures give rise to easily resolvable Q.S., even where the five bonds to tin are identical as in $SnCl_5^-$ (*364*). Almost all tin(II) compounds give resolvable Q.S., presumably because of the pyramidal, three-coordinated structure common in this valence state (*363*).

The possible explanations for the absence of resolvable Q.S. in an asymmetric compound include the following: (a) the finite e.f.g. is time-averaged to zero over the lifetime of the excited state; (b) there is negligible difference between the bonds tin makes with various elements as experienced by the nuclear quadrupole, and thus the individual identities of the atoms in an array of basic T_d or O_h symmetry about tin can sometimes be ignored; and (c) the admixture of *d* character into the bonding wave functions of the tin atom will contribute appreciably to the e.f.g. at the tin nucleus and give rise to resolvable Q.S. only where it can take place.

We can discuss these possibilities one at a time. Time averaging (a) can be accomplished in three ways: (i) nuclear—in which rotation or pulsation of the nonspherical nucleus would time-average the nuclear quadrupole moment to zero over the lifetime of the excited state; (ii) electronic—in which rearrangement of the field axes in the solid (equivalent to the rearrangement of the bonds or to rearrangement of atoms surrounding tin in the solid) would time-average the field gradients about tin to produce apparent cubic symmetry within the lifetime of the excited state; and

(iii) thermal—in which the thermal motions of the atoms in the solid would broaden the energy levels to an apparent broad singlet.

Broadening is not what is observed, however. Many of the resonances under discussion are found to be sharp singlets even when the new, narrow-line sources are used. It is difficult to imagine how the gross translational motions required of the ligand atoms or groups in (ii) could possibly take place in a solid at liquid nitrogen temperatures, or especially to be rapid with respect to 10^{-8} sec.

The most primitive view toward the differences in the bonds formed by tin (b) would come from comparisons of electronegativity differences as set out in Table VIII. The compound $[(C_6H_5)_3Sn]_4Pb$ shows a single sharp

TABLE VIII

ELECTRONEGATIVITY DIFFERENCES, ΔE.N., BETWEEN CARBON AND OTHER ELEMENTS IN C_n—Sn—E_{4-n} [a]

No quadrupole splitting		Quadrupole splitting	
Element E	ΔE.N.	Element E	ΔE.N.
H	−0.40	F	+1.60
Li	−1.53	Cl	+0.33
Na	−1.49	Br	+0.24
Ge	−0.48	I	−0.29
Sn	−1.80	O	+1.00
Pb	−1.95	S	−0.06
		N	+0.57

[a] Allred-Rochow values used, $C=2.50$; Pauling values and Mulliken values lead to similar conclusions.

resonance line yet the difference in electronegativity between carbon on the one side of the tin atom and lead on the other is greater than between carbon and any other element listed. By contrast, bromine, iodine, and sulfur have electronegativities close to carbon, yet organotin(IV) bromides, iodides, and sulfides give rise to large Q.S. values.

The suggestion embodied in (c), however, is worthy of careful consideration, since experiments which give direct information concerning the presence of $(p \rightarrow d)$–π bonding are few, and Mössbauer spectroscopy may have a part to play here. Indeed examination of Tables VI and VII reveals that all the compounds in the first are organotin(IV) derivatives containing

H, Li, Na, Ge, Sn, or Pb atoms directly bonded to tin, while all the compounds in the second have tin attached to F, Cl, Br, I, N, O, S, etc.

Greenwood has been able to classify asymmetric tin(IV) compounds into two sets according to the atoms directly attached, as shown in Table VIII. Compounds where only atoms from the first list are attached will show no resolvable Q.S. These compounds are listed in Table VI. Likewise for atoms in the second list, and these compounds are shown in Table VII. Compounds in which tin is directly bonded to some atoms in the first list and some in the second will exhibit a resolvable Q.S. This generalization is known as Greenwood's rule (*96*, *114*, *311*).

The chief distinguishing characteristic of the atoms listed in Table VIII is that those on the right all possess lone pairs of electrons while none of those on the left do. A general treatment of the e.f.g., $\partial^2 V/\partial z^2$, of an axially asymmetric system has been given by Townes and Dailey, who state: "It is possible that in some of the heavier atoms where *d*-orbitals are expected to be important, terms due to the mixing of *s*- and *d*-states will contribute appreciably to $\partial^2 V/\partial z^2$" (*394*).

The role of *d* orbitals in the bonding of elements of the second and lower rows of the periodic table to adjacent atoms holding lone pairs was discussed theoretically over a decade ago (*357*), and since that time an enormous amount of experimental evidence pertaining to the compounds formed by elements in the fourth group has been correlated on this basis. A combination of atoms from each list would produce a situation of imbalance in π-bonding effects at the tin atom which could give rise to a resolvable Q.S. This situation is the basis for Greenwood's rule (*96*, *114*, *311*).

b. *Exceptions to Greenwood's Rule.* A critical discussion of the resolution of quadrupole splitting in ^{119m}Sn spectra must include a careful definition of terms. In practice the resolution of resonance lines is limited by the natural linewidth discussed in Sections II,E,7 and II,F,3. Observed resonance lines are never as narrow as the theoretical value of 2Γ because of various broadening effects already discussed. In addition, although tin source materials which produce resonances approaching the natural linewidth are now generally available ($Ba^{119m}SnO_3$ lines are, for example, only 7% more broad), the data which were used for the most part to establish the generalization discussed in the last section were obtained using $^{119m}SnO_2$, which itself has a small Q.S. It is noteworthy, however, that most of the reported data fall cleanly into two categories—those in which the Q.S. is easily evident to the naked eye, and those in which a singlet resonance considered to be reasonably "narrow" for that particular source material is observed. The discussion to follow refers mainly to spectra for which the Q.S. can be recognized without the use of curve-fitting techniques.

Greenwood's rule is currently based on 161 compounds. In Fig. 8 are structural formulas representing 32 compounds which give resolvable Q.S. and in which the tin atoms are surrounded by four carbon atoms and

Resolvable Q.S.: I

A. σ - Skeletal V_{zz}.
B. π - Interaction along the Sn-C Bond.
C. 5 - Coordination.

$R_3Sn-C\equiv N$

$R_2Sn(C=N=S)_2$

$R_nSn-(C_6F_5)_{4-n}$

$(CH_3)_nSn-(C_6F_3EE')_{4-n}$

$R_nSn-(C_6Cl_5)_{4-n}$

$(C_6H_5)_2Sn(C_6F_4)_2$

E = F; E' = H
E = $(CH_3)_3Sn$; E' = F
E = F; E' = $(CH_3)_3Sn$
E = Br; E' = F

$(CH_3)_3Sn(X)C=C(X)E$

X = E = F
X = F; E = H
X = E = Cl

$R_3Sn-C\equiv C-P(O)(OR)_2$

$E\,Sn(CH_3)_2-C_6H_4E'\cdot Cr(CO)_3$

E = CH_3; E' = H
E = C_6H_5; E' = H
E = $C_6H_5\cdot Cr(CO)_3$; E' = H
E = CH_3; E' = $Sn(CH_3)_3$

FIG. 8. Resolvable quadrupole splitting: I. These structural formulas represent 32 compounds studied.

thus stand as exceptions. Noting the discussion in the last section, three reasonable explanations for the resolution of Q.S. in these compounds are available: (a) that a large e.f.g. exists in the σ-skeleton since the organic groups at tin are in all cases sp^3—sp or sp^3—sp^2 pairs, or involve polarizing perhaloalkyl and perhaloaryl groups, or in two cases involve a phenyl ring engaged in bonding with a transition metal; (b) that a $(p \rightarrow d)$—π interaction

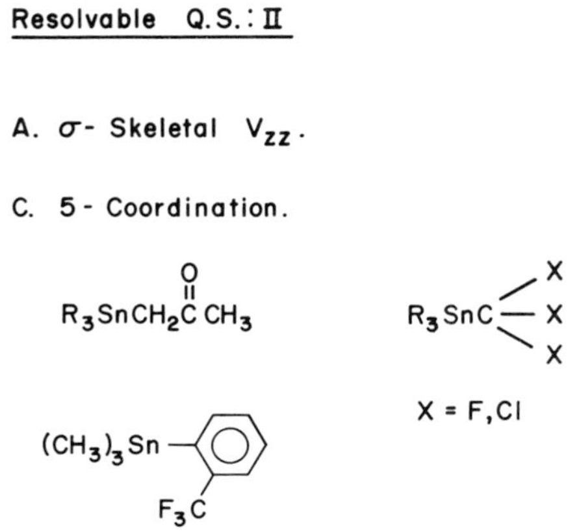

Resolvable Q.S.: II

A. σ- Skeletal V_{zz}.

C. 5 - Coordination.

$R_3SnCH_2C(=O)CH_3$

R_3SnCX_3

X = F, Cl

$(CH_3)_3Sn-C_6H_4-CF_3$

FIG. 9. Resolvable quadrupole splitting: II. These structural formulas represent 6 compounds studied.

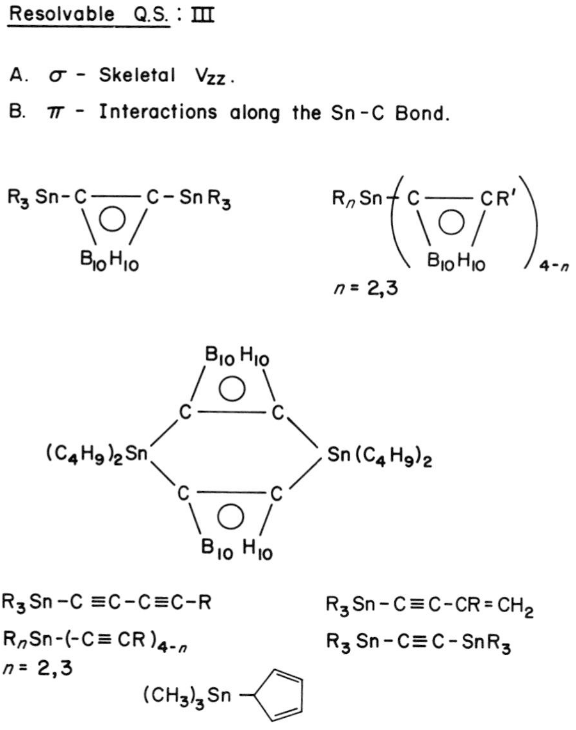

Resolvable Q.S.: III

A. σ - Skeletal V_{zz}.

B. π - Interactions along the Sn-C Bond.

$R_3Sn-C(B_{10}H_{10})C-SnR_3$

$R_nSn(C(B_{10}H_{10})CR')_{4-n}$

n = 2,3

$(C_4H_9)_2Sn(C(B_{10}H_{10})C)_2Sn(C_4H_9)_2$

$R_3Sn-C\equiv C-C\equiv C-R$

$R_3Sn-C\equiv C-CR=CH_2$

$R_nSn-(-C\equiv CR)_{4-n}$

n = 2,3

$R_3Sn-C\equiv C-SnR_3$

$(CH_3)_3Sn-C_5H_5$

FIG. 10. Resolvable quadrupole splitting: III. These structural formulas represent 26 compounds studied.

exists along the tin–carbon σ-bond which enhances the e.f.g. by population of the empty tin $5d$ orbitals since in each case listed in Fig. 8 one of the atoms adjacent to tin is a part of a π-system; (c) that five-coordination exists at tin through *intra*molecular interaction with one of the substituents on the α- or β-carbon atom. In trialkyltin cyanides higher coordination is achieved through the terminal nitrogen atom to produce a linear polymer in the solid (*389*). The physical properties of the other compounds, many of which are liquids, seem to rule out *inter*molecular interactions. The phenyltin–transition metal carbonyls could conceivably involve a $(d \rightarrow d)$–π across-space interaction (*334a*).

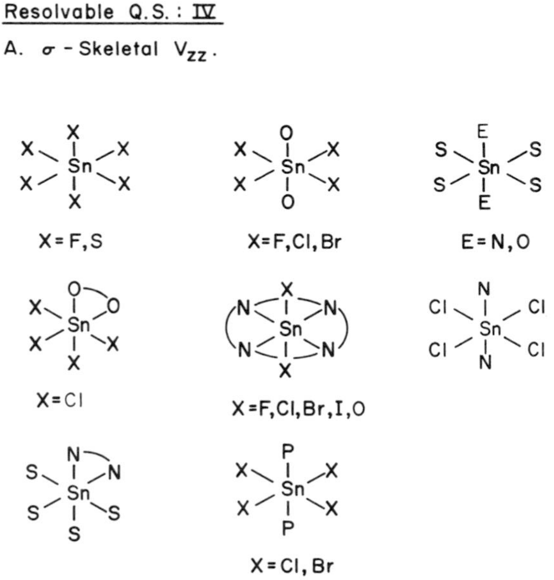

Resolvable Q.S. : IV

A. σ - Skeletal V_{zz}.

X = F, S

X = F, Cl, Br

E = N, O

X = Cl

X = F, Cl, Br, I, O

X = Cl, Br

FIG. 11. Resolvable quadrupole splitting: IV. These structural formulas represent 41 compounds studied.

Figure 9 includes 6 compounds for which only explanations (a) and (c) seem possible. Figure 10 includes 26 compounds for which only explanations (a) and (b) are possible. All the compounds represented in Figs. 8, 9, and 10 depart from T_d symmetry at the tin atom.

Figure 11 represents 41 additional compounds which depart from O_h symmetry; but show resolvable Q.S. Only explanation (a) seems reasonable.

The only explanation common to all these situations is the one involving an enhanced e.f.g. along the σ-bonds. In Figs. 8–11 are represented 105 compounds; in addition, 7 compounds which show resolvable Q.S. where tin is attached to a transition metal are represented in Fig. 12. In these systems, apart from explanation (a), the resolvable Q.S. can be rationalized by the population of the empty tin 5*d* orbitals from filled *d* orbitals of the

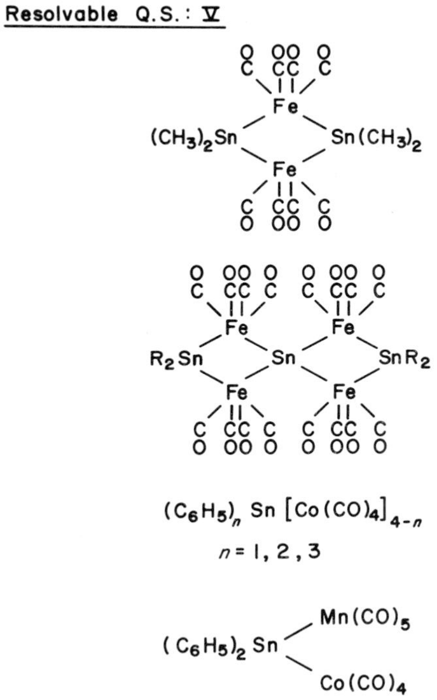

Resolvable Q.S.: V

$[(CH_3)_2SnFe(CO)_4]_2$

$R_2Sn[Fe(CO)_4]_2Sn[Fe(CO)_4]_2SnR_2$

$(C_6H_5)_n Sn [Co(CO)_4]_{4-n}$

$n = 1, 2, 3$

$(C_6H_5)_2 Sn[Mn(CO)_5][Co(CO)_4]$

FIG. 12. Resolvable quadrupole splitting: V. These structural formulas represent 7 compounds studied.

transition metal in a $(d \rightarrow d)$–π interaction. Thus, in summary, while the generalization concerning the appearance of resolvable Q.S. can be established on the basis of 161 compounds, there are 112 compounds which stand as exceptions.

We can now discuss the origin of the resolvable Q.S. in the 112 compounds which violate the rule. In Fig. 13 are represented the structural formulas of 46 compounds known to give singlet spectra. In each case there exists the possibility of a $(p \rightarrow d)$–π interaction along the tin–carbon σ-bond [explanation (b)]. In some cases the chance for such an interaction is enhanced by the substitution of π-electron-repelling groups in the para positions of phenyl substituents, yet no Q.S. is resolved.

In Fig. 14 are represented a further 21 compounds where five-coordination can be achieved in an intramolecular fashion [explanation (c)], yet no resolvable Q.S. is found. From the data from these 67 test molecules, if it

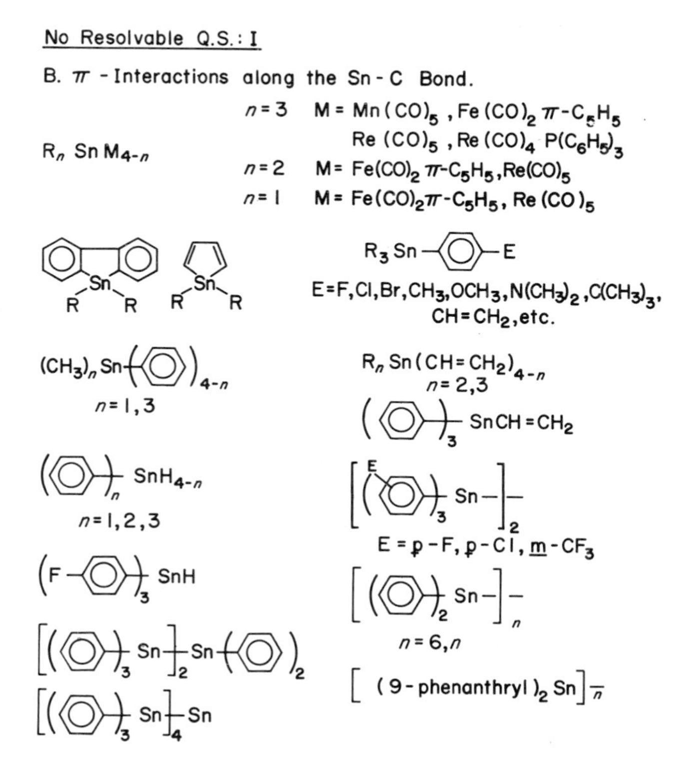

FIG. 13. No resolvable quadrupole splitting: I. These structural formulas represent 46 compounds studied.

can be assumed that intermolecular effects are unimportant (certainly not negligible in the case of the alkyltin cyanides at least), then it can be concluded that the predominant effect giving rise to a large enough e.f.g. to resolve in the Mössbauer experiment is the e.f.g. along the σ-bond. The case of the tin–transition metal compounds is treated separately in Section IV,E.

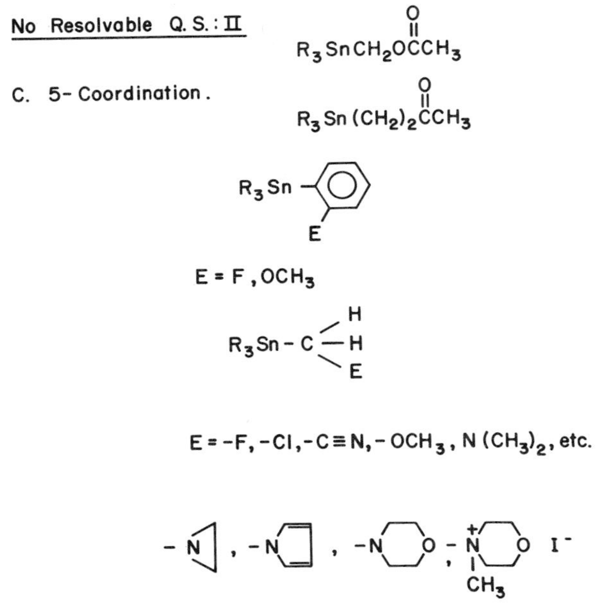

No Resolvable Q. S.: II

C. 5-Coordination.

$R_3SnCH_2OC(=O)CH_3$

$R_3Sn(CH_2)_2C(=O)CH_3$

R_3Sn–C_6H_4–E

E = F, OCH_3

R_3Sn–CH_2–E

E = –F, –Cl, –C≡N, –OCH_3, $N(CH_3)_2$, etc.

FIG. 14. No resolvable quadrupole splitting: II. These structural formulas represent 21 compounds studied.

c. *Quadrupole Splitting and 5d-Orbital Occupation.* The SCMO method discussed in Section III,B,1 has been applied to the problem of determining the 5*d*-orbital occupation and resulting $(p \to d)$–π bonding orders in several organotin(IV) compounds, but the results of the calculations do not seem to argue convincingly that the resolvable Q.S. is associated with either high total 5*d*-orbital occupation or high average $(p \to d)$–π bond order (*311*). Further detailed theoretical work on this problem is needed.

The overlap of filled orbitals on atoms adjacent to tin may be with 6*p* rather than 5*d* orbitals (*120*), but nothing in our current data allows us to distinguish between the two possibilities. The two levels are presumably reasonably close in energy. Recent estimates indicate, however, that population of 3*d* orbitals in copper produces approximately 6 or 7 times the effective e.f.g. that similar population of the 4*p* orbital would (*369*).

Among experiments capable of distinguishing between the effects discussed above is the measurement of the sign of the principal axis of the electric field gradient at the tin nucleus, discussed in Section III,C,3. An e.f.g. produced by $(p \to d)$–π bonding would give rise to an excess of charge along the tin–substituent bond direction, while electron release would produce a deficiency of charge along this bond. The sign of the e.f.g. should, accordingly, be opposite for the two cases (*74*). Unfortunately, the use of tin p orbitals in π-interactions could not be distinguished in this way (*257a*).

The determination of the magnitude of the e.f.g. at the tin nucleus in an asymmetric compound known to give a singlet resonance of narrow line-width can be carried out for polar compounds by analysis of microwave spectral lines. Although none of the stable tin nuclei possess quadrupole moments in their ground states, ^{119m}Sn with nuclear spin $\frac{3}{2}$ is quadrupolar, and an isotopically substituted compound containing ^{119m}Sn could be used. To improve chances for the determination, the concentration of the ^{119m}Sn-labeled compound would have to be greater than 10%, and the compound chosen so as to have a large dipole moment for greater line intensity.

2. *The Point Charge Approximation*

In Section II,E,2 it was stated that the electric field gradient at the tin nucleus could be treated as arising from the surrounding electrons as distorted from spherical symmetry by the atoms directly bonded to tin. In this section we consider a treatment wherein the atoms directly bonded to tin are approximated by a point charge. Equation (13) relates ΔE_Q to V_{zz} which is the principal moment of the e.f.g., equal to $\partial^2 V/\partial z^2 = eq$. The complete expression for q simplifies in the case of tin to

$$q = (1-\gamma_\infty) \sum q_i[(3\cos^2\theta - 1)/r_i{}^3] \tag{22}$$

where γ_∞ is an antishielding factor, and q_i is the magnitude of the ith charge whose coordinates are r_i and θ_i. Octahedral cis–trans isomers (point symmetry group D_{4h} and C_{2v}) are amenable to treatment by applying Eq. (13) to arrangements of electric charge whose symmetries correspond to the molecular point groups of the two compounds types. Figure 15 compares the two arrangements, both of which possess the axial symmetry required for Eq. (13) to apply. Assuming equal charges, equal antishielding factors, γ_∞, and equal internuclear distances, r, in both cases the ratio of expected Q.S. values can be calculated:

$$\frac{[\Delta E_Q]_{trans}}{[\Delta E_Q]_{cis}} = \frac{\frac{1}{2}e^2 Q[q]_{trans}}{\frac{1}{2}e^2 Q[q]_{cis}} = \frac{[q]_{trans}}{[q]_{cis}} = \frac{(1-\gamma_\infty)4q/r^3}{(1-\gamma_\infty)2q/r^3} = 2 \tag{23}$$

The 1:2 ratio of the magnitudes of the Q.S. for cis and trans isomers holds good roughly for a wide variety of SnA_2B_4 complexes tested, and the actual values for complexes of the type R_2SnX_4 where the X atom is Cl, or N, or O as part of an organic ligand are approximately $[Q.S.]_{cis} \sim 2$ and $[Q.S.]_{trans} \sim 4$ mm/sec (*94*). A simple extension of these ideas shows that complexes

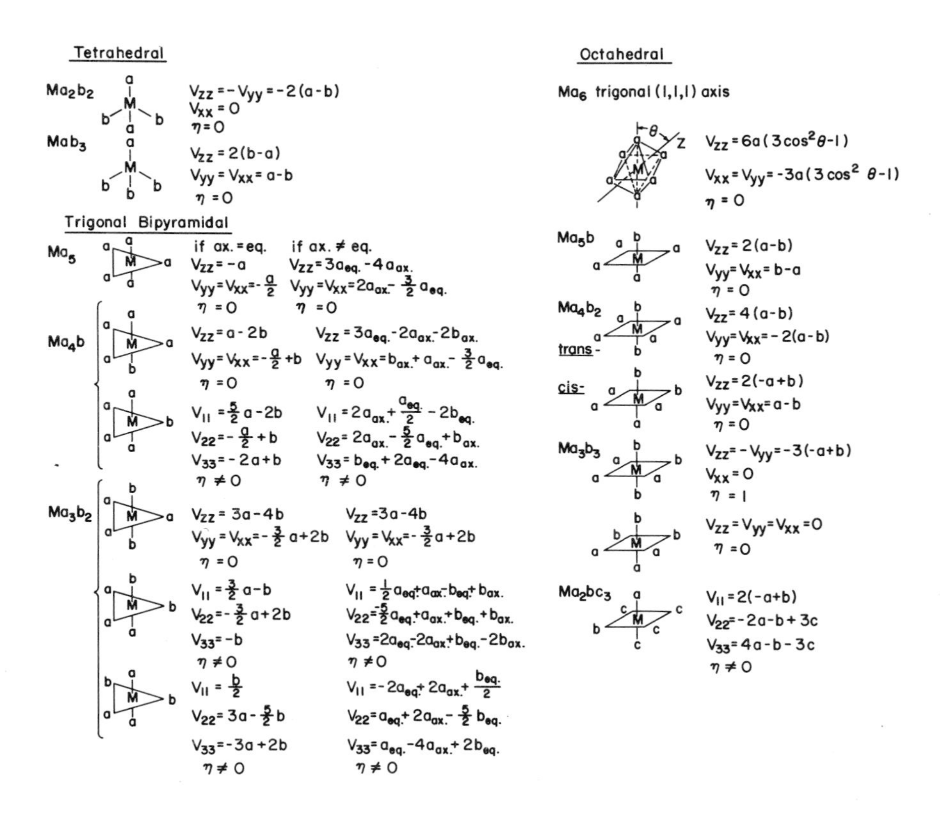

FIG. 15. Electric field gradients and asymmetry parameters, for various arrangements.

of the type $SnAB_5$ develop the same field gradient as in the [Q.S.] *cis*-SnA_2B_4 case (*351*). In the tetrahedral series, calculations indicate that compounds of the type SnA_2B_2 should have a Q.S. value 1.16 times that for $SnAB_3$ (*324*).

The ^{119m}Sn Q.S. values thus emerge as a powerful tool in structure determination as well as for the characterization of novel tin compounds.

3. *The Sign of the Principal Axis of the Electric Field Gradient*

The parameter ΔE_Q in Eq. (13) has both a magnitude and a sign. The magnitude is the Q.S., but ΔE_Q also carries the sign of V_{zz}, the principal axis of the electric field gradient (*245*), chosen so that $|V_{zz}| \geqslant |V_{yy}| \geqslant |V_{xx}|$. Two independent parameters determine the e.f.g.: V_{zz} and the asymmetry parameter, η, defined as in Eq. (12). For axial symmetry $\eta = 0$; its maximum value is unity.

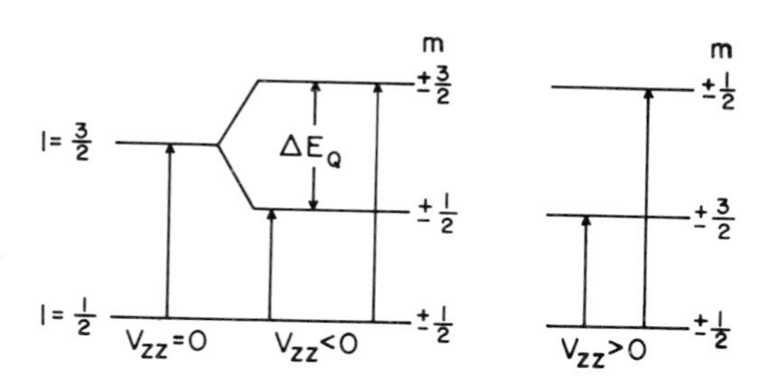

FIG. 16. The sign of the electric field gradient.

These parameters cannot be evaluated from the Q.S. data of such Mössbauer nuclides as ^{119m}Sn alone because of the nature of the $I = \frac{3}{2}$ to $\frac{1}{2}$ transition (see Fig. 5), where the degeneracy of the split levels is only partially lifted in that $\pm m$ have the same energy. The sign of V_{zz} can be measured by application of a strong magnetic field which splits the residual degeneracy. This method is applicable to powders.

A second method can be applied to a crystal for which the principal axis, z, makes an angle Θ with the incoming γ-ray. The situation with respect to the sign of V_{zz} is given in Fig. 16. The sign may be determined by observing the intensity ratio

$$\frac{I(\pm\frac{3}{2})}{I(\pm\frac{1}{2})} = \frac{1 + \cos^2 \Theta}{\frac{5}{3} - \cos^2 \Theta} \tag{24}$$

Thus for $\Theta = 0$, the intensity ratio will be 3, and, for $\Theta = \pi/2$, 0.6. Therefore, by measuring the intensity ratio as a function of angle Θ the sign of V_{zz} can be determined uniquely.

The application of an external magnetic field to a powder showing a Q.S. spectrum will, if the magnetic and quadrupolar interactions are comparable in magnitude, result in a differential broadening of the two lines of the doublet spectrum. Analysis of the broadening permits determination of the sign of V_{zz}.

Recently the determination of the sign of V_{zz} in $(CH_3)_2SnF_2$ has been reported by this method (*324*). Dimethyltin difluoride is isomorphous with SnF_4, incorporating flat planes of bridging fluorine atoms with the linear C—Sn—C axis perpendicular (*390*). The recoil-free fraction in the plane of the fluorine atoms is 40 times the value perpendicular to this plane, showing the relative freedom of motion of the tin atom perpendicular to the plane. V_{zz} lies along the C—Sn—C axis with the same sign as that in tin(II) oxide (*324*). Tin(IV) oxide and dimethyltin molybdate and dichloride have recently been examined (*112a*).

The sign of V_{zz} is important because most theories of the chemical bond–valence bond, ligand field, and molecular orbital treatments—predict the sign of V_{zz}. Determination of the sign can help in the choice of the most appropriate theoretical description for each case.

4. *Quadrupole Splitting and Molecular Symmetry*

The application of tin Mössbauer results to the elucidation of molecular symmetries is limited by an apparently large number of cases of a symmetric tin(IV) compounds in which the magnitude of the Q.S. is small compared with the relatively large natural linewidth for ^{119m}Sn. The generalization embodied in Greenwood's rule is not without use, however, since the magnitudes of the Q.S. values of those compounds which violate the rule are smaller usually than those which follow it, and the compounds which violate the rule usually have some interesting or special feature. It has recently been suggested that Q.S. > 2.5 mm/sec is unlikely to be observed unless greater than four coordination is found at tin (*191a*). It is also apparent that for homologous series of compounds the results of point charge calculations can yield predictions of the magnitudes of the Q.S. values to be expected. The direction of the principal axis and the sign of the e.f.g. has only just begun to be exploited in yielding useful information.

5. *Relationships Between the Isomer Shift and Quadrupole Splitting*

a. *Tin(II)*. No satisfactory relationship between these two important parameters has yet been derived for either valence state of tin. The Q.S. values obtained from tin(II) compounds are consistent with either of the generally proposed tin(II) structures, a $5s^2 5p^2$ configuration with right angles at tin, or a hybridized structure with wider bond angles (*363*). It is found generally that the Q.S. decreases as the I.S. increases. In a plot of I.S. vs. Q.S. it appears that most points lie near one of two straight lines whose slopes differ by a factor of 2 but which have the same intercept. The existence of the two branches has been interpreted by explaining that the compounds on the upper branch are those in which the covalent bond is linear with only P_x character involved in the wave function of the tin(II) atom, while planar bonds are proposed for the compounds on the lower branch, with P_x and p_y contributions present in equal amounts (*159, 160*). The real situation appears to be more complex, however, and it must be noted that $SnCl_2 \cdot 2\,H_2O$ which falls on the upper line has a structure in which the tin atom is pyramidal (*373*). In addition, several tin(II)–oxygen heterocycles which cannot possibly possess linear O—Sn—O bonds (*24, 280*) are found on the upper branch.

b. *Tin(IV): The ρ Value.* The ratio of the quadrupole splitting to the isomer shift value with respect to SnO_2, called ρ, was used early on to derive information concerning the coordination number of tin(IV) compounds based on the observation that ρ values greater than 2.1 are associated with coordination numbers greater than four, while values of 1.8 or lower are associated with four-coordination (*124, 198*).

The conclusions to be drawn from the much wider range of data now available are mixed since several compounds known to contain tin atoms in five- and six-coordinated sites exhibit ρ values below 1.8. The systematics of the value of ρ for various coordination numbers at tin are a reflection of two kinds of changes which take place on conversion of tin from four-coordination to higher coordination: (a) the I.S. value generally decreases, and (b) the Q.S. value generally increases. For example, while point charge calculations (see Section III,C,2) give the e.f.g. ratio for different stereochemical situations for any compound type and geometric shape, it is known that for the octahedral SnR_2B_4 complexes, the trans isomers show Q.S. values in the range of ~4 mm/sec while the figure is ~2 mm/sec for the cis isomers (*94*). From a study of the mixed five- and six-coordinated organotin(IV) salts of the type $[SnR_2B_4]^+[SnR_2C_3]^-$, it can be concluded that the values for equatorial arrangements of ligands in trigonal bipyramidal SnR_2B_3 species are not very different from that for trans octahedral SnR_2B_4 species. Likewise $SnRB_2C_3$ and $SnRB_5$ species appear to have Q.S. values of ~2 mm/sec while SnR_3B_2 species give Q.S. values in the range of 4 mm/sec (*76*). With a Q.S. value of 4 mm/sec, it is not likely that a tin(IV) species would have an I.S. value sufficiently high to bring the ρ

ratio below 1.8, as such high I.S. values could only belong to a tin(II) compound, especially in the light of the shift toward lower positive values seen on increased coordination. In addition, since so many high coordination number tin(IV) compounds have I.S. values in the region of 1 mm/sec, even a Q.S. value of ~ 2 will produce a ratio of greater than 2.1 for ρ. The interested reader is invited to peruse the tables of data and draw his own conclusions concerning the usefulness of the ρ parameter.

6. *The Relationship Between Quadrupole Splitting and the Nuclear Quadrupole Resonance Frequency of Attached Atoms*

Both the Mössbauer quadrupole splitting and the nuclear quadrupole resonance (n.q.r.) frequency measure the variation of electric field gradients in nuclei, and for directly bonded atoms it is reasonable that in a homologous series of compounds the variations in e.f.g. at each nucleus arise because of the redistribution of p electrons in the bonding σ-orbitals. An empirical equation (*49*) describes the relation of the bromine-81 n.q.r. frequencies, ν (averaged over the crystallographic splittings), to the ^{119m}Sn Q.S. values, Δ, in the organotin bromides R_3SnBr:

$$\nu\ (^{81}\mathrm{Br}) = 164.24 - 19.06\Delta \qquad (\mathrm{Mc/sec}) \tag{25}$$

Correlations between n.q.r. frequencies and Hammett–Taft σ^*-constants have been claimed and a similar empirical equation has been written for R_3SnBr where $R = C_6H_5$, C_4H_9, C_3H_7, C_2H_5, CH_3, and Br.

$$\Delta(^{119m}\mathrm{Sn}) = 3.15 - 0.38 \sum \sigma^* \qquad (\mathrm{mm/sec}) \tag{26}$$

C. The ^{119m}Sn Recoil-Free Fraction

Examples of tin compounds with a high recoil-free fraction, f', include SnO_2, SnO, R_2SnO, SnF_4, $(CH_3)_2Sn(OCHO)_2$, etc. The spectra of these compounds can be recorded at room temperature. The coefficient, f', as discussed in Section II,E,5 is related in the lattice dynamics of the solid to the displacement of the absorber tin atom from its equilibrium position, or, put another way, to the probability of finding the absorber atom a given distance from its equilibrium position. The value of f' should then also be a function of the binding force constants holding the absorber atom in the lattice, being larger the more rigid the binding in the lattice. Thus the magnitude of f' might correlate with lattice energy, heat of sublimation, and perhaps with melting point temperature, solubility, coordination number, the mass of the nearest-neighbor atoms or groups, etc., or even with the "ringing" sound produced when some compounds are shaken in a glass bottle.

The real situation appears to be very complex. Organotin compounds generally form molecular solids, i.e., crystals consisting of molecules which retain their identity when assembled in the solid, in which two kinds of forces are important—the binding of the tin atom in the molecule, and the binding of the molecule in the solid. The lattice force which affects the magnitude of f' will in general depend on contributions from both intra- and intermolecular forces.

The early claim of good correlation between f' and melting point (*54*) is clearly mistaken (*61*). Using a strictly homologous series of compounds of the formula R_2SnO it was found that an increase in the size of the R group from CH_3 to C_8H_{17} led to a monotonic decrease in the f' value (*8*), while the opposite trend was seen to be the case for a series of $(p\text{-}XC_6H_4)_2SnO$ compounds where X = H, Cl, Br, and I (*107*). These data from the earlier literature must, however, be considered in the light of more recent analyses of the errors involved in the determination of f' values (*128*, *212*). Later, careful work with organotin compounds suggests that earlier speculation on the relationship of the magnitude of the f' value to chemical behavior is inadequate to explain the lattice dynamics of organotin molecules. The conclusion, simply stated, is that there exists no simple functional dependence of f' on the following factors, considered independently (*216*): (a) the nearest-neighbor atom mass, the nearest-neighbor ligand mass, or the molecular weight of the molecule; (b) the coordination number at the tin atom; (c) bulk properties such as melting point or physical state; (d) the isomer shift or quadrupole splitting.

Nevertheless the value of f' is influenced by the nature of the microstructure. The tin compounds which give Mössbauer spectra easily at room temperature have one feature in common: the tin atom is held in a polymeric lattice. Compounds with higher values of f' such as bis(toluene-3,4-dithiolato)tin and the alkyltin formates are known to form a network lattice where there are strong intermolecular bonds (*385*, *386*). The tin–oxygen heterocycle *o*-phenylenedioxytin(II), which shares the structural feature of the planar chelating ligand (*91*), likewise exhibits a resonance at room temperature (*24*). It is interesting that bis(1,2-ethanedithiolato)tin, in which the organic chelating group lacks the requirement for planarity, shows a much weaker resonance at room temperature than its toluene analog (*91*), as do the tin–oxygen heterocycles where additional substitution either on the organic group (*24*) or at the tin atom (*397*) apparently disrupts somewhat the original structure of the solid with its intermolecular binding. The data for the alkyltin oxides can be understood in the same terms.

Although the dependence of the value of f' on the presence of a polymeric lattice seems to be established, it would be hazardous to use such a qualitative measure of f' value as the presence or absence of a resonance at ambient temperatures as a test of polymeric binding in the solid. The strength of such binding must also play a role. Certainly the absence of a resonance at room temperature gives no information, although its presence may be significant.

D. Line Asymmetries in ^{119m}Sn Doublet Spectra

The Goldanskii-Karyagin effect discussed in Section II,E,6 arises from a strongly anisotropic recoil-free fraction which can come about from fastening tin atoms in polymer chains or planes, adsorption at surfaces or interfaces, etc. The one- or two-dimensional intermolecular bonding is one of the typical examples of strongly anisotropic interactions from the tin atom, and the formation of such network solids is now recognized as a common feature of organotin chemistry (*385*). In addition, the atoms which when attached to tin produce large quadrupolar splittings are just those which would lead to additional bonding to the tin atom. For example, the crystal structures of trimethyltin fluoride and hydroxide show that these compounds are one-dimensional linear polymeric chains with van der Waals forces between methyl groups in neighboring chains (*354*, *385*). Likewise the tin atoms in trimethyltin cyanide are pentacoordinated to form infinite chains along the crystal *c* axis through the C≡N group. The X-ray anisotropic thermal parameters indicate that the mean square displacement of the tin atom is least in the direction of the chain axis (*389*). and the eccentricity of the vibrational ellipsoid is maximized in an intermediate range of temperature. These studies have been extended to two-dimensional polymeric dioctyltin oxide (*214a*). At low and high temperatures the thermal motion tends more toward a vibrational sphere, and the Goldanskii-Karyagin effect may vanish. In addition, the ratio of line intensities may reverse as a function of temperature, as observed with triphenyltin hydroxide and trimethyltin cyanide (*214*).

It remains to be seen if the observation of a Goldanskii-Karyagin effect can be used as a test of polymeric intermolecular network lattices in organotin compounds.

IV

APPLICATIONS OF ^{119m}Sn MÖSSBAUER SPECTROSCOPY TO PROBLEMS IN ORGANOTIN CHEMISTRY

A. Tin Assay

The simplest chemical use of the Mössbauer effect is the detection and assay of specific nuclei. This application encompasses the first two of the three categories discussed in Section I. Although a '49er-type prospecting kit for gold (another Mössbauer nuclide) is still awaited, Soviet scientists have developed a portable spectrometer weighing less than 7 lb designed for the analysis of mineralogical tin-bearing specimens in the field. These static spectrometers set for the determination of SnO_2 (cassiterite) in ores and minerals have been manufactured in the Soviet Union since 1965. The method gives measurements of better accuracy than conventional, wet analytical methods and is nondestructive as well (*255*, *368*). The general technique would seem to be applicable to any procedure involving repetitive analysis, such as "on-stream" processes in industry, so long as a suitable source material can be fabricated with the chemical composition of the product, obviating the need for a mover. This application might lend itself to resonant detection discussed in Section II,D,2. The method has potential for the nondestructive determination of tin in different environments (valence state, coordination number, site symmetry, etc.) in the same sample. The suggestion has been put forward that a Mössbauer spectrometer ride in a Moon-probe in order to transmit spectra of tin-bearing minerals on the lunar surface (*374*). The requirements for a technique giving quantitative analytical results from Mössbauer spectra have been discussed (*191b*, *299a*).

B. The ^{119m}Sn Mössbauer Label

The method of labeling is widely used today to study chemical systems. Both radioactive and stable isotopes can be used as the label, and the analysis for the presence of the isotope can be carried out by a variety of radiochemical and other methods. The Mössbauer effect opens up several new possibilities for the study of the course of reactions, or to monitor physical processes such as diffusion or precipitation. Many examples of the method in its different variations could be given. One type of application might involve preparing samples containing ^{119m}Sn atoms, and following the fate of these by testing for the 23.8 keV γ-ray. Another procedure would involve labeling a molecule by trialkyltin groups and then following it through a course of reactions by ^{119m}Sn Mössbauer spectroscopy. ^{119}Sn atoms in natural abundance have been used as a probe to measure magnetic fields (*26, 44, 45, 55, 65, 79, 92, 101, 111, 112, 116, 129a, 150, 163, 169, 185, 186*) by the nuclear Zeeman effect discussed in Section II,E,4, or to detect ferroelectric phase changes (*36, 68, 127, 176, 188, 192a*), electron distributions and the presence of intermetallic compounds in alloys (*12, 18, 26, 44, 50–53, 55–57, 67, 77, 78, 92, 101, 130, 131, 133a, 139, 161, 169, 185, 186, 196, 279*), different crystalline modifications in simple salts (*84*), or gross changes in pressure (*121, 188, 190*), or to measure the effects of radiation damage (*2, 4, 99*). Since recoil-free absorption only occurs in solids it is easy to conceive of the study of phase transitions by Mössbauer spectroscopy, and tin metal (m.p. 323° C) has been studied in this way (*46*). It is found that the resonance fails to fall off as sharply when the phase transition temperature is reached if impure tin metal is used (*161, 162*), constituting a rather special application of a criterion of purity known to organic chemists for over a hundred years!

C. Valency State

The separation of isomer shift values in Sn(IV) and Sn(II) compounds about the value of white tin [commonly quoted as +2.65 mm/sec (*160*)], as discussed in Section III,B,2, has been applied with benefit to several types or organotin systems.

1. R_2Sn Compounds

^{119m}Sn Mössbauer spectroscopy has been used to investigate the diorganotin compounds, R_2Sn, known for over 100 years as examples of organic derivatives of tin(II). These compounds give I.S. values below that of β-tin (*109*), and corroboration for the reformulation of these systems as tin(IV) has come from chemical, NMR, and X-ray evidence (*363*). The change in physical properties of the initial R_2Sn product suggests a process such as

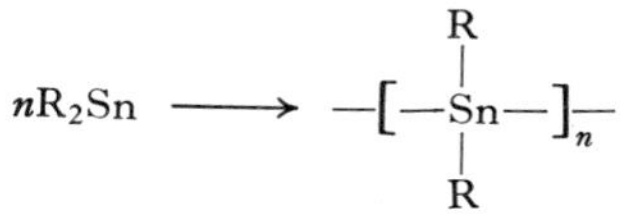

$$nR_2Sn \longrightarrow -[-\overset{\displaystyle R}{\underset{\displaystyle R}{Sn}}-]_n- \qquad (27)$$

to form a system with tin–tin bonds. The slow oxidation of di-*n*-butyltin to $[(n\text{-}C_4H_9)_2SnO]_n$ on exposure to air can be followed by Mössbauer spectroscopy (*109*). Presumably larger R groups would slow down the rate of polymerization. Monomeric di(9-phenanthryl)tin gives a singlet resonance with an I.S. characteristic of a tin(IV) compound (*20*), but the sample was apparently contaminated with oxidation products, and the matter needs reinvestigation and should be extended to other bulky systems with vinylic bonds. The tin(II)-substituted carboranes constitute a genuine example of an organotin(II) species, and the spectra show slow oxidation on exposure of an ethereal solution to air, precipitating a species containing tin(IV) (*2*). Two additional compounds in the literature are claimed to be stable organic derivatives of tin(II): dicyclopentadienyltin(II) (*358*) and dihydrodibenzostannepin (*376*). The spectrum of the former has recently been reported (*117c*).

2. *Tin(II)–Oxygen Heterocycles*

Isomer shift values of the tin–oxygen heterocycles of the general formula

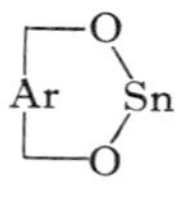

$$Ar\left\langle\begin{matrix} -O \\ \\ -O \end{matrix}\right\rangle Sn$$

enable differentiation between two possible structures which might be proposed to explain the apparent associated nature of these solids as compared to their carbon, silicon, and germanium analogs—a structure with tin–tin bonds by analogy with the compounds of formula $[R_2Sn]_n$ discussed above, in which the valence state is tin(IV); or an association of tin(II) monomers held together by $O \rightarrow Sn$ intermolecular bonds. The high I.S. values for these compounds serve to rule out the former (*24*). The hydrolysis of these systems in air gives rise to a resonance characteristic of tin(IV) oxide. Hydrolysis in a nitrogen atmosphere gives the expected tin(II) oxide (*24*).

3. *Tin-Containing Transition Metal Compounds*

The reaction of tin(II) halides with transition metal halides has been extensively investigated, and the products variously described as containing tin(II) donor groups or tin(IV)–metal bonds (*21a*, *363*). The I.S. data obtained for these systems represent evidence that all the tin–transition metal compounds studied should be considered as derivatives of tin(IV) (*93a*). Structural data (*388*) can be taken as corroborating the assignment of tin(IV) in these compounds.

4. *Metal Incorporation in Tin Porphyrins*

Metal tetrapyrroles are important in biological systems and the tin porphyrin has been used as a model system to study the incorporation of the metal atom into the ring. Starting with tin(II) materials, the incorporation can be monitored by visible and Mössbauer spectroscopy. The pattern of bands in the visible spectrum moves through three stages from the neutral, metal-free porphyrin to the tin-containing final product. The Mössbauer spectra also reflect these electronic changes in the porphyrin ring. It is found that while the intermediate tin–porphyrin complex contains tin(II), tin has been converted to tin(IV) on incorporation into the porphyrin ring. The singlet spectrum of the final product is consistent with its formulation as a 2:1 species, probably a sandwich structure (*293*) similar to the antiprismatic eight-coordinate structure reported for the tin phthalocyanine system (*348*). The departure from noncubic symmetry here would not be expected to give rise to large electric field gradients on the basis of point charge calculations (*324*, *360*, *364*).

D. Solution Interactions

Solvents play an important role in determining the course and the rate of organometallic reactions. Electron-donating aprotic solvents interact with metal atoms in organometallic compounds in solution. Figure 17 shows the quadrupole splitting value of dibutyltin dichloride measured at different molar ratios of various common solvents. Apparently the coordination of solvent molecules increases the electric field gradient at the tin nucleus from that found in the neat solid dibutyltin dichloride. From Fig. 17 it is possible to rank the solvents according to donor ability as DMSO > DMF > HMPA > DME > THF > DEE > diethyl ether. The break in the curves occurs at a mole ratio of 2–3:1. Further dilution causes no further change in

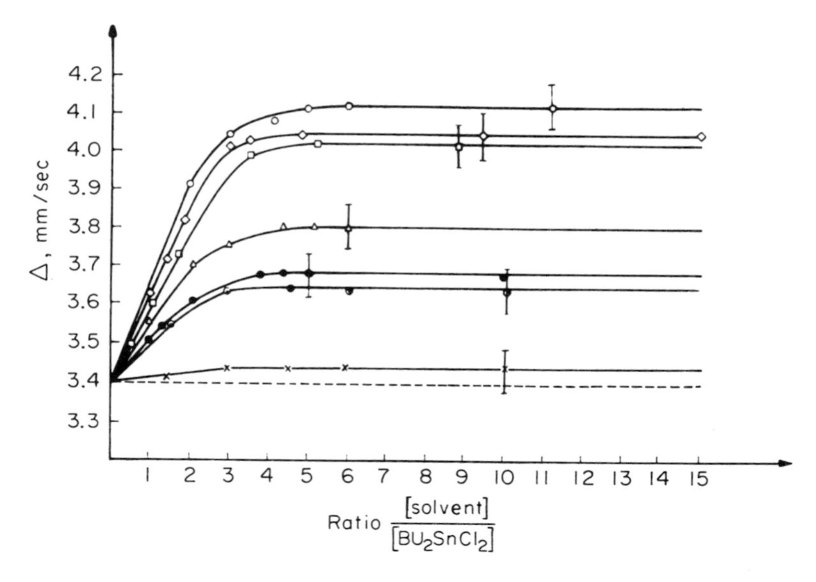

FIG. 17. The quadrupole splitting values measured at different molar ratios of solvent/dibutyltin dichloride: (o) dimethyl sulfoxide (DMSO); (◇) dimethylformamide (DMF); (□) hexamethyltriamidophosphate (HMPA); (△) dimethoxyethane (DME); (●) tetrahydrofuran (THF); (⊙) diethoxyethane (DEE); (**×**) diethyl ether.

the Q.S. value (*108*). In another study the Q.S. was found to increase generally with the dipole moment of the solvent to $\mu = 1.6$ D, and decrease somewhat at $\mu = 3$ D. The dependence on concentration is like that shown in Fig. 17 (*6*). Solvent-dependent spectra have also been recorded for triphenyltin lithium solutions (*32a*).

E. The Nature of the Tin–Transition Metal Bond

In Section IV,C,3 the valence state of tin in transition metal compounds was discussed. It is apparent from Fig. 18 that the I.S. increases monotonically with the substitution of transition metal atoms, M, in either $R_{4-n}SnM_n$ or $X_{4-n}SnM_n$. This corresponds to an increase in $|\psi(0)|^2$, viewed presumably isotropically from the tin nucleus. The NMR $J(^{119}Sn—C—^{1}H)$ in the methyltin derivatives is also related in the Fermi contact mechanism to the *s* distribution at tin, in this case directed along the bonding axes to carbon. The NMR data indicate that the increase in $|\psi_{ns}(0)|^2$ at the tin nucleus is accompanied by a decrease in the *s* character of the tin–carbon bond with metal substitution in $(H_3C)_{4-n}SnM_n$, and dictate a parallel

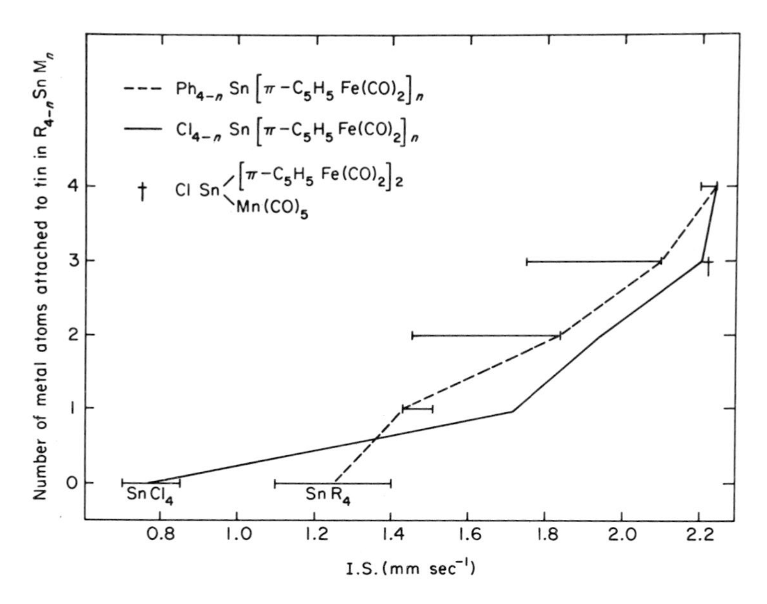

FIG. 18. Isomer shift vs. transition metal substitution at tin in $R_{4-n}SnM_n$ and $X_{4-n}SnM_n$. (The horizontal bars represent the range of values reported.)

concentration of *s* character in the tin–transition metal bond. The enhanced *s* character in this bond is reflected in the larger than tetrahedral angle M—Sn—M and smaller than tetrahedral angles C—Sn—C and X—Sn—X, and also in the tendency for short internuclear distances *d*(Sn—M) and long *d*(Sn—X) (*93*). The population of empty tin 5*d* orbitals through $(d \rightarrow d)$–π bonding from the attached transition metal would reduce the I.S. by shielding. Thus if such π-interactions are present at all they do not predominate over the other factors responsible for the distribution of electrons at tin.

F. Radiation Damage in Organotin Compounds

Irradiation of di-*n*-butyltin sulfate with ^{60}Co γ-rays produces a resonance in the tin(II) region which can be assigned to $SnSO_4$, indicating that fission of the tin–carbon bonds has occurred. Other spectral features are assigned to $(n\text{-}C_4H_9)_2SnSO_3$. Irradiation in air results in oxidation to SnO_2 (*4*). Radiation damage in tin(II) oxalate (*17b*) and the polymer $[(n\text{-}C_4H_9)_2Sn(OCOCCH_3CH_2)]_n$ has also been followed by Mössbauer spectroscopy (*4*). Irradiation of a tetraphenyltin and stannic iodide mixture with 1.6

meV electrons gives rise to a spectrum containing components due to $(C_6H_5)_nSnI_{4-n}$ (*99*). The stabilization of carbon-chain polymers to oxidation by use of organotin compounds has been studied using dibutyltin dimaleate in polyethylene; the radiation damage from ^{60}Co γ-rays can be followed by Mössbauer spectroscopy (*2*).

G. Adsorption of Organotin Compounds on Surfaces

Mössbauer spectroscopy, because of its sensitivity to the strength and angular distribution of binding and to the density of *s* electrons at the nucleus can be used to study the nature and range of molecular forces in the surface zone. In such experiments using refractory oxide substrates, the adsorbant will be transparent to γ-rays, and the usual transmission geometry can be used. Studies of this type should aid in understanding adsorption and catalytic phenomena. For example, the spectrum of tetramethyltin adsorbed on γ-aluminum oxide or silica gel gives rise to new resonances due to Sn—O bond formation, especially at elevated temperatures. The spectrum of tetramethyltin adsorbed on activated carbon under similar conditions with temperatures up to 300° C is unchanged. Atmospheric oxygen does not participate in these processes. The resonance of adsorbed liquid tetramethyltin can be observed at room temperature (*143*, *144*).

H. To Study the Course of Reaction

Previous sections have mentioned the hydrolysis–oxidation of tin(II)–oxygen heterocycles (Section IV,C,2), the oxidation of compounds of the formula $(R_2Sn)_n$ in air (Section IV,C,1), and the radiation-induced reaction between tetraphenyltin and tin(IV) iodide (Section IV,F). The possibilities for further studies of this kind are very great. In recent examples, the action of *n*-butyllithium on triethylvinyltin has been studied for various mole ratios (7), a mechanism for the reaction of tin(IV) chloride with lithium aluminum hydride in acid medium has been suggested (*38*), and the transformation from tin(II) chloride to tin(II) oxide during resin vulcanization followed (*149*).

I. Structures in Solution

There exist few rigorous physical methods for determining the structures of dissolved species. If it can be assumed that in the frozen solvent the organotin species are in identical environments as in the liquid solution, then Mössbauer data can be used as an adjunct in the problem of determining structure. Much effort has recently been focused on the structures of the organotin–transition metal compounds, and it is of interest to learn if the structural features observed for single crystals are preserved in solution. Changes in internuclear distances would have a marked effect on I.S. values, as shown by compression experiments (*352*, *353*, *396*), in which it has been estimated that a change of $\backsim$0.02 Å could be readily detected from changes in the I.S. (*119*). Thus structures which arise from packing could be differentiated from those which are consequences of the bonding. Using both ^{57}Fe and ^{119m}Sn Mössbauer results it was shown that the seemingly anomalous internuclear distances and bond angles in solid $(C_6H_5)_3Sn[\pi\text{-}C_5H_5Fe(CO)_2]$ and $Cl_3Sn[\pi\text{-}C_5H_5Fe(CO)_2]$ are a reflection of the bonding in these molecules, while in $Cl_2Sn[\pi\text{-}C_5H_5Fe(CO)_2]_2$ the spectrum in the glassy matrix differs from that in the solid with superimposed doublets arising from two types of tin atoms. These can be interpreted as resulting from two rotational isomers obtained by rotation about the metal–metal bond (*119*).

Structures of tin solids often involve higher coordination numbers through bridging atoms. Monomeric molecules might revert to T_d symmetry at tin in solution, and the changes in symmetry might be amenable to study by Mössbauer techniques. Unfortunately, the disruption of the crystal lattice, it seems, can only be brought about by supplying the type of interaction in solution which the tin atom enjoyed in the solid state. Thus the solvents which serve to dissolve the bridged organotin solids all possess donor atoms which apparently give the tin species a similar or higher coordination number in the resulting solution. On the other hand, distortions in the structure arising from nonspecific interactions in the crystal can be distinguished if they are relieved in solution.

J. *Intramolecular Interactions of Distant Atoms*

Because Mössbauer parameters seem relatively insensitive to changes of atoms and groups remote in organotin molecules, and because molecules of the type R_3SnR which depart from T_d symmetry only slightly do not show resolvable Q.S., it is possible to study intramolecular interactions directly involving tin. Such interactions which change coordination number at tin serve to produce resolvable Q.S.

Where resolvable Q.S. is expected in the absence of additional interactions, it may be a difficult matter to decide on the merits of structures such as

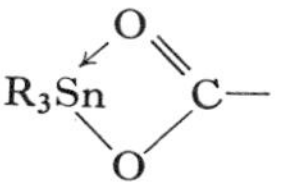

(I) (*359,385*) 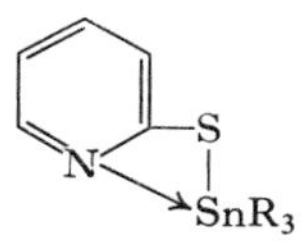 (II) (*184*) 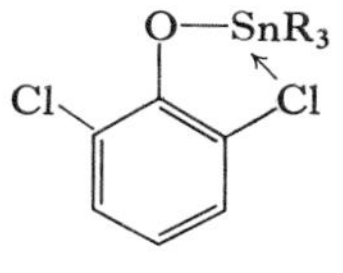 (III) (*184*) 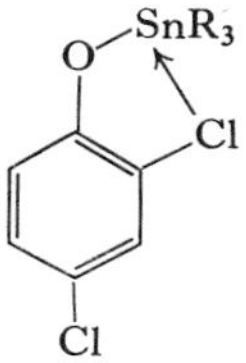 (IV) (*184*)

However, when a resolvable Q.S. is observed where none is expected, then it may arise from intramolecular interaction from a donor atom remote in the molecule. For example, a structure such as

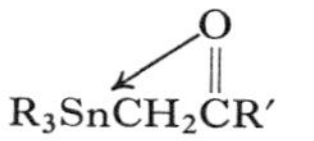

$$R_3SnCH_2\overset{\overset{O}{\|}}{C}R'$$

may be responsible for the observed resolvable Q.S. and the shift of ν(C=O) to lower energies lacking in $R_3SnCH_2CH_2\overset{\overset{O}{\|}}{C}R$ and $R_3SnCH_2O\overset{\overset{O}{\|}}{C}H$ (*146*). Failure to resolve Q.S. from the spectra of the compounds represented in Fig. 14 has been used to rule out structures involving intramolecular interactions such as

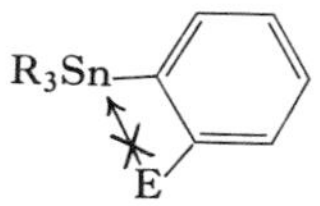

R_3Sn—C_6H_4—E and R_3Sn—CH_2—E (*365*).

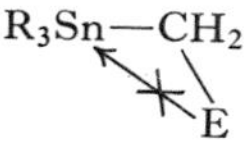

K. Derivation of Molecular Orbital Parameters from Mössbauer Data

Certain experimental methods yield information related to the problem of determining the electron distributions in complex molecules, and hence are useful in semiempirical calculations. These methods include ESR, NMR, n.q.r., and optical spectra. As seen in Sections II,E,1 and 2, I.S. and Q.S. data can be used to estimate electron densities and electron field gradients, and these in turn are related to the parameters of a molecular orbital calculation. Mössbauer data may, therefore, be added to those obtained in other ways (*30a*, *31*, *32*). An especially interesting case is the molecule SnI_4, for which complete Mössbauer data for both tin and iodine

(iodine has two Mössbauer nuclei) may be sufficient to determine all the parameters of the molecular orbitals in the molecule. Two independent studies of tin(IV) iodide have recently appeared (*63*, *118*).

L. Structures in the Solid

Information concerning the structures of organotin compounds can be assembled from a variety of spectroscopic methods. Examination of derivatives of di- and trimethyltin(IV) in the tin–carbon stretching region of the infrared yields information concerning the configuration of methyl groups about tin, the absence of ν_{sym}(Sn—C) taken as a sign of linear dimethyltin, or planar trimethyltin configurations. The NMR $J(^{119}Sn—C—^{1}H)$ value is indicative of the coordination number at tin. In derivatives containing carbonyl groups the IR ν(C=O) can be used to infer coordination through the carbonyl group or the presence of free carbonyl groups. In derivatives of inorganic anions IR can reveal departures from symmetry which arise from coordination to tin. Added to these parameters, the ^{119m}Sn Mössbauer I.S. and Q.S. can provide further confirmation of structure by specifying valence state and the electronic situation and site symmetry at the tin atom.

APPENDIX I

A BIBLIOGRAPHY OF ^{119m}Sn MÖSSBAUER SPECTROSCOPY

Note: References preceded by an asterisk were added in proof.

A. Research Papers and Notes

*1. M. A. Abidov, G. S. Zhdanov, and R. N. Kuz'min, *Uporyadochen. at. Ego Vlixan. Svoist. Splav* (Metallofiz.) **20**, 144–7 (1968).

1a. A. Yu. Aleksandrov, Yu. V. Baldokhin, R. P. Braginskii, V. I. Gol'danskii, L. A. Korytko, S. S. Leshchenko, and E. E. Finkel, *Khim. Vys. Energ.* **2**, 331 (1968).

*1b. A. Yu. Aleksandrov, S. M. Berlyant, V. L. Karpov, L. A. Korytko, and E. E. Finkel, *Vysokomol. Soedin. Ser. A* **11**, 2695 (1969).

1c. A. Yu. Aleksandrov, S. M. Berlyant, V. L. Karpov, S. S. Leshchenko, O. Yu. Okhlobystin, E. E. Finkel, and V. S. Shpinel, *Polymer Sci.* (*USSR*) (*English Transl.*) **6**, 2334 (1964).

2. A. Yu. Aleksandrov, V. I. Bregadze, V. I. Goldanskii, L. I. Zakharkin, O. Yu. Okhlobystin, and V. V. Khrapov, *Dokl. Akad. Nauk SSSR* **165**, 593 (1965).

3. A. Yu. Aleksandrov, N. N. Delyagin, K. P. Mitrofanov, L. S. Polak, and V. S. Shpinel, *Soviet Phys. JETP* (*English Transl.*) **16**, 879 (1963).

4. A. Yu. Aleksandrov, N. N. Delyagin, K. P. Mitrofanov, L. S. Polak, and V. S. Shpinel, *Soviet Phys. JETP* (*English Transl.*) **16**, 1467 (1963).

5. A. Yu. Aleksandrov, N. N. Delyagin, K. P. Mitrofanov, L. S. Polak, and V. S. Shpinel, *Dokl. Akad. Nauk SSSR* **148**, 126 (1963).
6. A. Yu. Aleksandrov, Ya. G. Dorfman, O. L. Lependina, K. P. Mitrofanov, M. V. Plotnikova, L. S. Polak, A. Ya. Temkin, and V. S. Shpinel, *Russ. J. Phys. Chem. (English Transl.)* **38**, 1185 (1964).
7. A. Yu. Aleksandrov, V. I. Gol'danskii, L. A. Korytko, V. A. Malizev, and N. A. Plate, *Vysokomol. Soedin.* **B10**, 209 (1968).
8. A. Yu. Aleksandrov, K. P. Mitrofanov, O. Yu. Okhlobystin, L. S. Polak, and V. S. Shpinel, *Proc. Acad. Sci. USSR, Phys. Chem. Sect.* (*English Transl.*) **153**, 974 (1963).
9. A. Yu. Aleksandrov, O. Yu. Okhlobystin, L. S. Polak, and V. S. Shpinel, *Proc. Acad. Sci. USSR, Phys. Chem. Sect.* (*English Transl.*) **157**, 768 (1964).
10. S. M. Aleksandrov, T. V. Malesheva, and S. S. Rodin, *Geokhimiya* p. 1104 (1967).
11. L. A. Alekseev, *Phys. Metals Metallog.* (*USSR*) (*English Transl.*) **20**, 153 (1965).
12. L. A. Alekseev and P. L. Gruzin, *Proc. Acad. Sci. USSR, Phys. Chem. Sect.* (*English Transl.*) **160**, 33 (1965).
13. L. A. Alekseev, P. L. Gruzin, U. L. Rodionov, and I. I. Shtan', *Fiz. Metal. i Metalloved.* **26**, 49 (1968).
*13a. L. A. Alekseev, P. L. Gruzin, and U. L. Rodionov, *Fiz. Metal. i Metalloved.* **27**, 1112 (1969).
*13b. L. A. Alekseev, P. L. Gruzin, and U. L. Rodionov, *Fiz. Metal. i Metalloved.* **28**, 550 (1969).
14. N. E. Alekseevskii, P. Z. Hien, V. G. Shapiro, and V. S. Shpinel, *Soviet Phys. JETP* (*English Transl.*) **16**, 559 (1963).
14a. N. E. Alekseevskii and A. P. Kiryanov, *Zh. Eksperim. i Teor. Fiz., Pisma, v Redaktsiyu* **9**, 92 (1969).
15. N. E. Alekseevskii, A. P. Kiryanov, V. I. Nizhankovskii, and Yu. A. Samarskii, *JETP Letters* (*English Transl.*) **2**, 171 (1965).
15a. N. E. Alekseevskii, A. P. Kiryanov, Yu. A. Samarskii, and V. I. Tsebro, *Dokl. Akad. Nauk SSSR* **186**, 1284 (1969).
*15b. K. M. Ali, D. Cunningham, M. J. Frazer, J. D. Donaldson, and B. J. Senior, *J. Chem. Soc, A* p. 2836 (1969).
16. T. Anderson and P. Oestergaard, *Trans. Faraday Soc.* **64**, 3014 (1968).
17. A. M. Babeshkin, A. A. Bekker, and V. I. Gotlib, *Vestn. Mosk. Univ.* p. 34 (1966).
*17a. A. M. Babeshkin, A. Bekker, E. N. Efremov, and A. N. Nesmeyanov, *Vestn. Mosk. Univ. Khim.* **24**, 40 (1969).
*17b. A. M. Babeshkin, A. Bekker, E. N. Efremov, and A. N. Nesmeyanov, *Vestn. Mosk. Univ. Khim.* **24**, 78 (1969).
17c. A. M. Babeshkin, A. A. Bekker, A. N. Nesmeyanov, P. B. Fabrichnyi, and K. V. Pokholok, *Radiokhimiya* **10**, 752 (1968).
17d. A. M. Babeshkin, K. V. Pokholok, A. A. Bekker, and A. N. Nesmeyanov, *Radiokhimiya* **9**, 668 (1967).
18. J. Baijal and U. Baijal, *J. Phys. Soc. Japan* **21**, 1457 (1966).
19. N. P. Balabanov, B. A. Komissarova, A. A. Sorokin, and V. S. Shpinel, *Nauchn. Tr. Vgssh. Pedagog. Inst., Plovdiv, Mat., Fiz., Khim., Biol.* **5**, 49 (1967).
20. V. I. Baranovskii, B. E. Dzevitskii, L. M. Krizhanskii, and B. I. Rogozev, *J. Struct. Chem.* (*USSR*) (*English Transl.*) **7**, 754 (1966).
21. V. I. Baranovskii, G. M. Gorodinskii, L. M. Krizhanskii, B. I. Rogozev, and S. B. Tomilov, *Radiokhimiya* **8**, 365 (1968).

21a. V. I. Baranovskii, V. P. Sergeev, and B. E. Dzevitskii, *Dokl. Akad. Nauk SSSR* **184**, 632 (1969).
22. R. Barloutand, E. Cotton, J.-L. Picou, and J. Quidort, *Compt. Rend.* **250**, 319 (1960).
23. R. Barloutand, J. P. Picou, and C. Tzara, *Compt. Rend.* **250**, 2705 (1960).
*23a. G. M. Bartenev and A. D. Tsyganov, *Dokl. Akad. Nauk SSSR* **181**, 627 (1968).
24. A. J. Bearden, H. S. Marsh, and J. J. Zuckerman, *Inorg. Chem.* **5**, 1260 (1966).
24a. A. A. Bekker, *Vestn. Mosk. Univ., Ser. II: Khim.* **22**, 83 (1967); *Chem. Abstr.* **69**, 6964 (1968).
*24b. V. N. Belogurov, V. F. Vasilev, E. Luksa, P. E. Senkov, and V. Vanaga, *Latv. PSR Zinat. Akad. Vestis Fiz. Teh. Zinat. Ser.* p. 63 (1969).
25. K. P. Belov and I. S. Lyubutin, *Zh. Eksperim. i Teor. Fiz.* **49**, 747 (1965).
26. K. P. Belov and I. S. Lyubutin, *JETP Letters* (*English Transl.*) **1**, 16 (1965).
26a. V. F. Belov and I. S. Zheludev, *Zh. Eksperim. i Teor. Fiz., Pis'ma v Redaktsiyu* **6**, 843 (1967).
27. L. M. Belyaev, I. S. Lyubutin, L. N. Demyanets, T. V. Dmitrieva, and L. P. Mitina, *Fiz. Tverd. Tela* **11**, 528 (1969).
*27a. L. M. Belyaev, I. S. Lyubutin, and T. V. Dmitrieva, *Fiz. Metal. i Metalloved.* **25**, 187 (1968).
28. V. A. Belyakov, *Phys. Letters* **16**, 279 (1965).
29. V. A. Bekyakov, *Soviet Phys. JETP* (*English Transl.*) **22**, 578 (1966).
30. N. Benczer-Koller, *Phys. Rev.* **134B**, 1205 (1964).
30a. H. L. Berger and H. A. Medicus, *Phys. Rev.* (1970) (in press).
30b. I. B. Bersuker, *Theoret. Exptl. Chem.* (*English Transl.*) **1**, 450 (1965).
31. I. B. Bersuker, V. I. Gol'danskii, and E. F. Makarov, *Theoret. Exptl. Chem.* (*English Transl.*) **1**, 452 (1965).
32. I. B. Bersuker, V. I. Gol'danskii, and E. F. Makarov, *Soviet Phys. JETP* (*English Transl.*) **22**, 485 (1966).
32a. K. A. Bilevich, V. I. Gol'danskii, V. Ya. Rochev, and V. V. Khrapov, *Izv. Akad. Nauk SSSR, Ser. Khim.* p. 1705 (1969).
33. G. Bliznikov and K. Petrov, *Z. Anorg. Allgem. Chem.* **354**, 307 (1967).
*33a. J.-P. Bocquet, Y. Y. Chu, G. T. Emery, and M. L. Perlman, *Phys. Rev.* **167**, 1117 (1968).
34. J.-P. Bocquet, Y. Y. Chu, O. C. Kistner, M. L. Perlman, and G. T. Emery, *Phys. Rev. Letters* **17**, 809 (1966).
35. V. A. Bokov, G. V. Novikov, O. B. Proskuryakov, Yu. G. Saksonov, V. A. Trukhtanov, and S. I. Yushchuk, *Fiz. Tverd. Tela* **10**, 1080 (1968).
36. V. A. Bokov, V. P. Romanov, and V. V. Chekin, *Soviet Phys.-Solid State* (*English Transl.*) **7**, 1521 (1965).
*36a. B. I. Boltaks, S. I. Bondarevskii, P. P. Seregin, and V. T. Shipatov, *Fiz. Tverd. Tela* **11**, 1839 (1969).
36b. S. I. Bondarevskii and P. P. Seregin, *Fiz. Tverd. Tela* **10**, 3454 (1968).
37. T. Bontschev, D. Christov, Kl. Burin, and Iv. Mandzhukov, *Z. Physik* **190**, 278, (1966).
38. T. Bontschev, D. Christov, Kl. Burin, and Iv. Mandzhukov, *Z. Anorg. Allgem. Chem.* **347**, 199 (1966).
38a. T. Bontchev, A. Jordanov, and A. Minikova, *Nucl. Instr. Methods* **69**, 36 (1969).
39. T. Bontchev, B. Skorchev, S. Ormandziev, O. Emersleben, D. Christov, P. Kamenov, and G. Danailov, *Godishnik Sofiskiya Univ., Fiz.-Mat. Fak.* **58**, 71 (1963–1964).
40. T. Bontchev, I. Vassilev, T. Sapundzhiev, and M. Evtimov, *Nature* **217**, 96 (1968).

41. F. Borsa, R. G. Barnes, and R. A. Reese, *Phys. Status Solidi* **19**, 359 (1967).
42. B. J. Bowles and T. E. Cranshaw, *Phys. Letters* **17**, 258 (1965).
43. A. J. F. Boyle, D. St. P. Bunbury, and C. Edwards, *Proc. Phys. Soc.* (*London*) **79**, 416 (1962).
44. A. J. F. Boyle, D. St. P. Bunbury, and C. Edwards, *Phys. Rev. Letters* **5**, 553 (1960).
45. A. J. F. Boyle, D. St. P. Bunbury, and C. Edwards, *Proc. Phys. Soc.* (*London*) **77**, 1062 (1961).
46. A. J. F. Boyle, D. St. P. Bunbury, C. Edwards, and H. E. Hall, *Proc. Phys. Soc.* (*London*) **77**, 129 (1961).
47. A. J. F. Boyle, D. St. P. Bunbury, C. Edwards, and H. E. Hall, *Proc. Phys. Soc.* (*London*) **76**, 165 (1960).
48. H. Brafman, M. Greenshpan, and R. H. Herber, *Nucl. Instr. Methods* **42**, 245 (1966).
49. E. V. Bryuchova, G. K. Semin, V. I. Goldanskii, and V. V. Khrapov, *Chem. Commun.* p. 491 (1968).
50. V. A. Bryukhanov, N. N. Delyagin, and Yu. Kagan, *Soviet Phys. JETP* (*English Transl.*) **19**, 563 (1964).
51. V. A. Bryukhanov, N. N. Delyagin, and Yu. Kagan, *Soviet Phys. JETP* (*English Transl.*) **18**, 945 (1964).
52. V. A. Bryukhanov, N. N. Delyagin, and R. N. Kuz'min, *Soviet Phys. JETP* (*English Transl.*) **19**, 98 (1964).
53. V. A. Bryukhanov, N. N. Delyagin, R. N. Kuz'min, and V. S. Shpinel, *Soviet Phys. JETP* (*English Transl.*) **19**, 1344 (1964).
54. V. A. Bryukhanov, N. N. Delyagin, A. A. Opalenko, and V. S. Shpinel, *Soviet Phys. JETP* (*English Transl.*) **16**, 310 (1963).
55. V. A. Bryukhanov, N. N. Delyagin, and V. S. Shpinel, *Soviet Phys. JETP* (*English Transl.*) **15**, 818 (1962).
56. V. A. Bryukhanov, N. N. Delyagin, and V. S. Shpinel, *Soviet Phys. JETP* (*English Transl.*) **20**, 55 (1965).
57. V. A. Bryukhanov, N. N. Delyagin, and V. S. Shpinel, *Soviet Phys. JETP* (*English Transl.*) **20**, 1400 (1965).
58. V. A. Bryukhanov, N. N. Delyagin, B. Zvenglinskii, and V. S. Shpinel, *Soviet Phys. JETP* (*English Transl.*) **13**, 499 (1961).
59. V. A. Bryukhanov, V. I. Goldanskii, N. N. Delyagin, L. A. Korytko, E. F. Makarov, I. P. Suzdalev, and V. S. Shpinel, *Soviet Phys. JETP* (*English Transl.*) **16**, 321 (1963).
60. V. A. Bryukhanov, V. I. Goldanskii, N. N. Delyagin, E. F. Makarov, and V. S. Shpinel, *Soviet Phys. JETP* (*English Transl.*) **15**, 443 (1962).
61. V. A. Bukarev, *Soviet Phys. JETP* (*English Transl.*) **17**, 579 (1963).
62. S. Bukshpan, *Solid State Commun.* **6**, 477 (1968).
63. S. Bukshpan and R. H. Herber, *J. Chem. Phys.* **46**, 3375 (1967).
63a. B. F. Burnham and J. J. Zuckerman, *J. Am. Chem. Soc.* **92**, 1547 (1969).
64. V. A. Burov, V. A. Krasilnikov, and O. Yu. Sukharevskaya, *Soviet Phys. JETP* (*English Transl.*) **16**, 837 (1963).
65. G. A. Bykov, G. K. Ryasnyin, and V. S. Shpinel, *Soviet Phys.-Solid State* (*English Transl.*) **7**, 1343 (1965).
*65a. J. S. Charlton, M. Cordey-Hayes, and I. R. Harris, *J. Less Common Metals* **20**, 105 (1970).
66. V. V. Chekin, *Zh. Eksperim. Teor. Fiz.* **54**, 1829 (1968).
*66a. V. V. Chekin, O. P. Balkashin, and G. D. Sultanov, *Ukr. Fiz. Zh.* **14**, 105 (1969).

*66b. V. V. Chekin, L. E. Danilenko, and A. L. Kaplienko, *Soviet Phys. JETP (English Transl.)* **24**, 472 (1967).
67. V. V. Chekin and V. G. Nanmov, *Soviet Phys. JETP (English Transl.)* **23**, 355 (1966).
*67a. V. V. Chekin and V. G. Nanmov, *Soviet Phys. JETP (English Transl.)* **24**, 699 (1967).
68. V. V. Chekin, V. P. Romanov, B. I. Verkin, and V. A. Bokov, *JETP Letters (English Transl.)* **2**, 117 (1965).
69. V. V. Chekin, A. P. Vinnikov, and O. P. Balkashin, *Fiz. Tverd. Tela* **9**, 2992 (1967).
70. V. V. Chekin, A. P. Vinnikov, and I. A. Burakhovich, *Soviet Phys.-Solid State (English Transl.)* **10**, 225 (1968).
71. R. B. Chesler, F. Boehm, and R. T. Brockmeier, *Phys. Rev. Letters* **18**, 953 (1967).
71a. T. Chivers and J. R. Sams, *Chem. Commun.* p. 249 (1969).
72. M. Cordey-Hayes, *J. Inorg. & Nucl. Chem.* **26**, 915 (1964).
73. M. Cordey-Hayes, *J. Inorg. & Nucl. Chem.* **26**, 2306 (1964).
*73a. M. Cordey-Hayes and I. R. Harris, *Phys. Letters* **24A**, 80 (1967).
73b. M. Cordey-Hayes, R. D. Kemmitt, R. D. Peacock, and G. D. Rimmer, *J. Inorg. & Nucl. Chem.* **31**, 1515 (1969).
74. M. Cordey-Hayes, R. D. Peacock, and M. Vucelic, *J. Inorg. & Nucl. Chem.* **29**, 1177 (1967).
*74a. R. F. Dalton and K. Jones, *Inorg. Nucl. Chem. Letters* **5**, 785 (1969).
75. C. G. Davies and J. D. Donaldson, *J. Chem. Soc. A* p. 946 (1968).
75a. C. G. Davies and J. D. Donaldson, *J. Inorg. & Nucl. Chem.* **30**, 2635 (1968).
75b. C. G. Davies, J. D. Donaldson, and W. B. Simpson, *J. Chem. Soc. A* p. 417 (1969).
76. N. W. G. Debye, E. Rosenberg, and J. J. Zuckerman, *J. Am. Chem. Soc.* **90**, 3234 (1968).
*76a. N. W. G. Debye and J. J. Zuckerman, *Develop. Appl. Spectrosc.* **8**, 267 (1970).
*76b. N. N. Delyagin, *Soviet Phys.-Solid State* **8**, 2748 (1967).
77. N. N. Delyagin, V. S. Shpinel, and V. A. Bryukhanov, *Soviet Phys. JETP (English Transl.)* **14**, 959 (1962).
78. N. N. Delyagin, V. S. Shpinel, V. A. Bryukhanov, and B. Zvenglinskii, *Soviet Phys. JETP (English Transl.)* **12**, 159 (1961).
79. N. N. Delyagin, V. S. Shpinel, V. A. Bryukhanov, and B. Zvenglinskii, *Soviet Phys. JETP (English Transl.)* **12**, 619 (1960).
79a. J. R. deVoe, *Natl. Bur. Std. (U.S.), Tech. Note* **451**, (1969).
*79b. J. Devooght, M. Gielen, and S. Lejeune, *J. Organometal. Chem.* **21**, 333 (1970).
80. I. Dezsi, N. A. Eissa, L. Keszthelyi, B. Molnar, and D. L. Nagy, *Phys. Status Solidi* **30**, 215 (1968).
*80a. H. Z. Dokuzoguz, L. H. Bowen, and H. H. Stadelmaier, *J. Phys. Chem. Solids*, **31**, 1565 (1970).
81. J. D. Donaldson and A. Jelen, *J. Chem. Soc., A* p. 1448 (1968).
82. J. D. Donaldson and A. Jelen, *J. Chem. Soc., A* p. 2244 (1968).
*82a. J. D. Donaldson and D. G. Nicholson, *J. Chem. Soc., A* p. 145 (1970).
*82b. J. D. Donaldson and D. G. Nicholson, *Inorg. Nucl. Chem. Letters* **6**, 151 (1970).
83. J. D. Donaldson, D. G. Nicholson, and B. J. Senior, *J. Chem. Soc., A* p. 2928 (1968).
84. J. D. Donaldson, R. Oteng, and B. J. Senior, *Chem. Commun.* p. 618 (1965).
*84a. J. D. Donaldson and B. J. Senior, *J. Chem. Soc., A* p. 2358 (1969).
85. J. D. Donaldson and B. J. Senior, *J. Chem. Soc., A* p. 1796 (1966).
86. J. D. Donaldson and B. J. Senior, *J. Chem. Soc., A* p. 1798 (1966).
87. J. D. Donaldson and B. J. Senior, *J. Chem. Soc., A* **p.** 1821 (1967).
87a. J. D. Donaldson and B. J. Senior, *J. Inorg. & Nucl. Chem.* **31**, 881 (1969).

87b. M. A. Doskey and C. Curran, *Inorg. Chim. Acta* **3**, 169 (1969).
87c. V. N. Dubinin, *Teor. i Eksperim. Khim.* **5**, 429 (1969).
88. V. N. Dubinin, S. L. Kordyuk, V. I. Lisichenko, and O. N. Smoilovs'kii, *Ukr. Fiz. Zh.* **10**, 1368 (1965).
89. V. N. Dubinin, S. L. Kordyuk, V. I. Lisichenko, N. N. Polovina, and O. N. Smoilovs'kii, *Theoret. Exptl. Chem.* (*English Transl.*) **2**, 99 (1966).
*89a. B. E. Dzevitskii and V. F. Sukhoverkhov, *Izv. Sibirsk. Otd. Akad. Nauk SSSR, Ser. Khim. Nauk* p. 54 (1968).
90. M. Eibschütz, E. Herman, and S. Shtrikman, *J. Phys. Chem. Solids* **28**, 1633 (1967).
91. L. M. Epstein and D. K. Straub, *Inorg. Chem.* **4**, 1551 (1965).
92. G. Fabri, E. Germagnoli, M. Musci, and G. C. Locati, *Nuovo Cimento* [10] **40B**, 8410 (1965).
*92a. D. S. Faleev, G. S. Zhdanov, and R. N. Kuzmin, *Fiz. Metal. i Metalloved.* **27**, 792 (1969).
93. D. E. Fenton and J. J. Zuckerman, *J. Am. Chem. Soc.* **90**, 6226 (1968).
93a. D. E. Fenton and J. J. Zuckerman, *Inorg. Chem.* **8**, 1771 (1969).
93b. D. E. Fenton, R. R. Gould, P. G. Harrison, T. B. Harvey, III, G. M. Omietanski, K. C.-T. Sze, and J. J. Zuckerman, *Inorg. Chim. Acta* **4**, 235 (1970).
94. B. W. Fitzsimmons, N. J. Seeley, and A. W. Smith, *Chem. Commun.* p. 390 (1968).
94a. B. W. Fitzsimmons, N. J. Seeley, and A. W. Smith, *J. Chem. Soc., A* p. 143 (1969).
95. B. F. E. Ford, B. V. Liengme, and J. R. Sams, *Chem. Commun.* p. 1333 (1968).
95a. B. F. E. Ford, B. V. Liengme, and J. R. Sams, *J. Organometal. Chem.* (*Amsterdam*) **19**, 53 (1969).
95b. B. Gassenheimer and R. H. Herber, *Inorg. Chem.* **8**, 1120 (1969).
95c. A. Gelberg, *Rev. Roumaine Phys.* **14**, 183 (1969).
96. T. C. Gibb and N. N. Greenwood, *J. Chem. Soc., A* p. 43 (1966).
97. B. G. Gokhale, R. B. Chesler, and F. Boehm, *Phys. Rev. Letters* **18**, 957 (1967).
98. V. I. Goldanskii, B. V. Borshazovskii, E. F. Makarov, R. A. Stukan, K. N. Anisimov, N. E. Kolobova, and V. V. Skripkin, *Teor. Eksperim. Khim.* **3**, 478 (1967).
99. V. I. Goldanskii, G. M. Gorodinskii, S. V. Karyagin, L. A. Korytko, L. M. Krizhanskii, E. F. Markarov, I. P. Suzdalev, and V. V. Khrapov, *Proc. Acad. Sci. USSR, Phys. Chem. Sect.* (*English Transl.*) **147**, 766 (1962).
100. V. I. Goldanskii, V. V. Khrapov, V. Ya. Rochev, T. N. Sumarokova, and D. E. Surpina, *Dokl. Akad. Nauk SSSR* **183**, 364 (1968).
101. V. I. Goldanskii, M. N. Levisheva, E. F. Makarov, G. V. Novikov, and V. A. Trukhtanov, *JETP Letters* (*English Transl.*) **4**, 42 (1966).
102. V. I. Goldanskii and E. F. Makarov, *Phys. Letters* **14**, 111 (1965).
103. V. I. Goldanskii, E. F. Makarov, and V. V. Khrapov, *Soviet Phys. JETP* (*English Transl.*) **17**, 508 (1963).
104. V. I. Goldanskii, E. F. Makarov, and V. V. Khrapov, *Phys. Letters* **3**, 344 (1963).
105. V. I. Goldanskii, E. F. Makarov, and R. A. Stukan, *J. Chem. Phys.* **47**, 4048 (1967).
106. V. I. Goldanskii, E. F. Makarov, R. A. Stukan, T. N. Sumarokova, V. A. Trukhtanov, and V. V. Khrapov, *Proc. Acad. Sci. USSR, Phys. Chem. Sect.* (*English Transl.*) **156**, 474 (1964).
107. V. I. Goldanskii, E. F. Makarov, R. A. Stukan, V. A. Trukhtanov, and V. V. Khrapov, *Proc. Acad. Sci. USSR, Phys. Chem. Sect.* (*English Transl.*) **151**, 598 (1963).
108. V. I. Goldanskii, O. Yu. Okhlobystin, V. Ya. Rochev, and V. V. Khrapov, *J. Organometal. Chem.* (*Amsterdam*) **4**, 160 (1965).

108a. V. I. Goldanskii, N. A. Plate, Yu. A. Purinson, and V. V. Khrapov, *Vysokomoleknl. Soedin*, **11**, 498 (1969).
109. V. I. Goldanskii, V. Ya. Rochev, and V. V. Khrapov, *Proc. Acad. Sci. USSR, Phys. Chem. Sect.* (*English Transl.*) **156**, 571 (1964).
110. V. I. Goldanskii, V. Ya. Rochev, V. V. Khrapov, B. E. Dzevitskii, and V. F. Sukhoverkhov, *Izv. Sibirsk. Otd. Akad. Nauk SSSR, Ser. Khim. Nauk* p. 22 (1968).
111. V. I. Goldanskii, V. A. Trukhtanov, M. N. Devisheva, and V. F. Belov, *JETP Letters* (*English Transl.*) **1**, 19 (1965).
112. V. I. Goldanskii, V. A. Trukhtanov, M. N. Devisheva, and V. F. Belov, *Phys. Letters* **15**, 317 (1965).
112a. B. A. Goodman and N. N. Greenwood, *Chem. Commun.* p. 1105 (1969).
113. G. M. Gorodinskii, L. M. Krizhanskii, and E. M. Kruglov, *Soviet Phys. JETP* (*English Transl.*) **16**, 1449 (1963).
*113a. N. N. Greenwood, P. G. Perkins, and D. H. Wall, *Phys. Letters* **28A**, 339 (1968).
114. N. N. Greenwood and J. N. R. Ruddick, *J. Chem. Soc., A* p. 1679 (1967).
*114a. P. L. Gruzin, G. N. Shlokov, and L. A. Alekeev, *Dokl. Akad. Nauk SSSR* **176**, 362 (1967).
115. M. P. Gupta and H. B. Mathur, *J. Phys. Chem. Solids* **29**, 1479 (1968).
116. S. S. Hanna, L. Meyer-Schutzmeister, R. S. Preston, and D. H. Vincent, *Phys. Rev.* **120**, 2211 (1960).
117. P. Hannaford, C. J. Howard, and J. W. G. Wignall, *Phys. Letters* **19**, 257 (1965).
*117a. P. Hannaford and J. W. G. Wignall, *Phys. Status Solidi* **35**, 809 (1969).
117b. P. G. Harrison and J. J. Zuckerman, *Chem. Commun.* p. 321 (1969).
117c. P. G. Harrison and J. J. Zuckerman, *Inorg. Nucl. Chem. Letters* **5**, 545 (1969).
117d. P. G. Harrison and J. J. Zuckerman, *J. Am. Chem. Soc.* **91**, 6885 (1969).
117e. P. G. Harrison and J. J. Zuckerman, *Inorg. Chem.* **9**, 175 (1970).
117f. P. G. Harrison and J. J. Zuckerman, *Inorg. Nucl. Chem. Letters* **6**, 5 (1970).
*117g. P. G. Harrison and J. J. Zuckerman, *J. Am. Chem. Soc.* **92**, 2577 (1970).
118. Y. Hazony, *J. Chem. Phys.* **49**, 159 (1968).
118a. Y. Hazony and R. H. Herber, *J. Inorg. & Nucl. Chem.* **31**, 321 (1969).
*118b. R. H. Herber, *Inorg. Chim. Acta* **3**, 85 (1969).
118c. R. H. Herber and H.-S. Cheng, *Inorg. Chem.* **8**, 2145 (1969).
119. R. H. Herber and Y. Goscinny, *Inorg. Chem.* **7**, 1293 (1968).
120. R. H. Herber and G. I. Parisi, *Inorg. Chem.* **5**, 769 (1966).
121. R. H. Herber and J. J. Spijkerman, *J. Chem. Phys.* **42**, 4312 (1965).
122. R. H. Herber and J. J. Spijkerman, *J. Chem. Phys.* **43**, 4057 (1965).
123. R. H. Herber and H. A. Stöckler, *Trans. N.Y. Acad. Sci.* [2] **26**, 929 (1964).
124. R. H. Herber, H. A. Stöckler, and W. T. Reichle, *J. Chem. Phys.* **42**, 2447 (1965).
125. P. Z. Hien and V. S. Shpinel, *Soviet Phys. JETP* (*English Transl.*) **17**, 268 (1963).
126. P. Z. Hien, V. S. Shpinel, A. S. Viskov, and Yu. N. Venevtsev, *Soviet Phys. JETP* (*English Transl.*) **17**, 1271 (1963).
127. P. Z. Hien, A. S. Viskov, V. S. Shpinel, and Yu. N. Venevtsev, *Soviet Phys. JETP* (*English Transl.*) **17**, 1465 (1963).
127a. J. C. Hill, R. S. Drago, and R. H. Herber, *J. Am. Chem. Soc.* **91**, 1644 (1969).
128. C. Hohenemser, *Phys. Rev.* **139**, A185 (1965).
129. D. Hristov, T. Bonchev, and K. Bourin, *Compt. Rend. Acad. Bulgar. Sci.* **19**, 293 (1966).
130. N. S. Ibraimov and R. N. Kuzmin, *Soviet Phys. JETP* (*English Transl.*) **21**, 70 (1965).
131. N. S. Ibraimov and R. N. Kuzmin, *Dokl. Akad. Nauk SSSR* **165**, 518 (1965).

132. N. S. Ibraimov, R. N. Kuzmin, and G. S. Zhdanov, *Soviet Phys. JETP* (*English Transl.*) **22**, 956 (1966).
132a. S. Ichiba, M. Mishima, and H. Negita, *Bull. Chem. Soc. Japan* **42**, 1486 (1969).
133. S. Ichiba, M. Mishima, H. Sakai, and H. Negita, *Bull. Chem. Soc. Japan* **41**, 49 (1968).
133a. S. Ichiba, H. Sakai, and H. Negita, *Bull. Chem. Soc. Japan* **41**, 2791 (1968).
134. A. P. Jain and T. E. Cranshaw, *Phys. Letters* **25A**, 425 (1967).
135. M. T. Jones, *Inorg. Chem.* **6**, 1249 (1967).
136. Yu. Kagan, *Soviet Phys. "Doklady"* (*English Transl.*) **6**, 881 (1961).
137. A. A. Kalmakov and N. Salakhutdinov, *Izv. Vysshikh Uchebn. Zavedenii, Tsvetn. Met.* **8**, 158 (1965).
138. A. V. Kalyamin, B. G. Lourie, A. V. Popov, and V. P. Romanov, *Fiz. Tverd. Tela* **10**, 3180 (1968).
139. C. R. Kanekar, K. R. P. Mallikarjuna Rao, and V. Udaya Shankar Rao, *Phys. Letters* **19**, 95 (1965).
140. C. R. Kanekar, K. R. P. Mallikarjuna Rao, and V. Udaya Shankar Rao, *Phys. Letters* **27A**, 85 (1968).
*140a. C. R. Kanekar, K. R. P. Mallikarjuna Rao, and V. Udaya Shankar Rao, *Phys. Letters* **28A**, 220 (1968).
141. A. N. Karasev, N. E. Kolobova, L. S. Polak, V. S. Shpinel, and K. N. Anisimov, *Theoret. Exptl. Chem.* **2**, 96 (1966).
142. A. N. Karasev, L. Ya. Margolis, and L. S. Polak, *Fiz. Tverd. Tela* **8**, 287 (1966).
143. A. N. Karasev, L. S. Polak, E. B. Shlikhter, and V. S. Shpinel, *Kinetics Catalysis* (*USSR*) (*English Transl.*) **6**, 630 (1965).
144. A. N. Karasev, L. S. Polak, E. B. Shlikhter, and V. S. Shpinel, *Russ. J. Phys. Chem.* (*English Transl.*) **39**, 1670 (1965).
145. S. V. Karyagin, *Dokl. Akad. Nauk SSSR* **148**, 110 (1963).
*145a. E. O. Kazimir, *U.S. At. Energy Comm.* NYO-906-86, 196 pp. (1969).
146. V. V. Khrapov, V. I. Goldanskii, A. K. Prokofiev, and R. G. Kostyanovskii, *J. Gen. Chem. USSR* (*English Transl.*) **37**, 1 (1967).
147. V. V. Khrapov, V. I. Goldanskii, A. K. Prokofiev, V. Ya. Rochev, and R. G. Kostyanovskii, *Izv. Akad. Nauk SSSR, Ser. Khim.* p. 1261 (1968).
148. D. Khristov, T. Bonchev, and K. Burin, *Compt. Rend. Acad. Bulgare Sci.* **19**, 293 (1966).
*148a. D. Khristov, T. Bonchev, and D. Dimov, *Kaut. Gummi Kunstst.* **23**, 15–16 (1970).
149. D. Khristov, T. Bonchev, B. Skortchev, D. Dimov, and S. Ormandziev, *Kautschuk Gummi Kunstoffe* **19**, 418 (1966).
150. O. C. Kistner, A. W. Sunyar, and J. B. Swan, *Phys. Rev.* **123**, 179 (1961).
*150a. B. A. Komissarova and A. A. Sorokin, *Soviet Phys. JETP* (*English Transl.*) **54**, 424 (1968).
151. B. A. Komissarova, A. A. Sorokin, and V. S. Shpinel, *Soviet J. Nucl. Phys.* (*English Transl.*) **1**, 444 (1965).
152. B. A. Komissarova, A. A. Sorokin, and V. S. Shpinel, *Soviet Phys. JETP* (*English Transl.*) **23**, 800 (1966).
152a. S. L. Kordyuk, *Izv. Vysshikh Uchebn. Zavedenii, Fiz.* **10**, 119 (1967); *Chem. Abstr.* **68**, 110029 (1968).
152b. S. L. Kordyuk, *Izv. Vysshikh Uchebn. Zavedenii, Fiz.* **12**, 150 (1969).
*152c. S. L. Kordyuk and V. I. Lisichenko, *Phys. Status Solidi* **35**, K127 (1969).
*152d. V. A. Kostroun and B. Crasemann, *Phys. Rev.* **174**, 1535 (1968).
152e. R. G. Kostyanovskii, A. K. Prokofiev, V. I. Goldanskii, V. V. Khrapov, and V. Ya. Rochev, *Izv. Akad. Nauk SSSR, Ser. Khim.* p. 270 (1968).

152f. V. Kothekar and V. S. Shpinel, *Zh. Strukt. Khim.* **10**, 37 (1969).
153. L. M. Krizhanskii, O. Yu. Okhlobystin, A. V. Popov, and B. I. Rogozev, *Proc. Acad. Sci. USSR, Phys. Chem. Sect.* (*English Transl.*) **160**, 142 (1965).
154. L. M. Krizhanskii, B. I. Rogozev, and A. V. Popov, *JETP Letters* (*English Transl.*) **3**, 382 (1966).
155. R. N. Kuz'min, N. S. Ibraimov, and G. S. Zhdanov, *Soviet Phys. JETP* (*English Transl.*) **23**, 219 (1966).
156. C. Lamborizio and I. Ortalli, *Nuovo Cimento* [10] **36**, 1059 (1965).
157. F. Lawson, *Nature* **215**, 955 (1967).
*157a. U. A. Lebedev, A. M. Babeshkin, A. N. Nesmeyanov, and E. V. Lamykin, *Vestn. Mosk. Univ.* **24**, 45 (1969).
158. Y.-F. Lee, *Ho Tsu K'o Hsueh* **4**, 25 (1965).
159. J. K. Lees and P. A. Flinn, *Phys. Letters* **19**, 186 (1965).
160. J. K. Lees and P. A. Flinn, *J. Chem. Phys.* **48**, 882 (1968).
*160a. M. Loewenhaupt and S. Huefner, *Phys. Letters* **30A**, 309 (1969).
161. G. Longworth, F. A. Deeney, and R. H. Packwood, *Phys. Letters* **19**, 188 (1965).
162. G. Longworth and R. H. Packwood, *Phys. Letters* **14**, 75 (1965).
163. V. A. Lyubimov and A. I. Alikhanov, *Soviet Phys. JETP* (*English Transl.*) **11**, 1375 (1960).
164. I. S. Lyubutin, *Fiz. Tverd. Tela* **8**, 643 (1966).
165. I. S. Lyubutin, E. F. Makarov, and V. A. Povitskii, *Fiz. Tverd. Tela* **10**, 534 (1968).
*165a. I. S. Lynbutin, V. A. Makarov, E. F. Makarov, and V. A. Povitskii, *JETP Letters* (*English Transl.*), **6**, 291 (1968).
166. I. S. Lyubutin and B. V. Mill, *Fiz. Tverd. Tela* **9**, 3145 (1967).
166a. M. Mahnig and E. Wicke, *Z. Naturforsch.* **24a**, 1258 (1969).
167. A. S. Marfunin and A. R. Mkrtchyan, *Geokhimiya* 498 (1968).
168. L. May and J. J. Spijkerman, *J. Chem. Phys.* **46**, 3272 (1967).
168a. W. Meisel, K. Hennig, and H. Schnorr, *Phys. Status Solidi* **34**, 577 (1969).
169. L. Meyer-Schutzmeister, R. S. Preston, and S. S. Hanna, *Phys. Rev.* **122**, 1717 (1961).
170. J. Miller and J. J. Moine, *Phys. Letters* **2**, 50 (1962).
171. K. P. Mitrofanov, M. V. Plotnikova, and V. Ya. Rochov, *Pribory i Tekhn. Eksperim.* **10**, 55 (1965).
172. K. P. Mitrofanov, M. V. Plotnikova, and V. S. Shpinel, *Soviet Phys, JETP* (*English Transl.*) **21**, 524 (1965).
173. K. P. Mitrofanov and V. S. Shpinel, *Soviet Phys. JETP* (*English Transl.*) **13**, 686 (1961).
174. K. P. Mitrofanov and T. A. Sidorov, *Soviet Phys.-Solid State* (*English Transl.*) **9**, 693 (1967).
175. K. P. Mitrofanov and T. A. Sidorov, *Soviet Phys.-Solid State* (*English Transl.*) **9**, 890 (1967).
176. K. P. Mitrofanov, A. S. Viskov, G. Ya. Driker, M. V. Plotnikova, P. Z. Hien, Yu. N. Venevtsev, and V. S. Shpinel, *Soviet Phys. JETP* (*English Transl.*) **19**, 260 (1964).
*176a. H. S. Möller, *Z. Phys.* **212**, 107 (1968).
177. H. S. Möller and R. L. Mössbauer, *Phys. Letters* **24A**, 416 (1967).
177a. D. Moras and R. Weiss, *Acta Cryst.* **B25**, 1726 (1969).
178. M. A. Mullins and C. Curran, *Inorg. Chem.* **7**, 2584 (1968).
179. M. A. Mullins and C. Curran, *Inorg. Chem.* **6**, 2017 (1967).
*179a. A. N. Murin, S. I. Bondarevskii, and P. P. Seregin, *Teor, Eksper, Khim.* **5**, 709 (1969).
*179b. A. N. Murin, S. I. Bondarevskii, and P. P. Seregin, *Soviet Radiochem.* **11**, 464 (1969).

*179c. A. N. Murin, B. G. Lur'e, S. I. Bondarevskii, and P. P. Seregin, *Fiz. Tverd. Tela* **10**, 2803 (1968).
180. C. Muzikar, V. Janovek, and V. Dvorak, *Phys. Status Solidi* **3**, K9 (1963).
181. J. Nasielski, N. Sprecher, J. Devooght, and S. Lejeune, *J. Organometal. Chem. (Amsterdam)* **8**, 97 (1967).
*181a. H. Negita, T. Okuda, and M. Mishima, *Bull. Chem. Soc. Japan* **42**, 2509 (1969).
182. A. N. Nesmeyanov, A. M. Babeshkin, A. A. Bekker, and V. Fano, *Radiokhimiya* **8**, 261 (1966).
183. A. N. Nesmeyanov, A. M. Babeshkin, A. A. Bekker, and V. Fano, *Radiokhimiya* **8**, 264 (1966).
183a. A. N. Nesmeyanov, V. I. Goldanskii, V. V. Khrapov, V. Ya. Rochev, D. N. Kravtsov, V. A. Pachevskaya, and E. M. Rokhlina, *Dokl. Akad. Nauk SSSR* **181**, 921 (1968).
*183b. A. N. Nesmeyanov, A. M. Babeshkin, E. N. Efremov, and A. A. Bekker, *Vestn. Mosk. Univ.* p. 107 (1967).
184. A. N. Nesmeyanov, V. I. Goldanskii, V. V. Khrapov, V. Ya. Rochev, D. N. Kravtsov, and E. M. Rokhlina, *Izv. Akad. Nauk SSSR, Ser. Khim.* p. 793 (1968).
185. V. I. Nikolaev, Yu. I. Shcherbina, and A. I. Karchevskii, *Soviet Phys. JETP (English Transl.)* **17**, 524 (1968).
186. V. I. Nikolaev, Yu. I. Shcherbina, and S. S. Yakimov, *Soviet Phys. JETP (English Transl.)* **18**, 878 (1964).
187. C. Nistor and T. Tinu, *Rev. Roumaine Phys.* **11**, 551 (1966).
188. V. N. Panyushkin, *Soviet Phys.-Solid State (English Transl.)* **10**, 1915 (1968).
189. V. N. Panyushkin and L. V. Rumyantseva, *Kristallografiya* **13**, 706 (1968).
190. V. N. Panyushkin and F. F. Voronov, *JETP Letters (English Transl.)* **2**, 97 (1965).
191. R. V. Parish and R. H. Platt, *Chem. Commun.* p. 1118 (1968).
191a. R. V. Parish and R. H. Platt, *J. Chem. Soc., A* p. 2145 (1969).
191b. P. A. Pella, J. R. deVoe, D. K. Snediker, and L. May, *Anal. Chem.* **41**, 46 (1969).
191c. A. A. Petrov, B. I. Rogozev, L. M. Krizhanskii, and V. S. Zavgorodnii, *Zh. Obshch. Khim.* **38**, 1196 (1968).
192. J. Philip, M. A. Mullins, and C. Curran, *Inorg. Chem.* **7**, 1895 (1968).
192a. M. V. Plotnikova, K. P. Mitrofanov, A. G. Kapyshev, Yu. N. Venevtsev, and V. S. Shpinel, *Izv. Akad. Nauk. SSSR, Ser. Fiz.* **33**, 1142 (1969).
193. M. V. Plotnikova, K. P. Mitrofanov, and V. S. Shpinel, *JETP Letters (English Transl.)* **3**, 209 (1966).
194. M. V. Plotnikova, K. P. Mitrofanov, and V. S. Shpinel, *Instr. Exptl. Tech. (English Transl.) (USSR)* **4**, 209 (1966).
195. M. V. Plotnikova, A. S. Viskov, K. P. Mitrofanov, V. S. Shpinel, and Yu. N. Venevtsev, *Izv. Akad. Nauk SSSR, Ser. Fiz.* **31**, 1112 (1967).
196. F. Pobell, *Z. Physik* **188**, 57 (1965).
196a. C. Poder and J. R. Sams, *J. Organometal. Chem. (Amsterdam)* **19**, 67 (1969).
196b. R. C. Poller and J. N. R. Ruddick. *J. Chem. Soc., A*, p. 2273 (1969).
*196c. R. C. Poller, J. N. R. Ruddick, M. Thevarasa, and W. R. McWhinnie, *J. Chem. Soc., A* p. 2327 (1969).
197. I. P. Polozova and P. P. Seregin, *Fiz. Tverd. Tela* **10**, 2536 (1968).
*197a. D. C. Price and R. Street, *Proc. Phys. Soc. London (Solid State Phys.)* Ser 2, **1**, 1258 (1968).
198. W. T. Reichle, *Inorg. Chem.* **5**, 87 (1966).
199. B. I. Rogozev, V. S. Zavgorodnii, L. M. Krizhanskii, and A. A. Petrov, *Zh. Obshch. Khim.* **38**, 2064 (1968).

200. S. L. Ruby, G. M. Kalvius, G. B. Beard, and R. E. Snyder, *Phys. Rev.* **159**, 239 (1967).
*200a. S. L. Ruby and G. K. Shenoy, *Phys. Rev.* **186**, 326 (1969).
*200b. S. L. Ruby, P. K. Tseng, H.-S. Cheng, and N. C. Li, *Chem. Phys. Letters* **2**, 39 (1968).
*200c. Yu. A. Samarskii and V. I. Tsebro, *Dokl. Akad. Nauk SSSR* **186**, 1284 (1969).
201. H. Sano and R. H. Herber, *J. Inorg. & Nucl. Chem.* **30**, 409 (1968).
201a. H. Sano and M. Kanno, *Chem. Commun.* p. 601 (1969).
202. V. G. Shapiro and V. S. Shpinel, *Soviet Phys. JETP* (*English Transl.*) **19**, 1321 (1964).
*202a. J. S. Shier and R. D. Taylor, *Solid State Commun.* **5**, 147 (1967).
*202b. J. S. Shier and R. D. Taylor, *Phys. Rev.* **174**, 346 (1968).
*202c. G. N. Shlokov, P. L. Gruzin, and E. J. Kuprianova, *Dokl. Akad. Nauk SSSR* **174**, 1144 (1967).
203. V. S. Shpinel, A. Yu. Aleksandrov, G. K. Ryasnyin, and O. Yu. Okhlobystin, *Soviet Phys. JETP* (*English Transl.*) **21**, 47 (1965).
204. V. S. Shpinel, V. A. Bryukhanov, and N. N. Delyagin, *Soviet Phys. JETP* (*English Transl.*) **13**, 1068 (1961).
205. V. S. Shpinel, V. A. Bruykhanov, and N. N. Delyagin, *Soviet Phys. JETP* (*English Transl.*) **14**, 1256 (1962).
206. V. S. Shpinel, V. A. Bryukhanov, V. Kothekar, and B. Z. Iofa, *Zh. Eksperim. i Teor. Fiz.* **53**, 23 (1967).
207. N. N. Shumilovskii, N. Salakhutdinov, and A. A. Kalmakov, *Izv. Akad. Nauk Uz. SSR, Ser. Tekhn. Nauk* **8**, 29 (1964).
208. C. M. Silcox Yoder and J. J. Zuckerman, *Inorg. Chem.* **6**, 163 (1967).
209. B. Skorchev, T. Bonchev, G. Danailov, I. Mandzhukov, and K. Burin, *Godishnik Sofiskaya Univ., Fiz. Mat. Fak.* **58**, 63 (1963).
210. D. L. Smith and J. J. Zuckerman, *J. Inorg. & Nucl. Chem.* **29**, 1203 (1967).
210a. N. S. Snyder, *Phys. Rev.* **178**, 537 (1969).
211. H. A. Stöckler and H. Sano, *Trans. Faraday Soc.* **64**, 577 (1968).
212. H. A. Stöckler and H. Sano, *Nucl. Instr. Methods* **44**, 103 (1966).
213. H. A. Stöckler and H. Sano, *Phys. Rev.* **165**, 406 (1968).
214. H. A. Stöckler and H. Sano, *Phys. Letters* **25A**, 550 (1967).
214a. H. A. Stöckler and H. Sano, *J. Chem. Phys.* **50**, 3813 (1969).
*214b. H. A. Stöckler and H. Sano, *Nat. Bur. Stand. Special Publ.* No. 301 (1969).
215. H. A. Stöckler, H. Sano, and R. H. Herber, *J. Chem. Phys.* **45**, 1182 (1966).
216. H. A. Stöckler, H. Sano, and R. H. Herber, *J. Chem. Phys.* **47**, 1567 (1967).
217. R. A. Stukan, V. I. Goldanskii, and E. F. Makarov, *Dokl. Akad. Nauk SSSR* **165**, 1347 (1965).
218. V. F. Sukhoverkhov and B. E. Dzevitskii, *Dokl. Akad. Nauk SSSR* **170**, 1099 (1966).
219. I. P. Suzdalev, M. Ya. Gen, V. I. Goldanskii, and E. F. Makarov, *Soviet Phys. JETP* (*English Transl.*) **24**, 79 (1967).
220. I. P. Suzdalev, V. I. Goldanskii, E. F. Makarov, A. S. Plachinda, and L. A. Korytko, *Soviet Phys. JETP* (*English Transl.*) **22**, 979 (1966).
221. I. P. Suzdalev, E. F. Makarov, I. Ya. Garzanov, and L. A. Korytko, *Kinetics Catalysis* (*USSR*) (*English Transl.*) **6**, 1002 (1965).
*221a. I. P. Suzdalev, A. S. Plachinda, and E. F. Makarov, *Soviet Phys. JETP* (*English Transl.*) **26**, 897 (1968).
222. I. P. Suzdalev, A. S. Plachinda, E. F. Makarov, and V. A. Dolzopolov, *Zh. Fiz. Khim.* **41**, 2831 (1967).

223. S. Trestianu, *Rev. Chim.* (*Bucharest*) **18**, 342 (1967).
*223a. P. K. Tseng and S. L. Ruby, *Chin. J. Phys.* (*Taipei*) **7**, 50 (1969).
224. C. Tzara and R. Barloutand, *Phys. Rev. Letters* **4**, 405 (1960).
225. R. A. Uher and R. A. Sorenson, *Nucl. Phys.* **86**, 1 (1966).
226. M. L. Unland and J. H. Letcher, *J. Chem. Phys.* **49**, 2706 (1968).
*226a. B. N. Veits, V. V. Grignalis, and V. D. Lisin, *Latv. PSR Zinat. Akad. Vestis Kim. Ser.* p. 744 (1969).
227. B. I. Verkin, V. V. Chekin, and A. P. Vinnikov, *Soviet Phys. JETP* (*English Transl.*) **24**, 16 (1967).
*227a. V. K. Voitovetskii, I. L. Korsunskii, and A. I. Larkin, *Phys. Letters* **27A**, 244 (1968).
227b. M. Vucelic, *Croat. Chem. Acta* **40**, 255 (1968).
228. S.-Y. Wang, Y.-F. Lee, and P. K. Tseng, *Chinese J. Phys.* **2**, 48 (1964).
*228a. R. W. J. Wedd and J. R. Sams, *Can. J. Chem.* **48**, 71 (1970).
229. W. H. Wiedemann, P. Kienle, and F. Pobell, *Z. Physik* **166**, 109 (1962).
230. J. M. Williams, *Proc. Phys. Soc.* (*London*) **C1**, 473 (1968).
*230a. J. M. Williams, *Proc. Phys. Soc. London* (*Solid State Phys.*) **2**, 2037 (1969).
*230b. D. E. Williams and C. W. Kocker, *J. Chem. Phys.* **52**, 1480 (1970).
*230c. B. Window, *Phys. Letters* **24A**, 659 (1967).
*230d. B. Window, *Proc. Phys. Soc.* (*London*) **2**, 2380 (1969).
231. L. J. Winters and D. T. Hill, *Inorg. Chem.* **4**, 1433 (1965).
232. M. Yaqub and C. Hohenemser, *Phys. Rev.* **127**, 2028 (1962).
232a. P. A. Yates, B. F. E. Ford, J. R. Sams, and F. Aubke, *Chem. Commun.* p. 791 (1969).
232b. H. Yoshida and R. H. Herber, *Radiochim. Acta* **12**, 14 (1969).
*232c. V. M. Zaporozhets, V. M. Ratnikov, V. K. Rgabkin, I. A. Timofeeva, Yu. V. Fedyunin, and G. N. Tsigelnitskii, *Razved. Okhr. Nedr.* **35**, 47 (1969).
232d. J. G. Zavistoski and J. J. Zuckerman, *J. Org. Chem.* **34**, 4197 (1969).
232e. I. S. Zheludev and V. F. Belov, *Izv. Akad. Nauk SSSR, Ser. Fiz.* **31**, 1117 (1967).
233. J. J. Zuckerman, *J. Inorg. & Nucl. Chem.* **29**, 2191 (1967).
234. V. S. Zykov, E. V. Petrovich, and Yu. P. Smirnov, *Soviet Phys. JETP* (*English Transl.*) **22**, 708 (1966).

B. Published Conference Reports

235. V. P. Alfimenko and A. V. Strelkov, eds., "Proceedings of the Conference on the Mössbauer Effect, Dubna, U.S.S.R." (English Transl.). Consultants Bureau, New York, 1962.
236. "Applications of the Mössbauer Effect in Chemistry and Solid-State Physics," Tech. Rept. Ser. No. 50. I.A.E.A., Vienna, 1966.
237. A. J. Bearden, *Rev. Mod. Phys.* **36**, 333 (1964).
238. D. M. J. Compton and A. H. Schoen, eds., "Transactions of the Second International Conference on the Mössbauer Effect." Wiley, New York, 1962.
238a. Faraday Society, *Symp. Faraday Soc.* **1** (1967).
239. H. Frauenfelder and H. Lustig, eds., "Proceedings of the First International Conference on the Mössbauer Effect." ASTIA, 1960.
240. I. J. Gruverman, ed., "Mössbauer Effect Methodology," Vol. I. Plenum Press, New York, 1965 (Vol. II, 1966; Vol. III, 1967; Vol. IV, 1968).
241. C. W. Seidel, ed., "The Mössbauer Effect and Its Application in Chemistry," Advances in Chemistry Series, Vol. 68. American Chemical Society, Washington, D.C., 1967.

C. Reviews

242. Anonymous, *Chem. Eng. News* 13 July 1964, p. 66.
243. N. Benczer-Koller and R. H. Herber, *in* "Chemical Applications of Mössbauer Spectroscopy" (V. I. Goldanskii and R. H. Herber, eds.), p. 114. Academic Press, New York, 1968.
244. P. R. Brady, P. R. Wigley, and P. R. F. Duncan, *Rev. Pure Appl. Chem.* **12**, 165 (1962).
245. R. L. Collins and J. C. Travis, *Mössbauer Effect Methodol.* **3**, 123 (1967).
246. M. Cordey-Hayes, *in* "Chemical Applications of Mössbauer Spectroscopy" (V. I. Goldanskii and R. H. Herber, eds.), p. 314. Academic Press, New York, 1968.
247. J. R. deVoe and J. J. Spijkerman, *Anal. Chem.* **38**, 382R (1966).
248. J. R. deVoe and J. J. Spijkerman, *Anal. Chem.* **40**, 472R (1968).
*248a. I. Dezsi, *Atomtech. Tajek*, **12**, 16 (1969).
249. J. F. Duncan and R. M. Golding, *Quart. Rev. (London)* **19**, 36 (1965).
250. P. A. Flinn, *Advan. Chem. Ser.* **68**, 21 (1967).
251. E. Fluck, *Advan. Inorg. Chem. Radiochem.* **6**, 433 (1964).
252. E. Fluck, *Fortschr. Chem. Forsch.* **5**, 395 (1966).
253. E. Fluck, W. Kerler, and W. Neuwirth, *Angew. Chem. Intern. Ed. Engl.* **2**, 277 (1963).
254. V. I. Goldanskii, *Intern. Sci. Technol.* p. 40 (1963).
255. V. I. Goldanskii, *Angew. Chem. Intern. Ed. Engl.* **6**, 830 (1967).
256. V. I. Goldanskii, *At. Energy Rev.* **1**, 3 (1963).
256a. V. I. Goldanskii, *At. Energy* **26**, 142 (1969).
257. V. I. Goldanskii, V. V. Khrapov, O. Yu. Okhlobystin, and V. Ya. Rochev, *in* "Chemical Applications of Mössbauer Spectroscopy" (V. I. Goldanskii and R. H. Herber, eds.), p. 336. Academic Press, New York, 1968.
257a. V. I. Goldanskii, V. V. Khrapov, and R. A. Stukan, *Organometal. Chem. Rev.* **A4**, 225 (1969).
258. V. I. Goldanskii and E. F. Makarov, *in* "Chemical Applications of Mössbauer Spectroscopy" (V. I. Goldanskii and R. H. Herber, eds.), p. 1. Academic Press, New York, 1968.
259. N. N. Greenwood, *Endeavour* **27**, 33 (1968).
260. N. N. Greenwood, *Chem. Brit.* **3**, 56 (1967).
261. R. H. Herber, *J. Chem. Educ.* **42**, 180 (1965).
262. R. H. Herber, *Progr. Inorg. Chem.* **8**, 1 (1966).
263. R. H. Herber, *Mössbauer Effect Methodol.* **1**, 3 (1965).
264. R. H. Herber, *Ann. Rev. Phys. Chem.* **17**, 261 (1966).
265. R. H. Herber, *Advan. Chem. Ser.* **68**, 1 (1967).
266. R. H. Herber and H. A. Stöckler, *Proc. Conf. Chem. Effects Nucl. Transformations, Vienna*, 1964 Vol. II, p. 403. I.A.E.A., Vienna, 1965.
*266a. H. Hobert and D. Arnold, *Z. Chem.* **9**, 410 (1969).
267. M. C. Hobson, Jr., *J. Electrochem. Soc.* **115**, 10 (1968).
268. M. J. D. Low, *in* "The Solid-Gas Interface" (E. A. Flood, ed.), Vol. 2, p. 947. Marcel Dekker, New York, 1967.
268a. L. May, *Appl. Spectry.* **23**, 204 (1969).
269. L. May and J. J. Spijkerman, *Chemistry* **40**, 14 (1967).
270. S. L. Ruby, *Mossbauer Effect Method* **3**, 203 (1967).
271. H. Sano, *Genshiryoku Kogyo* **14**, 24 (1968).
272. H. Sano, *Kagaku No Ryoiki* **22**, 409 (1968).
272a. D. A. Shirley, *Ann. Rev. Phys. Chem.* **20**, 25 (1969).

273. D. K. Snediker, *Mossbauer Effect Method* **2**, 161 (1966).
274. J. J. Spijkerman, *Advan. Chem. Ser.* **68**, 105 (1967).
*274a. J. J. Spijkerman and P. A. Pella, *Crit. Rev. Anal. Chem.* **1**, 7 (1970).
275. G. Stolze, *Z. Chem.* **6**, 81 (1966).
276. G. K. Wertheim, *Am. J. Phys.* **31**, 1 (1963).
277. G. K. Wertheim, *Phys. Today* July, 1967, p. 31.
278. G. K. Wertheim, *Science* **144**, 253 (1964).
279. G. S. Zhdanov, N. S. Ibraimov, and R. N. Kuz'min, *Izv. Akad. Nauk SSSR, Neorgan. Mater.* **1**, 1660 (1965).
280. J. J. Zuckerman, *Mössbauer Effect Methodol.* **3**, 15 (1967).

D. Books

281. A. Abragam, "L'effect Mössbauer et ses applications a l'etude des champs internes." Gordon & Breach, New York, 1964.
282. H. Frauenfelder, "The Mössbauer Effect." Benjamin, New York, 1962.
283. V. I. Goldanskii and R. H. Herber, eds., "Chemical Applications of Mössbauer Spectroscopy." Academic Press, New York, 1968.
284. V. I. Goldanskii, "The Mössbauer Effect and Its Applications in Chemistry." Consultants Bureau, New York, 1964.
285. A. H. Muir, Jr., K. J. Ando, and H. M. Coogan, eds., "Mössbauer Effect Data Index, 1958–1965." Wiley (Interscience), New York, 1966.
286. A. H. Muir, Jr., K. J. Ando, and H. M. Coogan, "Mössbauer Effect Data Index." North Am. Aviation Sci. Center, Thousand Oaks, California, 1963, 1964, 1965.
*286a. H. Wegener, "Der Mossbauer-Effect un seine Anwendung in Physik und Chemie." Bibliographisches Institut, Mannhein, Germany, 1965.
287. G. K. Wertheim, "Mössbauer Effect: Principles and Applications." Academic Press, New York, 1964.

E. Papers Given at Meetings

287a. T. Auel and E. L. Amma, *Abstr. 156th Natl. Meeting Am. Chem. Soc., Atlantic City,* (1968).
288. R. Barloutand, "Proceedings of the First International Conference on the Mössbauer Effect" (H. Frauenfelder and H. Lustig, eds.), p. 22. ASTIA, 1960.
289. V. A. Belyakov, *Trans. 15th Ann. Conf. Nucl. Spectry Nucl. Struct., Minsk,* 1965; *Bull. Acad. Sci. USSR, Phys. Ser.* (*English Transl.*) **29**, 1189 (1965).
290. A. J. F. Boyle, D. St. P. Bunbury, and C. Edwards, *in* "Proceedings of the Second International Conference on the Mössbauer Effect" (D. M. J. Compton and H. A. Schoen, eds.), p. 267. Wiley, New York, 1962.
291. V. A. Bryukhanov, N. N. Delyagin, and Yu. P. Kagan, *Rev. Mod. Phys.* **36**, 470 (1964).
292. S. Bukshpan and R. H. Herber, *Abstr. Intern. Conf. Hyperfine Nucl. Spectry, Wellington, New Zealand, 1966.*
293. B. F. Burnham, and J. J. Zuckerman, *Abstr. 151st Natl. Meeting Am. Chem. Soc., Pittsburgh* (1966).
*293a. T. Chivers, *Abstr. CIC/ACS Joint Conf.* Toronto, May, 1970.
294. C. A. Clausen, III and M. L. Good, *Abstr. S. W. Reg. Meeting Am. Chem. Soc., Austin, Texas* (1968).

294a. C. A. Clausen, III and M. L. Good, *Abstr. 158th Natl. Meeting Am. Chem. Soc., New York* (1969).
295. G. T. Cocks and J. J. Zuckerman, *Abstr. 149th Natl. Meeting Am. Chem. Soc., Detroit* (1965).
296. M. Cordey-Hayes, *Rev. Mod. Phys.* **36**, 352 (1964).
297. M. Cordey-Hayes, *in* "Applications of the Mössbauer Effect in Chemistry and Solid-State Physics," Tech. Rept. Ser. No. 50, p. 156. I.A.E.A., Vienna, 1966.
*297a. W. R. Cullen, *Abstr. CIC/ACS Joint Conf.* Toronto, May, 1970.
*297b. W. R. Cullen, J. R. Sams, and J. A. Thompson, *Abstr. CIC/ACS Joint Conf.* Toronto, May, 1970.
297c. D. Cunningham, M. J. Frazer, and J. D. Donaldson, *Abstr. Chem. Soc. Autumn Meeting, Southampton, England* (1969).
298. C. Curran, M. A. Mullins, and J. Philip, *Abstr. 154th Natl. Meeting Am. Chem. Soc., Chicago* (1967).
299. C. Curran and M. D. O'Rourke, *Abstr. 154th Natl. Meeting Am. Chem. Soc., Chicago* (1967).
299a. N. W. G. Debye, D. E. Fenton, S. E. Ulrich, and J. J. Zuckerman, *Abstr. 158th Natl. Meeting Am. Chem. Soc., New York* (1969).
299b. N. W. G. Debye and J. J. Zuckerman, *Abstr. 20th Ann. Mid-Am. Symp. Spectry. Chicago* (1969).
299c. J. R. deVoe, *Abstr. 156th Natl. Meeting Am. Chem. Soc., Atlantic City* (1968).
299d. H. Z. Dokuzoguz, L. H. Bowen, H. H. Stadelmaier, and G. G. Long, *Abstr. 158th Natl. Meeting Am. Chem. Soc., New York* (1969).
300. J. D. Donaldson, *Abstr. Intern. Symp. Valence Reactivity, Oxford, England* (1968).
301. M. A. Doskey and C. Curran, *Abstr. 154th Natl. Meeting Am. Chem. Soc., Chicago* (1967).
302. M. Enuysal and J. J. Zuckerman, *Abstr. 156th Natl. Meeting Am. Chem. Soc., Atlantic City* (1968).
303. L. M. Epstein, *Abstr. 149th Natl. Meeting Am. Chem. Soc., Detroit* (1965).
303a. N. E. Erickson, *Abstr. 20th Ann. Mid-Am. Symp. Spectry., Chicago* (1969).
304. N. E. Erickson, M. Cefola, and E. Kazimir, *Abstr. 154th Natl. Meeting Am. Chem. Soc., Chicago* (1967).
304a. N. E. Erickson, M. Cefola, and E. Kazimir, *Abstr. 157th Natl. Meeting Am. Chem. Soc., Minneapolis* (1969).
305. D. E. Fenton and J. J. Zuckerman, *Abstr. 156th Natl. Meeting Am. Chem. Soc., Atlantic City* (1968).
305a. D. C. Fetherstone and J. F. Lefelhocz, *Abstr. 157th Natl. Meeting Am. Chem. Soc., Minneapolis* (1969).
306. J. Fink and P. Kienle, *in* "Applications of the Mössbauer Effect in Chemistry and Solid-State Physics," Tech. Rept. Ser. No. 50, p. 227. I.A.E.A., Vienna, 1966.
307. P. A. Flinn and S. L. Ruby, *Rev. Mod. Phys.* **36**, 352 (1964).
307a. B. F. E. Ford, B. V. Liengme, and J. R. Sams, *Abstr. Northwest Reg. Meeting Am. Chem. Soc., Salt Lake City* (1969).
307b. B. F. E. Ford, C. Poder, and J. R. Sams, *Abstr. 4th Intern. Conf. Organometal. Chem., Bristol, England* (1969).
308. T. C. Gibb and N. N. Greenwood, *in* "Applications of Mössbauer Effect in Chemistry and Solid-State Physics," Tech. Rept. Ser. No. 50, p. 163. I.A.E.A., Vienna, 1966.
309. V. I. Gol'danskii, V. V. Khrapov, and E. F. Makarov, *Rev. Mod. Phys.* **36**, 461 (1964).

310. V. I. Goldanskii, O. Yu. Okhlobystin, V. Ya. Rochev, and V. V. Khrapov, *in* "Applications of the Mössbauer Effect in Chemistry and Solid-State Physics," Tech. Rept. Ser. No. 50, p. 223. I.A.E.A., Vienna, 1966.
311. N. N. Greenwood, P. G. Perkins, and D. H. Wall, *Proc. Symp. Mössbauer Effect, London*, 1967; *Symp. Faraday Soc.* **1**, 90 (1968).
312. S. S. Hanna, J. Heberle, J. Diaz, and R. W. Reno, *Rev. Mod. Phys.* **36**, 407 (1964).
313. S. S. Hanna, L. Meyer-Schutzmeister, R. S. Preston, and D. H. Vincent, *Bull. Am. Phys. Soc.* [2] **5**, 429 (1960).
313a. P. G. Harrison, *Abstr. 158th Natl. Meeting Am. Chem. Soc., New York* (1969).
313b. P. G. Harrison and J. J. Zuckerman, *Abstr. 157th Natl. Meeting Am. Chem. Soc.,* Minneapolis (1969).
313c. P. G. Harrison and J. J. Zuckerman, *Abstr. 158th Natl. Meeting Am. Chem. Soc., New York* (1969).
313d. Y. Hazony and R. H. Herber, *Abstr. 156th Natl. Meeting Am. Chem. Soc., Atlantic City* (1968).
314. R. H. Herber, *in* "Applications of the Mössbauer Effect in Chemistry and Solid-State Physics," Tech. Rept. Ser. No. 50, p. 120. I.A.E.A., Vienna, 1966.
315. R. H. Herber, *in* "Applications of the Mössbauer Effect in Chemistry and Solid-State Physics," Tech. Rept. Ser. No. 50, p. 121. I.A.E.A., Vienna, 1966.
316. R. H. Herber, *Proc. Symp. Mössbauer Effect, London, 1967*; *Symp. Faraday Soc.* **1** (1970) (in press).
317. R. H. Herber, *Abstr. 148th Natl. Meeting Am. Chem. Soc., Chicago* (1964).
318. R. H. Herber, *Abstr. 148th Natl. Meeting Am. Chem. Soc., Chicago* (1964).
319. R. H. Herber, *Abstr. 149th Natl. Meeting Am. Chem. Soc., Detroit* (1965).
320. R. H. Herber, *Abstr. 3rd Middle Atlantic Reg. Meeting Am. Chem. Soc., Philadelphia* (1968).
321. R. H. Herber, *Abstr. 154th Natl. Meeting Am. Chem. Soc., Chicago* (1967).
321a. R. H. Herber, *Abstr. 158th Natl. Meeting Am. Chem. Soc., New York* (1969).
*321b. R. H. Herber, *Abstr. CIC/ACS Joint Conf.* Toronto, May, 1970.
321c. R. H. Herber and H.-S. Cheng, *Abstr. 4th Intern. Conf. Organometal. Chem., Bristol, England* (1969).
322. R. H. Herber and H. A. Stöckler, *in* "Applications of the Mössbauer Effect in Chemistry and Solid-State Physics," Tech. Rept. Ser. No. 50, p. 110. I.A.E.A., Vienna, 1966.
323. J. Herberle, M. Schulhof, and S. S. Hanna, *Rev. Mod. Phys.* **36**, 407 (1964).
*223a. C. R. Kanekar, K. R. P. Mallikarjuna Rao, and V. Udaya Shankar Rao, *Proc. Nucl. Phys. Solid State Phys. Sympos.* 11th, Kanpur, India, 1967, *Solid State Phys. Chem. Abstr.* **69**, 91548 (1968).
324. E. O. Kazimir, M. Cefola, and N. E. Erickson, *Abst. 156th Natl. Meeting Am. Chem. Soc., Atlantic City* (1968).
325. O. C. Kistner, *in* "Proceedings of the First International Conference on the Mössbauer Effect" (H. Frauenfelder and H. Lustig, eds.), p. 28. ASTIA, 1960.
326. O. C. Kistner, V. Jaccarino, and L. R. Walker, *in* "Proceedings of the Second International Conference on the Mössbauer Effect" (D. M. J. Compton and A. H. Schoen, eds.), p. 264. Wiley, New York, 1962.
327. O. C. Kistner and J. B. Swan, *Bull. Am. Phys. Soc.* [2] **6**, 51 (1961).
328. C. J. Meechan and A. H. Muir, Jr., *Rev. Mod. Phys.* **36**, 438 (1964).
329. L. Meyer-Schutzmeister, *in* "Proceedings of the Second International Conference on the Mössbauer Effect" (D. M. J. Compton and A. H. Schoen, eds.), p. 190. Wiley, New York, 1962.

330. A. H. Muir, Jr., C. J. Meechan, U. Gonser, and H. Wiedersich, *Bull. Am. Phys. Soc.* [2] **7**, 505 (1962).
331. M. D. O'Rourke and C. Curran, *Abstr. 152nd Natl. Meeting Am. Chem. Soc., New York* (1966).
332. G. I. Parisi and R. H. Herber, *Abstr. 152nd Natl. Meeting Am. Chem. Soc., New York* (1966).
333. D. Petridis and C. Curran, *Abstr. 156th Natl. Meeting Am. Chem. Soc., Atlantic City* (1968).
334. J. Philip and C. Curran, *Abstr. 149th Natl. Meeting Am. Chem. Soc., Detroit* (1965).
334a. T. P. Poeth, B. R. Willeford, and J. J. Zuckerman, *Abstr. 4th Intern. Conf. Organometal. Chem., Bristol, England* (1969).
335. D. A. Shirley, *in* "Proceedings of the Second International Conference on the Mössbauer Effect" (D. M. J. Compton and A. H. Schoen, eds.), p. 255. Wiley, New York, 1962.
336. D. A. Shirley, *Rev. Mod. Phys.* **36**, 339 (1964).
337. V. S. Shpinel, V. A. Bryukhanov, V. Kothekar, B. Z. Iofa, and S. I. Semenov, *Proc. Symp. Mössbauer Effect, London,* 1967; *Symp. Faraday Soc.* **1** (1970) (in press).
338. J. J. Spijkerman, K. R. Swanson, P. A. Pella, and J. R. deVoe, *Abstr. 156th Natl. Meeting Am. Chem. Soc., Atlantic City* (1968).
339. H. A. Stöckler, *Abstr. 154th Natl. Meeting Am. Chem. Soc., Chicago* (1967).
340. W. H. Wiedemann, P. Kienle, and F. Pobell, *in* "Proceedings of the Second International Conference on the Mössbauer Effect" (D. M. J. Compton and A. H. Schoen, eds.), p. 210. Wildy, New York, 1962.
340a. C. I. Wynter and R. H. Herber, *Abstr. 158th Natl. Meeting Am. Chem. Soc., New York* (1969).
341. J. G. Zavistoski and J. J. Zuckerman, *Abstr. 154th Natl. Meeting Am. Chem. Soc., Chicago* (1967).
341a. J. G. Zavistoski and J. J. Zuckerman, *Abstr. Octavo Congr. Peruano Quim., Cuzco, Peru, 1968.*
342. J. J. Zuckerman, *Abstr. 152nd Natl. Meeting Am. Chem. Soc., New York* (1966).
343. J. J. Zuckerman, *Abstr. Intern. Symp. Valence Reactivity, Oxford, England* (1968).
344. J. J. Zuckerman, *Abstr. 3rd Middle Atlantic Reg. Meeting Am. Chem. Soc., Philadelphia* (1968).
345. J. J. Zuckerman, *Abstr. Central Reg. Meeting Am. Chem. Soc., Akron* (1968).
*345a. J. J. Zuckerman, *Abstr. 5th Middle Atlantic Reg. Meeting Am. Chem. Soc.* Newark, Del. (1970).

Additional References Cited

346. A. Yu. Aleksandrov, Candidate Dissertation, Inst. Petrol. Chem. Synthesis, Acad. Sci. U.S.S.R., Moscow, 1964 (quoted in V. I. Goldanskii and R. H. Herber, eds., "Chemical Applications of Mössbauer Spectroscopy." Academic Press, New York, 1968).
347. W. H. Baur, *Acta Cryst.* **9**, 515 (1956).
348. W. E. Bennett, private communication (1969).
349. H. Bent, *Chem. Rev.* **61**, 275 (1961).
350. G. Bergerhoff, *Acta Cryst.* **15**, 509 (1962).
351. R. R. Berrett and B. W. Fitzsimmons, *J. Chem. Soc., A* p. 525 (1967).
352. A. R. Champion and H. G. Drikamer, *J. Chem. Phys.* **47**, 2591 (1967).

353. A. R. Champion, R. W. Vaughan, and H. G. Drikamer, *J. Chem. Phys.* **47**, 2583 (1967).
354. H. C. Clark, R. J. O'Brien, and J. Trotter, *Proc. Chem. Soc.* p. 85 (1964); *J. Chem. Soc.* p. 2332 (1964).
355. R. L. Collins, *Mössbauer Effect Methodol.* **4**, 129 (1968).
356. R. D. Cowan, quoted as private communication in May and Spijkerman (*168*).
357. D. P. Craig, A. Maccoll, R. S. Nyholm, L. E. Orgel, and L. E. Sutton, *J. Chem. Soc.* p. 332 (1954).
358. L. D. Dave, D. F. Evans, and G. Wilkinson, *J. Chem. Soc.* p. 3684 (1959).
359. N. W. G. Debye, D. E. Fenton, and J. J. Zuckerman, unpublished results (1968).
360. N. W. G. Debye and J. J. Zuckerman, unpublished results (1969).
361. J. R. deVoe, *Natl. Bur. Std.* (*U.S.*), *Tech. Note* **248** (1964).
361a. J. R. deVoe, private communication (1969).
362. J. Devooght, M. Gielen, and S. Lejeune, private communication (1968).
363. J. D. Donaldson, *Progr. Inorg. Chem.* **8**, 287 (1966).
364. N. E. Erickson and E. O. Kazimir, private communication (1968).
365. D. E. Fenton and J. J. Zuckerman, unpublished results (1968).
366. N. Flitcroft and H. D. Kaesz, *J. Am. Chem. Soc.* **85**, 1377 (1963).
367. T. Gela, *J. Chem. Phys.* **24**, 1009 (1956).
368. V. I. Gol'danskii, private communication (1966).
369. C. B. Harris, *Inorg. Chem.* **7**, 1517 (1968).
370. W. Hofmann, *Z. Krist.* **92**, 161 (1935).
371. R. Hoppe and W. Dähne, *Naturwissenschaften* **49**, 254 (1962).
372. G. M. Kalvius, *Mössbauer Effect Methodol.* **1**, 163 (1965).
373. B. Kamenar and D. Grdenic, *J. Chem. Soc.* p. 770 (1961).
374. P. J. Klass, *Aviation Week & Space Technol.* **9**, 89 (1963).
375. V. V. Khrapov, Candidate Dissertation, Inst. Chem. Phys., Acad. Sci. U.S.S.R., Moscow, 1965 (quoted in V. I. Goldanskii and R. H. Herber, eds., "Chemical Applications of Mössbauer Spectroscopy." Academic Press, New York, 1968).
376. H. G. Kuivila and O. F. Beumel, *J. Am. Chem. Soc.* **80**, 3250 (1958).
377. M. Lister and L. E. Sutton, *Trans. Faraday Soc.* **37**, 393 (1941).
378. R. L. Livingston and C. N. R. Rao, *J. Chem. Phys.* **30**, 339 (1959).
379. M. L. Maddox, N. Flitcroft, and H. D. Kaesz, *J. Organometal. Chem.* (*Amsterdam*) **4**, 50 (1965).
380. J. A. Marley and T. C. MacAvoy, *J. Appl. Phys.* **32**, 2504 (1961).
381. K. P. Mitrofanov, N. V. Illiarionova and V. S. Shpinel, *Proc. Soviet Conf. Mössbauer Effect, Dubna*, 1962 English transl., p. 37. Consultant's Bureau, New York, 1963.
382. K. P. Mitrofanov, N. V. Illiarionova, and V. S. Shpinel, *Instr. Exptl. Tech.* (*USSR*) (*English Transl.*) **3**, 415 (1963).
383. M. J. Moore and L. Pauling, *J. Am. Chem. Soc.* **63**, 1392 (1941).
384. C. Nordling, *Arkiv Fysik* **15**, 241 (1959).
385. R. Okawara and M. Wada, *Advan. Organometal. Chem.* **5**, 137 (1967).
386. R. C. Poller, *Proc. Chem. Soc.* p. 312 (1963).
387. F. C. Ruegg, J. J. Spijkerman, and J. R. deVoe, *Rev. Sci. Instr.* **36**, 356 (1965).
388. R. E. Rundle and D. H. Olsen, *Inorg. Chem.* **3**, 596 (1964).
389. E. O. Schlemper and D. Britton, *Inorg. Chem.* **5**, 507 (1966).
390. E. O. Schlemper and W. C. Hamilton, *Inorg. Chem.* **5**, 995 and 2238 (1966).
391. H. Schröcke, *Neues Jahrb. Mineral., Monatsh.* p. 57 (1959).

392. O. I. Sumbaev and A. F. Mezentsev, *Soviet Phys. JETP* (*English Transl.*) **21**, 295 (1965).
393. O. I. Sumbaev, A. F. Mezentsev, V. I. Marushenko, E. V. Petrovich, and A. S. Rylnikov, *Soviet Phys. JETP* (*English Transl.*) **23**, 572 (1966).
394. C. H. Townes and B. P. Dailey, *J. Chem. Phys.* **17**, 782 (1949).
395. J. M. Van den Berg, *Acta Cryst.* **14**, 1002 (1961).
396. R. W. Vaughan and H. G. Drikamer, *J. Chem. Phys.* **47**, 468 (1967).
397. J. J. Zuckerman, unpublished results (1967).

APPENDIX II

^{119m}Sn MÖSSBAUER DATA FOR ORGANOTIN COMPOUNDS*

* Data marked with an asterisk were obtained at ambient temperatures, the remainder at 77° K.

TABLE 1

R_4Sn

Compound	I.S. (mm/sec)	Q.S. (mm/sec)	ρ=Q.S./I.S.	Source	References
$(CH_3)_4Sn$	1.59±0.05	0	0	SnO_2	*74*
	1.35±0.05	0	0	SnO_2	*147*
	1.30	0	0	—	*375*
	1.29±0.05	0	0	SnO_2	*191*
	1.25±0.10	0	0	SnO_2	*143*
	1.22±0.06	0	0	Mg_2Sn	*120*
	1.21±0.09	0	0	Pd(Sn)	*211*
	1.19±0.09	0	0	Pd(Sn)	*216*
	1.19±0.09	0	0	Pd(Sn)	*215*
$(ClCH_2)_4Sn$	1.30	0	0	—	*375*
$(CH_2{=}CH)_4Sn$	1.22±0.05	0	0	Pd(Sn)	*191a*
$(C_2H_5)_4Sn$	1.33±0.08	0	0	SnO_2	*5*
	1.30	0	0	—	*375*
$(n\text{-}C_3H_7)_4Sn$	1.30±0.07	0	0	SnO_2	*5*
	1.30	0	0	—	*375*
$(n\text{-}C_4H_9)_4Sn$	1.35±0.10	0	0	SnO_2	*5*
	1.30±0.10	0	0	SnO_2	*3*
	1.30	0	0	—	*375*
$(C_6H_5)_4Sn$	1.40±0.05	0	0	SnO_2	*72*
	1.35±0.08	0	0	SnO_2	*109*
	1.27±0.05	0	0	SnO_2	*191*
	1.25±0.10	0	0	SnO_2	*5*
	1.25±0.08	0	0	SnO_2	*146*
	1.22±0.09	0	0	Pd(Sn)	*216*
	1.22±0.09	0	0	Pd(Sn)	*215*
	1.22±0.09	0	0	Pd(Sn)	*211*
	1.21±0.02	0	0	SnO_2	*124*
	1.20±0.15	0	0	SnO_2	*59*
	1.19±0.01	0	0	Mg_2Sn	*160*
	1.15±0.10	0	0	SnO_2	*96*
$(C_6H_5)_4Sn$/polymethylmethacrylate	1.2±0.15	0	0	SnO_2	*59*
$(p\text{-}ClC_6H_4)_4Sn$	1.35	0	0	—	*375*
	1.25±0.08	0	0	SnO_2	*146*
$(m\text{-}CF_3C_6H_4)_4Sn$	1.28±0.02	0	0	SnO_2	*124*
$(p\text{-}CF_3C_6H_4)_4Sn$	1.29±0.02	0	0	SnO_2	*124*

(*Continued*)

TABLE 1 (*Continued*)

Compound	I.S. (mm/sec)	Q.S. (mm/sec)	ρ=Q.S./I.S.	Source	References
$(C_6F_5)_4Sn$	1.22 ± 0.05	0	0	SnO_2	*72*
	1.04 ± 0.09	0	0	Pd(Sn)	*211*
$(C_6Cl_5)_4Sn$	1.32 ± 0.05	0	0	—	*73a*
$(C_6H_{11})_4Sn$	1.52 ± 0.02	0	0	SnO_2	*124*
[*sym*-$(CH_3)_3C_6H_2]_4Sn$	1.17 ± 0.06	0	0	SnO_2	*397*
	1.15 ± 0.06	0	0	SnO_2	*360*
$(C_6H_5OC_6H_4)_4Sn$	0.90 ± 0.06	0	0	SnO_2	*397*
$[C_6H_5C(CH_3)CH_2]_4Sn$	1.34 ± 0.02	0	0	SnO_2	*124, 198*
$(N{\equiv}CCH_2CH_2)_4Sn$	1.30 ± 0.07	0	0	SnO_2	*5*
Tetrakis(2-thiophenolato)tin	0.79 ± 0.06*	0	0	SnO_2	*397*
Spiro-Bistannole	1.30 ± 0.06	0	0	SnO_2	*341, 232d*

TABLE 2

$(RE)_4Sn$

Compound	I.S. (mm/sec)	Q.S. (mm/sec)	ρ=Q.S./I.S.	Source	References
$(CH_3\overset{\overset{O}{\parallel}}{C}O)_4Sn$	0.18	0	0	—	*262*
$(HC{\equiv}C\overset{\overset{O}{\parallel}}{C}O)_4Sn$	0 ± 0.08	0	0	—	*106*
	0 ± 0.08*	0	0	—	*375*
$(NCS)_4Sn$	0.56 ± 0.02	0	0	$BaSnO_3$	*95b*
$(C_5H_5S)_4Sn$	1.17 ± 0.06	0	0	SnO_2	*397*
Bis(1,2-ethanedithiolato)tin	1.45	0.98	0.675	Mg_2Sn	*91*
Bis(3,4-toluenedithiolato)tin	1.32	1.52	1.15	Mg_2Sn	*91*
	1.37*	1.37*	1.00	Mg_2Sn	*91*
	1.26 ± 0.09	1.53 ± 0.09	1.21	Pd(Sn)	*216*

TABLE 3

R_3SnR'

Compound	I.S. (mm/sec)	Q.S. (mm/sec)	ρ=Q.S./I.S.	Source	References
$(CH_3)_3SnCH{=}CH_2$	1.3	0	0	—	*375*
	1.30 ± 0.05	0	0	SnO_2	*191*
	1.13 ± 0.05	0	0	SnO_2	*9*
$(CH_3)_3SnC_5H_5$	1.05 ± 0.06	1.05 ± 0.06	1.00	$BaSnO_3$	*117d*
$(CH_3)_3SnC_6H_5$	1.26 ± 0.05	0	0	SnO_2	*74*
	1.25 ± 0.05	0	0	SnO_2	*9*
	1.16 ± 0.05	0	0	Pd(Sn)	*191*
	1.08	0	0	—	*375*
$(CH_3)_3SnC_6H_4CH{=}CH_2$	1.30 ± 0.05	0	0	SnO_2	*9*

(*Continued*)

TABLE 3 (*Continued*)

Compound	I.S. (mm/sec)	Q.S. (mm/sec)	ρ=Q.S./I.S.	Source	References
$[(CH_3)_3SnC_6H_4\overset{\vert}{C}H—CH_2—]_n$	1.25 ± 0.05	0	0	SnO_2	*9*
$(CH_3)_3SnCH_2\overset{O}{\overset{\Vert}{C}}CH_3$	1.23 ± 0.05	2.08 ± 0.05	1.69	SnO_2	*147*
$(CH_3)_3SnCH_2O\overset{O}{\overset{\Vert}{C}}CH_3$	1.35 ± 0.05	0	0	SnO_2	*147*
$(CH_3)_3SnCH_2F$	1.38 ± 0.08	0	0	SnO_2	*146*
$(CH_3)_3SnCF_3$	1.31 ± 0.05	1.38 ± 0.05	1.05	Pd(Sn)	*191, 191a*
$(CH_3)_3SnCCl_3$	1.25 ± 0.06	1.60 ± 0.12	1.28	$BaSnO_3$	*397*
$(CH_3)_3SnCH_2Cl$	1.32 ± 0.08	0	0	SnO_2	*146*
	1.20 ± 0.05	0	0	SnO_2	*147*
$(CH_3)_3SnCH_2Cl/DMF$	1.16–1.24 ± 0.05	0.4–0.6 ± 0.05	0.35–0.48	SnO_2	*147*
$(CH_3)_3SnCH_2Cl/DMSO$	1.30 ± 0.05	0.50 ± 0.05	0.38	SnO_2	*147*
$(CH_3)_3SnCH_2Cl/THF$	1.30 ± 0.05	0.60 ± 0.05	0.46	SnO_2	*147*
$(CH_3)_3SnCH_2OCH_3$	1.38 ± 0.08	0	0	SnO_2	*146*
N-(Trimethylstannylmethyl)aziridine	1.32 ± 0.08	0	0	SnO_2	*146*
N-(Trimethylstannylmethyl)pyrrole	1.38 ± 0.08	0	0	SnO_2	*146*
N-(Trimethylstannylmethyl)morpholine	1.38 ± 0.08	0	0	SnO_2	*146*
N-Methyl,*N*-(trimethylstannylmethyl)-morpholinium iodide	1.17 ± 0.08	0	0	SnO_2	*146*
$(CH_3)_3SnC_6F_5$	1.27 ± 0.05	1.31 ± 0.05	1.03	Pd(Sn)	*191, 191a*
$(CH_3)_3SnC_6F_4$-*p*-H	1.24 ± 0.03	1.08 ± 0.03	0.87	—	*71a*
$(CH_3)_3SnC_6Cl_5$	1.32 ± 0.05	1.09 ± 0.05	0.67	Pd(Sn)	*191, 191a*
	1.17 ± 0.06	2.06 ± 0.12	1.76	$BaSnO_3$	*397*
$(CH_3)_3SnC{\equiv}CC_6H_5$	1.23 ± 0.05	1.17 ± 0.05	0.95	Pd(Sn)	*191, 191a*
	1.20 ± 0.05	1.45 ± 0.05	1.21	SnO_2	*199*
$(CH_3)_3SnC{\equiv}C—CH(CH_3)_2$	1.15 ± 0.05	1.06 ± 0.05	0.92	SnO_2	*199*
$(CH_3)_3Sn—X{\equiv}C—C(CH_3){=}CH_2$	1.24 ± 0.05	1.30 ± 0.05	1.05	SnO_2	*199*
$(CH_3)_3Sn—C{\equiv}C—C{\equiv}C—C_2H_5$	1.20 ± 0.05	1.80 ± 0.05	1.50	SnO_2	*199*
$(CH_3)_3SnCF{=}CF_2$	1.32 ± 0.06	1.28 ± 0.12	0.97	$BaSnO_3$	*397*
$(CH_3)_3SnCCl{=}CCl_2$	1.31 ± 0.05	1.24 ± 0.05	0.95	Pd(Sn)	*191a*
$(CH_3)_3SnCF{=}CHF$	1.30 ± 0.06	1.14 ± 0.12	0.88	$BaSnO_3$	*397*
$(CH_3)_3SnC_6H_4$-*o*-F	1.30 ± 0.06	0	0	$BaSnO_3$	*365*
$(CH_3)_3SnC_6H_4$-*o*-OCH_3	1.26 ± 0.06	0	0	$BaSnO_3$	*365*
$(CH_3)_3SnC_6H_4$-*o*-CF_3	1.21 ± 0.03	0.66 ± 0.03	0.55	—	*71a*
$(CH_3)_3SnC_6H_4$-*p*-$N(CH_3)_2$	1.30 ± 0.05	0	0	SnO_2	*74*
	1.26 ± 0.06	0	0	$BaSnO_3$	*365*
$(CH_3)_3SnC_6H_4$-*p*-$C(CH_3)_3$	1.28 ± 0.05	0	0	SnO_2	*74*
$(CH_3)_3SnC_6H_4$-*p*-OCH_3	1.30 ± 0.05	0	0	SnO_2	*74*
$(CH_3)_3SnC_6H_4$-*p*-F	1.23 ± 0.03	0	0	—	*71a*
$(CH_3)_3SnC_6H_4$-*p*-Cl	1.34 ± 0.05	0	0	SnO_2	*74*
$(CH_3)_3SnC_6H_4$-*p*-$Sn(CH_3)_3$	1.67 ± 0.06	0	0	$BaSnO_3$	*334a*
$(CH_3)_3SnC{\equiv}N$	1.29	2.96	2.30	—	*375*
	1.39 ± 0.02	3.12 ± 0.02	2.24	$BaSnO_3$	*95b*
$(CH_3)_3SnC_6H_5 \cdot Cr(CO)_3$	1.67 ± 0.06	0.72 ± 0.06	0.43	$BaSnO_4$	*334a*
$(CH_3)_3SnCH_2C_6H_5 \cdot Cr(CO)_3$	1.67 ± 0.06	0.59 ± 0.06	0.35	$BaSnO_3$	*334a*
1,4-$(CH_3)_3SnC_6H_5 \cdot Cr(CO)_3$	1.69 ± 0.06	0.72 ± 0.06	0.43	$BaSnO_3$	*334a*
$(CH_3)_2Sn[C_6H_5 \cdot Cr(CO)_3](C_6H_5)$	1.74 ± 0.06	0.64 ± 0.06	0.37	$BaSnO_3$	*334a*
$(CH_3)_2Sn[C_6H_5 \cdot Cr(CO)_3]_2$	1.75 ± 0.06	0.89 ± 0.06	0.51	$BaSnO_3$	*334a*
$(C_6H_5C{\equiv}C)_3SnC_4H_9$	0.81 ± 0.05	1.72 ± 0.05	2.12	Pd(Sn)	*191a*
$(CH_2{=}CH)_3SnC_6H_5$	1.25 ± 0.05	0	0	Pd(Sn)	*191, 191a*
$(C_2H_5)_3SnCH_3$	1.35 ± 0.08	0	0	SnO_2	*146*
$(C_2H_5)_3Sn(n$-$C_3H_7)$	1.35 ± 0.08	0	0	SnO_2	*146*
$(C_2H_5)_3Sn—C{\equiv}CH$	1.44 ± 0.05	1.42 ± 0.05	0.99	SnO_2	*191c, 199*
$(C_2H_5)_3Sn—C{\equiv}CCH_3$	1.37 ± 0.05	1.22 ± 0.05	0.89	SnO_2	*191c, 199*

(*Continued*)

TABLE 3 (*Continued*)

Compound	I.S. (mm/sec)	Q.S. (mm/sec)	ρ=Q.S./I.S.	Source	References
$(C_2H_5)_3Sn{-}C{\equiv}CC_2H_5$	1.35±0.05	1.05±0.05	0.78	SnO_2	*191c, 199*
$(C_2H_5)_3SnC{\equiv}C{-}CH(CH_3)_2$	1.36±0.05	1.09±0.05	0.80	SnO_2	*199*
$(C_2H_5)_3SnC{\equiv}C{-}C_3H_5$-*cyclo*	1.38±0.05	1.25±0.05	0.91	SnO_2	*199*
$(C_2H_5)_3SnC{\equiv}CC_6H_5$	1.38±0.05	1.48±0.05	1.07	SnO_2	*191c, 199*
$(C_2H_5)_3SnC{\equiv}CCl$	1.39±0.05	1.75±0.05	1.26	SnO_2	*191c, 199*
$(C_2H_5)_3SnC{\equiv}CBr$	1.40±0.05	1.70±0.05	1.21	SnO_2	*199*
$(C_2H_5)_3SnC{\equiv}CSn(C_2H_5)_3$	1.40	1.00	0.71	—	*375*
	1.38±0.05	1.18±0.05	0.86	SnO_2	*199*
$(C_2H_5)_3SnC{\equiv}C{-}P(O)(OC_2H_5)_2$	1.42±0.05	2.40±0.05	1.69	SnO_2	*191c, 199*
$[(C_2H_5)_3Sn\overset{\mid}{C}H{-}CH_2{-}]_n$	1.40	0	0	—	*375*
$(C_2H_5)_3SnCH_2\overset{O}{\overset{\Vert}{C}}CH_3$	1.45±0.10	1.00±0.05	0.69	SnO_2	*8*
	1.29±0.05	0	0	SnO_2	*147*
$(C_2H_5)_3Sn(CH_2)_2\overset{O}{\overset{\Vert}{C}}CH_3$	1.37±0.05	0	0	SnO_2	*147*
$(C_2H_5)_3SnCH_2O\overset{O}{\overset{\Vert}{C}}CH_3$	1.35±0.05	0	0	SnO_2	*147*
$(C_2H_5)_3SnCH_2Cl$	1.43±0.08	0	0	SnO_2	*146*
$(C_2H_5)_3SnCH_2C{\equiv}N$	1.29±0.08	0	0	SnO_2	*146*
$(C_2H_5)_3SnCH_2OCH_3$	1.35±0.08	0	0	SnO_2	*146*
$(C_2H_5)_3SnCH_2N(CH_3)_2$	1.35±0.08	0	0	SnO_2	*146*
N-(Triethylstannylmethyl)aziridine	1.35±0.08	0	0	SnO_2	*146*
N-(Triethylstannylmethyl)pyrrole	1.29±0.08	0	0	SnO_2	*146*
N-(Triethylstannylmethyl)morpholine	1.43±0.08	0	0	SnO_2	*146*
$(C_2H_5)_3SnC{\equiv}N$	1.41±0.02	3.19±0.02	2.26	$BaSnO_3$	*95b*
	1.36±0.06	3.08±0.12	2.26	$BaSnO_3$	*397*
	1.29	2.96	2.30	—	*375*
n-$C_3H_7)_3SnC{\equiv}CH$	1.42±0.05	1.37±0.05	0.97	SnO_2	*199*
$(n$-$C_3H_7)_3SnC{\equiv}N$	1.39±0.06	3.00±0.12	2.16	$BaSnO_3$	*397*
	1.37±0.02	3.27±0.02	2.39	$BaSnO_3$	*95b*
$(n$-$C_4H_9)_3SnC{\equiv}CH$	1.40±0.05	1.42±0.05	1.01	SnO_2	*191c, 199*
$(n$-$C_4H_9)_3SnCH_2\overset{O}{\overset{\Vert}{C}}CH_3$	1.26±0.06	1.21±0.12	0.96	$BaSnO_3$	*365*
$(C_6H_5)_3SnCH_3$	1.91	0	0	—	*375*
$(C_6H_5)_3SnCH{=}CH_2$	1.28±0.05	0	0	Pd(Sn)	*191, 191a*
$(C_6H_5)_3SnC_6H_4$-*o*-CH_3	1.30±0.08	0	0	SnO_2	*146*
$(C_6H_5)_3SnC_6H_4$-*p*-CH_3	1.30±0.08	0	0	SnO_2	*146*
$(C_6H_5)_3SnC_6H_4$-*p*-$CH{=}CH_2$	1.30±0.08	0	0	SnO_2	*146*
$(C_6H_5)_3SnC_6H_4$-*p*-Cl	1.30±0.08	0	0	SnO_2	*146*
$(C_6H_5)_3SnC_6H_4$-*p*-Br	1.30±0.08	0	0	SnO_2	*146*
$(C_6H_5)_3SnC_6F_5$	1.43±0.05	1.10±0.05	0.74	SnO_2	*73*
	1.30±0.05	0.90±0.05	0.69	Pd(Sn)	*191*
	1.25±0.09	0.98±0.09	0.79	Pd(Sn)	*211*
$C_6H_5)_3SnC_6Cl_5$	1.27±0.05	0.84±0.05	0.66	Pd(Sn)	*191, 191a*
$(C_6F_5)_3SnCH_3$	1.19±0.09	1.14±0.09	0.96	Pd(Sn)	*211*
$(C_6F_5)_3SnC_6H_5$	1.16±0.09	0.92±0.09	0.80	Pd(Sn)	*211*
$(C_6F_5)_3Sn$-*p*-$CH_3C_6H_4$	1.18±0.09	1.02±0.09	0.87	Pd(Sn)	*211*
1,2-$[(CH_3)_3Sn]_2C_6F_4$	1.26±0.03	0.85±0.03	0.68	—	*71a*
1,4-$[(CH_3)_3Sn]_2C_6F_4$	1.20±0.03	1.20±0.03	1.00	—	*71a*
1,4-$[(CH_3)_3Sn]_2C_6Cl_4$	1.26±0.03	1.10±0.03	0.87	—	*71a*
$(C_6Cl_5)_3SnC_6H_5$	1.21±0.05	0.8±0.05	0.67	—	*73b*

TABLE 4

R_2SnR_2

Compound	I.S. (mm/sec)	Q.S. (mm/sec)	ρ=Q.S./I.S.	Source	References
$(CH_3)_2Sn(C_6F_5)_2$	1.34±0.06	1.29±0.06	0.96	$BaSnO_3$	*365*
	1.25±0.09	1.48±0.09	1.18	Pd(Sn)	*211*
	1.23±0.03	1.56±0.03	1.27	—	*71a*
$(CH_3)_2Sn(C_6F_4$-*o*-$Br)_2$	1.25±0.03	1.41±0.03	1.13	—	*71a*
$(CH_3)_2Sn(CH_2Cl)_2$	7.30	0	0	—	*375*
$(C_2H_5)_2Sn(CH{=}CH_2)_2$	1.20	0	0	—	*375*
$(C_3H_7)_2Sn(C{\equiv}CC_3H_7)_2$	1.27±0.05	1.60±0.05	1.26	Pd(Sn)	*191a*
1,1-Dimethyl-2,3,4,5-tetraphenylstannole	1.23±0.06	0	0	SnO_2	*341, 232d*
1,1-Divinyl-2,3,4,5-tetraphenylstannole	1.25±0.06	0	0	SnO_2	*341, 232d*
Hexaphenylstannole	1.19±0.06	0	0	SnO_2	*341, 232d*
$(C_4H_9)_2Sn(C_6Cl_5)_2$	1.43±0.05	1.23±0.05	0.86	—	*73b*
9,9-Diphenyl-9-stannafluorene	1.20±0.06	0	0	SnO_2	*397*
$(C_6H_5)_2Sn(C_6F_5)_2$	1.22±0.09	1.11±0.06	0.91	Pd(Sn)	*211*
$(C_6H_5)_2Sn(C_6Cl_5)_2$	1.35±0.05	1.23±0.05	1.91	Pd(Sn)	*191a*
	1.60±0.05	1.05±0.05	0.67	—	*73b*
9,9-Diphenyl-9-stannaperfluorofluorene	1.22±0.06	1.31±0.06	1.08	$BaSnO_3$	*365*
(*p*-$CH_3C_6H_4)_2Sn(C_6F_5)_2$	1.22±0.09	1.18±0.09	0.97	Pd(Sn)	*211*

TABLE 5

ORGANOTIN(IV) HYDRIDES, R_nSnH_{4-n}

Compound	I.S. (mm/sec)	Q.S. (mm/sec)	ρ=Q.S./I.S.	Source	References
$n=0$					
SnH_4	1.27±0.06	0	0	SnO_2	*120*
	1.2±0.1	0	0	SnO_2	*37*
$n=1$					
CH_3SnH_3	1.24±0.06	0	0	Mg_2Sn	*120*
	1.15±0.05	0	0	SnO_2	*74*
iso-$C_3H_7SnH_3$	1.46±0.06	0	0	Mg_2Sn	*120*
	1.40±0.06	0	0	SnO_2	*120*
n-$C_4H_9SnH_3$	1.44±0.06	0	0	Pd(Sn)	*120*
$C_6H_5SnH_3$	1.40±0.06	0	0	Pd(Sn)	*120*
$n=2$					
$(CH_3)_2SnH_2$	1.23±0.06	0	0	SnO_2	*120*
	1.22±0.06	0	0	Mg_2Sn	*120*
(*n*-$C_3H_7)_2SnH_2$	1.30	0	0	—	*375*
(*n*-$C_4H_9)_2SnH_2$	1.45±0.07	0	0	SnO_2	*9*
	1.42±0.06	0	0	Pd(Sn)	*120*
$(C_6H_5)_2SnH_2$	1.38±0.06	0	0	Pd(Sn)	*120*
	1.28±0.09	0	0	Pd(Sn)	*216*
$n=3$					
$(CH_3)_3SnH$	1.24±0.06	0	0	Mg_2Sn	*120*
$(C_2H_5)_3SnH$	1.30	0	0	—	*375*
(*n*-$C_3H_7)_3SnH$	1.45±0.05	0	0	SnO_2	*9*
(*n*-$C_4H_9)_3SnH$	1.45±0.05	0	0	SnO_2	*9*
	1.41±0.06	0	0	Pd(Sn)	*120*
(iso-$C_4H_9)_3SnH$	1.45±0.05	0	0	SnO_2	*9*
$(C_6H_5)_3SnH$	1.45±0.05	0	0	SnO_2	*9*
	1.39±0.06	0	0	Pd(Sn)	*120*
	1.28±0.09	0	0	Pd(Sn)	*216*
(*p*-$FC_6H_4)_3SnH$	1.37±0.02	0	0	SnO_2	*124*
(*n*-$C_4H_9)_2SnHCl$	1.56±0.06	3.34±0.06	2.14	Pd(Sn)	*120*

TABLE 6

COMPOUNDS WITH TIN–TIN BONDS

Compound	I.S. (mm/sec)	Q.S. (mm/sec)	ρ=Q.S./I.S.	Source	References
$[(CH_3)_3Sn]_2$	1.46±0.05	0	0	Pd(Sn)	*191, 191a*
$[(C_2H_5)_3Sn]_2$	1.55±0.05	0	0	SnO_2	*9*
	1.45±0.80	0	0	SnO_2	*109*
$[(C_6H_5)_3Sn]_2$	1.55±0.07	0	0	SnO_2	*9*
	1.41±0.02	0	0	SnO_2	*124*
	1.38±0.09	0	0	Pd(Sn)	*216*
	1.35±0.09	0	0	Pd(Sn)	*215*
	1.30±0.10	0	0	SnO_2	*96*
$[(p\text{-}FC_6H_4)_3Sn]_2$	1.33±0.02	0	0	SnO_2	*124*
$[(p\text{-}ClC_6H_4)_3Sn]_2$	1.44±0.02	0	0	SnO_2	*124*
$[(m\text{-}CF_3C_6H_4)_3Sn]_2$	1.40±0.02	0	0	SnO_2	*124*
	1.40±0.08	0	0	SnO_2	*146*
$[(C_6H_5)_3Sn]_2Sn(C_6H_5)_2$	1.06±0.10	0	0	SnO_2	*96*
$[(C_6H_5)_3Sn]_4Sn$	1.56±0.09	0	0	Pd(Sn)	*216*
	1.56±0.09	0	0	Pd(Sn)	*215, 216*
	1.33±0.10	0	0	SnO_2	*96*
$[(C_6H_5)_2Sn]_6$	1.56±0.09	0	0	Pd(Sn)	*215*
$[(n\text{-}C_4H_9)_2Sn]_n$	1.55±0.08	0	0	SnO_2	*109*
$[(C_6H_5)_2Sn]_n$	1.42±0.08	0	0	SnO_2	*109*
$[(9\text{-Phenanthryl})_2Sn]_n$	1.8±0.05	0	0	—	*20*
$[(C_2H_5)_2SnCl]_2$	1.42	3.22	2.27	—	*375*
	1.4±0.2	3.1±0.2	2.22	SnO_2	*59*
	1.34±0.08	3.34±0.08	2.49	SnO_2	*107*

TABLE 7

ORGANOTIN COMPOUNDS WITH NON-TRANSITION METALS

Compound	I.S. (mm/sec)	Q.S. (mm/sec)	ρ=Q.S./I.S.	Source	References
$[(C_6H_5)_3SnLi$	1.40±0.07	0	0	SnO_2	*9*
$(CH_3)_3SnNa$	1.38±0.05	0	0	SnO_2	*74*
$[(C_6H_5)_3Sn]_4Ge$	1.13±0.10	0	0	SnO_2	*96*
$[(C_6H_5)_3Sn]_4Sn$	1.56±0.09	0	0	Pd(Sn)	*216*
	1.33±0.10	0	0	SnO_2	*96*
$[(C_6H_5)_3Sn]_4Pb$	1.39±0.10	0	0	SnO_2	*96*

TABLE 8

ORGANOTIN HALIDES, R_3SnX

Compound	I.S. (mm/sec)	Q.S. (mm/sec)	ρ=Q.S./I.S.	Source	References
X=F					
$(CH_3)_3SnF$	1.35±0.08	3.93±0.08	2.91	Mg_2Sn/SnO_2	*362*
	1.30*	3.60*	2.77	SnO_2	*322*
	1.28±0.05	3.86±0.05	3.02	Pd(Sn)	*191*
	1.28±0.05	3.86±0.05	3.02	SnO_2	*74*
	1.27±0.09	3.87±0.05	3.04	Pd(Sn)	*213*
	1.26	3.77	2.99	SnO_2	*322*
	1.25±0.02	3.73±0.02	2.98	Mg_2Sn	*160*

(*Continued*)

TABLE 8 (*Continued*)

Compound	I.S. (mm/sec)	Q.S. (mm/sec)	ρ=Q.S./I.S.	Source	References
	1.18±0.03	3.47±0.03	2.94	SnO_2	*124*
$(C_2H_5)_3SnF$	1.47±0.05	3.72±0.05	2.53	Mg_2Sn/SnO_2	*362*
	1.35	3.50	2.59	—	*375*
$(N{\equiv}CCH_2CH_2)_3SnF$	1.35±0.10	3.50±0.10	2.59	SnO_2	*5*
$(n\text{-}C_3H_7)_3SnF$	1.47±0.05	3.70±0.05	2.52	Mg_2Sn/SnO_2	*361*
$(n\text{-}C_4H_9)_3SnF$	1.31±0.05	3.70±0.05	2.82	Mg_2Sn/SnO_2	*361*
$(iso\text{-}C_4H_9)_3SnF$	1.47±0.05	3.60±0.05	2.45	Mg_2Sn/SnO_2	*362*
$(C_6H_5)_3SnF$	1.29±0.05	3.90±0.05	3.02	SnO_2	*73*
	1.25±0.05	3.53±0.05	2.82	Pd(Sn)	*191*
	1.25	3.45	2.76	—	*375*
	1.17±0.03	3.34±0.03	2.85	SnO_2	*124*
$[C_6H_5C(CH_3)_2CH_2]_3SnF$	1.33±0.03	2.79±0.03	2.09	SnO_2	*124*
X=Cl					
$(CH_3)_3SnCl$	1.64	3.67	2.24	—	*375*
	1.54±0.05	3.50±0.05	2.27	SnO_2	*73*
	1.44±0.06	3.01±0.12	2.09	SnO_2	*76*
	1.43±0.05	3.70±0.05	2.59	Mg_2Sn/SnO_2	*362*
	1.43±0.05	3.41±0.05	2.38	SnO_2	*74*
	1.43±0.03	3.32±0.03	2.32	—	*127a*
	1.42±0.05	3.41±0.05	2.40	Pd(Sn)	*191*
	1.41±0.09	3.41±0.09	2.42	Pd(Sn)	*211*
	1.40±0.03	3.09±0.03	2.21	SnO_2	*124*
	1.36±0.04	3.23±0.04	2.37	Mg_2Sn	*160*
	1.12±0.10	3.15±0.10	2.81	SnO_2	*181*
$(CH_3)_3SnCl/CCl_4$	1.17±0.10	2.42±0.10	2.10	SnO_2	*181*
$(CH_3)_3SnCl/C_6H_6$	1.42±0.03	3.36±0.03	2.36	—	*127a*
$(C_2H_5)_3SnCl$	1.62±0.05	3.57±0.05	2.20	Mg_2Sn/SnO_2	*362*
	1.30	3.24	2.49	—	*375*
$(n\text{-}C_3H_7)_3SnCl$	1.62±0.05	3.30±0.05	2.04	Mg_2Sn/SnO_2	*362*
$(n\text{-}C_4H_9)_3SnCl$	1.65±0.10	3.30±0.10	2.00	SnO_2	*5*
	1.65	3.30	2.00	—	*375*
	1.58±0.06	3.40±0.06	2.15	Pd(Sn)	*120*
	1.38±0.05	3.53±0.05	2.56	Mg_2Sn/SnO_2	*362*
	1.36±0.10	2.78±0.10	2.04	SnO_2	*181*
$(iso\text{-}C_4H_9)_3SnCl$	1.61±0.05	3.20±0.05	1.99	Mg_2Sn/SnO_2	*362*
$(C_6H_5)_3SnCl$	1.45±0.05	2.55±0.05	1.76	SnO_2	*73*
	1.4±0.2	2.4±0.2	1.71	SnO_2	*59*
	1.38±0.08	2.50±0.08	1.81	SnO_2	*107*
	1.37±0.03	2.45±0.03	1.79	SnO_2	*124*
	1.37±0.08	2.45±0.08	1.79	SnO_2	*146*
	1.35	2.44	1.81	—	*375*
	1.34±0.09	2.46±0.09	1.84	Pd(Sn)	*211*
	1.34±0.09	2.89±0.09	2.16	Pd(Sn)	*216*
	1.31±0.05	2.56±0.05	1.96	Pd(Sn)	*191*
	1.25±0.05	2.55±0.05	2.04	SnO_2	*73*
$(C_6H_5CH_2)_3SnCl$	1.48	2.80	1.89	—	*375*
$[C_6H_5C(CH_3)_2CH_2]_3SnCl$	1.39±0.03	2.65±0.03	1.90	SnO_2	*124*
$C_6H_5CH{=}C(C_6H_5)$ —$C(C_6H_5){=}C(C_6H_5)Sn(CH_3)_2Cl$	1.27±0.06	2.68±0.12	2.11	SnO_2	*341, 232d*
$(ClCH_2)_3SnCl$	1.52	2.55	2.09	—	*373*
$(O_2NCH_2)_3SnCl$	0.00±0.08	0.00±0.08	0	SnO_2	*106*
$(p\text{-}ClC_6H_4)_3SnCl$	1.37±0.03	2.49±0.03	1.81	SnO_2	*124*
$(C_6F_5)_3SnCl$	1.21±0.05	1.55±0.05	1.28	SnO_2	*73*
$[(C_2H_5)_2SnCl]_2$	1.42	3.22	2.27	—	*375*
	1.4±0.2	3.1±0.2	2.22	SnO_2	*59*
	1.34±0.08	3.34±0.08	2.49	SnO_2	*107*
Tris(phenylcarboranyl)tin chloride	1.17±0.05	0.4±0.04	0.34	SnO_2	*1*

(*Continued*)

TABLE 8 (*Continued*)

Compound	I.S. (mm/sec)	Q.S. (mm/sec)	ρ=Q.S./I.S.	Source	References
X=Br					
$(CH_3)_3SnBr$	1.49±0.05	3.25±0.05	2.18	Pd(Sn)	*191*
	1.49±0.05	3.25±0.05	2.18	SnO_2	*74*
	1.45±0.05	3.45±0.05	2.38	—	*49*
	1.38±0.09	3.28±0.09	2.38		*211*
	1.30±0.10	2.98±0.10	2.28	SnO_2	*181*
	1.30±0.08	3.60±0.05	2.77	Mg_2Sn/SnO_2	*362*
$(C_2H_5)_3SnBr$	1.62±0.08	3.17±0.05	1.96	Mg_2Sn/SnO_2	*362*
	1.62±0.05	3.45±0.05	2.13	—	*49*
	1.38±0.10	2.82±0.10	2.06	SnO_2	*181*
$(n\text{-}C_3H_7)_3SnBr$	1.67±0.08	3.26±0.05	1.95	Mg_2Sn/SnO_2	*362*
	1.46±0.05	2.92±0.05	2.00	—	*49*
	1.46	2.92	2.00	—	*375*
$(n\text{-}C_4H_9)_3SnBr$	1.70	3.30	1.94	—	*375*
	1.70±0.10	3.30±0.10	1.94	SnO_2	*5*
	1.50±0.05	3.30±0.05	2.20	—	*49*
	1.33±0.08	3.32±0.05	2.50	$MgSn/SnO_2$	*362*
$(iso\text{-}C_4H_9)_3SnBr$	1.60±0.08	3.07±0.05	1.92	Mg_2Sn/SnO_2	*362*
	1.40	2.40	1.71	—	*375*
$(C_6H_5)_3SnBr$	1.40±0.05	2.40±0.05	1.71	—	*49*
	1.40±0.05	2.51±0.05	1.79	SnO_2	*73*
	1.37±0.05	2.48±0.05	1.81	Pd(Sn)	*191*
$[C_6H_5C(CH_3)_2CH_2]_3SnBr$	1.42±0.02	2.65±0.02	1.87	SnO_2	*124*
$(N{\equiv}CCH_2CH_2)_3SnBr$	1.48±0.08	3.04±0.08	2.06	SnO_2	*5*
$(m\text{-}CF_3C_6H_4)_3SnBr$	1.22±0.02	1.94±0.02	1.59	SnO_2	*124*
$(C_6F_5)_3SnBr$	1.26±0.05	1.60±0.05	1.27	SnO_2	*73*
X=I					
$(CH_3)_3SnI$	1.48±0.05	3.05±0.05	2.06	Pd(Sn)	*191*
	1.48±0.05	3.05±0.05	2.06	SnO_2	*74*
$(C_2H_5)_3SnI$	1.55±0.08	2.77±0.05	1.79	Mg_2Sn/SnO_2	*362*
$(n\text{-}C_3H_7)_3SnI$	1.46	2.70	1.85	—	*375*
$(n\text{-}C_4H_9)_3SnI$	1.39±0.08	2.40±0.05	1.73	Mg_2Sn/SnO_2	*362*
$(iso\text{-}C_4H_9)_3SnI$	1.63±0.08	2.55±0.05	1.57	Mg_2Sn/SnO_2	*362*
$(C_6H_5)_3SnI$	1.77±0.05	2.05±0.05	1.16	—	*49*
	1.41±0.08	2.05±0.08	1.46	SnO_2	*146*
	1.20±0.05	2.25±0.05	1.88	Mg_2Sn/SnO_2	*362*
$[C_6H_5C(CH_3)_2CH_2]_3SnI$	1.41±0.03	2.40±0.03	1.70	SnO_2	*124*
$(N{\equiv}CCH_2CH_2)_3SnI$	1.45±0.08	2.96±0.08	2.04	SnO_2	*5*
$(p\text{-}FC_6H_4)_3SnI$	1.23±0.03	1.92±0.03	1.56	SnO_2	*124*

TABLE 9

ORGANOTIN HALIDES, R_2SnX_2

Compound	I.S. (mm/sec)	Q.S. (mm/sec)	ρ=Q.S./I.S.	Source	References
X=F					
$(n\text{-}C_4H_9)_2SnF_2$	1.50	3.90	2.60	—	*375*
	1.45±0.15	3.9±0.2	2.70	SnO_2	*3*
X=Cl					
$(CH_3)_2SnCl_2$	1.68±0.05	3.85±0.05	2.29	SnO_2	*73*
	1.61±0.05	3.85±0.05	2.24	SnO_2	*74*
	1.55	3.60	2.32	—	*375*
	1.54±0.06	3.33±0.12	2.16	$BaSnO_3$	*76*
	1.53±0.03	3.41±0.03	2.24	SnO_2	*124*
	1.52±0.09	3.62±0.09	2.38	Pd(Sn)	*211*

(*Continued*)

TABLE 9 *(Continued)*

Compound	I.S. (mm/sec)	Q.S. (mm/sec)	ρ=Q.S./I.S.	Source	References
$(C_2H_3)_2SnCl_2$	1.35±0.06	3.08±0.12	2.28	SnO_2	*360*
$(C_2H_5)_2SnCl_2$	1.7±0.3	3.3±0.3	1.94	SnO_2	*59*
	1.49±0.06	3.13±0.12	2.10	SnO_2	*360*
$(C_2H_5)_2SnCl_2$/dichloroethane	1.4±0.2	3.0±0.2	2.14	SnO_2	*59*
$(C_2H_5)_2Sn(CH_2Cl)Cl$	1.51	3.40	2.26	—	*375*
$(n\text{-}C_3H_7)_2SnCl_2$	1.70±0.3	3.60±0.3	2.12	SnO_2	*59*
	1.62±0.06	3.18±0.12	1.96	SnO_2	*360*
$(n\text{-}C_4H_9)_2SnCl_2$	1.60±0.2	3.25±0.15	2.03	SnO_2	*3*
	1.60±0.05	3.25±0.05	2.03	SnO_2	*6*
	1.5±0.2	3.4±0.2	2.27	SnO_2	*59*
$(C_6H_5)_2SnCl_2$	1.52±0.05	2.98±0.05	1.96	SnO_2	*73*
	1.4±0.2	2.8±0.2	2.00	SnO_2	*59*
	1.40±0.05	2.80±0.05	2.00	SnO_2	*6*
	1.38±0.06	2.75±0.12	1.99	SnO_2	*76*
	1.37±0.07	2.76±0.07	2.01	Pd(Sn)	*178*
	1.34±0.09	2.89±0.09	2.16	Pd(Sn)	*211*
	1.34±0.09	2.89±0.09	2.16	Pd(Sn)	*216*
	1.31±0.03	2.66±0.03	2.03	SnO_2	*124*
$(C_6H_{11})_2SnCl_2$	1.59±0.03	3.40±0.03	2.14	SnO_2	*124*
Bis(phenylcarboranyl)tin dichloride	1.25±0.06	0.90±0.05	0.72	SnO_2	*2*
X=Br					
$(CH_3)_2SnBr_2$	1.59±0.09	3.41±0.09	2.14	Pd(Sn)	*211*
$(C_2H_5)_2SnBr_2$	1.68±0.06	3.37±0.12	2.44	$BaSnO_3$	*360*
$(n\text{-}C_4H_9)_2SnBr_2$	1.70±0.15	3.15±0.50	1.85	SnO_2	*59*
	1.70±0.05	3.20±0.05	1.88	SnO_2	*6*
	1.40	3.45	2.46	—	*375*
Bis(phenylcarboranyl)tin dibromide	0.90±0.05	0.80±0.04	0.89	SnO_2	*1*
X=I					
$(C_2H_5)_2SnI_2$	1.31±0.05	3.21±0.05		—	*49*
$(n\text{-}C_4H_9)_2SnI_2$	1.80	2.40		—	*375*
	1.80±0.15	2.90±0.15	1.61	SnO_2	*3*

TABLE 10

ORGANOTIN HALIDES, $RSnX_3$

Compound	I.S. (mm/sec)	Q.S. (mm/sec)	ρ=Q.S./I.S.	Source	References
$n\text{-}C_4H_9SnCl_3$	1.70±0.10	3.40±0.10	2.00	SnO_2	*5*
	1.31±0.06	1.83±0.12	1.40	SnO_2	*76*
$C_6H_5SnCl_3$	2.8±0.3	4.8±0.3	1.72	SnO_2	*59*
	1.27±0.09	1.80±0.09	1.42	Pd(Sn)	*211*
CH_3SnBr_3	1.41±0.09	1.91±0.09	1.36	Pd(Sn)	*211*

TABLE 11

ORGANOTIN(IV) HYDROXIDES AND ALKOXIDES

Compound	I.S. (mm/sec)	Q.S. (mm/sec)	ρ=Q.S./I.S.	Source	References
$(CH_3)_3SnOH$	1.19±0.05	2.91±0.05	2.53	SnO_2	*74*
	1.14±0.09	2.97±0.09	2.60	Pd(Sn)	*213*
	1.07±0.03	2.71±0.03	2.53	SnO_2	*124*
$(C_2H_5)_3SnOH$	1.35	3.24	2.40	—	*375*
	1.35±0.07	3.00±0.07	2.22	SnO_2	*5*
$(n\text{-}C_4H_9)_3SnOH$	1.46	3.24	2.22	—	*375*
$(C_6H_5)_3SnOH$	1.35±0.08	2.70±0.08	2.00	SnO_2	*107*
	1.18±0.03	2.68±0.03	2.28	SnO_2	*124*
	1.02	1.19	1.17	—	*375*
$[C_6H_5C(CH_3)_2CH_2]_3SnOH$	1.13±0.03	1.08±0.03	0.96	SnO_2	*124, 198*
$(C_2H_5)_3SnOCH_3$	1.41	2.86	2.03	—	*37*
	1.41±0.05	2.86±0.05	2.03	SnO_2	*147*
$(C_2H_5)_3SnOC(CH_3)_3$	1.40±0.05	2.59±0.05	1.85	SnO_2	*147*
	1.30	2.59	1.99	—	*375*
$(C_2H_5)_3SnOC_6H_5$	1.49±0.06	3.09±0.06	2.08	Pd(Sn)	*183a*
$(C_2H_5)_3SnOC_6H_5/CCl_4$	1.42±0.06	3.04±0.06	2.14	Pd(Sn)	*183a*
$(C_2H_5)_3SnOC_6H_5/C_6H_6$	1.50±0.06	3.14±0.06	2.09	Pd(Sn)	*183a*
$(C_2H_5)_3SnOC_6H_5/CHCl_3$	1.48±0.06	3.07±0.06	2.08	Pd(Sn)	*183a*
$(C_2H_5)_3SnOC_6H_5/C_4H_8O$	1.48±0.06	3.32±0.06	2.24	Pd(Sn)	*183a*
$(C_2H_5)_3SnOC_6H_5/CH_3COCH_3$	1.45±0.06	3.34±0.06	2.30	Pd(Sn)	*183a*
$(C_2H_5)_3SnOC_6H_5/CH_3COOC_2H_5$	1.44±0.06	3.17±0.06	2.20	Pd(Sn)	*183a*
$(C_2H_5)_3SnOC_6H_5/C_5H_5N$	1.46±0.06	3.29±0.06	2.26	Pd(Sn)	*183a*
$(C_2H_5)_3SnOC_6H_5/CH_3SOCH_3$	1.46±0.06	3.34±0.06	2.29	Pd(Sn)	*183a*
$(C_2H_5)_3SnOC_6H_5/HCON(CH_3)_2$	1.48±0.06	3.31±0.06	2.24	Pd(Sn)	*183a*
$(C_2H_5)_3SnOC_6H_5/CH_3CN$	1.48±0.06	3.31±0.06	2.24	Pd(Sn)	*183a*
$(C_2H_5)_3SnOC_6H_5/CH_3OC_2H_4OCH_3$	1.48±0.06	3.31±0.06	2.24	Pd(Sn)	*183a*
$(C_2H_5)_3SnOC_6H_5/C_6H_5COOC_2H_5$	1.43±0.06	3.21±0.06	2.24	Pd(Sn)	*183a*
$(C_2H_5)_3SnOC_6H_5/C_6H_5N(CH_3)_2$	1.46±0.06	3.21±0.06	2.20	Pd(Sn)	*183a*
$(C_2H_5)_3SnOC_6H_5/CH_3SCN$	1.45±0.06	3.59±0.06	2.48	Pd(Sn)	*183a*
$(C_2H_5)_3SnOC_6H_5/C_6H_5NO_2$	1.45±0.06	3.17±0.06	2.18	Pd(Sn)	*183a*
$(C_2H_5)_3SnOC_6H_5/C_6H_5CHO$	1.47±0.06	3.35±0.06	2.28	Pd(Sn)	*183a*
$(C_2H_5)_3SnOC_6H_5/C_6H_5CN$	1.45±0.06	3.38±0.06	2.33	Pd(Sn)	*183a*
$4\text{-}(C_2H_5)_3SnOC_6H_4OCH_3$	1.46±0.06	3.20±0.06	2.20	Pd(Sn)	*183a*
$4\text{-}(C_2H_5)_3SnOC_6H_4OCH_3$/pyridine	1.43±0.06	3.28±0.06	2.30	Pd(Sn)	*183a*
$4\text{-}(C_2H_5)_3SnOC_6H_4F$	1.48±0.06	3.30±0.06	2.23	Pd(Sn)	*183a*
$4\text{-}(C_2H_5)_3SnOC_6H_4F$/pyridine	1.38±0.06	3.31±0.06	2.40	Pd(Sn)	*183a*
$4\text{-}(C_2H_5)_3SnOC_6H_4Br$	1.46±0.06	3.07±0.06	2.10	Pd(Sn)	*183a*
$4\text{-}(C_2H_5)_3SnOC_6H_4Br$/pyridine	1.36±0.06	3.34±0.06	2.46	Pd(Sn)	*183a*
$4\text{-}(C_2H_5)_3SnOC_6H_4CHO$	1.50±0.06	3.82±0.06	2.54	Pd(Sn)	*183a*
$4\text{-}(C_2H_5)_3SnOC_6H_4CHO$/pyridine	1.45±0.06	3.44±0.06	2.38	Pd(Sn)	*183a*
$4\text{-}(C_2H_5)_3SnOC_6H_4SCN$	1.49±0.06	3.35±0.06	2.25	Pd(Sn)	*183a*
$4\text{-}(C_2H_5)_3SnOC_6H_4SCN$/pyridine	1.45±0.06	3.31±0.06	2.28	Pd(Sn)	*183a*
$4\text{-}(C_2H_5)_3SnOC_6H_4NO_2$	1.50±0.06	3.55±0.06	2.36	Pd(Sn)	*183a*
$4\text{-}(C_2H_5)_3SnOC_6H_4NO_2$/pyridine	1.47±0.06	3.56±0.06	2.42	Pd(Sn)	*183a*
$4\text{-}(C_2H_5)_3SnOC_6H_4N(CH_3)_2$	1.41±0.06	2.96±0.06	2.10	Pd(Sn)	*183a*
$4\text{-}(C_2H_5)_3SnOC_6H_4N(CH_3)_2$/pyridine	1.36±0.06	3.00±0.06	2.20	Pd(Sn)	*183a*
$4\text{-}(C_2H_5)_3SnOC_6H_4CH_3$	1.49±0.06	3.10±0.06	2.08	Pd(Sn)	*183a*
$4\text{-}(C_2H_5)_3SnOC_6H_4CH_3$/pyridine	1.40±0.06	3.28±0.06	2.34	Pd(Sn)	*183a*
$4\text{-}(C_2H_5)_3SnOC_6H_4Cl$	1.51±0.06	3.10±0.06	2.05	Pd(Sn)	*183a*
$4\text{-}(C_2H_5)_3SnOC_6H_4Cl$/pyridine	1.38±0.06	3.38±0.06	2.44	Pd(Sn)	*183a*
$4\text{-}(C_2H_5)_3SnOC_6H_4I$	1.50±0.06	3.14±0.06	2.09	Pd(Sn)	*183a*
$4\text{-}(C_2H_5)_3SnOC_6H_4I$/pyridine	1.38±0.06	3.38±0.06	2.45	Pd(Sn)	*183a*
$4\text{-}(C_2H_5)_3SnOC_6H_4COOCH_3$	1.45±0.06	3.24±0.06	2.23	Pd(Sn)	*183a*
$4\text{-}(C_2H_5)_3SnOC_6H_4COOCH_3$/pyridine	1.42±0.06	3.42±0.06	2.41	Pd(Sn)	*183a*
$4\text{-}(C_2H_5)_3SnOC_6H_4CN$	1.48±0.06	3.31±0.06	2.24	Pd(Sn)	*183a*
$4\text{-}(C_2H_5)_3SnOC_6H_4CN$/pyridine	1.45±0.06	3.46±0.06	2.38	Pd(Sn)	*183a*
$(n\text{-}C_3H_7)_3SnOCH_3$	1.40	2.81	2.00	—	*375*
$(C_6H_5)_3SnOC_6H_4NO_2$	1.40	2.02	1.44	—	*375*

(Continued)

TABLE 11 (*Continued*)

Compound	I.S. (mm/sec)	Q.S. (mm/sec)	ρ=Q.S./I.S.	Source	References
$(CH_3)_2Sn(OCH_3)_2$	0.99±0.03	2.31±0.03	2.34	SnO_2	*124*
$(C_2H_5)_2Sn(OCH_3)_2$	1.08	2.38	2.20	—	*375*
$(n\text{-}C_4H_9)_2Sn(OC_2H_5)_2$	1.30±0.05	2.00±0.07	1.54	SnO_2	*9*
o-Phenylenedioxytin dimethyl	1.14±0.10	3.24±0.12	2.84	SnO_2	*397*
o-Phenylenedioxytin di-*n*-butyl	1.29±0.10	3.40±0.12	2.64	SnO_2	*397*
2,2′-Diphenylenedioxytin dimethyl	1.15±0.06	3.23±0.12	2.81	SnO_2	*397*
1,3-Dichloro-2-phenoxytin triethyl	1.50±0.05	3.00±0.05	2.00	SnO_2	*184*
1,3-Dichloro-2-phenoxytin triethyl/pyridine	1.74±0.05	3.61±0.05	2.08	SnO_2	*184*
1,3-Dichloro-2-phenoxytin triphenyl	1.36±0.05	2.46±0.05	1.81	SnO_2	*184*
1,3-Dichloro-2-phenoxytin triphenyl/pyridine	1.45±0.05	2.90±0.05	2.00	SnO_2	*184*
1,3-Dichloro-4-phenoxytin triethyl	1.34±0.05	2.86±0.05	2.14	SnO_2	*184*
1,3-Dichloro-4-phenoxytin triethyl/pyridine	1.39±0.05	3.47±0.05	2.50	SnO_2	*184*
1,3-Dichloro-4-phenoxytin triphenyl	1.34±0.05	2.07±0.05	1.54	SnO_2	*184*
1,3-Dichloro-4-phenoxytin triphenyl/pyridine	1.58±0.05	2.87±0.05	1.82	SnO_2	*184*
3,5-Dichloro-4-triethylstannoxypyridine	1.51±0.05	3.77±0.05	2.50	SnO_2	*184*
3,5-Dichloro-4-triethylstannoxypyridine/pyridine	1.65±0.05	3.74±0.05	2.27	SnO_2	*184*
3,5-Dichloro-4-triphenylstannoxypyridine	1.31±0.05	3.20±0.15	2.44	SnO_2	*184*
3,5-Dichloro-4-triphenylstannoxypyridine/pyridine	1.29±0.05	3.24±0.05	2.51	SnO_2	*184*
3,5-Dichloro-2-triethylstannoxypyridine	1.56±0.05	2.86±0.05	1.83	SnO_2	*184*
3,5-Dichloro-2-triethylstannoxypyridine/pyridine	1.65±0.05	3.47±0.05	1.79	SnO_2	*184*
3,5-Dichloro-2-triphenylstannoxypyridine	1.31±0.05	2.35±0.05	1.79	SnO_2	*184*
3,5-Dichloro-2-triphenylstannoxypyridine/pyridine	1.34±0.05	2.77±0.05	2.07	SnO_2	*184*
$(CH_3)_3SnON{=}C(CH_3)_2$	1.40±0.06	2.93±0.06	2.09	$BaSnO_3$	*117e*
$(CH_3)_3SnON{=}C_6H_{10}$	1.43±0.06	2.96±0.06	2.07	$BaSnO_3$	*117e, 117f*
$(CH_3)_3SnON{=}C_6H_{10}$/butylbenzene	1.37±0.06	3.00±0.06	2.19	$BaSnO_3$	*117e*
$(C_2H_5)_3SnON{=}C_6H_{10}$	1.58±0.06	1.96±0.06	1.24	$BaSnO_3$	*117e, 117f*
$(n\text{-}C_3H_7)_3SnON{=}C_6H_{10}$	1.42±0.06	2.03±0.06	1.43	$BaSnO_3$	*117e, 117f*
$(n\text{-}C_4H_9)_3SnON{=}C_6H_{10}$	1.48±0.06	1.76±0.06	1.19	$BaSnO_3$	*117e, 117f*
$(C_6H_5)_3SnON{=}C_6H_{10}$	1.38±0.06	1.44±0.06	1.04	$BaSnO_3$	*117e, 117f*

TABLE 12

ORGANOSTANNOXANES, $(R_3Sn)_2O$

Compound	I.S. (mm/sec)	Q.S. (mm/sec)	ρ=Q.S./I.S.	Source	References
$[(n\text{-}C_4H_9)_3Sn]_2O$	1.20±0.05	1.15±0.10	0.96	SnO_2	*5*
	1.29±0.05	1.56±0.05	1.21	Pd(Sn)	*191a*
$[(C_6H_5)_3Sn]_2O$	1.08±0.03	2.15±0.03	2.00	SnO_2	*124*
$[(C_6F_5)_3Sn]_2O$	1.21±0.05	2.13±0.05	1.76	SnO_2	*73*
$[(n\text{-}C_4H_9)_2SnCl]_2O$	1.40	3.24	2.32	—	*375*
$[(n\text{-}C_4H_9)_2SnOH]_2O$	1.50±0.10	3.20±0.10	2.14	SnO_2	*5*
$[(CH_3)_2SnOC({=}O)CH_3]_2O$	1.38	3.57	2.58	SnO_2	*322*
	1.33*	3.54*	2.66	SnO_2	*322*
$[(n\text{-}C_4H_9)_2SnOC({=}O)CH_3]_2O$	1.30±0.08	3.24±0.08	2.49	SnO_2	*107*

(*Continued*)

TABLE 12 (*Continued*)

Compound	I.S. (mm/sec)	Q.S. (mm/sec)	ρ=Q.S./I.S.	Source	References
$[(n\text{-}C_4H_9)_2SnO\overset{\overset{O}{\|}}{C}(CH_2)_3CH_3]_2O$	1.53±0.06	3.28±0.05	2.14	SnO_2	*153*
$[(n\text{-}C_4H_9)_2SnO\overset{\overset{O}{\|}}{C}(CH_2)_5CH_2Cl]_2O$	1.48±0.02	3.25±0.05	2.19	SnO_2	*153*
$[(n\text{-}C_4H_9)_2SnO\overset{\overset{O}{\|}}{C}(CH_2)_7CH_2Cl]_2O$	1.44±0.02	3.25±0.04	2.26	SnO_2	*153*
$[(n\text{-}C_4H_9)_2SnO\overset{\overset{O}{\|}}{C}(CH_2)_{16}CH_3]_2O$	1.51±0.05	3.25±0.04	2.16	SnO_2	*153*
	1.48±0.05	3.26±0.04	2.20	SnO_2	*153*
$[(C_2H_5)_2SnO\overset{\overset{O}{\|}}{C}C_6H_5]_2O$	1.40	3.24	2.32	—	*375*
$CH_3\overset{\overset{O}{\|}}{C}O[(n\text{-}C_4H_9)_2SnO]_4O\overset{\overset{O}{\|}}{C}CH_3$	1.03	2.49	2.42	—	*375*
$CH_3\overset{\overset{O}{\|}}{C}O[(n\text{-}C_4H_9)_2SnO]_8O\overset{\overset{O}{\|}}{C}CH_3$	1.02	2.26	2.22	—	*375*

TABLE 13

ORGANOTIN(IV) OXIDES, $[R_2SnO]_n$

Compound	I.S. (mm/sec)	Q.S. (mm/sec)	ρ=Q.S./I.S.	Source	References
$[(CH_3)_2SnO]_n$	1.00±0.05	2.00±0.10	2.00	SnO_2	*8*
	0.92±0.03	1.92±0.03	2.08	SnO_2	*124*
	0.92±0.08	1.82±0.08	1.98	SnO_2	*107*
$[(C_2H_5)_2SnO]_n$	1.05±0.05	2.10±0.10	2.00	SnO_2	*8*
$[(n\text{-}C_3H_7)_2SnO]_n$	1.1±0.3	2.4±0.3	2.18	SnO_2	*59*
	1.10±0.08	2.10±0.08	1.91	SnO_2	*107*
	1.1	2.04	1.86	—	*375*
$[(n\text{-}C_4H_9)_2SnO]_n$	1.8±0.15	2.9±0.15	1.61	SnO_2	*3*
	1.15±0.10	2.08±0.20	1.81	SnO_2	*96*
	1.05±0.10	2.20±0.20	2.10	SnO_2	*3*
	1.00±0.05	2.00±0.10	2.00	SnO_2	*8*
	0.98±0.08	2.06±0.08	2.10	SnO_2	*107*
	0.95±0.10	2.2±0.20	2.32	SnO_2	*3*
$(n\text{-}C_5H_{11})_2SnO]_n$	1.08	2.06	1.91	—	*375*
	1.08±0.08	2.11±0.08	1.95	SnO_2	*107*
$[(C_6H_5)_2SnO]_n$	0.95±0.03	1.87±0.03	1.96	SnO_2	*124*
	0.88±0.08	1.73±0.08	1.97	SnO_2	*107*
	0.88±0.08	1.73±0.08	1.97	SnO_2	*146*
$[(p\text{-}ClC_6H_4)_2SnO]_n$	0.88±0.08	1.73±0.08	1.97	SnO_2	*107*
	0.88±0.08	1.73±0.08	1.97	SnO_2	*146*
$[(p\text{-}BrC_6H_4)_2SnO]_n$	0.92±0.08	1.83±0.08	1.99	SnO_2	*107*
	0.92±0.08	1.83±0.08	1.99	SnO_2	*146*
$[(p\text{-}IC_6H_4)_2SnO]_n$	0.86±0.08	1.73±0.08	2.02	SnO_2	*146*
	0.84±0.08	1.73±0.08	2.06	SnO_2	*107*
$[(C_6H_{13})_2SnO]_n$	1.00±0.05	2.00±0.10	2.00	SnO_2	*8*
$[(C_8H_{17})_2SnO]_n$	1.00±0.05	2.00±0.10	2.00	SnO_2	*8*
	0.96±0.09*	2.05±0.09*	1.05	—	*214a*

TABLE 14

ORGANOSTANNONIC ACIDS

Compound	I.S. (mm/sec)	Q.S. (mm/sec)	ρ=Q.S./I.S.	Source	References
C_2H_5SnOOH	0.70	1.70	2.44	—	*346*
	0.12	0	0	—	*375*
n-C_4H_9SnOOH	0.70	1.65	2.36	—	*346*
	0.74	1.80	2.48	Pd(Sn)	*191a*

TABLE 15

ORGANOTIN CARBOXYLATES

Compound	I.S. (mm/sec)	Q.S. (mm/sec)	ρ=Q.S./I.S.	Source	References
$R_3SnO\overset{O}{\overset{\|}{C}}R'$					
$(CH_3)_3SnO\overset{O}{\overset{\|}{C}}CH_3$	1.75	3.52	2.01	SnO_2	*322*
	1.31 ± 0.06	3.57 ± 0.12	2.72	$BaSnO_3$	*359*
	1.35 ± 0.03	3.68 ± 0.03	2.72	$BaSnO_3$	*95, 95a, 196a*
	1.34 ± 0.03	3.47 ± 0.03	2.59	SnO_2	*124*
$(CH_3)_3SnO\overset{O}{\overset{\|}{C}}CH_2F$	1.37 ± 0.06	3.86 ± 0.10	2.82	$BaSnO_3$	*359*
$(CH_3)_3SnO\overset{O}{\overset{\|}{C}}CHF_2$	1.40 ± 0.06	4.02 ± 0.10	2.87	$BaSnO_3$	*359*
$(CH_3)_3SnO\overset{O}{\overset{\|}{C}}CF_3$	1.42 ± 0.06	4.18 ± 0.10	2.94	$BaSnO_3$	*359*
	1.38 ± 0.03	4.22 ± 0.06	3.05	$BaSnO_3$	*196a*
$(CH_3)_3SnO\overset{O}{\overset{\|}{C}}CH_2Cl$	1.41 ± 0.03	3.89 ± 0.03	2.76	$BaSnO_3$	*196a*
$(CH_3)_3SnO\overset{O}{\overset{\|}{C}}CHCl_2$	1.37 ± 0.03	4.08 ± 0.03	2.98	$BaSnO_3$	*196a*
$(CH_3)_3SnO\overset{O}{\overset{\|}{C}}CCl_3$	1.44 ± 0.03	4.15 ± 0.03	2.88	$BaSnO_3$	*196a*
$(CH_3)_3SnO\overset{O}{\overset{\|}{C}}CH_2Br$	1.34 ± 0.03	3.90 ± 0.03	2.91	$BaSnO_3$	*196a*
$(CH_3)_3SnO\overset{O}{\overset{\|}{C}}CBr_3$	1.43 ± 0.03	4.13 ± 0.03	2.89	$BaSnO_3$	*196a*
$(CH_3)_3SnO\overset{O}{\overset{\|}{C}}CH_2I$	1.37 ± 0.03	3.83 ± 0.03	2.80	$BaSnO_3$	*196a*
$(CH_3)_3SnO\overset{O}{\overset{\|}{C}}C{\equiv}C\overset{O}{\overset{\|}{C}}OSn(CH_3)_3$	1.40	3.81	2.72	SnO_2	*322*
$(C_2H_5)_3SnO\overset{O}{\overset{\|}{C}}CH_3$	1.60 ± 0.2	3.20 ± 0.2	2.00	SnO_2	*59*
	1.38	3.50	2.54	—	*375*

(Continued)

TABLE 15 (*Continued*)

Compound	I.S. (mm/sec)	Q.S. (mm/sec)	ρ=Q.S./I.S.	Source	References
$(C_2H_5)_3SnO\overset{\overset{O}{\|}}{C}C(CH_3){=}CH_2$	1.35±0.2	3.00±0.2	2.22	SnO_2	*60*
$[(C_2H_5)_3SnO\overset{\overset{O}{\|}}{C}C(CH_3)CH_2]_n$	1.5±0.2	3.0±0.2	2.00	SnO_2	*60*
$(n\text{-}C_4H_9)_3SnO\overset{\overset{O}{\|}}{C}CH_3$	1.38±0.06	3.71±0.12	2.69	$BaSnO_3$	*359*
	1.46±0.03	3.64±0.03	2.50	$BaSnO_3$	*95a*
	1.40	3.40	2.43	—	*375*
	1.38	3.67	2.66	SnO_2	*322*
	1.31±0.06	3.40±0.06	2.60	SnO_2	*397*
$(n\text{-}C_4H_9)_3SnO\overset{\overset{O}{\|}}{C}CH_3$/cumene	1.45±0.06	3.59±0.12	2.48	$BaSnO_3$	*359*
$(n\text{-}C_4H_9)_3SnO\overset{\overset{O}{\|}}{C}CH_2F$	1.42±0.06	3.96±0.12	2.79	$BaSnO_3$	*359*
	1.30±0.06	3.60±0.06	2.77	SnO_2	*397*
$(n\text{-}C_4H_9)_3SnO\overset{\overset{O}{\|}}{C}CHF_2$	1.59±0.06	3.92±0.12	2.46	$BaSnO_3$	*359*
$(n\text{-}C_4H_9)_3SnO\overset{\overset{O}{\|}}{C}CF_3$	1.62±0.06	4.04±0.12	2.49	$BaSnO_3$	*359*
$(n\text{-}C_4H_9)_3SnO\overset{\overset{O}{\|}}{C}CF_3$/cumene	1.54±0.06	3.95±0.12	2.56	$BaSnO_3$	*359*
$(n\text{-}C_4H_9)_3SnO\overset{\overset{O}{\|}}{C}CH_2Cl$	1.40±0.06	3.94±0.12	2.81	$BaSnO_3$	*359*
$(n\text{-}C_4H_9)_3SnO\overset{\overset{O}{\|}}{C}CHCl_2$	1.47±0.06	4.00±0.12	2.72	$BaSnO_3$	*359*
$(n\text{-}C_4H_9)_3SnO\overset{\overset{O}{\|}}{C}CCl_3$	1.57±0.06	3.96±0.12	2.52	$BaSnO_3$	*359*
	1.36±0.06	3.68±0.06	2.71	SnO_2	*397*
$(n\text{-}C_4H_9)_3SnO\overset{\overset{O}{\|}}{C}C(CH_3){=}CH_2$	1.45±0.07	3.70±0.10	2.56	SnO_2	*9*
$[(n\text{-}C_4H_9)_3SnO\overset{\overset{O}{\|}}{C}C(CH_3)CH_2]$	1.50±0.07	3.10±0.10	2.06	SnO_2	*9*
$(C_6H_5)_3SnO\overset{\overset{O}{\|}}{C}H$	1.37±0.03	3.58±0.03	2.61	$BaSnO_3$	*95a*
$(C_6H_5)_3SnO\overset{\overset{O}{\|}}{C}CH_3$	1.27±0.03	3.40±0.03	2.68	$BaSnO_3$	*95, 95a*
	1.08	2.70	2.50	—	*375*
$(C_6H_5)_3SnO\overset{\overset{O}{\|}}{C}CH_2CH_3$	1.33±0.03	3.43±0.03	2.57	$BaSnO_3$	*95a*
$(C_6H_5)_3SnO\overset{\overset{O}{\|}}{C}(CH_2)_2\overset{\overset{O}{\|}}{C}CH_3$	1.29±0.03	3.43±0.03	2.66	$BaSnO_3$	*95, 95a*

Continued)

TABLE 15 (*Continued*)

Compound	I.S. (mm/sec)	Q.S. (mm/sec)	ρ=Q.S./I.S.	Source	References
$(C_6H_5)_3SnOC(=O)C(CH_3)=CH_2$	1.21	2.26	1.87	SnO_2	*95*
	1.15 ± 0.1	2.10 ± 0.2	1.83	SnO_2	*59*
	1.10	2.20	2.00	—	*375*
$(C_6H_5)_3SnOC(=O)(CH_2)_4CH_3$	1.32 ± 0.03	3.43 ± 0.03	2.60	$BaSnO_3$	*95a*
$(C_6H_5)_3SnOC(=O)(CH_2)_6CH_3$	1.29 ± 0.03	3.35 ± 0.03	2.60	$BaSnO_3$	*95a*
$(C_6H_5)_3SnOC(=O)(CH_2)_7CH_3$	1.28 ± 0.03	3.36 ± 0.03	2.62	$BaSnO_3$	*95a*
$(C_6H_5)_3SnOC(=O)(CH_2)_8CH_3$	1.27 ± 0.03	3.43 ± 0.03	2.72	$BaSnO_3$	*95a*
$(C_6H_5)_3SnOC(=O)(CH_2)_{10}CH_3$	1.24 ± 0.03	3.41 ± 0.03	2.75	$BaSnO_3$	*95a*
$(C_6H_5)_3SnOC(=O)(CH_2)_{14}CH_3$	1.25 ± 0.03	3.44 ± 0.03	2.75	$BaSnO_3$	*95a*
$(C_6H_5)_3SnOC(=O)(CH_2)_{16}CH_3$	1.26 ± 0.03	3.33 ± 0.03	2.64	$BaSnO_3$	*95a*
$(C_6H_5)_3SnOC(=O)(CH_2)_7CH=CH(CH_2)_7CH_3$	1.27 ± 0.03	3.38 ± 0.03	2.66	$BaSnO_3$	*95a*
$(C_6H_5)_3SnOC(=O)CH(C_2H_5)C_4H_9$-*n*	1.21 ± 0.03	2.26 ± 0.03	1.87	$BaSnO_3$	*95, 95a*
$(C_6H_5)_3SnOC(=O)C(CH_3)_3$	1.21 ± 0.03	2.40 ± 0.03	1.98	$BaSnO_3$	*95a*
$(C_6H_5)_3SnOC(=O)C(CH_3)=CH_2$	1.21 ± 0.03	2.26 ± 0.03	1.87	$BaSnO_3$	*95a*
$[C_6H_5C(CH_3)_2CH_2]_3SnOC(=O)CH_3$	1.35 ± 0.03	2.45 ± 0.03	1.81	SnO_2	*124, 198*
$R_2Sn[OC(=O)R']_2$					
$(CH_3)_2Sn(OC(=O)H)_2$	1.45	4.72	3.26	SnO_2	*322*
	1.37*	4.52*	3.30	SnO_2	*322*
	1.14	4.47	3.94	Pd(Sn)	*216*
$(CH_3)_2Sn(OC(=O)C_5H_4N)_2$	1.28	4.43	3.47	SnO_2	*322*
$(CH_3)_2Sn(OC(=O)C_6H_5)_2$	1.40	3.96	2.82	SnO_2	*322*
$(CH_3)_2Sn(CH_3C(=O)C_2H_4C(=O)CH_3)_2$	1.18	3.93	3.33	SnO_2	*322*

(*Continued*)

TABLE 15 (*Continued*)

Compound	I.S. (mm/sec)	Q.S. (mm/sec)	ρ=Q.S./I.S.	Source	References
$(n\text{-}C_4H_9)_2Sn(O\overset{\overset{O}{\|}}{C}CH_3)_2$	1.40±0.10	3.45±0.10	2.46	SnO_2	*5*
	1.34±0.08	3.50±0.08	2.61	SnO_2	*107*
$(n\text{-}C_4H_9)_2Sn(O\overset{\overset{O}{\|}}{C}CH_2Cl)_2$	1.60±0.10	3.65±0.10	2.28	SnO_2	*5*
	1.46	3.56	2.44	—	*375*
$(n\text{-}C_4H_9)_2Sn(O\overset{\overset{O}{\|}}{C}CHCl_2)_2$	1.54	3.73	2.42	—	*375*
$(n\text{-}C_4H_9)_2Sn(O\overset{\overset{O}{\|}}{C}CCl_3)_2$	1.65±0.10	3.80±0.10	2.30	SnO_2	*5*
	1.50±0.05	4.00±0.05	2.67	SnO_2	*375*
$(n\text{-}C_4H_9)_2Sn(O\overset{\overset{O}{\|}}{C}C_2H_5)_2$	1.49±0.04	3.70±0.06	2.48	SnO_2	*143*
$(n\text{-}C_4H_9)_2Sn[O\overset{\overset{O}{\|}}{C}C(CH_3){=}CH_2]_2$	1.45±0.07	3.90±0.12	2.69	SnO_2	*9*
	1.40±0.20	3.50±0.20	2.50	SnO_2	*5*
$(n\text{-}C_4H_9)_2Sn[O\overset{\overset{O}{\|}}{C}C(CH_3)CH_2]_n$	1.40±0.07	3.25±0.10	2.32	SnO_2	*9*
$(n\text{-}C_4H_9)_2SnC_4H_2O_4$	1.50±0.10	3.50±0.10	2.34	SnO_2	*5*
$(n\text{-}C_4H_9)_2Sn(O\overset{\overset{O}{\|}}{C}C_4H_9\text{-}n)_2$	1.47±0.02	3.23±0.04	2.20	SnO_2	*143*
$(n\text{-}C_4H_9)_2Sn(O\overset{\overset{O}{\|}}{C}C_4H_8Cl)_2$	1.50±0.05	3.41±0.03	2.28	SnO_2	*143*
$(n\text{-}C_4H_9)_2Sn(O\overset{\overset{O}{\|}}{C}C_6H_5)_2$	1.62	3.44	2.12	SnO_2	*322*
	1.57	3.56	2.27	—	*375*
$(n\text{-}C_4H_9)_2Sn(O\overset{\overset{O}{\|}}{C}C_6H_{13}\text{-}n)_2$	1.46±0.02	3.64±0.04	2.49	SnO_2	*143*
$(n\text{-}C_4H_9)_2Sn(O\overset{\overset{O}{\|}}{C}C_6H_{12}Cl\text{-}n)_2$	1.43±0.02	3.35±0.02	2.34	SnO_2	*143*
$(n\text{-}C_4H_9)_2Sn(O\overset{\overset{O}{\|}}{C}C_7H_{15}\text{-}n)_2$	1.45±0.10	3.45±0.10	2.38	SnO_2	*5*
	1.35±0.08	3.45±0.08	2.56	SnO_2	*107*
$(n\text{-}C_4H_9)_2Sn(O\overset{\overset{O}{\|}}{C}C_8H_{16}Cl\text{-}n)_2$	1.55±0.05	3.39±0.06	2.18	SnO_2	*143*
$(n\text{-}C_4H_9)_2Sn(O\overset{\overset{O}{\|}}{C}C_9H_{19}\text{-}n)_2$	1.49±0.02	3.61±0.03	2.42	SnO_2	*143*
$(n\text{-}C_4H_9)_2Sn(O\overset{\overset{O}{\|}}{C}C_{11}H_{23}\text{-}n)_2$	1.48±0.02	3.41±0.05	2.31	SnO_2	*143*
	1.45±0.20	3.50±0.20	2.42	SnO_2	*5*
	1.34±0.08	3.35±0.08	2.50	SnO_2	*107*
$(n\text{-}C_4H_9)_2Sn(O\overset{\overset{O}{\|}}{C}C_{14}H_{29}\text{-}n)_2$	1.24±0.06	3.10±0.02	2.50	SnO_2	*143*

(*Continued*)

TABLE 15 (*Continued*)

Compound	I.S. (mm/sec)	Q.S. (mm/sec)	ρ=Q.S./I.S.	Source	References
$(n\text{-}C_4H_9)_2Sn(O\overset{O}{\overset{\|}{C}}C_{14}H_{28}Cl\text{-}n)_2$	1.30±0.03	2.89±0.04	2.22	SnO_2	*143*
$(n\text{-}C_4H_9)_2Sn(O\overset{O}{\overset{\|}{C}}C_{17}H_{35}\text{-}n)_2$	1.45±0.10	3.30±0.10	2.27	SnO_2	*5*
	1.36±0.08	3.56±0.08	2.62	SnO_2	*107*
$(n\text{-}C_4H_9)_2\underset{OCH_3}{\underset{\vert}{Sn}}O\overset{O}{\overset{\|}{C}}CH_3$	1.30	3.24	2.49	—	*375*
$(n\text{-}C_4H_9)_2\underset{Cl}{\underset{\vert}{Sn}}O\overset{O}{\overset{\|}{C}}H\cdot H_2O$	1.44	3.47	2.41	SnO_2	*322*
$(n\text{-}C_4H_9)_2SnO\overset{O}{\overset{\|}{C}}CH{=}CH\overset{O}{\overset{\|}{C}}O$ (cyclic, Sn–O bridged)	1.25	3.62	2.89	SnO_2	*322*
$(C_6H_5)_2SnOC(C_6H_5)C_2H_4C(CH_3)CO$	1.72	2.03	1.18	SnO_2	*322*
$RSn[O\overset{O}{\overset{\|}{C}}R']_3$					
$n\text{-}C_4H_9Sn(O\overset{O}{\overset{\|}{C}}C(CH_3){=}CH_2)_3$	1.40±0.07	4.25±0.20	3.04	SnO_2	*9*
$[n\text{-}C_4H_9Sn(O\overset{O}{\overset{\|}{C}}C(CH_3)CH_2)_3]_n$	1.55±0.10	3.45±0.15	2.23	SnO_2	*9*

TABLE 16

ORGANOTIN(IV) SULFUR COMPOUNDS

Compound	I.S. (mm/sec)	Q.S. (mm/sec)	ρ=Q.S./I.S.	Source	References
$[(CH_3)_2SnS]_n$	1.24	1.51	1.22	—	*375*
$[(n\text{-}C_4H_9)_2SnS]_n$	0.90±0.20	1.90±0.20	2.11	SnO_2	*3*
$[(C_6H_5)_2SnS]_n$	1.19	1.29	1.08	—	*375*
$[(C_6H_5)_3Sn]_2S$	1.22±0.03	1.17±0.03	0.96	SnO_2	*124*
$(C_2H_5)_3SnSC_4H_9$	1.60±0.05	1.80±0.05	1.13	SnO_2	*184*
$(C_2H_5)_3SnSC_4H_9$/pyridine	1.63±0.05	1.94±0.09	1.19	SnO_2	*184*
$(C_2H_5)_3SnSC_6H_5$	1.62±0.05	2.07±0.05	0.83	SnO_2	*183a, 184*
$(C_2H_5)_3SnSC_6H_5$/pyridine	1.65±0.05	2.85±0.05	1.73	SnO_2	*184*
4-$(C_2H_5)_3SnSC_6H_4CH_3$	1.45±0.06	2.08±0.06	1.43	Pd(Sn)	*183a*
4-$(C_2H_5)_3SnSC_6H_4CH_3$/pyridine	1.45±0.06	2.79±0.06	1.93	Pd(Sn)	*183a*
4-$(C_2H_5)_3SnSC_6H_4NO_2$	1.48±0.06	2.41±0.06	1.63	Pd(Sn)	*183a*
4-$(C_2H_5)_3SnSC_6H_4NO_2$/pyridine	1.53±0.06	3.11±0.06	2.03	Pd(Sn)	*183a*
4-$(C_2H_5)_3SnSC_6H_4N(CH_3)_2$	1.50±0.06	1.96±0.06	1.31	Pd(Sn)	*183a*
4-$(C_2H_5)_3SnSC_6H_4N(CH_3)_2$/pyridine	1.52±0.06	2.41±0.06	1.59	Pd(Sn)	*183a*
4-$(C_2H_5)_3SnC_6H_4Cl$	1.51±0.06	2.18±0.06	1.44	Pd(Sn)	*183a*
4-$(C_2H_5)_3SnSC_6H_4Cl$/pyridine	1.51±0.06	2.96±0.06	1.96	Pd(Sn)	*183a*
4-$(C_2H_5)_3SnSC_6H_4F$	1.52±0.06	2.31±0.06	1.52	Pd(Sn)	*183a*

(*Continued*)

TABLE 16 (*Continued*)

Compound	I.S. (mm/sec)	Q.S. (mm/sec)	ρ=Q.S./I.S.	Source	References
4-$(C_2H_5)_3SnSC_6H_4F$/pyridine	1.44±0.06	2.87±0.06	1.99	Pd(Sn)	*183a*
4-$(C_2H_5)_3SnSC_6H_4OCH_3$	1.52±0.06	2.15±0.06	1.41	Pd(Sn)	*183a*
4-$(C_2H_5)_3SnSC_6H_4OCH_3$/pyridine	1.52±0.06	2.70±0.06	1.78	Pd(Sn)	*183a*
$(C_6H_5)_3SnSC_6H_5$	1.40±0.05	1.16±0.05	0.83	SnO_2	*184*
$(C_6H_5)_3SnSC_6H_5$/pyridine	1.52±0.05	2.34±0.05	1.54	SnO_2	*184*
4-Triethylstannthiopyridine	1.55±0.05	3.05±0.05	1.98	SnO_2	*184*
4-Triethylstannthiopyridine/pyridine	1.62±0.05	3.08±0.05	1.90	SnO_2	*184*
4-Triphenylstannthiopyridine	1.37±0.05	2.61±0.05	1.90	SnO_2	*184*
4-Triphenylstannthiopyridine/pyridine	1.36±0.05	2.54±0.05	1.87	SnO_2	*184*
2-Triethylstannthiopyridine	1.56±0.05	2.14±0.05	1.37	SnO_2	*184*
2-Triethylstannthiopyridine/pyridine	1.30±0.05	2.60±0.05	2.00	SnO_2	*184*
2-Triphenylstannthiopyridine	1.36±0.05	1.58±0.05	1.16	SnO_2	*184*
2-Triphenylstannthiopyridine/pyridine	1.45±0.05	1.72±0.05	1.19	SnO_2	*184*
1,2-Ethanedithioatotin dimethyl	1.35	2.33	1.73	Mg_2Sn	*91*
1,2-Ethanedithiolatotin diphenyl	1.36	1.69	1.24	Mg_2Sn	*91*
3,4-Toluenedithiolatotin dimethyl	1.36	2.62	1.93	Mg_2Sn	*91*
3,4-Toluenedithiolatotin diphenyl	1.33	1.93	1.45	Mg_2Sn	*91*
$(CH_3)_3SnSCN$	1.40±0.02	3.77±0.02	2.69	$BaSnO_3$	*95b*
$(C_2H_5)_3SnSCN$	1.57±0.02	3.80±0.02	2.42	$BaSnO_3$	*95b*
$(C_4H_9)_3SnSCN$	1.60±0.02	3.69±0.02	2.31	$BaSnO_3$	*95b*
$(C_6H_5)_3SnSCN$	1.35±0.02	3.87±0.02	2.86	$BaSnO_3$	*95b*
$(CH_3)_2Sn(SCN)_2$	1.48±0.02	3.87±0.02	2.62	$BaSnO_3$	*95b*
$(C_2H_5)_2Sn(SCN)_2$	1.56±0.02	3.96±0.02	2.54	$BaSnO_3$	*95b*
$(C_4H_9)_2Sn(SCN)_2$	1.56±0.02	3.88±0.02	2.49	$BaSnO_3$	*95b*
$(C_4H_9)_2Sn(SCN)_2$/methyl THF	1.47±0.05	3.98±0.05	2.72	$BaSnO_3$	*95b*
$(C_4H_9)_2Sn(SCN)_2/CH_3CN$	1.49±0.05	3.86±0.05	2.59	$BaSnO_3$	*95b*
$C_4H_9Sn(SCN)_3$	1.43±0.02	1.46±0.02	1.02	$BaSnO_3$	*95b*

TABLE 17

ORGANOTIN(IV) NITROGEN COMPOUNDS

Compound	I.S. (mm/sec)	Q.S. (mm/sec)	ρ=Q.S./I.S.	Source	References
$(CH_3)_3SnN_3$	1.24±0.03	3.23±0.03	2.60	SnO_2	*124*
$(C_6H_5)_3SnN_3$	1.40±0.03	3.19±0.03	2.28	SnO_2	*124*
$[C_6H_5C(CH_3)_2CH_2]_3SnN_3$	1.33±0.03	2.48±0.03	1.86	SnO_2	*124*
$(CH_3)_3Sn$(imidazole)	1.64±0.03	2.76±0.03	2.37	SnO_2	*124*
$(C_4H_9)_3Sn$(imidazole)	1.37±0.05	2.87±0.05	2.10	Pd(Sn)	*191a*
$(C_6H_5)_3Sn$(imidazole)	1.25±0.05	2.73±0.05	2.18	Pd(Sn)	*191a*
$(CH_3)_3Sn$(1,2,4-triazole)	1.27±0.03	2.96±0.03	2.33	SnO_2	*124*
$(C_6H_5)_3Sn$(1,2,4-triazole)	1.29±0.03	2.76±0.03	2.14	SnO_2	*124*
$(CH_3)_3Sn$(benzimidazole)	1.20±0.03	2.87±0.03	2.39	SnO_2	*124*
$(C_6H_5)_3Sn$(benzimidazole)	1.19±0.03	2.59±0.03	2.17	SnO_2	*124*
$(CH_3)_3Sn$(1,2,3-benztriazole)	1.31±0.03	2.48±0.03	1.89	SnO_2	*124*
$(C_6H_5)_3Sn$(1,2,3-benztriazole)	1.31±0.03	2.98±0.01	2.28	SnO_2	*124*
$(C_2H_5)_3Sn—N(NO_2)CH_3$	1.49	3.53	2.37	SnO_2	*231*
$(C_4H_9)_2Sn(NCS)_2$	1.54±0.07	3.90±0.07	2.53	Pd(Sn)	*178*
$(C_6H_5)_2Sn(NCS)_2$	1.45±0.07	3.96±0.07	2.73	Pd(Sn)	*178*

TABLE 18

ORGANOTIN DERIVATIVES OF INORGANIC ACIDS

Compound	I.S. (mm/sec)	Q.S. (mm/sec)	ρ=Q.S./I.S.	Source	References
$(CH_3)_3SnNO_3$	1.44±0.05	4.14±0.05	2.80	SnO_2	*74*
$[C_6H_5C(CH_3)_2CH_2]_3SnNO_3$	1.40±0.02	3.18±0.02	2.28	SnO_2	*124*
$(CH_3)_2SnSO_4$	1.611	5.003	3.10	—	*232a*
	1.572*	4.94*	3.14	—	*232a*
$(CH_3)_2Sn(NO_3)_2$	1.28±0.06	3.90±0.06	3.05	SnO_2	*397*
$(CH_3)_2Sn(OH)NO_3$	1.28±0.05	3.52±0.05	2.75	SnO_2	*74*
$(CH_3)_2SnMoO_4$	1.25±0.06	3.92±0.12	3.14	$BaSnO_3$	*359*
	1.52±0.05	4.10±0.05	2.70	SnO_2	*227a*
$(CH_3)_2SnWO_4$	1.12±0.06	3.18±0.12	2.84	$BaSnO_3$	*359*
	1.49±0.05	3.53±0.05	2.37	SnO_2	*227a*
$(CH_3)_2SnCO_3$	1.56±0.06	2.49±0.12	1.60	$BaSnO_3$	*359*
$(CH_3)_2SnCO_3/AgCl$	1.29±0.06	2.90±0.12	2.25	$BaSnO_3$	*359*
$(CH_3)_2SnC_2O_4 \cdot H_2O$	1.26±0.06	4.42±0.06	3.50	$BaSnO_3$	*359*
	1.65±0.05	4.65±0.05	2.82	SnO_2	*227a*
$(CH_3)_3Sn(SO_3F)_2$	1.82	5.54	3.04	—	*232a*
	1.77*	5.41*	3.06	—	*232a*
$(CH_3)_2Sn(SO_3CF_3)_2$	1.79	5.51	3.08	—	*232a*
	1.78*	5.51*	3.10	—	*232a*
$(CH_3)_2Sn(SO_3Cl)_2$	1.75	5.20	2.97	—	*232a*
	1.72*	5.18*	3.02	—	*232a*
$(CH_3)_2Sn(SO_3CH_3)_2$	1.52	5.05	3.32	—	*232a*
	1.54*	5.03*	3.27	—	*232a*
$(CH_3)_2Sn(SO_3C_2H_5)_2$	1.52	4.91	3.24	—	*232a*
	1.51*	4.83*	3.20	—	*232a*
$[C_6H_5C(CH_3)_2CH_2]_3SnClO_4$	1.57±0.02	3.83±0.02	2.44	SnO_2	*124*
	1.4	4.0	2.86	—	*375*
$(n\text{-}C_4H_9)_2SnSO_3$	1.3±0.2	4.0±0.2	3.1	SnO_2	*3*
$(n\text{-}C_4H_9)_2SnSO_4$	1.8±0.15	4.8±0.15	2.7	SnO_2	*3*
	1.52	4.75	3.12	—	*375*
$(CH_3)_2SnO \cdot Sn(CH_3)_2CrO_4$	1.38±0.05	2.98±0.05	2.16	SnO_2	*227a*

TABLE 19

ORGANOTIN(IV) TRANSITION METAL COMPOUNDS

Compound	I.S. (mm/sec)	Q.S. (mm/sec)	ρ=Q.S./I.S.	Source	References
R_nSnM_{4-n}					
$n=0$					
$Sn[Fe(CO)_2\pi\text{-}C_5H_5]_4$	2.14	0	0	—	*98*
$Sn[Co(CO)_4]_4$	1.96±0.06	0	0	$BaSnO_3$	*93, 93a*
$(CH_3)_2SnFe_2(CO)_8\mathit{Sn}Fe_2(CO)_8Sn(CH_3)_2$	2.20±0.10	0	0	SnO_2	*135*
$n=1$					
$C_6H_5Sn[Fe(CO)_2\pi\text{-}C_5H_5]_3$	2.00	0	0	—	*98*
$C_6H_5Sn[Co(CO)_4]_3$	1.54±0.06	1.28±0.12	0.83	SnO_2	*93*
$C_6H_5Sn[Re(CO)_5]_3$	1.75±0.10	0	0	SnO_2	*141*
$n=2$					
$(CH_3)_2Sn[Fe(CO)_2\pi\text{-}C_5H_5]_2$	1.68	0	0	—	*262*
$(CH_3)_2SnFe(CO)_8Sn(CH_3)_2$	1.47±0.10	1.22±0.10	0.83	SnO_2	*135*
$(CH_3)_2\mathit{Sn}Fe_2(CO)_8SnFe(CO)_8\mathit{Sn}(CH_3)_2$	1.45±0.10	1.24±0.10	0.86	SnO_2	*135*
$(C_2H_5)_2Sn[Fe(CO)_2\pi\text{-}C_5H_5]_2$	1.74	0	0	—	*262*

(Continued)

TABLE 19 (*Continued*)

Compound	I.S. (mm/sec)	Q.S. (mm/sec)	ρ=Q.S./I.S.	Source	References
$(n\text{-}C_4H_9)_2SnFe(CO)_8Sn(n\text{-}C_4H_9)_2$	1.70±0.10	1.26±0.10	0.74	SnO_2	*135*
	1.70	1.26	0.74	—	*135*
$(C_6H_5)_2Sn[Fe(CO)_2\pi\text{-}C_5H_5]_2$	1.74	0	0	—	*98*
$(C_6H_5)_2Sn[Co(CO)_4]_2$	1.68±0.07	1.15±0.07	0.68	SnO_2	*141*
$Mn(CO)_5$ $(C_6H_5)_2Sn$ $Co(CO)_4$	1.65±0.07	1.15±0.07	0.70	SnO_2	*141*
$(C_6H_5)_2Sn[Re(CO)_5]_2$	1.70±0.07	0	0	SnO_2	*141*
$n=3$					
$(C_6H_5)_3SnFe(CO)_2\pi\text{-}C_5H_5$	1.50±0.02	0	0	$BaSnO_3$	*119*
	1.43	0	0	—	*98*
	1.43	0	0	—	*262*
$(C_6H_5)_3SnFe(CO)_2\pi\text{-}C_5H_5$/poly(methyl methacrylate)	1.50±0.02	0	0	$BaSnO_3$	*119*
$(C_6H_5)_3SnMn(CO)_5$	1.45±0.07	0	0	SnO_2	*141*
$(C_6H_5)_3SnCo(CO)_5$	1.50±0.07	1.0±0.07	0.67	SnO_2	*141*
$(C_6H_5)_3Re(CO)_5$	1.45±0.07	0	0	SnO_2	*141*
$(C_6H_5)_3SnRe(CO)_4P(C_6H_5)_3$	1.50±0.07	0	0	SnO_2	*141*
X_nSnM_{4-n}					
$n=1$					
$ClSn[Mn(CO)_5]_3$	1.92±0.05	1.55±0.07	0.81	SnO_2	*98*
	1.92	1.55	0.81	—	*98*
$Fe(CO)_2\pi\text{-}C_5H_5$ $ClSn$ $Mn(CO)_5$	2.10	2.02	0.96	—	*98*
$ClSn[Re(CO)_5]_3$	1.82	1.60	0.88	—	*98*
$Cl(C_6H_5)_2SnMn(CO)_5$	1.62±0.05	2.60±0.07	1.60	SnO_2	*141*
$Cl(C_6H_5)_2SnCo(CO)_4$	1.56±0.05	2.22±0.07	1.42	SnO_2	*141*
$BrSn[Re(CO)_5]_3$	1.82±0.07	1.60±0.07	0.88	SnO_2	*141*
$n=2$					
$Cl_2Sn[Fe(CO)_2\pi\text{-}C_5H_5]_2$	2.12	2.46	1.16	—	*98*
	1.95±0.02	2.38±0.02	1.22	$BaSnO_3$	*119, 316*
	1.94	2.37		—	*262*
$Cl_2Sn[Fe(CO)_2\pi\text{-}C_5H_5]_2$/poly(methyl methacrylate)	1.96±0.02	2.25±0.02	1.15	$BaSnO_3$	*119, 316*
	1.31±0.02	2.29±0.02	1.75		
$Mn(CO)_5$ Cl_2Sn $Mo(CO)_3\pi\text{-}C_5H_5$	1.98±0.08	2.0±0.08	1.01	SnO_2	*141*
$Mn(CO)_5$ Cl_2Sn $Re(CO)_5$	1.96±0.05	2.48±0.07	1.27	SnO_2	*141*
	1.96	2.48	1.27	—	*98*
$n=3$					
$Cl_3SnFe(CO)_2\pi\text{-}C_5H_5$	1.90	1.90	1.00	—	*262*
	1.74±0.02	1.77±0.02	1.02	$BaSnO_3$	*119, 316*
	1.62	1.43	0.88	—	*98*
$Cl_3SnFe(CO)_2\pi\text{-}C_5H_5$/methyl THF	1.54±0.05	1.64±0.05	1.07	$BaSnO_3$	*119, 316*
$Cl_3SnFe(CO)_2\pi\text{-}C_5H_5$/poly(methyl methacrylate)	1.66±0.02	1.78±0.02	1.07	$BaSnO_3$	*119, 316*
$Cl_3SnMn(CO)_5$	1.73±0.05	1.56±0.07	0.90	SnO_2	*141*

(*Continued*)

TABLE 19 *(Continued)*

Compound	I.S. (mm/sec)	Q.S. (mm/sec)	ρ=Q.S./I.S.	Source	References
$Cl_3SnRh[P(C_6H_5)_3]_3$	1.78±0.06	1.73±0.12	0.97	$BaSnO_3$	*93a*
$Cl_3SnIr[C_8H_{12}]_2$	1.80±0.06	1.64±0.12	0.91	$BaSnO_3$	*93a*
$Br_3SnMn(CO)_5$	1.84±0.10	1.44±0.10	0.78	SnO_2	*141*
$(Cl_3Sn)_2Ru[(CH_3)_4N]_2Cl_2$	1.93±0.06	1.64±0.12	0.85	$BaSnO_3$	*93a*
$(Cl_3Sn)_2Pt[(CH_3)_4N]_2Cl_2$	1.80±0.06	1.61±0.12	0.89	$BaSnO_3$	*93a*
$(Cl_3Sn)_2Pt[(C_2H_5)_4N]_2Cl_2$	1.56±0.06	1.61±0.12	1.03	$BaSnO_3$	*93a*
$(Cl_3Sn)_2Pt_3(C_8H_{12})_3CH_3NO_2$	1.50±0.06	1.20±0.12	0.80	$BaSnO_3$	*93a*
$(Cl_3Sn)_4Rh_2[(CH_3)_4N]Cl_2$	1.90±0.06	1.62±0.12	0.85	$BaSnO_3$	*93a*
$(Cl_3Sn)_5Pt[(C_2H_5)_4N]$	1.64±0.06	1.53±0.12	0.93	$BaSnO_3$	*93a*

TABLE 20

CARBORANE DERIVATIVES

Compound	I.S. (mm/sec)	Q.S. (mm/sec)	ρ=Q.S./I.S.	Source	References
Tripropyl(carboranyl)tin	1.45±0.07	1.65±0.08	1.14	SnO_2	*2*
Tripropyl(phenylcarbonyl)tin	1.35±0.05	1.50±0.07	1.11	SnO_2	*2*
Triphenyl(carboranyl)tin	1.05±0.05	0.95±0.05	0.91	SnO_2	*2*
Triphenyl(phenylcarboranyl)tin	1.30±0.07	1.20±0.06	0.92	SnO_2	*2*
Bis(tripropylstannyl(carborane	1.45±0.05	1.50±0.05	1.03	SnO_2	*2*
Bis(triphenylstannyl)carborane	0.95±0.05	0.70±0.04	0.74	SnO_2	*2*
Bis(phenylcarboranyl)tin dibutyl	1.20±0.06	1.70±0.08	1.42	SnO_2	*2*
$B_{10}H_{10}$ (O) C—C $(C_4H_9)_2Sn$ $Sn(C_4H_9)_2$ C—C (O) $B_{10}H_{10}$	1.20±0.03	1.60±0.04	1.33	SnO_2	*2*
Bis(phenylcarboranyl)tin dichloride	1.25±0.06	0.90±0.05	0.72	SnO_2	*2*
Bis(phenylcarboranyl)tin dibromide	0.90±0.05	0.80±0.04	0.89	SnO_2	*2*
Tris(phenylcarboranyl)tin chloride	1.20±0.05	0.4±0.04	0.34	SnO_2	*2*
Bis(phenylcarboranyl)tin	2.95	1.90	0.64	SnO_2	*2*

TABLE 21

TIN(IV) HALIDE COMPLEXES WITH ORGANIC LIGANDS

Compound	I.S. (mm/sec)	Q.S. (mm/sec)	ρ=Q.S./I.S.	Source	References
$SnF_4 \cdot B$					
2 C_2H_5OH	−0.32±0.06	0	0	—	*110*
2 Dimethoxyethane	−0.32±0.06	0	0	—	*110*
1 THF	−0.24±0.06	1.26±0.12	5.24	—	*110*
	−0.20±0.06*	1.44±0.12*	7.20	—	*110*
2 THF	−0.10±0.06	1.08±0.12	10.80	—	*110*
	−0.15±0.06	0	0	—	*110*
3 THF	−0.28±0.06	0	0	—	*110*
	−0.25±0.06*	0	0	—	*110*

(Continued)

TABLE 21 (*Continued*)

Compound	I.S. (mm/sec)	Q.S. (mm/sec)	ρ=Q.S./I.S.	Source	References
2 C_5H_5N	-0.29 ± 0.06	0	0	—	*110*
2 $(C_2H_5)_2O$	-0.38 ± 0.06	0	0	—	*110*
2 DMSO	-0.30 ± 0.06	0	0	—	*110*
$SnCl_4\cdot B$					
2 $(n\text{-}C_4H_9)_3P$	0.87 ± 0.07	1.0 ± 0.07	1.15	Pd(Sn)	*192*
2 C_4H_8S	0.81 ± 0.08	0	0	SnO_2	*106*
2 $(C_6H_5)_3P$	0.72 ± 0.05	0	0	SnO_2	*227b*
2 $(NH_2)_2C{=}S$	0.70 ± 0.07	0	0	Pd(Sn)	*106*
	0.95 ± 0.08	0	0	SnO_2	*106*
2 C_4H_8O	0.70 ± 0.08	0	0	SnO_2	*106*
	$0.43\pm5\%$	$1.14\pm5\%$	2.65	SnO_2	*133*
$CH_3S(CH_2)_2SCH_3$	0.70 ± 0.07	0	0	Pd(Sn)	*192*
$(CH_3)_2N(CH_2)_2N(CH_3)_2$	0.61 ± 0.07	0	0	Pd(Sn)	*192*
$CH_3O(CH_2)_2OCH_3$	0.51 ± 0.07	0.80 ± 0.07	1.57	Pd(Sn)	*192*
2 C_5H_5N	0.51 ± 0.07	0	0	Pd(Sn)	*192*
	0.00 ± 0.08	0	0	SnO_2	*106*
2 $H_2N(CH_2)_2NH_2$	0.50 ± 0.08	0	0	SnO_2	*106*
$(C_5H_{10}N)_3P{=}S$	0.49 ± 0.07	0	0	Pd(Sn)	*192*
$C_{10}H_8N_2$	0.47 ± 0.07	0	0	Pd(Sn)	*192*
2 $(C_2H_5)_2O$	$0.45\pm5\%$	$1.10\pm5\%$	2.45	SnO_2	*133*
	0.59 ± 0.05	1.20 ± 0.05	2.04	SnO_2	*227b*
2 $O(CH_2)_4O$	$0.45\pm5\%$	$1.10\pm5\%$	2.45	SnO_2	*133*
2 8-Hydroxyquinoline	0.45	0	0	—	*114*
2 $C_6H_4(OH)CHO\text{-}p$	$0.45\pm5\%$	0	0	SnO_2	*132a*
$(C_4H_8N)_3P{=}S$	0.43 ± 0.07	0	0	Pd(Sn)	*192*
$C_5H_5N\cdot CH_3\overset{O}{\overset{\|}{C}}OH$	0.43 ± 0.08	0	0	SnO_2	*106*
2 CH_3OH	$0.43\pm5\%$	$0.70\pm5\%$	1.63	SnO_2	*133*
2 $CH_3C{\equiv}N$	$0.43\pm5\%$	$0.70\pm5\%$	1.63	SnO_2	*133*
2 $n\text{-}C_3H_7OH$	$0.43\pm5\%$	$0.50\pm5\%$	1.16	SnO_2	*133*
2 C_6H_5CHO	$0.42\pm5\%$	$0.80\pm5\%$	1.91	SnO_2	*132a*
2 $C_6H_5CH{=}CHCHO$	$0.42\pm5\%$	$0.75\pm5\%$	1.78	SnO_2	*132a*
8-Hydroxyquinoline	0.42	0	0	—	*114*
Bipyridyl	0.42	0	0	—	*114*
	0.58	0	0	SnO_2	*227b*
$[(C_6H_5)_2\overset{C}{\overset{\|}{P}}]_2NH$	0.40	0	0	—	*114*
2 $CH_3CH(NH_2)\overset{O}{\overset{\|}{C}}OH$	0.40 ± 0.08	0	0	SnO_2	*106*
2 $C_6H_5CH{=}CH\overset{O}{\overset{\|}{C}}OH$	$0.40\pm5\%$	0.92	2.30	SnO_2	*132a*
2 $(CH_3)_2C{=}O$	$0.40\pm5\%$	Small	—	SnO_2	*133*
2 $(CH_3)_2S{=}O$	0.37 ± 0.07	0	0	Pd(Sn)	*192*
	0.44 ± 0.05	0	0	SnO_2	*227b*
2 $(C_6H_5)_3P{=}O$	0.35 ± 0.07	0.50 ± 0.07	1.43	Pd(Sn)	*192*
2 $[(CH_3)_2N]_2C{=}O$	0.35 ± 0.07	0.75 ± 0.07	2.14	Pd(Sn)	*192*
2 $(CH_2)_5C{=}O$	$0.35\pm5\%$	0	0	SnO_2	*133*
$(CH_3)_2CHOH$	$0.35\pm5\%$	$0.70\pm5\%$	2.00	SnO_2	*133*
2 $C_6H_5\overset{O}{\overset{\|}{C}}OH$	$0.35\pm5\%$	$1.16\pm5\%$	3.32	SnO_2	*132a*
2 $C_6H_5(OCH_3)CHO\text{-}p$	$0.35\pm5\%$	$0.64\pm5\%$	1.83	SnO_2	*132a*
2 *p*-Phenylenediamine	0.35	0	0	—	*114*
2 $C_6H_5(OH)CHO\text{-}o$	$0.34\pm5\%$	0.92	2.72	SnO_2	*132a*
2 C_2H_5OH	$0.33\pm5\%$	$0.70\pm5\%$	2.12	SnO_2	*133*
$OC_2H_5\cdot C_2H_5OH$	$0.33\pm5\%$	Small	—	SnO_2	*133*
2 $[(CH_3)_2N]_3P{=}O$	0.31 ± 0.07	0.70 ± 0.07	2.26	Pd(Sn)	*192*

(*Continued*)

TABLE 21 (*Continued*)

Compound	I.S. (mm/sec)	Q.S. (mm/sec)	ρ=Q.S./I.S.	Source	References
$C_5H_{11}N \cdot CH_3\overset{O}{\overset{\|}{C}}OH$	0.31 ± 0.08	0	0	SnO_2	*106*
$4\ (CH_3)_2CHOH$	$0.30 \pm 5\%$	0	0	SnO_2	*133*
$2\ C_6H_5CH{=}CHCH_2OH$	$0.27 \pm 5\%$	0	0	SnO_2	*132a*
$2\ C_6H_5CH{=}CHCOOC_2H_5$	$0.25 \pm 5\%$	1.20	4.80	SnO_2	*132a*
$3\ H_2N(CH_2)_2NH_2$	0.22 ± 0.08	0	0	SnO_2	*106*
$4\ H_2N(CH_2)_2NH_2$	0.11 ± 0.08	0	0	SnO_2	*106*
$2\ H_2N(CH_2)_4NH_2$	0.11 ± 0.08	0	0	SnO_2	*106*
$3\ H_2N(CH_2)_4NH_2$	0.11 ± 0.08	0	0	SnO_2	*106*
$2\ (CH_3)_2(CH)_2NH_2\overset{O}{\overset{\|}{C}}OH$	0.00 ± 0.08	0	0	SnO_2	*106*
$2\ C_5H_{11}N \cdot 2\ CH_3\overset{O}{\overset{\|}{C}}OH$	0.00 ± 0.08	0	0	SnO_2	*106*
2 Dimethylformamide	0.00 ± 0.06	0	0	SnO_2	*208*
$SnBr_4 \cdot B$					
$2\ C_4H_8S$	0.99 ± 0.07	0	0	Pd(Sn)	*192*
$CH_3S(CH_2)_2SCH_3$	0.97 ± 0.07	0	0	Pd(Sn)	*192*
$2\ [(CH_3)_2N]_2C{=}S$	0.94 ± 0.07	0	0	Pd(Sn)	*192*
$CH_3O(CH_2)_2OCH_3$	0.81 ± 0.07	0	0	Pd(Sn)	*192*
$2\ (H_2N)_2C{=}S$	0.80 ± 0.08	0	0	SnO_2	*106*
$2\ C_5H_5N$	0.74 ± 0.07	0	0	Pd(Sn)	*192*
$C_{10}H_8N_2$	0.73 ± 0.07	0	0	Pd(Sn)	*192*
$[(CH_3)_2N]C{=}O$	0.70 ± 0.07	0.85 ± 0.07	1.21	Pd(Sn)	*192*
$(CH_3)_2S{=}O$	0.66 ± 0.07	0	0	Pd(Sn)	*192*
Bipyridyl	0.66	0	0	—	*114*
$[(C_6H_5)_2\overset{O}{\overset{\|}{P}}]_2NH$	0.63	0	0	—	*114*
$2\ (C_6H_5)_3P{=}O$	0.63 ± 0.07	0.61 ± 0.07	0.97	Pd(Sn)	*192*
$2\ (C_6H_5)_3P$	0.63 ± 0.07	0.66 ± 0.07	1.05	Pd(Sn)	*192*
$(C_4H_8N)_3P{=}S$	0.62 ± 0.07	0	0	Pd(Sn)	*192*
$2\ [(CH_3)_2N]_3P{=}O$	0.56 ± 0.07	0.76 ± 0.07	1.36	Pd(Sn)	*192*
$2\ H_2N(CH_2)_2\overset{O}{\overset{\|}{C}}OH$	0.55 ± 0.08	0	0	SnO_2	*106*
$2\ H_2N(CH_2)_2NH_2$	0.43 ± 0.08	0	0	SnO_2	*106*
$3\ H_2N(CH_2)_2NH_2$	0.32 ± 0.08	0	0	SnO_2	*106*
$2\ H_2N(CH_2)_6NH_2$	0.22 ± 0.08	0	0	SnO_2	*106*
$4\ H_2N(CH_2)_4NH_2$	0.13 ± 0.08	0	0	SnO_2	*106*
$4\ H_2N(CH_2)_2NH_2$	0.00 ± 0.08	0	0	SnO_2	*106*
$3\ H_2N(CH_2)_6NH_2$	0.00 ± 0.08	0	0	SnO_2	*106*
$SnI_4 \cdot B$					
Bipyridyl	0.95	0	0	—	*114*
$2\ H_2N(CH_2)_2NH_2$	0.43 ± 0.08	0	0	SnO_2	*114*
$3\ H_2N(CH_2)_2NH_2$	0.12 ± 0.08	0	0	SnO_2	*114*
$4\ H_2N(CH_2)_2NH_2$	0.00 ± 0.08	0	0	SnO_2	*114*
Miscellaneous					
$SnF_2(ACAC)_2$	-0.06 ± 0.06	0	0	SnO_2	*360*
$SnCl_3(OC_2H_5) \cdot C_2H_5OH$	0.44 ± 0.05	0	0	SnO_2	*227b*
$SnCl_2$(8-hydroxyquinoline)$_2$	0.30	0	0	SnO_2	*114*
$SnCl_2(ACAC)_2$	0.25	0	0	SnO_2	*114*
	0.30 ± 0.06	0	0	SnO_2	*360*

(*Continued*)

TABLE 21 (*Continued*)

Compound	I.S. (mm/sec)	Q.S. (mm/sec)	ρ=Q.S./I.S.	Source	References
$SnCl_2[C_6H_5\overset{O}{\overset{\|}{C}}CH\overset{O}{\overset{\|}{C}}CH_3]_2$	0.18	0	0	SnO_2	*114*
$SnCl_2\{[(C_6H_5)_2\overset{O}{\overset{\|}{P}}]_2N\}_2$	0.06	0	0	SnO_2	*114*
$SnBr_2(ACAC)_2$	0.45±0.06	0	0	SnO_2	*360*
$SnBr_2\{[(C_6H_5)_2\overset{O}{\overset{\|}{P}}]_2N\}_2$	0.17	0	0	SnO_2	*114*
$SnI_2\{[(C_6H_5)_2\overset{O}{\overset{\|}{P}}]_2N\}_2$	0.40	0	0	SnO_2	*114*
$PcSnF_2$[a]	0.00±0.08	0.56±0.08	—	Pd(Sn)	*215*
$PcSnCl_2$[a]	0.30±0.08	0.99±0.08	—	Pd(Sn)	*215*
$PcSnBr_2$[a]	0.28±0.08	1.13±0.08	—	Pd(Sn)	*215*
$PcSnI_2$[a]	0.00±0.08	0.56±0.08	—	Pd(Sn)	*215*
$PcSn(OH)_2$[a]	0.06±0.08	0.47±0.08	—	Pd(Sn)	*215*

[a] Pc = phthalocyanine.

TABLE 22

ORGANOTIN(IV) HALIDE COMPLEXES

Compound	I.S. (mm/sec)	Q.S. (mm/sec)	ρ=Q.S./I.S.	Source	References
R_3SnX					
$(CH_3)_3SnCl$					
C_5H_5N	1.53±0.05	3.52±0.05	2.30	—	*127a*
	1.45±0.05	3.44±0.05	2.36	SnO_2	*74*
	1.42±0.03	3.49±0.03	2.36	SnO_2	*124, 198*
	1.33±0.09	3.44±0.09	2.58	Pd(Sn)	*216*
HMPA	1.44±0.03	3.52±0.03	2.44	—	*127a*
DMA	1.50±0.04	3.69±0.04	2.46	—	*127a*
PMPO	1.44±0.03	3.45±0.03	2.40	—	*127a*
TPPO	1.45±0.03	3.49±0.03	2.48	—	*127a*
$(CH_3)_3SnBr$					
Benzo[*h*]quinoline	1.43±0.10	2.86±0.10	2.00	SnO_2	*181*
Acridine	1.34±0.10	3.26±0.10	2.56	SnO_2	*181*
Quinoline	1.34±0.10	3.20±0.10	2.40	SnO_2	*181*
Isoquinoline	1.34±0.10	3.14±0.10	2.35	SnO_2	*181*
Benzo[*f*]quinoline	1.32±0.10	3.38±0.10	2.56	SnO_2	*181*
Phenanthridine	1.30±0.10	3.06±0.10	2.34	SnO_2	*181*
Pyridine	1.30±0.10	3.18±0.10	2.44	SnO_2	*181*
$(C_2H_5)_3SnBr$					
Pyridine	1.43±0.10	3.06±0.10	2.15	SnO_2	*181*
Benzo[*f*]quinoline	1.39±0.10	2.92±0.10	2.10	SnO_2	*181*
Isoquinoline	1.33±0.10	2.66±0.10	2.00	SnO_2	*181*
Acridine	1.30±0.10	3.00±0.10	2.30	SnO_2	*181*
Phenanthridine	1.29±0.10	2.52±0.10	1.96	SnO_2	*181*
Benzo[*h*]quinoline	1.26±0.10	2.42±0.10	1.98	SnO_2	*181*
Quinoline	1.11±0.10	2.60±0.10	2.34	SnO_2	*181*

(*Continued*)

TABLE 22 (*Continued*)

Compound	I.S. (mm/sec)	Q.S. (mm/sec)	ρ=Q.S./I.S.	Source	References
$(n\text{-}C_4H_9)_3SnCl$					
Pyridine	1.36±0.10	2.84±0.10	2.08	SnO_2	*181*
Benzo[*f*]quinoline	1.36±0.10	2.80±0.10	2.06	SnO_2	*181*
Phenanthridine	1.33±0.10	2.82±0.10	2.12	SnO_2	*181*
Benzo[*f*]quinoline	1.32±0.10	2.82±0.10	2.14	SnO_2	*181*
Acridine	1.29±0.10	2.76±0.10	2.14	SnO_2	*181*
Quinoline	1.25±0.10	2.76±0.10	2.20	SnO_2	*181*
Isoquinoline	1.21±0.10	2.82±0.10	2.34	SnO_2	*181*
R_2SnX_2					
$(CH_3)_2SnCl_2$					
2 C_5H_5N	1.37±0.05	3.83±0.05	2.80	SnO_2	*74*
2 (2-C_5H_4N)	1.45±0.05	4.02±0.05	2.78	SnO_2	*74*
2,2′-Bipyridyl	1.55	4.09	2.64	SnO_2	*314*
	1.39±0.09	4.08±0.09	2.94	Pd(Sn)	*216*
o-Phenanthroline	1.32	4.03	3.06	SnO_2	*314*
$(n\text{-}C_4H_9)_2SnCl_2$					
2,2′-Bipyridyl	1.56±0.09	3.83±0.09	2.46	Pd(Sn)	*179*
o-Phenanthroline	1.69±0.09	4.07±0.09	2.41	Pd(Sn)	*179*
$(C_6H_5)_2SnCl_2$					
2,2′-Bipyridyl	1.22±0.07	3.39±0.07	2.78	Pd(Sn)	*178*
	1.35±0.2	3.90±0.2	2.89	$BaSnO_3$	*94a*
o-Phenanthroline	1.21±0.07	3.37±0.07	2.79	Pd(Sn)	*178*
	1.28±0.2	3.70±0.2	2.89	$BaSnO_3$	*94a*
$(n\text{-}C_4H_9)_2SnBr_2$					
2,2′-Bipyridyl	1.62±0.09	3.95±0.09	2.44	Pd(Sn)	*179*
o-Phenanthroline	1.63±0.09	3.94±0.09	2.42	Pd(Sn)	*179*
$(n\text{-}C_4H_9)_2SnI_2$					
2,2′-Bipyridyl	1.70±0.09	3.82±0.09	2.24	Pd(Sn)	*179*
o-Phenanthroline	1.69±0.09	3.75±0.09	2.22	Pd(Sn)	*179*

TABLE 23

ORGANOTIN(IV) IONS

Compound	I.S. (mm/sec)	Q.S. (mm/sec)	ρ=Q.S./I.S.	Source	References
Based on $n\text{-}C_4H_9SnCl_3$					
$[n\text{-}C_4H_9SnCl_2\cdot\text{terpyridyl}]_2^+ [n\text{-}C_4H_9SnCl_5]^{2-}$	1.07±0.06	1.94±0.12	1.81	$BaSnO_3$	*76*
$[n\text{-}C_4H_9SnCl_2\cdot\text{terpyridyl}]^+ [B(C_6H_5)_4]^-$	1.09±0.06	1.76±0.12	1.61	SnO_2	*76*
$[n\text{-}C_4H_9SnCl_2\cdot\text{terpyridyl}]^+ClO_4^-$	0.92±0.06	1.74±0.12	1.89	$BaSnO_3$	*76*
$[(C_2H_5)_4N]_2^+ [n\text{-}C_4H_9SnCl_5]^{2-}$	1.07±0.06	1.86±0.12	1.74	SnO_2	*76*
Based on $C_6H_5SnCl_3$					
$[C_5H_5N]_2^+[C_6H_5SnCl_5]^{2-}$	1.10±0.2	1.92±0.2	1.75	$BaSnO_3$	*94a*
Based on $(CH_3)_2SnCl_2$					
$[(CH_3)_2SnCl\cdot\text{terpyridyl}]^+ [(CH_3)_2SnCl_3]^-$	1.38±0.06	3.31±0.12	2.40	$BaSnO_3$	*76*
$[(CH_3)_2SnCl\cdot\text{terpyridyl}]^+[B(C_6H_5)_4]^-$	1.46±0.06	3.58±0.12	2.45	SnO_2	*76*
$[(CH_3)_2SnCl\cdot\text{terpyridyl}]^+I^-$	1.38±0.06	3.56±0.12	2.58	SnO_2	*76*
$[(CH_3)_2SnCl\cdot\text{terpyridyl}]^+ClO_4$	1.38±0.06	3.50±0.12	2.54	SnO_2	*76*

(*Continued*)

TABLE 23 (*Continued*)

Compound	I.S. (mm/sec)	Q.S. (mm/sec)	ρ=Q.S./I.S.	Source	References
$[(C_2H_5)_4N]^+ [(CH_3)_2SnCl_3]^-$	1.40±0.06	3.30±0.12	2.36	SnO_2	*76*
$[(CH_3)_2Sn(H_2O)_nOH]^+$	1.37	3.90	2.85	SnO_2	*114*
$[C_5H_6N]_2{}^+ [(CH_3)_2SnCl_4]^{2-}$	1.59±0.2	4.32±0.2	2.72	$BaSnO_3$	*94, 94a*
Based on $(C_6H_5)_2SnCl_2$					
$[(C_6H_5)_2SnCl\cdot terpyridyl]^+ [(C_6H_5)_2SnCl_3]^-$	1.17±0.06	2.88±0.12	2.46	$BaSnO_3$	*76*
$[(C_6H_5)_2SnCl\cdot terpyridyl]^+ [B(C_6H_5)_4]^-$	1.20±0.06	3.24±0.12	2.70	SnO_2	*76*
$[(C_6H_5)_2SnCl\cdot terpyridyl]^+ClO_4{}^-$	1.24±0.06	3.01±0.12	2.42	SnO_2	*76*
$[(C_2H_5)_4N]^+[(C_6H_5)_2SnCl_3]^-$	1.25±0.06	2.62±0.12	2.10	SnO_2	*76*
$[C_5H_6N]_2{}^+[(C_6H_5)_2SnCl_4]^{2-}$	1.44±0.2	3.80±0.2	2.64	$BaSnO_3$	*94, 94a*
Based on $(CH_3)_3SnCl$					
$[(C_2H_5)_4N]^+[(CH_3)_3SnCl_2]^-$	1.24±0.06	3.23±0.12	2.60	SnO_2	*76*
$[(CH_3)_3Sn(H_2O)_2]^+[B(C_6H_5)_4]^-$	1.42±0.06	4.10±0.12	2.89	$BaSnO_3$	*76*
Based on $SnCl_4$					
$[SnCl_3\cdot terpyridyl]_2{}^+[SnCl_6]^{2-}$	1.62±0.06	0	0	SnO_2	*76*
$[(C_2H_5)_4N]^+[SnCl_5]^-$	0.59±0.05	0.77±0.05	1.30	Pd(Sn)	*191a*

TABLE 24

MISCELLANEOUS COMPLEXES

Compound	I.S. (mm/sec)	Q.S. (mm/sec)	ρ=Q.S./I.S.	Source	References
$(C_6H_5)_3Sn$(8-hydroxyquinoline)	1.07±0.05	1.75±0.05	1.64	$BaSnO_3$	*196b*
$(CH_3)_2Sn\{[(C_6H_5)_2P(=O)]_2N\}_2$	1.28	4.18	3.27	SnO_2	*114*
$(CH_3)_2Sn$(8-hydroxyquinoline)$_2$	0.88±0.05	1.98±0.05	2.25	$BaSnO_3$	*196b*
	0.85	1.93	2.27	SnO_2	*114*
	0.77±0.2	1.98±0.2	2.57	$BaSnO_3$	*94a*
	0.77	1.98	2.57	SnO_2	*314*
$(CH_3)_2Sn(ACAC)_2$	1.18±0.2	3.93±0.2	3.33	$BaSnO_3$	*94, 94a*
$(C_2H_5)_2Sn$(8-hydroxyquinoline)$_2$	0.99±0.05	2.02±0.05	2.04	$BaSnO_3$	*196b*
$(C_3H_7)_2Sn$(8-hydroxyquinoline)$_2$	1.02±0.2	2.20±0.2	2.16	$BaSnO_3$	*94a*
	0.98±0.05	2.08±0.05	2.12	$BaSnO_3$	*196b*
$(C_4H_9)_2Sn$(8-hydroxyquinoline)$_2$	1.10±0.2	2.21±0.2	2.01	$BaSnO_3$	*94a*
	1.02±0.05	2.04±0.05	2.00	$BaSnO_3$	*196b*
	0.93±0.07	2.05±0.07	2.21	Pd(Sn)	*178*
$(C_6H_5)_2Sn$(8-hydroxyquinoline)$_2$	0.83±0.2	1.78±0.2	2.15	$BaSnO_3$	*94, 94a*
	0.78±0.05	1.64±0.05	2.10	$BaSnO_3$	*196b*
	0.72±0.07	1.63±0.07	2.27	Pd(Sn)	*178*
	0.64	1.53		—	*314*
$(C_8H_{17})_2Sn$(8-hydroxyquinoline)$_2$	1.13±0.05	1.86±0.05	1.64	$BaSnO_3$	*196b*
$(CH_3)_2SnCl$(8-hydroxyquinoline)	1.26±0.05	3.12±0.05	2.48	$BaSnO_3$	*196b*
$(C_2H_5)_2SnCl$(8-hydroxyquinoline)	1.34±0.05	3.13±0.05	2.34	$BaSnO_3$	*196b*
$(C_2H_5)_2SnBr$(8-hydroxyquinoline)	1.39±0.05	3.08±0.05	2.22	$BaSnO_3$	*196b*
$(C_2H_5)_2SnI$(8-hydroxyquinoline)	1.43±0.05	2.85±0.05	1.99	$BaSnO_3$	*196b*
$(C_2H_5)_2SnNCS$(8-hydroxyquinoline)	1.31±0.05	3.07±0.05	2.34	$BaSnO_3$	*196b*
$(C_3H_7)_2SnCl$(8-hydroxyquinoline)	1.31±0.05	2.78±0.05	2.12	$BaSnO_3$	*196b*
$(C_4H_9)_2SnCl$(8-hydroxyquinoline)	1.40±0.05	3.21±0.05	2.28	$BaSnO_3$	*196b*
$(C_8H_{17})_2SnCl$(8-hydroxyquinoline)	1.56±0.05	3.36±0.05	2.15	$BaSnO_3$	*196b*
$(C_6H_5)_2SnCl$(8-hydroxyquinoline)	1.12±0.05	2.40±0.05	2.16	$BaSnO_3$	*196b*
	1.08±0.07	2.39±0.07	2.19	Pd(Sn)	*178*

(*Continued*)

TABLE 24 (*Continued*)

Compound	I.S. (mm/sec)	Q.S. (mm/sec)	ρ=Q.S./I.S.	Source	References
$(C_6H_5)_2Sn(ACAC)_2$	0.74±0.2	2.14±0.2	2.89	—	*94, 94a*
$C_4H_9SnCl(8\text{-hydroxyquinoline})_2$	0.84±0.05	1.67±0.05	1.99	$BaSnO_3$	*196b*
$C_6H_5SnCl(8\text{-hydroxyquinoline})_2$	0.66±0.05	1.48±0.05	2.24	$BaSnO_3$	*196b*
$C_4H_9Sn(8\text{-hydroxyquinoline})_3$	0.69±0.05	1.82±0.05	2.64	$BaSnO_3$	*196b*
$Sn[(OCH_2CH_2)_2NCH_3]_2$	0.45±0.05	0	0	SnO_2	*152e*
	0.50±0.05*	—	—	SnO_2	*152e*
$CH_3OSn(OCH_2CH_2)_3N$	0.22±0.05	0	0	SnO_2	*152e*
	0.30±0.05*	0	0	SnO_2	*152e*
$(CH_3)_2NH \cdot 2\ Sn(OCH_3)_4$	0.22±0.05	0	0	SnO_2	*152e*
	0.31±0.05*	0	0	SnO_2	*152e*
$(C_2H_3)_2NH \cdot 2\ Sn(OC_2H_5)_4$	0.18±0.05	0	0	SnO_2	*152e*
$(CH_3)_2NH \cdot 2\ Sn(OC_2H_5)_4/(C_2H_5)_3N$	0.40±0.05	0	0	SnO_2	*152e*
Bis-(1,2-ethanedithiolato)tin · dipyridine	1.16	1.84	1.58	Mg_2Sn	*91*
o-phenanthroline	1.07	1.00	0.93	Mg_2Sn	*91*
Bis-(3,4-toluenedithiolato)tin · dipyridine	1.07	1.69	1.58	Mg_2Sn	*91*
2 DMSO	1.06	1.62	1.53	Mg_2Sn	*91*
2 $(C_2H_5)_3N$	0.61	0.84	1.38	Mg_2Sn	*91*
o-phenanthroline	1.12	1.26	1.12	Mg_2Sn	*91*
2,2-bipyridyl	0.93	0.92	0.99	Mg_2Sn	*91*
3,4-Toluenedithiolatodimethyltin · dipyridine	1.37	2.28	1.74	Mg_2Sn	*91*
o-phenanthroline	1.11	2.05	1.85	Mg_2Sn	*91*
3,4-Toluenedithiolatodiphenyltin · dipyridine	1.35	1.76	1.30	Mg_2Sn	*91*
1,2-Ethanedithiolatodimethyltin · dipyridine	1.36	2.25	1.65	Mg_2Sn	*91*
1,2-Ethanedithiolatodiphenyltin · dipyridine	1.33	1.76	1.32	Mg_2Sn	*91*
o-phenanthroline	1.11	1.76	1.59	Mg_2Sn	*91*
$(C_4H_9)_2Sn(NCS)_2 \cdot 2,2'$-bipyridyl	1.43±0.07	4.04±0.07	2.82	Pd(Sn)	*178*
o-phenanthroline	1.42±0.07	4.18±0.07	2.95	Pd(Sn)	*178*
8-hydroxyquinoline	1.33±0.07	3.25±0.07	2.44	Pd(Sn)	*178*
$(C_6H_5)_2Sn(NCS)_2 \cdot 2,2'$-bipyridyl	0.82±0.07	2.13±0.07	2.60	Pd(Sn)	*178*
o-phenanthroline	0.81±0.07	2.34±0.07	2.89	Pd(Sn)	*178*
8-hydroxyquinoline	0.98±0.07	2.48±0.07	2.53	Pd(Sn)	*178*

TABLE 25

DIVALENT COMPOUNDS

Compound	I.S. (mm/sec)	Q.S. (mm/sec)	ρ=Q.S./I.S.	Source	References
$(C_5H_5)_2Sn$	3.73±0.06	0.65±0.06	0.17	$BaSnO_3$	*117d*
Bis(phenylcarboranyl)tin	2.95	1.90	0.64	SnO_2	*2*
Tin(II) oxalate	3.90±0.10	1.4±0.10	0.36	SnO_2	*72*
	3.59±0.02	1.52±0.02	0.42	Mg_2Sn	*160*
	3.29±0.09	1.36±0.09	0.41	Mg_2Sn	*228*
	3.16±0.06	1.48±0.12	0.47	$BaSnO_3$	*359*
Tin(II) phthalate	3.00±0.10	1.35±0.12	0.45	$BaSnO_3$	*365*
$Sn(C_2H_3O_2)_2$	3.35±0.04	1.67±0.04	0.50	Mg_2Sn	*160*

TABLE 25 *(Continued)*

Compound	I.S. (mm/sec)	Q.S. (mm/sec)	ρ=Q.S./I.S.	Source	References
$SnC_4H_4O_6$	3.11±0.02	1.94±0.02	0.62	Mg_2Sn	*160*
$(C_6H_5O)_2Sn$	2.68±0.06	2.19±0.06	0.82	SnO_2	*365*
PcSn	2.88±0.08	1.44±0.08	0.50	Pd(Sn)	*215*
o-Phenylenedioxytin(II)	2.95±0.06	1.76±0.06	0.60	SnO_2	*24*
	2.95±0.06*	1.53±0.06*	0.52*	SnO_2	*24*
2,3-Toluenedioxytin(II)	3.09±0.06	1.89±0.06	0.61	SnO_2	*24*
2,3-Naphthylenedioxytin(II)	3.08±0.06	1.82±0.06	0.5	SnO_2	*24*
2,2′-Biphenylenedioxytin(II)	3.13±0.06	1.98±0.06	0.63	SnO_2	*24*
2,2′-Biphenylenedicarbamatotin(II)	3.46±0.06	1.56±0.06	0.45	$BaSnO_3$	*117c*
$Sn(SC_6H_5)_2$	2.79±0.06	1.43±0.06	0.51	SnO_2	*365*
$Sn(O\overset{\overset{O}{\Vert}}{C}H)_2$	3.15±0.05	1.56±0.05	0.50	SnO_2	*81*
$Sn(O\overset{\overset{O}{\Vert}}{C}CH_3)_2$	3.31±0.05	1.77±0.05	0.54	SnO_2	*81*
$Sn(O\overset{\overset{O}{\Vert}}{C}C_2H_5)_2$	3.31±0.05	1.89±0.05	0.57	SnO_2	*81*
$Sn(O\overset{\overset{O}{\Vert}}{C}_{11}C_3H_7)$	3.30±0.05*	1.86±0.05*	0.56*	SnO_2	*81*
$Sn[(\overset{\overset{O}{\Vert}}{C}CH(CH_3)_2]_2$	3.33±0.05*	1.84±0.05*	0.55*	SnO_2	*81*
$Sn[O\overset{\overset{O}{\Vert}}{C}C(CH_3)_3]_2$	3.35±0.05*	1.88±0.05*	0.56*	SnO_2	*81*
$Sn[O\overset{\overset{O}{\Vert}}{C}C(C_2H_5)_3]_2$	3.34±0.05*	1.86±0.05*	0.56*	SnO_2	*81*
$Sn(O\overset{\overset{O}{\Vert}}{C}CH_2Cl)_2$	3.20±0.05	1.66±0.05	0.52	SnO_2	*81*
	3.23±0.05*	1.69±0.05*	0.52*	SnO_2	*81*
$Sn(O\overset{\overset{O}{\Vert}}{C}CCl_3)_2$	3.48±0.05	1.64±0.05	0.47	SnO_2	*81*
	3.43±0.05*	1.63±0.05*	0.48*	SnO_2	*81*
$Sn(O\overset{\overset{O}{\Vert}}{C}CCl_3)_2$	3.29±0.05*	1.78±0.05*	0.54*	SnO_2	*81*
$Sn(O\overset{\overset{O}{\Vert}}{C}CH_2F)_2$	3.10±0.05	1.76±0.05	0.57	SnO_2	*81*
	3.17±0.05*	1.85±0.05*	0.58*	SnO_2	*81*
$Sn(O\overset{\overset{O}{\Vert}}{C}CHF_2)_2$	3.25±0.05	1.75±0.05	0.54	SnO_2	*81*
	3.19±0.05*	1.78±0.05*	0.56*	SnO_2	*81*
$Sn(O\overset{\overset{O}{\Vert}}{C}CF_3)_2$	3.16±0.05*	1.76±0.05*	0.56*	SnO_2	*81*
$Sn(O\overset{\overset{O}{\Vert}}{C}CHClCH_3)_2$	3.22±0.05*	1.70±0.05*	0.54*	SnO_2	*81*
$Sn(O\overset{\overset{O}{\Vert}}{C}CH_2CH_2Cl)_2$	3.27±0.05*	1.83±0.05*	0.56*	SnO_2	*81*

TABLE 26

DIVALENT COMPLEXES

Compound	I.S. (mm/sec)	Q.S. (mm/sec)	ρ=Q.S./I.S.	Source	References
$SnCl_2 \cdot B$					
Bipyridyl	3.47	1.05	0.30	Pd(Sn)	*87b, 301*
	3.33±0.06	0.64±0.12	0.19	SnO_2	*360*
o-Phenanthroline	3.55	1.03	0.29	Pd(Sn)	*87b, 301*
2 *p*-Toluidine	3.41	1.22	0.36	Pd(Sn)	*87b, 301*
Terpyridyl	3.11	1.12	0.36	Pd(Sn)	*87b 301*
PMAQ	3.27	1.10	0.34	Pd(Sn)	*87b, 301*
8-Aminoquinoline	3.39	1.30	0.38	Pd(Sn)	*87b, 301*
DPSO	3.07±0.06	1.36±0.12	0.44	SnO_2	*360*
DMSO	3.06±0.06	1.32±0.12	0.43	SnO_2	*360*
$SnBr_2 \cdot B$					
o-Phenanthroline	3.55	0.83	0.23	Pd(Sn)	*87b, 301*
2 *p*-Toluidine	3.49	0.94	0.27	Pd(Sn)	*87b, 301*
SnCl·B					
Oxine	3.04	1.70	0.56	Pd(Sn)	*87b, 301*
Sn·2 B					
Sal_2phen	2.99	1.34	0.45	Pd(Sn)	*87b*
2 Anthranilate	3.14	1.77	0.56	Pd(Sn)	*87b*
2 Picolinate	3.04	1.81	0.60	Pd(Sn)	*87b*
2 Oxine	2.84	1.70	0.60	Pd(Sn)	*87b, 301*
2 Quinoldate	2.98	1.78	0.60	Pd(Sn)	*87b*
Dipicolinate	3.15	1.63	0.52	Pd(Sn)	*87b*
Salts of $HSnCl_3$					
$C_6H_5N(C_2H_5)_2H^+$	3.55±0.05	0.60±0.05	0.17	SnO_2	*129*
$(C_2H_5)_3NH^+$	3.53±0.05	1.05±0.05	0.30	SnO_2	*129*
$C_2H_5NH_3^+$	3.25±0.05	0	0	SnO_2	*129*
$C_5H_5NH_3^+$	3.23±0.05	1.05±0.05	0.33	SnO_2	*129*
$(C_2H_5)_2NH_2^+$	2.95±0.05	0.90±0.05	0.31	SnO_2	*129*
$(CH_3)_2NH_2^+$	2.95±0.05	0.95±0.05	0.32	SnO_2	*129*
$C_5H_5NH^+$	2.95±0.05	0.50±0.05	0.17	SnO_2	*129*
$H_2N(CH_2)_2NH_3^+$	2.85±0.05	0.55±0.05	0.19	SnO_2	*129*
Miscellaneous					
$Sn_2(EDTA) \cdot H_2O$	3.38	1.57	0.46	Pd(Sn)	*87b*
$Na_2Sn(EDTA) \cdot 2\ H_2O$	3.57	1.25	0.35	Pd(Sn)	*87b*
Sn_2ETTA	3.26	1.83	0.56	Pd(Sn)	*87b*

Organic Complexes of Lower-Valent Titanium

R. S. P. COUTTS and P. C. WAILES

Division of Applied Chemistry, C.S.I.R.O.
Melbourne, Australia

I

INTRODUCTION

Early interest in the organic chemistry of titanium was centered mainly on the alkoxides, or titanates, primarily because of their ease of preparation from titanium tetrachloride and alcohols, and also because these derivatives have found use in heat-resistant paints and in the treatment of textiles, wood, and paper.

In more recent years the expansion in the volume of research on organic titanium derivatives corresponds with the increase in research in metal-organic chemistry in general. There seems little doubt, however, that present interest in derivatives of lower-valent titanium is due in no small measure to the ability of this element, generally complexed with another metal, to bring about the polymerization of olefins as well as the formation of complexes of dinitrogen, and its subsequent reduction to ammonia. This interest is expected to continue as the approach to such catalysts becomes less empirical and knowledge of their structures becomes more important.

Titanium is in Group IV of the Periodic Table and is the first of the transition elements. In line with its outer electronic configuration of $3d^2 4s^2$, its maximum and also its most stable valence is 4, but it is the lower oxidation states, namely, 3 and to a lesser extent 2 and below, with which we shall be concerned in this review.

With few exceptions the organic complexes of lower-valent titanium are extremely sensitive to oxygen. In many cases oxidation is so rapid that the compounds are pyrophoric in air. The efficient use of vacuum line and glove-box techniques then becomes extremely important. In addition, the reactivity towards nitrogen of many compounds of titanium in a highly reduced form means that argon remains the only readily available blanketing gas.

The isolation of titanium metal and the preparation of its halides, from which most of its organic derivatives are prepared, have been well documented by Brauer (*12*). Titanium is the ninth most abundant element on earth and is the most persistent constituent of all rocks and sediments. It occupies a larger proportion of the known terrestrial matter than zinc, copper, and lead combined and is five to ten times more abundant than sulfur or phosphorus. With difficulties in the refinement of the metal largely overcome, the future for titanium and its derivatives seems assured.

In the review which follows, the term "organic complexes of titanium" is taken to include not only true organotitanium compounds with carbon-to-titanium bonds, but also compounds containing organic groups bonded to titanium by almost any other element.

In the tables accompanying each chapter the room temperature magnetic moment for each complex is listed. Those cases for which moments at more than one temperature have been measured are indicated by superscript ^{T}. Electronic transition bands due to *d–d* transitions are also listed, but in any titanium complex containing different ligands the distortions are so great and the symmetry is so low that any conclusions based on spectral data must be tentative. For a theoretical treatment of the spectra and magnetics of titanium compounds the reader is referred to Clark (*23*) and references therein.

II

ADDITION COMPLEXES OF TITANIUM TRIHALIDES

A. Preparation

The simplest organic derivatives of lower-valent titanium are addition compounds of the di- and trihalides. All of the lower-valent halides are polymeric with bridging halogens but these bridges are broken by polar solvents and other donor ligands to give a great variety of addition compounds of ever-increasing number.

When the ligand is a liquid the complexes may be prepared directly from the reactants by dissolving the halide in the ligand. In many cases the conditions under which this is carried out determine the number of ligands which coordinate to each titanium atom. Compare, for example, the dioxane complexes, in which either one, two, or three dioxane molecules are attached to titanium trichloride according to the reaction conditions (*65*). Displacement of one coordinated ligand by another is also a useful method of preparation, employed successfully by Fowles and co-workers, who found that trimethylamine could be displaced from $TiX_3 \cdot 2\,N(CH_3)_3$ by a variety of ligands including pyridine, bipyridyl, dioxane, and others, to give complexes of the type $TiX_3 \cdot 3L$ or $TiX_3 \cdot 2\,L$ (*73*).

In Table I known complexes are listed according to donor atom. Most are complexes containing ligands coordinated through oxygen or nitrogen, but

TABLE I

ADDITION COMPLEXES OF TITANIUM TRIHALIDES[a,b]

Compound	Probable structure	Color	Visible spectra (kK) Solid	Solution (ε)	μ_{eff} (BM, 20° C)	References
	O-Coordinated					
Ethers						
$TiCl_3 \cdot 3$ THF	Octahedral	Sky blue	14.7	—	1.72	*21, 24, 99, 106, 159, 160*
$TiBr_3 \cdot 3$ THF	Octahedral	Green	12.4 14.0	13.25 (4)	1.75	*63*
$TiI_3 \cdot 3$ THF	Octahedral	Red-brown	10.9 14.2	10.8 14.1	1.64	*69*
$TiCl_3 \cdot 2$ THF	—	Green	—	—	—	*145*
$2\ TiCl_3 \cdot 3\ (CH_2OCH_3)_2$	ψ-Oct., bridging ether or $[TiCl_2 \cdot 2\ (CH_2OCH_3)_2][TiCl_4(CH_2OCH_3)_2]$	Blue	12.4 13.8	— —	1.74^T	*49, 65, 115*
$2\ TiBr_3 \cdot 3\ (CH_2OCH_3)_2$	Oct., as for chloride	Green	13.0	14.2 (12)	1.67	*49, 63*
$TiI_3 \cdot 2\ (CH_2OCH_3)_2$	$[TiI_2 \cdot 2\ (CH_2OCH_3)_2]^+I^-$	Yellow	11.25 14.7	—	1.73	*69*
$TiCl_3 \cdot 3$(O◯O) (dioxane)	Oct., only one O coord.	Blue-green	13.4 15.2	—	1.69	*65*
$TiCl_3 \cdot 2$(O◯O) (dioxane)	ψ-Oct., dimer, Cl bridge	Blue-green	12.5 14.8	—	1.72	*24, 49, 65, 160*
$TiCl_3 \cdot$ O◯O (dioxane)	Oct., polymer, Cl and diox. bridge, both O's coord.	Blue-green	13.5	—	1.77^T	*65, 115*
$TiBr_3 \cdot 3$(O◯O) (dioxane)	Oct., one O coord.	Green	12.5 14.1	13.6	1.75	*63, 72*
$TiI_3 \cdot 3$(O◯O) (dioxane)	Oct., only one O coord.	Red-brown	11.4 14.1	14.4 (15)	1.64	*69*
$TiCl_3 \cdot 2$(O◯S) (oxathiane)	—	Green	—	15.0	1.58	*4, 72*
$TiCl_3 \cdot$ O◯S (oxathiane)	Likely to involve S	Brown	13.5	—	1.71	*49, 65, 72, 115*

$TiBr_3 \cdot 2$(O S)	—	Yellow-brown	—	14.2	1.60	*4, 72*
$TiCl_3 \cdot 2$(O NCH_3)	Coord. through O	Green	—	15.0	1.62	*72*
$TiBr_3 \cdot 3$(O NCH_3)	As for chloride	Yellow-brown	—	14.25	1.49	*72*
$H[TiCl_4 \cdot O(C_2H_5)_2]$	—	Yellow-brown	16.6	—	0.78^T	*78*
Ketones						
$TiCl_3 \cdot 3\ OC(CH_3)_2$	Oct.	Brown	—	15.4 (37)	1.61	*24, 65*
$TiCl_3 \cdot 2\ OC(C_2H_5)_2$	Oct., probably Cl bridge	Green	—	15.6 (140)	1.61	*65*
$TiCl_3 \cdot 2\ OCPh_2$	Oct., probably Cl bridge	Steel blue	15.6	—	—	*65*
Alcohols						
$TiCl_3 \cdot 3\ CH_3OH$	Oct.	Pale blue	13.8 16.9	13.4 15.1	1.79^T	*78*
$TiCl_3 \cdot 4\ CH_3OH$	$[TiCl_2(CH_3OH)_4]Cl$, probably *cis*	Blue	15.4 18.2	—	1.79^T	*77*
$TiCl_3 \cdot 4$ (iso-C_3H_7OH)	$[TiCl_2(ROH)_4]Cl$	Blue	—	16.7 (9)	1.74^T	*159, 160*
$TiCl_3 \cdot 4$ (sec-C_4H_9OH)	$[TiCl_2(ROH)_4]Cl$	Blue	—	16.1 (9)	1.77^T	*159, 160*
$TiCl_3 \cdot 4$ (cyclo-$C_6H_{11}OH$)	$[TiCl_2(ROH)_4]Cl$	Blue	—	16.1 (8)	1.81^T	*159, 160*
$TiBr_3 \cdot 4$ (iso-C_3H_7OH)	$[TiBr_2(C_3H_7OH)_4]Br$	Green	—	—	1.75^T	*159, 160*
$TiCl_3 \cdot 5\ CH_3OH$	$[TiCl(CH_3OH)_5]Cl_2$	Pale blue	15.2 18.6	15.1 16.8 (5)	1.79^T	*77*
$(C_5H_6N)_2[TiCl_5(CH_3OH)_2]$	Unknown	Green	12.9 15.6	14.0 14.8	1.76^T	*77*
$C_5H_6N \cdot [TiCl_4(CH_3OH)_2]$	Oct., probably *cis*	Turquoise	12.9 15.7	12.7 14.6	1.79^T	*78*
$(C_5H_6N)_2[TiCl_5 \cdot CH_3OH]$	Oct.	Yellow	11.4 13.6	—	1.79^T	*78*
$TiCl_3 \cdot 6\ (CH_3OH)$	$[Ti(CH_3OH)_6]Cl_3$, oct.	Blue	—	15.1 16.8	—	*78, 80*
$TiCl_3 \cdot 6\ (C_2H_5OH)$	$[Ti(C_2H_5OH)_6]Cl_3$, oct.	Blue	—	—	—	*80*
$TiCl_3 \cdot 6$ (iso-C_3H_7OH)	$[Ti(C_3H_7OH)_6]Cl_3$, oct.	Blue	—	—	—	*80*
Acids, amides, etc.						
$CsTiCl_5 \cdot CH_3CO_2H$	Oct.	Green	—	—	1.84^T	*116*
$TiCl_3 \cdot 2$ (OC NH_2 N)	Bonded through amide and ring N	Red-brown	—	—	2.08^T	*116*

(*Continued*)

TABLE I (*Continued*)

Compound	Probable structure	Color	Visible spectra (kK)		μ_{eff} (BM, 20° C)	References
			Solid	Solution (ϵ)		
$TiI_3 \cdot 6$ urea	$(Ti[OC(NH_2)_2]_6)I_3$, oct.	Blue	16.4 18.2	—	1.69^T	*81, 112, 115, 160*
$TiI_3 \cdot 6$ acetamide	$(Ti[NH_2COCH_3]_6)I_3$, oct.	Blue	—	—	—	*81*
$TiCl_3 \cdot 3$ DMF	Oct.	Blue	—	—	} 1.63–1.65	*47*
$TiCl_3 \cdot 3$ MF	Oct.	Blue	—	—		
$TiCl_3 \cdot 3$ F	Oct.	Blue	—	—		
$\left[Ti\left(OC\begin{smallmatrix}NH-CH_2\\NH-CH_2\end{smallmatrix}\right)_6\right]Cl_3 \cdot 2C_2H_5OH$	Oct.	Blue	15.6 17.0	—	1.79	*10*
$\left[Ti\left(OC\begin{smallmatrix}NH-CH_2\\NH-CH_2\end{smallmatrix}\right)_6\right]I_3$	Oct.	Blue	15.4 17.0	—	1.81	*10*
$\left[Ti\left(OC\begin{smallmatrix}N(C_6H_5)-NCH_3\\CH=CCH_3\end{smallmatrix}\right)_6\right]Br_3 \cdot 2C_2H_5OH$	Oct.	Green	15.0 16.5	—	1.88	*10*
$\left[Ti\left(OC\begin{smallmatrix}N(C_6H_5)-NCH_3\\CH=CCH_3\end{smallmatrix}\right)_6\right]I_3$	Oct.	Green	15.4 17.0	—	1.81	*10*
N-Coordinated						
Nitriles						
$TiCl_3 \cdot 3\ CH_3CN$	ψ-Oct., monomeric	Light blue	—	14.7 (15) 17.2 (31)	1.71^T	*22, 25, 53, 65, 107, 116*

$TiCl_3 \cdot 3\ C_2H_5CN$	ψ-Oct., monomeric	Blue	—	14.7 17.2	1.53	*53, 65*
$TiCl_3 \cdot 3\ C_3H_7CN$	ψ-Oct., monomeric	Blue	—	14.7 17.2	1.61	*53, 107*
$(C_2H_5)_4N[TiCl_4 \cdot 2\ CH_3CN)$	Oct., not known if *cis* or *trans*	Green	14.3 15.0	—	1.76^T	*115, 152*
$TiBr_3 \cdot 3\ CH_3CN$	ψ-Oct.	Green	—	16.3 (500)	1.51	*53, 72*
$(C_2H_5)_4N[TiBr_4 \cdot 2\ CH_3CN]$	Oct.	—	12.7 14.8	—	—	*152*
$(C_5H_6N)_2[TiCl_5 \cdot CH_3CN]$	Oct.	Yellow-green	—	13.6 15.2	1.76^T	*77, 78*
$TiI_3 \cdot 4\ CH_3CN$	$[TiI_2 \cdot (CH_3CN)_4]I$, Oct.	Red-brown	16.0	15.9	1.62	*69*
$Ti(CH_3CN)_6I_9$	$[Ti(CH_3CN)_6][I_3]_3$, oct.	Black	—	—	1.80	*82*
Pyridine, bipyridyl, etc.						
$TiCl_3 \cdot 3\ py$	Oct.	Green	16.5	—	1.63	*64, 125, 167*
$TiCl_3\ 2\ py \cdot CH_3CO_2C_2H_5$	—	Light brown	—	—	—	*144*
$TiCl_3 \cdot py$	—	Gray	—	—	—	*75*
$TiBr_3 \cdot 3\ py$	ψ-Oct., monomeric	Green	14.5 16.0	14.5 16.5	1.71	*64, 73*
$TiI_3 \cdot 3\ py$	Oct.	Tan	11.9 14.8	11.8 14.2	1.69	*69*
$TiCl_3 \cdot 2\ \alpha\text{-pic}$	*trans*-Trigonal bipyramidal	Green-blue	7.3 16.4	7.5 15.9	1.62	*49, 64*
$TiBr_3 \cdot 2\ \alpha\text{-pic}$	As for chloride above	Green	6.5 15.8	—	1.69	*49, 73*
$TiI_3 \cdot 2\ \alpha\text{-pic}$	As for chloride above	Tan	5.7	—	1.65	*49, 69*
$TiCl_3 \cdot 3\ \gamma\text{-pic}$	ψ-Oct., monomer	Green	14.7 16.8	14.8 16.7	1.75^T	*64, 115*
$TiBr_3 \cdot 3\ \gamma\text{-pic}$	ψ-Oct., monomer	Green	16.0	15.8 (58)	1.70	*73*
$TiI_3 \cdot 3\ \gamma\text{-pic}$	ψ-Oct.	Tan	12.9 20.9	15.0 (250) 20.0	1.89	*69*
$TiCl_3 \cdot 2\ bipy$	$[TiCl_2(bipy)_2]Cl$	Colorless	—	—	—	*163*
$TiBr_3 \cdot 2\ bipy$	$[TiBr_2(bipy)_2]Br$	Purple	16.0 19.3	15.9 19.1	—	*68*
$2\ TiCl_3 \cdot 3\ bipy$	$[TiCl_2(bipy)_2]^+[TiCl_4(bipy)]^-$	Dark blue	} 13.5 15.8	17.8	1.68	*68*
$2\ TiBr_3 \cdot 3\ bipy$	As for chloride	—	15.9 18.7	15.4 18.5	1.72	*68, 73*
$2\ TiI_3 \cdot 3\ bipy$	As for chloride	Brown	10.8 15.5 20.0	18.9	1.39	*69*
$TiBr_3 \cdot 2\ bipy \cdot CH_3CN$	$[TiBr_2(bipy)_2]^+Br^-$, CH_3CN; CH_3CN not coord.	Purple	16.4 19.1	15.2 15.9 19.1	2.06	*68*
$TiBr_3 \cdot 2\ bipy \cdot CHCl_3$	$[TiBr_2(bipy)_2]^+Br^-$, $CHCl_3$	Purple	16.3 18.9	15.2 15.9 19.1	1.85	*68*

(*Continued*)

TABLE I (*Continued*)

Compound	Probable structure	Color	Visible spectra (kK) Solid	Solution (ϵ)	μ_{eff} (BM, 20° C)	References
$TiCl_3 \cdot$bipy	ψ-Oct., dimer, Cl bridge	Dark blue	13.5 15.8	—	1.72	*66*
$TiBr_3 \cdot$bipy	ψ-Oct., dimer, Br bridge	Purple	12.9 15.9 18.7	15.2 18.0	1.88	*68*
$TiCl_3 \cdot$bipy$\cdot CH_3CN$	Oct.	Purple-violet	—	15.2 17.4	1.74	*66*
$TiCl_3 \cdot$bipy$\cdot C_2H_5CN$	Oct.	Violet	17.0	14.9 17.2	1.67	*66*
$TiCl_3 \cdot 2$ phen	—	Yellow	—	—	0.37 ?	*108*
$TiI_3 \cdot 2$ phen	$[TiI_2(phen)_2]I$	Brown	14.3 19.6	18.7	1.39	*69*
$TiCl_3 \cdot 2\ N(CH_3)_3$	*trans*-Trigonal bipyramidal	Blue	6.1 15.1	6.6 (88) 15.1 (17)	1.73	*3, 49, 64, 153*
$TiBr_3 \cdot 2\ N(CH_3)_3$	*trans*-Trigonal bipyramidal	Green	5.1 14.1	—	1.71^T	*49, 64, 115, 153*
$TiI_3 \cdot 2\ N(CH_3)_3$	*trans*-Trigonal bipyramidal	Red-brown	13.4 19.0	13.0	—	*69*
$TiCl_3 \cdot$terpy	Oct., monomer	Dark green	—	—	—	*19, 47*
$TiCl_3 \cdot 2$ piperidine $CH_3CO_2C_2H_5$	—	Light brown	—	—	—	*144*
Amines						
$TiCl_3 \cdot 4$ en	Oct., bridging en	Pale blue	13.9	—	1.66^T	*54, 115*
$TiBr_3 \cdot 4$ en	Oct., bridging en	Pale blue	14.1	—	1.58^T	*54, 115*
$TiCl_3 \cdot 3$ en	$[Ti(en)_3]^{3+}3\ Cl^-$	Blue	13.5	—	1.67^T	*24, 116*
$TiCl_3 \cdot 3$ pen	$[Ti(pen)_3]^{3+}3\ Cl^-$	Blue	14.0	—	1.66	*24*
$TiCl_3 \cdot 2$ dien	$[Ti(dien)_2]^{3+}3\ Cl^-$	Blue	—	—	1.42^T	*116*
$TiCl_3 \cdot 3$ (NH O) [morpholine ring]	*N*-Coordinated	Blue	13.3 15.4	—	1.60	*65*

$TiCl_3 \cdot 2\,L \cdot CH_3CO_2C_2H_5$						
L = *o*-, *m*-, and *p*-aminophenol,	—	Brown	—	—	—	*144*
o-, *m*-, and *p*-aminobenzoic acid,		Brown	—	—	—	*144*
o-, *m*-, and *p*-nitroaniline,		Yellow to brown	—	—	—	*144*
p-aminoacetanilide		Yellow	—	—	—	*144*
		S-Coordinated				
$TiCl_3 \cdot 2\,S(CH_3)_2$	Polymeric, bridging mechanism unknown	Brown	12.1 17.3	12.1 15.6 (25)	1.03^T	*70*
$TiBr_3 \cdot 2\,S(CH_3)_2$	Polymeric, bridging mechanism unknown	Brown	12.5	11.8 14.3 (12)	1.67	*70*
$TiI_3 \cdot 2\,S(CH_3)_2$	Polymeric, bridging mechanism unknown	Black	—	—	1.67	*70*
$TiCl_3 \cdot 2$ S	Polymeric, bridging mechanism unknown	Gray	12.2 17.3	11.8 15.3	1.12^T	*70*
$TiBr_3 \cdot 2$ S	Polymeric, bridging mechanism unknown	Brown	12.9	11.9 13.8 (13)	1.72	*70*
$TiI_3 \cdot 2$ S	Polymeric, bridging mechanism unknown	Brown	10.8	10.8 12.6 (13)	—	*70*
		P-Coordinated				
$TiCl_3(C_2H_4[P(C_2H_5)_2]_2)$	—	Dark brown	—	—	—	*21*
		As-Coordinated				
$TiCl_3 \cdot H_2O \cdot D$	Oct., monomeric	Red	—	—	0.91	*166*
$TiBr_3 \cdot H_2O \cdot D$	Oct., monomeric	Red	—	—	0.88	*166*

[a] bipy = 1,1′-bipyridyl; D = *o*-phenylenebis(dimethylarsine); dien = diethylenetriamine; DMF = dimethylformamide; en = ethylenediamine; F = formamide; MF = methylformamide; pen = propylenediamine; phen = 1,10-phenanthroline; α- and γ-pic = α- and γ-picoline; py = pyridine; terpy = 1,1′,1″-terpyridyl; THF = tetrahydrofuran.

[b] *T* indicates cases for which moments have been measured at more than one temperature.

TABLE II

COMPLEXES OF TYPE $TiX_n \cdot (3-n)L$[a]

Compound	Probable structure	Color	Visible spectra (kK) Solid	Visible spectra (kK) Solution (ε)	μ_{eff} (BM, 20° C)	References
Alkoxides						
$Ti(OCH_3)_3$	Polymeric, O bridge, oct.	Yellow-green	10.0	—	Diamag.	*1, 2, 77*
$Ti(OC_2H_5)_3$	Polymeric	Blue	—	—	—	*2, 114*
$Ti(OC_3H_7\text{-}n)_3$	Polymeric	Pink-lilac	—	—	—	*137*
$Ti(OC_4H_9\text{-}n)_3$	Polymeric	Pink-lilac	—	—	—	*137*
$TiCl_2(OCH_3) \cdot 2\,CH_3OH$	Trinuclear cluster, OCH_3 bridges	Red	10.0	—	1.0^T	*189*
$TiCl(OCH_3)_2 \cdot CH_3OH$	Trinuclear	Dark brown	10.0	—	—	*189*
Carboxylates and Phosphate						
$Ti_2(C_2O_4)_3 \cdot 10\,H_2O$	Pentagonal bipyramid, 7 coord. Ti	Yellow-brown	9.4 12.3	—	1.65^T	*52, 56, 160, 165*
$NH_4[Ti(C_2O_4)_2 \cdot 2\,H_2O]$ also K, Rb	Oct., bridging oxalate	Orange	12.8	—	1.76^T	*56, 154, 160*
$Ti(OCOCH_3)Cl_2$	Oct., bridging acetate	Dark brown	—	13.0 18.4 (for these three compounds)	2.38^T	*116*
$Ti(OCOCH_3)Cl_2 \cdot CH_3CO_2H$	Oct.	—	—		1.70^T	*116*
$Ti(OCOCH_3)_2Cl$	Oct., 2 acetate bridges	Yellow-brown	—		1.61^T	*116*
$MTi(EDTA) \cdot n\,H_2O$ M = H, Li, Na, K, Rb, Cs, NH_4, Ba/2	Oct.	Blue to purple	—	12.8 18.0	1.63– 1.82	*143*
$Ti[O_2P(OCH_3)_2]_3$	Oct.	Pink	20.0	—	—	*79*
β-Diketonates						
$Ti(acac)_3$	Monomeric, strongly distorted oct.	Blue	—	15.2 (870) 16.5 (1120) 17.9 (930)	1.68^T	*2, 5, 20, 48, 58, 142, 156*
$Ti(F_6\text{-}acac)_3$	Monomeric, distort. oct.	Blue	—	—	—	*74*
$Ti(benzoylac)_3$	Monomeric, distort, oct.	Green	—	12.8 (800) 14.1 (880) 15.9 (670)	1.67^T	*48, 58*

Ti(3-CNacac)$_3$	Monomeric, distort. oct.	Purple	—	16.1 (810) 17.3 (1000) 18.5 (910)	—	*48*
Ti(dibenzoylCH$_2$)$_3$	Monomeric, distort. oct.	Green	—	—	1.66	*48*
Ti(F$_3$thenoylac)$_3$	Monomeric, distort. oct.	Green	—	12.1 (2600) 13.5 (2380) 15.3 (1320)	1.66	*48*
Ti(acac)$_2$Cl	Dimeric, bridging Cl	Red-violet	16.6 18.5	17.4 (430) 18.8 (417)	1.39^T	*141, 156*
Ti(acac)Cl$_2$	Insol., probably polymeric	Red	16.9 17.6	18.7 (519)	1.70^T	*156*
Amido Complexes						
Ti[N(CH$_3$)$_2$]$_3$	$[(CH_3)_2N]_2Ti\langle N(CH_3)_2 \rangle_2 Ti[N(CH_3)_2]_2$ (Ti—Ti bridged by two N(CH$_3$)$_2$ groups)	Red-brown oil	—	—	Diamag.	*2*
Ti[N(C$_2$H$_5$)$_2$]$_3$	As for CH$_3$ above?	—	—	—	—	*2*
Ti[N(CH$_3$)$_2$]$_3$·O(C$_2$H$_5$)$_2$	—	Red-brown oil	—	—	Diamag.	*2*
Ti[N(CH$_3$)$_2$]$_2$·N(C$_2$H$_5$)$_2$	—	—	—	—	—	*2*
Ti[N(CH$_3$)$_2$]$_2$·N(iso-C$_3$H$_7$)$_2$	—	—	—	—	—	*2*
Ti[N(CH$_3$)$_2$]$_2$·N[Si(CH$_3$)$_3$]$_2$	—	—	—	—	—	*2*
Borohydride						
Ti(BH$_4$)$_3$	—	Green	—	—	—	*96*

[a] T indicates cases for which moments have been measured at more than one temperature.

sulfur-, phosphorus-, and arsenic-bonded compounds are included. Space does not permit a detailed discussion of each type, but despite their great variety it would appear that the titanium(III) ion is mostly hexacoordinate. For this reason, the most common complex is of stoichiometry $TiX_3 \cdot 3\ L$.

When the number of coordinating ligands is other than 3, hexacoordination of titanium is achieved by bridging through halogen or through bidentate ligands, or by forming ionic species. Examples of all of these types are shown in Table I.

Notable exceptions to the pseudo-octahedral symmetry of most of these compounds are those of type $TiX_3 \cdot 2\ L$, where X = Cl, Br, or I and L = $N(CH_3)_3$ or α-picoline. Although originally thought to be octahedral (*64*), these have recently been assigned a five-coordinate, trans trigonal bipyramidal structure on the basis of X-ray crystallographic data from the bromide complex (*153*). Bands in the near-infrared around 4.5–7.0 kK are believed to be characteristic of this configuration (*49*).

In addition to the compounds formed with amines, nitriles, and ethers, two series of alcohol complexes are known. From $TiCl_3$ or $TiBr_3$ and isopropanol, *sec*-butanol or cyclohexanol, complexes of formula $TiX_3 \cdot 4\ ROH$ have been isolated (*159*). These are probably ionic with hexacoordinate titanium, viz., $[Ti(ROH)_4X_2]^+X^-$. From $TiCl_3$ in methanol all of the monomeric complexes $[TiCl_n(CH_3OH)_{6-n}]^{(3-n)+}$, where $n = 1$–6, have now been prepared and characterized (*77*, *78*). The existence of the species $[Ti(ROH)_6]^{3+}$, where R = CH_3, C_2H_5, C_3H_7, in solution has been demonstrated but the compounds were not isolated (*80*).

Several sulfur-bonded complexes of type $TiX_3 \cdot 2\ L$ have been prepared by Fowles, Lester, and Walton (*70*). All show magnetic exchange between neighboring titanium atoms so that their structure is probably polymeric with bridging ligands and not trigonal bipyramidal like the trimethylamine and α-picoline adducts.

The only phosphine complex known is $TiCl_3 \cdot (C_2H_4[P(C_2H_5)_2]_2)$, prepared by Chatt and Hayter (*21*) as a dark brown solid from the two reactants in boiling benzene.

Hexacoordination of titanium in the two adducts of σ-phenylenebis(dimethylarsine) with titanium trichloride and titanium tribromide has been achieved by the formation of monohydrates, viz., $TiX_3 \cdot D \cdot H_2O$, where D = $C_6H_4(As[CH_3]_2)_2$ (*166*).

From a practical point of view the importance of many of these complexes lies in their usefulness in preparing titanium compounds which may not be accessible otherwise. The use of $TiX_3 \cdot 2\ N(CH_3)_3$ in this regard has already been mentioned, and complexes such as $HTiCl_4 \cdot O(C_2H_5)_2$ may often be substituted for titanium trichloride in the preparation of neutral $TiX_3 \cdot 3\ L$ complexes (*78*).

It has been claimed (*106*) that the tetrahydrofuran adduct of titanium trichloride disproportionates several hundred degrees below $TiCl_3$ itself, according to Eq. (1). Since $TiCl_4 \cdot 2$ THF is volatile such a process should constitute a useful synthesis of titanium dichloride, but in fact the residue is low in chlorine and contains, in addition to $TiCl_3$, carbonaceous matter (*183*).

$$2\ TiCl_3 \cdot 3\ THF \rightarrow TiCl_4 \cdot 2\ THF + TiCl_2 + 4\ THF \quad (1)$$

B. Visible Spectra

As stated above, in many of the complexes of titanium trihalides there is little doubt that the central metal ion is in a pseudo-octahedral environment. In most cases the visible spectrum of the compounds shows an asymmetric absorption band in the 14–16 kK region, which is typical of octahedrally coordinated titanium(III). With some complexes, distortions occur which result in a lowering of symmetry. As a result the ^2E_g and $^2T_{2g}$ terms are split and distinct shoulders or multiplet structures appear in the spectrum. The solid state reflectance spectrum is sometimes shifted relative to the solution spectrum, possibly because of site distortions.

C. Magnetics

In most cases the magnetic moment at room temperature only is available. Those cases for which moments at more than one temperature have been measured are marked in Table I with superscript ^{T}. At room temperature most are close to the spin-only value for a d^1 system (1.73 BM), but lowering of the moment with temperature by exchange through bridging ligands would be expected and in some case has been demonstrated.

Many of the structural proposals in Table I are based on visible spectra, magnetic data, molar conductance, and molecular weight determinations. In those cases where the complexes are so insoluble that solution data is excluded, then structural predictions must of necessity be based on magnetics and solid state spectra alone. It should be pointed out that interpretations based on these two properties can lead to erroneous conclusions and care should be taken in the interpretation of such data. It is to be expected, therefore, that as further X-ray crystal structures are determined, some of the probable structures in Table I may need some adjustment.

III

COMPLEXES OF TYPE $TiX_n \cdot (3-n)L$

A. *Alkoxides of Titanium(III) (Titanites)*

The structural chemistry of titanium alkoxides is dominated by the formation of polynuclear molecular clusters with bridging alkoxide groups. The mode and degree of association in alkyl titanates is reasonably well understood and has been adequately covered by Feld and Cowe (*57*). Similar alkoxy bridges exist in the few titanium(III) compounds known, and these offer efficient pathways for magnetic interaction between neighboring titanium atoms. As a result all of these derivatives have low magnetic moments.

From titanium trichloride and lithium methoxide in anhydrous methanol, the trimethoxide, $[Ti(OCH_3)_3]_n$, was obtained by Martin, Winter, and co-workers (*1*), as a yellow-green polymeric solid. Magnetic interaction between metal atoms is so strong that the complex is diamagnetic. Higher homologs have been obtained by reduction of the corresponding tetra-alkoxides (titanates) by sodium or potassium. In 1928, MacCorquodale and Adkins reported (*114*) the preparation of blue triethoxytitanium in 87% purity by reduction of $Ti(OC_2H_5)_4$ with sodium in ethanol, and Nesmeyanov and collaborators have obtained pink-lilac alkoxides by potassium and alcohol reductions of the tetrapropoxide and tetrabutoxide (*137*).

From one equivalent of titanium trimethoxide and two of titanium trichloride, Winter has isolated (*189*) a red complex, $[TiCl_2(OCH_3) \cdot 2\,CH_3OH]_3$, the magnetic moment of which (1.0 BM per titanium atom) is virtually independent of temperature and indicative of the trinuclear cluster (I).

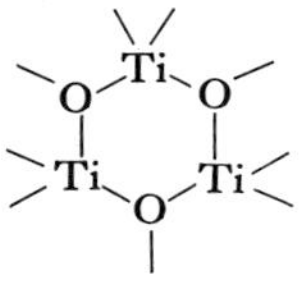

(I)

On reversing the proportions of the reactants, a dark brown complex was obtained, $TiCl(OCH_3)_2 \cdot CH_3OH$, which is also believed to contain a trinuclear cation $[Ti(OCH_3)_2 \cdot CH_3OH]^{3+}$ (*189, 190*). Both of these compounds absorb in the visible region around 10 kK, giving spectra very similar to that of $Ti(OCH_3)_3$.

The most recent work is described in a communication from Bradley, Lappert, and co-workers (*2*), in which titanium trimethoxide and triethoxide are formed by the action of methanol or ethanol on the tris(dimethylamido) compound $Ti[(NCH_3)_2]_3$, but as yet no details are available.

It should be mentioned that alkoxides of lower-valent titanium are formed from sodium naphthalide reductions of titanium tetraalkoxides in nitrogen fixation experiments, but none of the reduced species were isolated (see Section IX,B).

B. *Carboxylates of Titanium(III) (Acylates)*

Much of the early work in this field was carried out by Stähler, Grossman, and others during the early part of this century by treatment of titanous chloride with various carboxylic acids and derivatives. This early work has been reviewed by Feld and Cowe (*57*) and although some of the products were not isolated and many were not characterized, several interesting carboxylates resulted.

The oxalato compounds $Ti_2(ox)_3 \cdot 10\ H_2O$, and $MTi(ox)_2 \cdot 2\ H_2O$, where M = K, Rb, or NH_4, were prepared by Stähler in 1905 (*165*) and have been reinvestigated by Eve and Fowles recently (*56*). The potassium, ammonium, and rubidium compounds are polymeric and spectral evidence suggests that the titanium is in an octahedral environment provided by bridging oxalato groups. The water molecules are not coordinated to the titanium atoms and can be removed from the ammonium and potassium salts by heating.

Although the decahydrate $Ti_2(ox)_3 \cdot 10\ H_2O$ was originally given an octahedral configuration (*56*), X-ray data has shown the titanium to be seven-coordinate in a pentagonal bipyramid with one oxalato group bridging the two titanium atoms (*52*).

From titanium trichloride in acetic anhydride and acetic acid McDonald, Thompson, and Larsen (*116*) have prepared acetate complexes in which one or two acetato ligands have replaced chloride, i.e., $Ti(OCOCH_3)_{1\,or\,2}Cl_{2\,or\,1}$. Despite good analytical results, there is a possibility that with excess acetic anhydride replacement of chloride is a continuous process without the production of unique compounds.

Many complexes of titanium(III) with ethylenediaminetetraacetic acid (EDTA) were prepared by Podlahová and Podlaha (*143*). All of these highly colored compounds, of general formula $MTi(EDTA)\cdot n\,H_2O$, where $M = Ba/2$ or an alkali metal, have magnetic moments around the spin-only value and their visible spectra are indicative of octahedral titanium.

An isolated phosphato complex was prepared by Gutmann and Beer (*79*) from $TiCl_3\cdot 3\,CH_3CN$ and trimethylphosphate. Methyl chloride was eliminated, giving the pink octahedral complex $Ti(O_2P[OCH_3]_2)_3$ in which the phosphato ligands are bidentate.

C. β-Diketonates of Titanium(III)

The tris(acetylacetonate) of titanium(III) was prepared by Chakravarti in 1958 from titanium trichloride and acetylacetone in benzene using gaseous ammonia as a base (*20*). The same compound has since been prepared by others (*5*, *48*, *156*), using similar methods, and by displacement of dimethylamine from $Ti(NMe_2)_3$ with acetylacetone (*2*). From benzoylacetone, dibenzoylmethane, trifluorothenoylacetone, and 3-cyanoacetylacetone, Cox, Lewis, and Nyholm (*48*) have prepared similar tris(β-diketonates). All of these complexes are intensely colored and monomeric, with magnetic moments in the range 1.66–1.68 BM at room temperature.

The extinction coefficients of their bands in the visible spectra are around 1000 liters $mole^{-1}\ cm^{-1}$, which is high for *d–d* transitions. Nevertheless in the case of the tris(acetylacetonate) the major component of the band system has been assigned to a *d–d* transition, modified by mixing of the metal and ligand systems through low-lying π-orbitals (*48*, *142*). The shoulders on this main band have been attributed to vibrational fine structure (*5*, *142*).

It would be expected that distortion from octahedral symmetry in a complex with three symmetrical chelate rings would be small. In fact, from electron spin resonance (*101*), visible spectra (*5*, *142*), and magnetic measurements (*58*), the tris(acetylacetonate) has been shown to contain strong trigonal distortion.

In 1958 Pflugmacher, Carduck, and Zucketto (*141*) isolated a red complex from titanium trichloride and neat acetylacetone, to which was assigned a dimeric chlorine-bridged structure $[Ti(acac)_2Cl]_2$. The identity of this compound as a titanium(III) derivative has been disputed (*47*), but more recently Salzmann (*156*) has prepared all three acetylacetonates of general formula $Ti(acac)_nCl_{3-n}$, where $n = 1–3$, and has investigated their magnetics. $Ti(acac)_2Cl$ shows magnetic interaction between titanium atoms with a Néel point at 120° K, behavior which would be expected of the chlorine-bridged dimer proposed by Pflugmacher and co-workers (*141*).

In physical and chemical properties the compounds $Ti(acac)_nCl_{3-n}$ bear a striking resemblance to the corresponding cyclopentadienyl derivatives $(C_5H_5)_nTiCl_{3-n}$, in Section IV.

D. Amido Compounds of Titanium(III)

Dialkylamido compounds of titanium(III) are finding use as intermediates in the preparation of other complexes. Bradley, Lappert, and co-workers have recently reported the synthesis of $Ti(NR_2)_3$, where $R = CH_3$ and C_2H_5, from titanium trichloride and the lithium dialkylamide (*2*). The isopropyl and *sec*-butyl derivatives could not be made by this method. With protic reagents such as C_5H_6, $(C_2H_5)_2NH$, $(iso\text{-}C_3H_7)_2NH$, and $[(CH_3)_3Si]_2NH$ one of the dimethylamido groups of $Ti[N(CH_3)_2]_3$ was displaced by the new ligand.

Methanol and ethanol displaced all three amido ligands to give alkoxides, and acetylacetone gave the tris(β-diketonate), $Ti(acac)_3$. Insertion of carbon disulfide into $Ti[N(C_2H_5)_3]_3$ failed to give the titanium(III) diethyldithiocarbamate; instead disproportionation occurred to the titanium(IV) and titanium(II) dithiocarbamates. Disproportionation was also observed on attempted distillation of $XTi[N(CH_3)_2]_2$, where $X = N(CH_3)_2$, $N(C_2H_5)_2$, $N(iso\text{-}C_3H_7)_2$, giving $Ti[N(CH_3)_2]_4$ and TiX_2.

E. Phosphido Compounds of Titanium(III)

The only phosphido compounds of titanium(III) are the cyclopentadienyl derivatives, $[(\pi\text{-}C_5H_5)_2Ti \cdot PR_2]_2$, where $R = C_2H_5$ or C_4H_9, which will be dealt with in Section IV,B,4.

With titanium trichloride and lithium di(cyclohexyl)phosphide, Issleib and co-workers found that reduction occurred and only the titanium(II) compound, $Ti[P(C_6H_{11})_2]_2$, could be isolated (*99*).

F. Borohydride

A green borohydride of titanium(III), $Ti(BH_4)_3$, was described by Hoekstra and Katz (*96*). It was prepared from titanium tetrachloride by reaction with lithium borohydride and is much more unstable than the cyclopentadienyl derivative described in Section IV,B,4.

IV

ORGANOMETALLIC COMPOUNDS OF TITANIUM(III)

By far the major part of the work carried out in organotitanium chemistry has been concerned with cyclopentadienyl compounds in all valence states. The reasons for this are connected with the unique stabilizing influence exerted by the π-cyclopentadienyl ligands, which allows the isolation of compounds that would undoubtedly not survive in the presence of ligands other than cyclopentadienyl. Although advantageous where the isolation of new compounds is concerned, this stability can be a disadvantage in some types of catalytic processes.

A. Tris(cyclopentadienyl)titanium(III)

$(C_5H_5)_3Ti$ was first prepared in 1960 by Fischer and Löchner (*61*) in "low yield" from sodium cyclopentadienide and $(\pi\text{-}C_5H_5)_2TiCl_2$. A much better yield (70%) was obtained by Canty, Coutts, and Wailes (*18*) from $(\pi\text{-}C_5H_5)_2TiCl$. Over the range 100–300°K the magnetic moment was found to be independent of temperature and close to the spin-only value for a d^1 system. The solubility and volatility of $(C_5H_5)_3Ti$ are strong indications of its monomeric nature.

Under 150 atmospheres pressure of carbon monoxide at 80°C the tris(cyclopentadienyl) derivative is converted to the dicarbonyl, $(C_5H_5)_2Ti(CO)_2$ (*61*). It will also react immediately with dialkyl- and diaryl disulfides, RSSR, the color changing from green to red, giving an equilibrium mixture of thiolatotitanium(IV) compounds of type $(C_5H_5)_nTi(SR)_{4-n}$ (*36*).

B. Bis(cyclopentadienyl)titanium(III) Compounds

The ready availability of $(\pi\text{-}C_5H_5)_2TiCl$, both from reduction of $(\pi\text{-}C_5H_5)_2TiCl_2$ and from $TiCl_3$ with metal cyclopentadienides, has led to the widespread use of this compound as a starting material. Consequently this group is the largest of the organotitanium(III) compounds. A characteristic of many of the bis(cyclopentadienyl)titanium(III) complexes is the distorted tetrahedral environment around the titanium atom. To achieve this configuration the compounds will polymerize, solvate, or in some way coordinate a ligand into the fourth position. Polymerization generally leads to magnetic exchange between neighboring titanium atoms, resulting in low magnetic moments.

The visible spectral bands listed in Table III are believed to be due to *d–d* transitions but in some cases it is difficult to distinguish these from charge-transfer bands. In addition the shift in band maxima with changes in the ligands means that interpretation of the spectra is a difficult process which can give misleading results.

1. *Reduction of* $(\pi\text{-}C_5H_5)_2TiCl_2$

In polar organic solvents such as methanol, tetrahydrofuran, or acetone, bis(cyclopentadienyl)titanium dichloride will react rapidly with finely divided zinc, giving the green complex (II).

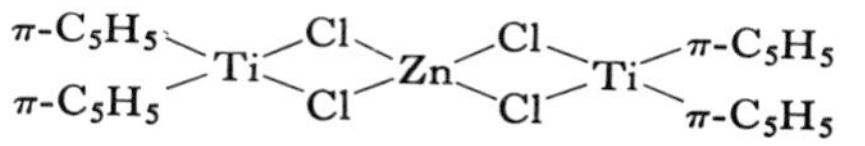

$$(\pi\text{-}C_5H_5)_2Ti\langle{}^{Cl}_{Cl}\rangle Zn\langle{}^{Cl}_{Cl}\rangle Ti(\pi\text{-}C_5H_5)_2$$

(II)

Similar but slower reductions occur in the presence of magnesium and aluminum (*187*). The zinc chloride complex, which gives only small amounts of $(\pi\text{-}C_5H_5)_2TiCl$ on attempted sublimation, is probably the same compound obtained by Birmingham, Fischer, and Wilkinson in 1955 (*9*), although its composition was not recognized at the time.

In the presence of thiocyanate, cyanate, cyanide, nitrate, etc., during the reduction, the chloride bridges are replaced by the more abundant anion (*187*). Contrary to a previous claim (*9*), as yet no satisfactory method has been found for removal of the zinc salt from these complexes in organic solvents to give $(\pi\text{-}C_5H_5)_2TiCl$, and in the use of the zinc complex for the preparation of other titanium(III) derivatives the presence of the zinc should not be overlooked. The lack of spin-pairing in the ESR spectrum of the zinc-reduced $(\pi\text{-}C_5H_5)_2TiCl_2$, for example, which has been attributed to the presence of a solvated monomer of $(\pi\text{-}C_5H_5)_2TiCl$ (*16*), is due to the fact that the magnetic moment of the zinc complex shows the spin-only value, independent of temperature, with no magnetic interaction between

TABLE III

ORGANOMETALLIC COMPOUNDS OF TITANIUM(III)[a]

Compound	Color	Visible spectra (kK)		μ_{eff} (BM, 20°C)	References
		Solid	Solution (ε)		
	Tris(cyclopentadienyl)titanium(III)				
$(C_5H_5)_3Ti$	Dark green	14.3 16.8	—	1.69^T	*18, 61*
	Bis(cyclopentadienyl)titanium(III) compounds				
Prepared in Air-Free Water					
$[(C_5H_5)_2TiCl]_2$	Green	8.85 13.3	10.0 13.9	1.6^T	*151*
$(C_5H_5)_2Ti$ picrate	Brown	—	—	2.3	*188*
$[(C_5H_5)_2Ti]_2SO_4$	Pale green	9.35 13.9	—	1.64^T	*39*
$[(C_5H_5)_2Ti]_2CO_3$	Pale blue	10.8 12.2 13.7	—	0.8^T	*39*
$(C_5H_5)_2Ti(acac)$	Deep blue	—	10.3 13.0 14.6 (61) 17.2 (43)	1.74^T	*42*

$(C_5H_5)_2Ti\langle O, O \rangle C—R$ (chelating carboxylate)					
R=H	Green	11.8 14.5	—	1.69^T	*35*
$R=CH_3$	Royal blue	10.6 13.9 16.7	—	1.71^T	*35*
$R=C_9H_{19}$	Royal blue	10.5 13.9 16.9	—	1.72^T	*35*
$R=C_{17}H_{35}$	Royal blue	10.9 13.9 16.7	—	1.55^T	*35*
$R=C_6H_5$	Dark green	10.4 13.3 17.2	—	1.62^T	*35*
$[(C_5H_5)_2Ti\langle O, O \rangle C]_2R'$					
$R'=—CH_2CH_2—$	Gray-blue	10.8 14.1 16.7	—	1.66^T	*35*
R=—CH=CH— (*cis*)	Pale green	10.2 13.9 16.7	—	1.61^T	*35*
R=—CH=CH— (*trans*)	Mauve	10.5 13.5 17.5	—	1.68^T	*35*
$(C_5H_5)_2Ti\langle S, O \rangle C—R$					
R=H	Dark green	10.0 13.8 16.4	—	1.64^T	*38*

(Continued)

TABLE III (*Continued*)

Compound	Color	Visible spectra (kK)		μ_{eff} (BM, 20°C)	References
		Solid	Solution (ϵ)		
$R=CH_3$	Dark green	10.6 13.7 15.8	—	1.74^T	*38*
$R=C_2H_5$	Dark green	10.4 13.2 15.9	—	1.64^T	*38*
$R=C_{17}H_{35}$	Dark green	10.5 13.3 15.9	—	1.55^T	*38*
$R=C_6H_5$	Teal blue	13.1 16.95	—	1.71^T	*38*
$(C_5H_5)_2Ti(S_2C{-}NR_2)$					
$R=H$	Pale green	—	13.3 (60) 16.0 (110)	1.60^T	*43, 44*
$R=CH_3$	Blue-green	—	13.3 (43) 16.3 (82) 21.7 (140)	1.64^T	*43, 44*
$R=C_2H_5$	Deep green	—	13.3 (43) 16.3 (79) 21.55 (176)	1.68^T	*43, 44*
$R=n\text{-}C_3H_7$	Deep green	—	13.3 (41) 16.45 (76)	1.63^T	*43, 44*

			21.5 (158)		
$R=n\text{-}C_4H_9$	Deep green	—	13.3 (47) 16.4 (87) 21.4 (179)	1.47^T	*43, 44*
$R=n\text{-}C_5H_{11}$	Deep green	—	13.3 (51) 16.5 (94) 21.4 (188)	—	*43, 44*
$R_2=—(CH_2)_5—$	Deep green	—	13.3 (43) 16.4 (78) 21.4 (140)	1.71^T	*43, 44*
$(C_5H_5)_2Ti(S_2C{-}O{-}R)$					
$R=CH_3$	Light blue	—	14.3 (55) 16.4 (82) 18.5 (126)	1.60^T	*45*
$R=C_2H_5$	Bright blue	—	14.3 (47) 16.5 (74) 18.6 (111)	1.54^T	*45*
$R=n\text{-}C_3H_7$	Bright blue	—	14.3 (49) 16.5 (77) 18.5 (115)	1.60^T	*45*
$R=n\text{-}C_4H_9$	Dark blue	—	14.3 (53) 16.5 (86) 18.5 (132)	1.63^T	*45*
$R=n\text{-}C_5H_{11}$	Dark blue	—	14.3 (52) 16.6 (85) 18.6 (128)	1.62^T	*45*
$[(C_5H_5)_2TiCN]_3$	Purple	—	12.9	1.03^T	*34*
$[(C_5H_5)_2TiNCS]_3$	Red-brown	—	12.0	1.00^T	*34*
$[(C_5H_5)_2TiNCSe]_3$	Chocolate brown	—	9.8 15.9 20.4	0.88^T	*36*

(Continued)

TABLE III (*Continued*)

Compound	Color	Visible spectra (kK)		μ_{eff} (BM, 20°C)	References
		Solid	Solution (ϵ)		
$(C_5H_5)_2TiNCO$	Green		9.7 12.8 15.4	1.64^T	*34*
$[(C_5H_5)_2Ti(H_2O)_3]_2[BPh_4]_2$	Pale blue	9.1 14.8	—	1.4^T	*31*
$[(C_5H_5)_2Ti(py)_2][BPh_4]$	Dark green	11.0 13.9	—	1.72^T	*31*
$[(C_5H_5)_2Ti(N{\equiv}CCH_3)_2][BPh_4]$	Bright blue	13.0 17.8	—	1.74^T	*31*
$([(\pi\text{-}C_5H_5)_2Ti]_2O)_n$	Deep blue	11.0 13.7 17.7	—	0.97^T	*31*
Prepared in Organic Media					
$[(C_5H_5)_2TiCl]_2$	Green	8.85 13.3	10.0 13.9	1.6^T	*151*
$[(C_5H_5)_2TiBr]_2$	Red-brown	—	—	—	*138*
$[(C_5H_5)_2TiI]_2$	Black-brown	—	—	—	*138*
$(C_5H_5)_2TiCl.py$	Red	—	9.5 (32) 12.3 (46) 13.9 (50) 19.3 (100)	1.72^T	*184*

$(C_5H_5)_2TiCl \cdot 4,4'$-bipy	Green	—	9.65 (40) 12.1 (60) 16.2 (90)	1.62^T	*184*
$[(C_5H_5)_2TiCl \cdot dipy]_2 \cdot dipy$	Blue	—	11.3 (72) 13.3 (65) 17.6 (180)	1.82^T	*40*
$[(C_5H_5)_2TiCl \cdot phen]_2 \cdot phen$	Mauve	—	11.6 (54) 13.0 (47) 17.85 (134)	1.85^T	*40*
$[(C_5H_5)_2TiCl \cdot phm]_2 \cdot phm$ (phm = *o*-phenylenediamine)	Pale green	—	9.1 (26) 13.5 (54) 14.3 (57)	1.94^T	*40*
$[(C_5H_5)_2TiCl \cdot picam]_2 \cdot picam$ (picam = α-picolylamine)	Fawn	—	13.4 (85) 17.2 (120)	1.78^T	*40*
$(C_5H_5)_2TiCl \cdot terpy$	Dark green	—	17.0	—	*36*
$[(C_5H_5)_2TiP(C_2H_5)_2]_2$	Violet	—	—	Diam.	*98, 105*
$[(C_5H_5)_2TiP(C_4H_9)_2]_2$	Violet	—	—	Diam.	*98, 105*
$(C_5H_5)_2Ti \cdot BH_4$	Violet	—	—	—	*138, 100*
$(C_5H_5)_2Ti \cdot BF_4$	Blue	—	—	—	*138*
$(C_5H_5)_2TiSn(C_6H_5)_3 \cdot THF$	Green	—	—	1.6	*37*
$(C_5H_5)_2TiGe(C_6H_5)_3 \cdot THF$	Green	—	—	1.6	*37*
$[(C_5H_5)_2TiC_6H_5]_2$	Olive green	12.3 14.9	—	Diam.	*46*
$[(C_5H_5)_2TiC{\equiv}CC_6H_5]_n$	Dark green	—	13.4 15.3	Diam.	*46, 169*
$[(C_5H_5)_2TiC{\equiv}CH]_n$	Black	—	—	—	*104*
$[(C_5H_5)_2TiC{\equiv}CTi(C_5H_5)_2]_n$	Blue	—	—	—	*104*
$(C_5H_5)_2Ti$-allyl	Violet	—	19.5 (364)	1.65	*120*
$(C_5H_5)_2Ti$-1-methylallyl	Blue-violet	—	18.55 (364)	1.67	*120*
$(C_5H_5)_2Ti$-2-methylallyl	Purple	—	16.8 (62) 20.1 (283)	1.72	*120*

(Continued)

TABLE III (*Continued*)

Compound	Color	Visible spectra (kK)		μ_{eff} (BM, 20°C)	References
		Solid	Solution (ϵ)		
$(C_5H_5)_2Ti$-1,3-dimethylallyl	Blue	—	17.3 (445)	1.72	*120*
$(C_5H_5)_2Ti$-1,1-dimethylallyl	Brown-red	—	—	1.48	*120*
$(C_5H_5)_2Ti$-1,2-dimethylallyl	Violet	—	19.15	—	*120*
$(C_5H_5)_2Ti$-1-methyl-3-ethylallyl	Blue	—	17.2	—	*121*
$(C_5H_5)_2Ti$-1,2,3-trimethylallyl	Violet	—	17.7	—	*121*
$[(C_5H_5)_2TiN(CH_3)_2]_2$	Red-brown	—	—	—	*2*
$[(C_5H_5)_2TiOCH_3]_n$	Dark brown	—	12.3 18.5	1.38^T	*36*
$[(C_5H_5)_2TiOC_2H_5]_n$	Dark brown	—	12.0 17.5	—	*36*
$[(C_5H_5)_2TiOC_4H_9$-*tert*$]_n$	Dark brown	—	12.5 16.9	—	*36*
$(C_9H_7)_2TiCl$	Yellow-red	—	—	—	*118*
$(C_9H_7)_2TiBr$	Brick red	—	—	—	*118*
$(C_9H_7)_2TiI$ $[(C_9H_7 = \text{indenyl})]$	—	—	—	—	*118*
Mono(cyclopentadienyl)titanium(III) compounds					
$C_5H_5TiCl_2$	Purple	9.6 14.1 19.6	—	1.69^T	*7, 18, 36*

$C_5H_5TiCl_2 \cdot 2\ py$	Green	—	15.3 22.5	—	*36*
$C_5H_5TiCl_2 \cdot bipy$	Blue-gray	—	14.3 19.6	—	*36*
$C_5H_5[(CH_3)_2N]Ti \langle N(CH_3)_2 \rangle_2 Ti[N(CH_3)_2]C_5H_5$	Red-brown	—	—	Diamag.	*2*
$C_5H_5TiC_8H_8$	Green	—	—	1.60	*170*
	Alkyl and aryl titanium(III) compounds				
CH_3TiCl_2	—	—	—	—	*110*
$CH_3TiCl_2 \cdot 3\ py$	Blue	—	—	—	*127*
$C_6H_5TiCl_2 \cdot 3\ py$	Blue	—	15.15	—	*127*
$(CH_3)_3Ti$	Green	—	—	—	*26*
$C_2H_5TiCl_2$	—	—	—	—	*139*
$C_8H_{17}TiCl_2$	—	—	—	—	*139*
$[Ti_3[C_6(CH_3)_6]_3Cl_6]Cl$	Violet	—	—	1.84 per trimer	*62*

[a] *T* indicates cases for which moments have been measured at more than one temperature.

titanium atoms (*155*, *184*). Its subsequent reactions with Grignard reagents and lithium alkyls cannot necessarily be equated with the reactions of (π-$C_5H_5)_2TiCl$ with these reagents.

If the reduction with zinc is carried out in air-free water, however, a bright blue solution containing the (π-$C_5H_5)_2Ti^+$ cation is obtained. Bis(cyclopentadienyl)titanium(III) compounds can then be precipitated from this solution by those anions which do not have insoluble zinc derivatives. The aqueous chemistry of (π-$C_5H_5)_2Ti^+$ will be covered below in Section IV,B,3.

The zinc complex (II) is in the same class as the halogen-bridged bimetallic species (π-$C_5H_5)_2TiX_2MR_2$. where M = boron, aluminum, gallium, or indium and R = alkyl or halogen, which are formed from reduced (π-$C_5H_5)_2TiCl_2$ and the trihalides or mixed alkyl halides of Group III elements. These are being extensively studied in connection with their Ziegler-Natta-type polymerization properties, and will be dealt with more fully later in Section IX,A.

For the preparation of (π-$C_5H_5)_2Ti^{III}$ compounds in organic media, (π-$C_5H_5)_2TiCl$ is the starting material of choice. It may be prepared from the bimetallic complexes mentioned above, e.g., (π-$C_5H_5)_2TiCl_2AlR_2$, by complexing the aluminum with trimethylamine or ether (*14*, *27*) according to Eq. (2),

$$(\pi\text{-}C_5H_5)_2Ti\langle{}^{Cl}_{Cl}\rangle Al\langle{}^{R}_{R} + (C_2H_5)_2O \longrightarrow (\pi\text{-}C_5H_5)_2TiCl + R_2AlCl{,}O(C_2H_5)_2 \quad (2)$$

From 0.25 mole of lithium aluminum hydride and (π-$C_5H_5)_2TiCl_2$ in tetrahydrofuran, (π-$C_5H_5)_2TiCl$ can be obtained in 70% yield by sublimation directly from the reaction mixture (*104*). Alternative preparations are from titanium trichloride and sodium cyclopentadienide (*130*), or best, magnesium cyclopentadienide (*151*). The latter reagent will not place any more than two cyclopentadienyl rings on titanium(III) halides.

2. *Properties of* (π-$C_5H_5)_2TiCl$

(π-$C_5H_5)_2TiCl$ is a green-brown, air-sensitive dimer (*130*) which oxidizes in air to give yellow oxygen-bridged polymers (*76*). The magnetic moment is low due to magnetic interaction, either through the bridging chlorines or by titanium–titanium bonding (*18*, *123*). In organic solvents the compound will split disulfides, giving thiolatotitanium(IV) derivatives (*33*), Eq. (3).

$$2\,(\pi\text{-}C_5H_5)_2TiCl + RSSR \longrightarrow 2\,(\pi\text{-}C_5H_5)_2Ti\begin{smallmatrix}SR\\Cl\end{smallmatrix} \qquad (3)$$

With organic azides, RN_3, nitrogen is liberated and the nitrogen-bridged compounds $[\pi\text{-}(C_5H_5)_2TiCl]_2NR$, where $R{=}C_6H_5$ or $p\text{-}ClC_6H_4$, are obtained (*32*). In halogenated solvents the monochloride will also abstract halogen rapidly giving red $(\pi\text{-}C_5H_5)_2TiCl_2$.

Several complexes of $(\pi\text{-}C_5H_5)_2TiCl$ with various nitrogen-containing ligands are known. Thus with bipyridyl, phenanthroline, α-picolylamine, and σ-phenylenediamine, the dimeric complexes (III) with bridging

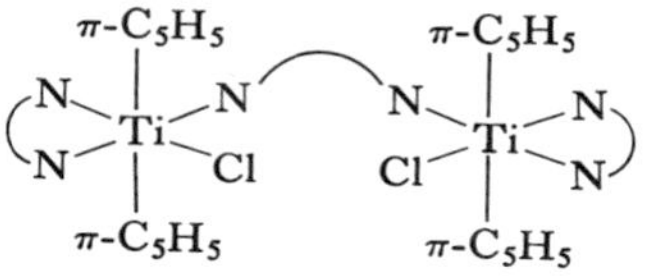

π-C₅H₅ π-C₅H₅
N N N N
Ti Ti
N Cl Cl N
π-C₅H₅ π-C₅H₅

(III)

bidentate ligands are precipitated (*40*), whereas by reduction of $(\pi\text{-}C_5H_5)_2TiCl_2$ with sodium pyridyl two more complexes were obtained (*184*). That in higher yield was $(\pi\text{-}C_5H_5)_2TiCl\cdot py$, a red air-sensitive monomer very soluble in organic solvents. A by-product was the green, less-soluble 4,4′-bipyridyl complex, $(\pi\text{-}C_5H_5)_2TiCl\cdot bipy$, the ligand of which was undoubtedly formed from sodium pyridyl. Magnetic measurements on both compounds show that the moments are around 1.6–1.7 BM and are independent of temperature.

A deep green terpyridyl adduct, $(C_5H_5)_2TiCl\cdot terpy$, can be formed from the two reactants in tetrahydrofuran over several days. Since the complex is sparingly soluble in organic solvents but dissolves readily in water, it is probably ionic in nature (*36*).

The diamagnetic, halogen-free titanium-aluminum derivative, $[(\pi\text{-}C_5H_5)_2TiAl(C_2H_5)_2]_2$, has been obtained by Natta and co-workers from $(\pi\text{-}C_5H_5)_2TiCl$ and triethylaluminum (*29, 132*). The same compound was prepared by Wailes and Weigold (*184*) from titanocene and triethylaluminum and will be discussed in Sections VII,A,2 and IX,A.

3. *Aqueous Chemistry of* $(\pi\text{-}C_5H_5)_2TiCl$

In air-free water $(\pi\text{-}C_5H_5)_2TiCl$ dissolves to give a bright blue solution which shows the molar conductance of a 1:1 electrolyte. Wilkinson and Birmingham (*188*) showed in 1954 that picrate and silicotungstate derivatives could be precipitated from solutions containing the $(\pi\text{-}C_5H_5)_2Ti^+$

ion, and more recently Coutts and Wailes have prepared a great range of new titanium(III) compounds using water as solvent. Of those compounds listed in Table III the carboxylates (*35*), thiocarboxylates (*38*), dithiocarbamates (*43*), xanthates (*45*), and sulfate (*39*) are all monomeric and volatile with magnetic moments which are virtually independent of temperature and close to the spin-only value for titanium(III) (1.73 BM). All of these derivatives are unusual in that the bidentate chelating ligands do not bridge but form four-membered rings with the titanium atom giving monomeric structures, e.g., carboxylates (IV) and sulfate (V).

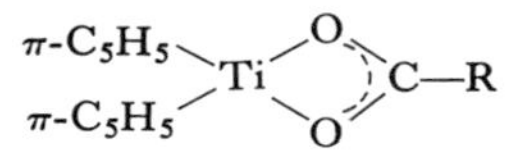

(IV) 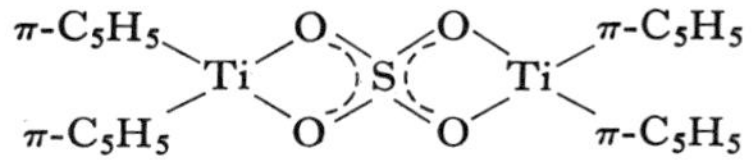 (V)

Although it has been claimed (*51*) that an acetylacetonate of π-$C_5H_5Ti^{III}$ does not form, the deep blue $(\pi$-$C_5H_5)_2Ti \cdot acac$ was obtained (*42*) by vigorously stirring acetylacetone in excess with an aqueous solution of $(\pi$-$C_5H_5)_2TiCl$. This monomeric derivative is extremely volatile and can be sublimed below 100° C under high vacuum.

The carbonato complex, $[(C_5H_5)_2Ti]_2CO_3$, can be prepared from either sodium carbonate or bicarbonate, as a pale blue solid which has low magnetic moments due to interaction between neighboring titanium atoms (*39*). This magnetic exchange may proceed via the π-electrons of the symmetric O—C—O group, by a mechanism similar to that proposed for copper formate (*140*), although metal–metal bonding is also possible. The third oxygen atom of the carbonato ligand may be involved in satisfying the coordination requirements of the titanium atom, as in (VI) for example. The insolubility in organic solvents of the carbonato relative to the sulfato derivative could be indication of this.

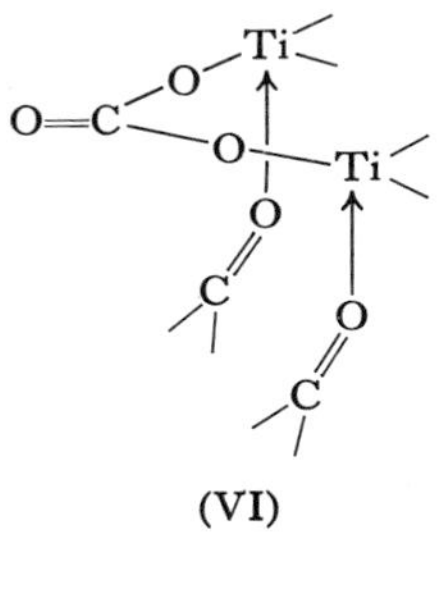

(VI)

The magnetic susceptibility of the carbonato compound could not be measured above 100° C due to decomposition. Carbon dioxide was liberated leaving a deep blue insoluble residue which is apparently a polymer of titanocene oxide, $([(\pi\text{-}C_5H_5)_2Ti]_2O)_n$. Its insolubility, involatility, and low magnetic moment (0.9 BM) suggest a highly polymerized structure, probably bridged through oxygen (*39*), as in (VII).

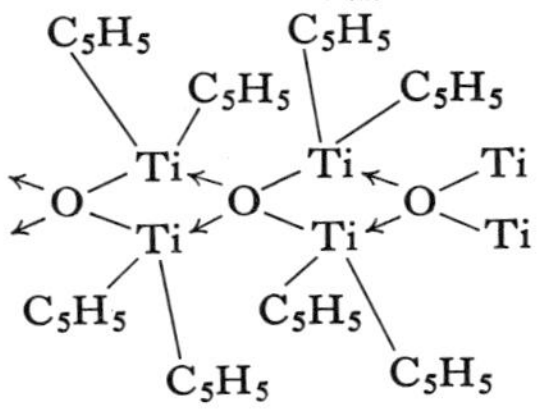

(VII)

A similar compound was obtained by pyrolysis of the pale blue hydrated tetraphenylborato derivative $[(\pi\text{-}C_5H_5)_2Ti \cdot 3\ H_2O]_2 \cdot 2\ BPh_4$, prepared by addition of $NaBPh_4$ to $(\pi\text{-}C_5H_5)_2TiCl$ in water (*31*). The tetraphenylborato group is noncoordinating and in the aquo complex the coordination number of the titanium ions has been increased by formation of hydrated species. Since water molecules in two different environments can be distinguished in the infrared spectrum, it is believed that bridging water is present, providing a pathway for magnetic exchange between the two titanium atoms.

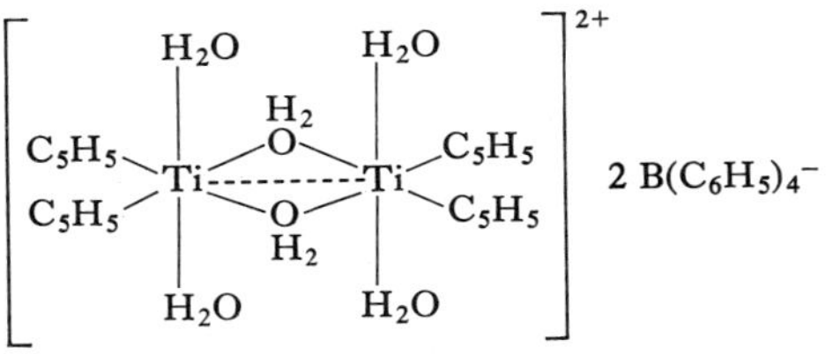

$2\ B(C_6H_5)_4^-$

(VIII)

From methanolic solutions of $(\pi\text{-}C_5H_5)_2TiCl$ and $NaBPh_4$ in the presence of methyl cyanide, the bright blue crystalline complex $[(\pi\text{-}C_5H_5)_2Ti \cdot 2\ N{\equiv}CCH_3]BPh_4$ was obtained (*31*), and could be converted to the corresponding pyridine complex $[(\pi\text{-}C_5H_5)_2Ti \cdot 2\ py]BPh_4$ by recrystallization from this solvent (*31*). In both of these compounds the variation of magnetic susceptibility with temperature follows a Curie-Weiss law, the moments being independent of temperature and close to 1.7 BM.

The pseudohalides $(\pi\text{-}C_5H_5)_2TiX$, where X=CN, NCS, NCO (*34*), and NCSe (*36*) have been prepared similarly in water as highly colored, air-sensitive solids. From infrared and mass spectral data the compounds X=NCO, NCS, and NCSe were shown to be iso derivatives bonded through nitrogen. The cyanide, isothiocyanate, and isoselenocyanate have uncorrected magnetic moments around 1 BM per titanium atom, which is independent of temperature over a limited range. This effect is claimed to be indicative of trinuclear metal clusters (*28*). Confirmation of the trimeric nature of the cyanide came from the mass spectrum. Whether the bridging ligands are linear, (IXa), or of the three-center type, (IXb), has not been determined.

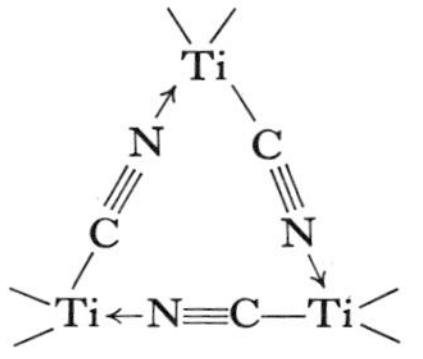

(IXa) 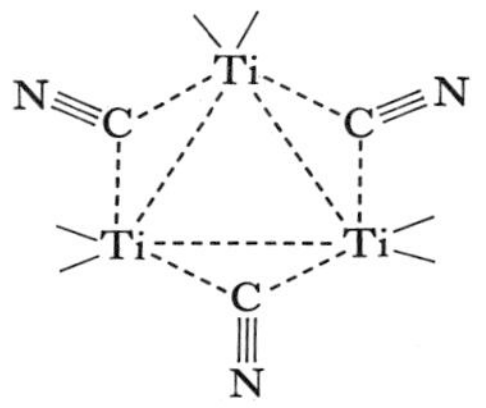 (IXb)

Surprisingly the pale green isocyanate does not show a reduced magnetic moment and thus differs from the other pseudohalides. It is more soluble and more volatile than the others and would appear to be monomeric.

Many attempts have been made to prepare the corresponding azido derivative $[(\pi\text{-}C_5H_5)_2TiN_3]$, but in water the product of the reaction between sodium azide and $(\pi\text{-}C_5H_5)_2TiCl$ liberates nitrogen and cyclopentadiene, giving yellow insoluble products (*41*). From the presence of an azide band in the infrared spectrum it seems likely that the compound is a polymer terminated by azide of type (X) [cf. the chloride polymers (*76*)].

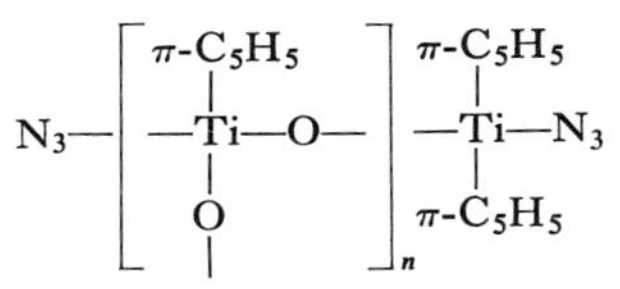

(X)

In dimethylformamide the solvated complex of the azide $(\pi\text{-}C_5H_5)_2TiN_3 \cdot DMF$, was obtained as a green unstable solid which decomposed at room temperature (*41*).

4. *Preparation of $(\pi\text{-}C_5H_5)_2Ti^{III}$ Compounds in Organic Media*

From $(\pi\text{-}C_5H_5)_2TiCl_2$ and Grignard reagents or other strongly reducing reactants, several bis(cyclopentadienyl)titanium(III) compounds have been isolated. Issleib and Häckert (*98*) obtained the bridged phosphido complex (XI), where $R=C_2H_5$ or $n\text{-}C_4H_9$, from $(\pi\text{-}C_5H_5)_2TiCl_2$ and

$$(\pi\text{-}C_5H_5)_2Ti(\mu\text{-}PR_2)_2Ti(\pi\text{-}C_5H_5)_2$$

(XI)

2 moles of $LiPR_2$. The violet compounds are diamagnetic and with methyl iodide give $(\pi\text{-}C_5H_5)_2TiI$ and the dimethyldialkylphosphonium iodide.

By reduction of the titanium(IV) compound with allyl Grignard reagents Jellinek and collaborators have prepared a series of allyltitanium(III) compounds substituted in the 1-, 2-, and 3-positions, of general structure

$$(\pi\text{-}C_5H_5)_2Ti[\eta^3\text{-}C(R)(R^1)\text{—}C(R^2)\text{—}C(R^3)(R^4)]$$

(XII)

(XII) (*83*, *120*). Several of the compounds have been prepared from $(\pi\text{-}C_5H_5)_2TiCl$ with 1 mole of allyl Grignard reagent (*121*), or with isopropylmagnesium bromide in the presence of dienes (*119*, *121*). The compounds are all monomeric and blue to violet in color; they have one unpaired electron per titanium atom. The allylic group occupies two coordination positions on the titanium atom, leading to the stable tetrahedral arrangement so common in compounds of this class.

As intermediates in the formation of these allyl derivatives and also in the reactions of both $(\pi\text{-}C_5H_5)_2TiCl_2$ and $(\pi\text{-}C_5H_5)_2TiCl_2ZnCl_2Ti(\pi\text{-}C_5H_5)_2$ with lithium alkyls and Grignard reagents, it has been suggested (*16*, *121*) that dihydride and dialkyl complexes are formed as intermediates. The evidence for the existence of such complexes, of type $[(\pi\text{-}C_5H_5)_2TiR_2]^-$, where $R=H$, CH_3, C_2H_5, etc., comes from ESR spectra, but as yet no hydride or alkyl derivative of $(\pi\text{-}C_5H_5)_2Ti^{III}$ has been isolated and characterized.

Note added in proof: The titanium(III) hydride $[(\pi\text{-}C_5H_5)_2TiH]_2$ has recently been isolated by Bercaw and Brintzinger as a purple solid from the reaction between gaseous H_2 and solid $(\pi\text{-}C_5H_5)_2Ti(CH_3)_2$ (*8a*).

The bimetallic hydride (XIII) has been suggested by Henrici-Olivé and Olivé as product of the reduction of $(\pi\text{-}C_5H_5)_2TiCl_2$ with sodium in the presence of $AlCl_3$ (*91*). The suggestion was made in order to explain six 1/2/1 triplets in the ESR spectrum of the reaction mixture, apparently due to the splitting by two equivalent hydrogen nuclei of the six-line spectrum caused by interaction of the unpaired titanium(III) electron with the aluminum nucleus ($I=\frac{5}{2}$).

$$(C_5H_5)_2Ti(\mu\text{-}H)_2AlCl_2$$

(XIII)

Lithium borohydride in ether will also reduce $(\pi\text{-}C_5H_5)_2TiCl_2$ giving $(\pi\text{-}C_5H_5)_2Ti\cdot BH_4$ (*138*), a volatile compound with double hydrogen bridge between titanium and boron.

$$(\pi\text{-}C_5H_5)_2Ti(\mu\text{-}H)_2BH_2$$

(XIV)

With HCl, HBr, HI, BCl_3, or BBr_3 the borohydride (XIV) is converted to the corresponding titanium(III) halides, $(\pi\text{-}C_5H_5)_2TiX$, while boron trifluoride afforded the tetrafluoroborate, $(\pi\text{-}C_5H_5)_2TiBF_4$, which is bridging through two fluorine atoms (*138*).

Compounds containing metal–metal bonds between elements of Groups IVA and IVB have been prepared. In particular titanium(III)–tin and titanium(III)–germanium compounds were isolated (*37*) as paramagnetic solvated complexes, $(\pi\text{-}C_5H_5)_2TiM(C_6H_5)_3\cdot THF$, where M = Sn or Ge, from the reaction between $(\pi\text{-}C_5H_5)_2TiCl$ and sodium tin triphenyl or lithium germanium triphenyl. The corresponding lead derivative could be formed as a bright green solution in tetrahydrofuran at low temperature but deposition of lead occurred rapidly at room temperature and the compound could not be isolated.

Recently the olive green phenyl derivative, $[(\pi\text{-}C_5H_5)_2TiC_6H_5]_2$ has been isolated (*46*) from the reaction between $(\pi\text{-}C_5H_5)_2TiCl$ and LiPh.

In this case the coordination number of the titanium has been satisfied by dimerization, probably bridging through phenyl groups.

$$\begin{matrix} C_5H_5 \\ C_5H_5 \end{matrix} \!\!>\! Ti \!<\!\! \begin{matrix} C_6H_5 \\ C_6H_5 \end{matrix} \!\!>\! Ti \!<\!\! \begin{matrix} C_5H_5 \\ C_5H_5 \end{matrix}$$

(XV)

Since the magnetic susceptibility of (XV) can be accounted for almost entirely by temperature-independent paramagnetism, spin-pairing of the electrons is quite strong and may involve metal–metal bonding.

The same phenyl derivative has been postulated as an intermediate in the pyrolysis of the titanium(IV) derivative $(\pi\text{-}C_5H_5)_2Ti(C_6H_5)_2$ to give titanocene (*148*), but it was never isolated from this pyrolysis.

The corresponding deep green phenylethynyl derivative, $(\pi\text{-}C_5H_5)_2TiC{\equiv}CC_6H_5$, is claimed from mass spectral evidence to be a dimer with bridging phenylethynyl groups (*169*). Phenylethynyl-bridged aluminum, gallium, indium, zinc, and cadmium derivatives all show $C{\equiv}C$ stretching bands in their infrared spectra around 2050–2120 cm^{-1} (*102*), whereas $(\pi\text{-}C_5H_5)_2TiC{\equiv}CC_6H_5$ shows no band in this region. This evidence is not in accord with a bridging dimer, nor is its extreme insolubility in polar solvents (*46*). The presence of a mass spectral peak at m/e for a dimer does not necessarily preclude the presence of a higher oligomer. It would seem likely that the triple bond is associated in a much more complex manner than a bridging dimer would require.

The related complexes, black $[(\pi\text{-}C_5H_5)_2TiC{\equiv}CH]_n$ and blue $[(\pi\text{-}C_5H_5)_2TiC{\equiv}CTi(\pi\text{-}C_5H_5)_2]_n$, have been isolated from reaction mixtures of the mono- and dimagnesium bromides of acetylene with $(\pi\text{-}C_5H_5)_2TiCl$ (*104*). Both compounds are air-sensitive and undoubtedly polymeric. Like the phenylethynyl derivative they show no acetylenic bands in their infrared spectra.

A recent communication (*2*) describes the preparation of the dimethylamido-bridged dimer, $[(\pi\text{-}C_5H_5)_2Ti\cdot N(CH_3)_2]_2$, and its use in the synthesis of titanium(III) derivatives by displacement of dimethylamine with protic reagents such as alcohols and metal hydrides, but details are not yet available.

The alkoxides $[(\pi\text{-}C_5H_5)_2TiOR]_n$ are chocolate brown solids which were obtained by Coutts and Wailes from $(\pi\text{-}C_5H_5)_2TiCl$ and the sodium alkoxide in tetrahydrofuran (*36*). The alkoxides are extremely soluble, even in light petroleum, and are extensively associated. The molecular weight values, in terms of multiples of the monomer are as follows: methoxide, 2.2 to 2.6 depending on concentration in boiling benzene; ethoxide, 2.5; and *tert*-butoxide, 1.4. Magnetic measurements on the methoxide over the temperature range 112° to 293° K reflect this association, the moments ranging from 1.03 to 1.38 BM. The electronic absorption spectrum of the *tert*-butoxide differs somewhat from that of the other homologs (Table III). In tetrahydrofuran a strong band around 16,900 cm^{-1} develops, which is probably caused by irradiation in the spectrophotometer since the same thing happens in sunlight, the color changing to deep blue simultaneously.

The bis(indenyl)titanium(III) halides, $(C_9H_7)_2TiX$, where X = Cl, Br, or I, are known. These are analogous to the cyclopentadienyl derivatives and were prepared by reduction of the corresponding titanium(IV) dihalides with triethylaluminum (*118*). The intermediate green complexes $(C_9H_7)_2TiX_2Al(C_5H_5)_2$ are tabulated in Table VIII, Section IX,A.

C. *Mono(cyclopentadienyl)titanium(III) Compounds*

This field has scarcely been touched and few complexes are known in which one cyclopentadienyl ring is attached to titanium(III). The first was prepared by Bartlett and Seidel (*7*) by the action of di(isobutyl)aluminum chloride on $(\pi\text{-}C_5H_5)_2TiCl_2$. The chlorido ligands remained untouched but one cyclopentadienyl group was removed, giving the purple $\pi\text{-}C_5H_5TiCl_2$.

A rather more convenient preparation in 85% yield is by zinc reduction of $\pi\text{-}C_5H_5TiCl_3$ in benzene in the presence of a stoichiometric amount of tetrahydrofuran (*41*). A purple precipitate of $\pi\text{-}C_5H_5TiCl_2$ appears almost immediately and after filtration can be extracted from unreacted zinc with tetrahydrofuran. Although the insolubility in nonpolar solvents and involatility of this compound would indicate some type of association, its magnetic moment is close to the spin-only value and is virtually independent of temperature (*18*). This behavior would not be expected of, say, a chlorine-bridged oligomer. The compound forms a blue-green crystalline tetrahydrofuranate and a green crystalline triethylamine complex, but these solvents are only weakly coordinated and on pumping under vacuum or washing with ether they are easily removed. The green pyridine complex $C_5H_5TiCl_2 \cdot 2\,py$ and the blue-gray bipyridyl complex $C_5H_5TiCl_2 \cdot bipy$ are rather more stable and can be isolated as well-defined complexes (*41*).

Differences in their solubilities and spectral properties seem to indicate different structures for these two derivatives.

Cyclopentadienylbis(dimethylamido)titanium(III) is reported to be formed by the action of cyclopentadiene on the tris(dimethylamido) derivative, $Ti(N[CH_3]_2)_3$ (*2*). One of the dimethylamido ligands of π-$C_5H_5Ti[N(CH_3)_2]_2$ is bridging and magnetic interaction between titanium atoms renders the compound virtually diamagnetic.

From $C_5H_5TiCl_3$ or $(C_5H_5)_2TiCl_2$ and the dipotassium salt of cyclooctatetraene, van Oven and de Liefde Meijer have recently isolated the green volatile titanium(III) derivative $C_5H_5TiC_8H_8$ (*170*). The magnetic moment of this complex is 1.6 BM and it is independent of temperature.

D. Alkyl and Aryl Titanium(III) Compounds

These are usually so thermally unstable that they cannot be isolated. Such is the case with trimethyltitanium, which has been obtained only as deep green solutions in tetrahydrofuran from titanium trichloride and methyllithium at $-50°$ to $-80°C$. Above $-20°C$ the solutions decompose, giving a gas and leaving a black residue (*26*).

The alkyltitanium dichlorides $RTiCl_2$, where $R=CH_3$ and C_8H_{17}, are mentioned in a French patent (*139*) as products of the reaction between titanium tetrachloride and the appropriate trialkylaluminum. Pyridine adducts of this class of compound, i.e., $RTiCl_2 \cdot 3$ py, where $R=CH_3$ and C_6H_5, were isolated by Japanese workers from the action of Grignard reagents on titanium trichloride in pyridine (*127*). The alkyl derivatives decompose at room temperature but the aryl is more stable. Despite the instability described by most workers, a recent communication from Kühlein and Clauss mentions the isolation of uncomplexed CH_3TiCl_2 for the first time and describes its use in ethylene polymerization (*110*), but details of its preparation and properties are lacking.

A novel complex of titanium has been isolated by Fischer and Röhrscheid (*62*) from titanium tetrachloride heated to 130°C with aluminum powder, aluminum chloride, and hexamethylbenzene. The complex, $(Ti_3[C_6(CH_3)_6]$-$Cl_6)Cl$, has a trinuclear cluster of titanium atoms with two bridging chlorides between each pair and one hexamethylbenzene molecule coordinated to each titanium atom. In line with its formulation as a trinuclear cluster, the violet compound has a magnetic moment of 1.84 BM, i.e., one unpaired electron per trinuclear unit.

From the same reactants in benzene instead of hexamethylbenzene, the complex $C_6H_6TiCl_2 \cdot 2\ AlCl_3$ has been isolated (*122*, *133*, *176*). This is a halogen-bridged titanium(III) complex with benzene coordinated to the central titanium atom. It is active in polymerization and nitrogen fixation and will be dealt with in Section IX,A.

V

ADDITION COMPLEXES OF TITANIUM DIHALIDES

Methods of preparation similar to those used for the trihalide complexes are generally successful, i.e., direct reaction between the dihalide and the donor ligand, but reaction times are necessarily longer and some ligands, e.g., pyridine, do not give clean products. Better results have been obtained by displacing methyl cyanide from $TiX_2 \cdot 2\ CH_3CN$, which can be formed in high yield from the two reactants (*71*). Although this method works

TABLE IV

ADDITION COMPLEXES OF TITANIUM DIHALIDES

Compound	Color	Visible spectra (kK) Solid	Solution	μ_{eff} (BM, 20°C)	References
		O-Coordinated			
$TiCl_2 \cdot 2$ THF	Dark brown	16.1 22.2	—	1.21	*67, 71*
$TiCl_2 \cdot 2$ THP	Black	14.3	—	0.99	*67, 71*
$TiCl_2 \cdot 2$ DMF	Green	—	—	1.17	*55*
		N-Coordinated			
$TiCl_2 \cdot 2\ CH_3CN$	Black	21.8	9.7 14.0	1.05^T	*67, 71*
$TiCl_2 \cdot 2$ py	Brown	24.4	25.2	1.14	*67, 71*
$TiCl_2 \cdot$ bipy	Dark blue	20.0	14.0 19.0	1.09	*67, 71*
$TiCl_2 \cdot$ phen	Dark blue	16.7	18.0	1.11^T	*67, 71*
$TiBr_2 \cdot 2\ CH_3CN$	Black	9.7	14.0	1.0^T	*67, 71*
$TiBr_2 \cdot$ bipy	Dark blue	15.4	17.0	1.10	*67, 71*

reasonably well with the dichloride, little success has been achieved with the bromide. As a result, the methyl cyanide and bypyridyl adducts remain the only *N*-coordinated complexes of $TiBr_2$ so far characterized. All of the dihalide complexes are dark brown or blue in color and are strong reducing agents. They are oxidized by air and react with water to produce hydrogen. Their magnetic moments are all in the range 0.99–1.35 BM, in accord with polymeric structures with bridging ligands, probably forming six-coordinate titanium. Their visible spectra show only weak shoulders superimposed on rising absorption in the ultraviolet region above 10 kK (Table IV).

VI

COMPLEXES OF TYPE $TiX_n \cdot (2-n)L$

A. *Alkoxides of Titanium(II)*

Titanium(II) alkoxides, $Ti(OR)_2$ where R = benzyl or allyl, are believed to be intermediates in the coupling of benzyl or allyl alcohol to bibenzyl or

TABLE V

COMPLEXES OF TYPE $TiX_n \cdot (2-n)L$

Compound	Probable structure	Color	Visible spectra (kK)		μ_{eff} (BM, 20°C)	References
			Solid	Solution (ϵ)		
β-Diketonates						
$Ti(acac)_2$	Polymeric	Red-brown	—	16.4 (110) 20.8 (207)	0.41^T	*156*
Amido Derivatives						
$(Ti[N(CH_3)_2]_2)_n$	Polymeric	Black-green	—	—	—	*2*
$(Ti[N(C_2H_5)_2]_2)_n$	Polymeric	Black-green	—	—	—	*2*
$(Ti[N(iso\text{-}C_3H_7)_2]_2)_n$	Polymeric	Black-green	—	—	—	*2*
Phosphido Derivative						
$Ti[P(C_6H_{11})_2]_2$	Monomeric	Black-brown	—	—	—	*99*
Dithiocarbamate						
$Ti[S_2CN(C_2H_5)_2]_2$	—	—	—	—	—	*2*

1,5-hexadiene (*172*). Impure titanium(II) benzoxide was obtained as a black, air-sensitive solid by reduction with metallic potassium, sodium naphthalide, or alkyllithium of the reaction product from $TiCl_3$ or $TiCl_4$ and benzyl alcohol. On being heated in glyme the black alkoxide generated bibenzyl. Coupling of saturated alcohols in the same manner was not successful.

B. β-Diketonate of Titanium(II)

No carboxylates of titanium(II) are known but the bis(acetylacetonato) derivative, $Ti(acac)_2$, was reported by Salzmann in 1968 (*156*). The red-brown product was prepared by reduction of $Ti(acac)_2Cl_2$ with sodium sand in tetrahydrofuran; it is almost diamagnetic and its insolubility and low chemical reactivity probably indicate a polymeric structure.

C. Amido Derivatives of Titanium(II)

Several dialkylamido derivatives have been mentioned in a recent communication (*2*). The green-black pyrophoric compounds, $Ti(NR_2)_2$ where $R = CH_3$, C_2H_5, or iso-C_3H_7, were obtained, as well as the corresponding titanium(IV) compounds, by disproportionation of the trivalent amido compounds $Ti(NR_2)_3$.

D. Bis(diethyldithiocarbamato)titanium(II)

Disproportionation was observed also on attempted insertion of carbon disulfide into $Ti[N(CH_3)_2]_3$. The bis- and tetra(diethyldithiocarbamato)-titanium derivatives were obtained (*2*).

E. Phosphido Derivative of Titanium(II)

On treatment of $TiCl_3 \cdot 3$ THF or $TiCl_4 \cdot 2$ THF with lithium di(cyclohexyl)phosphide, reduction occurred and the titanium(II) compound $Ti[P(C_6H_{11})_2]_2$ was isolated as a black-brown pyrophoric compound which behaves as a monomer in benzene (*99*). With iodine oxidation to the titanium (IV) species $TiI_2[P(C_6H_{11})_2]_2$ and $TiI_3 \cdot P(C_6H_{11})_2$ occurs.

VII

ORGANOMETALLIC COMPOUNDS OF TITANIUM(II)

A Bis(cyclopentadienyl)titanium(II) and Derivatives

1. *Preparation*

Although a preparation of bis(cyclopentadienyl)titanium (titanocene) from titanium dichloride was reported by A. K. Fischer and Wilkinson (*59*) in 1956, no one has yet succeeded in repeating this preparation (*185*). Other syntheses of $(C_5H_5)_2Ti$ are now available but there is some reason to believe that the bonding in the "titanocenes" prepared by the various methods is not consistent.

In 1962 Clauss and Bestian reported (*27*) that solutions of bis(cyclopentadienyl)dimethyltitanium in hexane deposited green crystalline $(C_5H_5)_2Ti$ on exposure to hydrogen at ambient temperatures.

$$(\pi\text{-}C_5H_5)_2Ti(CH_3)_2 + H_2 \rightarrow (C_5H_5)_2Ti + 2\ CH_4 \tag{4}$$

In fact, a solution of titanocene in tetrahydrofuran may be prepared directly from $(\pi\text{-}C_5H_5)_2TiCl_2$ and 2 moles of methyllithium in a hydrogen atmosphere. On treatment with halogens and other reagents the titanocene was oxidized to known titanium(IV) compounds, which is good reason to believe that both of the rings are π-bonded.

Russian workers have prepared $(C_5H_5)_2Ti$ from the same dimethyl derivative and also from the diphenyl derivative, by pyrolysis in hexane in a sealed tube at 90° C. The yield of green-black $(C_5H_5)_2Ti$ was reported to be 91% (*148*).

A later preparation of $(C_5H_5)_2Ti$ by Watt and co-workers (*186*) used strongly reducing sodium naphthalide to remove the two chloride ions from $(\pi\text{-}C_5H_5)_2TiCl_2$. Modifications of this reductive method employ sodium sand in toluene or tetrahydrofuran (*158*) or sodium amalgam (*162*). Interestingly, with one equivalent of anhydrous hydrogen chloride the "Watt titanocene" is converted fairly rapidly to a purple compound, $[(C_5H_5)_2TiCl]_n$, while a second equivalent slowly forms green, insoluble $[(C_5H_5)_2TiCl_2]_n$. Both of these products differ from the usual forms of the chlorides and these results were interpreted by Salzmann and Mosimann (*158*) as indicating the presence of two different types of ring–metal bonding, i.e., π- and σ-types. Support for this theory came from Köpf and Block (*109*), who used titanocene to split disulfides, diselenides, and iodine, to give

$(C_5H_5)_2TiX_2$, where X=SR, SeR, or I. The low yields of known compounds obtained possibly reflects the different types of ring–metal bonding present and the difficulty of changing to the bis(π-cyclopentadienyl) derivatives. In addition, Calderazzo, Salzmann, and Mosimann (*17*) obtained two different bipyridyl adducts of titanocene according to the method used (see below). The reactions reported below have been carried out using $(C_5H_5)_2Ti$ from reduction of the dichloride. There seems to have been little work done with the corresponding compound of Clauss and Bestian (*27*) or Razuvaev and co-workers (*148*). A comparison between the two should be made.

2. *Reactions of* $(C_5H_5)_2Ti$

$(C_5H_5)_2Ti$ is a dark green diamagnetic solid which is dimeric in benzene (*17, 158, 186*), although its mass spectrum shows no peaks at *m/e* greater than that of the monomer (*168*). The NMR spectrum shows four peaks between τ 3.3 and 4.1 (*158*).

With oxygen the peroxo compound $[(C_5H_5)_2TiO_2]$ was obtained, while nitric oxide produced the hyponitrite $(C_5H_5)_2TiNO$, which appears to be a polymer and is weakly paramagnetic (μ_{eff} 0.43 BM) (*157*).

"Titanocene" absorbs carbon monoxide slowly at room temperature and atmospheric pressure, giving low yields of the known dicarbonyl $(C_5H_5)_2Ti(CO)_2$ (*17*; see below).

Japanese workers have investigated the reactions of titanocene with acetylenes and have found that acetylene itself was readily polymerized at 30°C by $(C_5H_5)_2Ti$, giving red-black "polyacetylene" containing trans double bonds (*192*). Mass spectral evidence suggests (*168*) that the complex

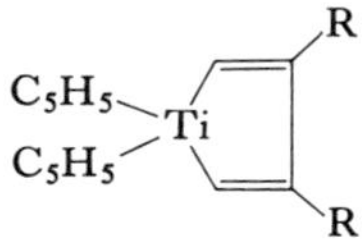

(XVIa) 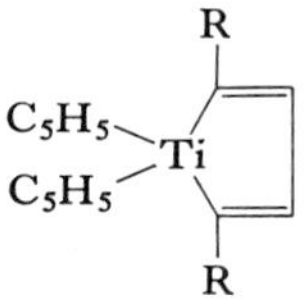 (XVIb)

from $(C_5H_5)_2Ti$ and methylacetylene has structure (XVIa) or (XVIb). Similar types of compounds have been isolated from the reactions between diphenylacetylene or phenylacetylene and $(C_5H_5)_2Ti(CO)_2$ (*124, 164*) or a mixture of titanium tetrachloride and excess sodium cyclopentadienide (*177*).

An interesting reaction between titanocene and boron halides was demonstrated by Nöth and collaborators (*161*); the halides are split giving purple titanium–boron-bonded derivatives as shown in Eq. (5), where

$$[(C_5H_5)_2Ti] + 2\,Y_2BX \longrightarrow (C_5H_5)_2Ti\begin{matrix} X \\ BY_2 \end{matrix} \tag{5}$$

X and Y = Cl and C_6H_5, Br and Br, or Cl and Cl.

With triethylaluminum in benzene in a sealed tube at 60° C "titanocene" undergoes an insertion reaction with liberation of ethane (*184*). The purple product obtained is diamagnetic and appears to be identical in every respect with the complex obtained by Natta and co-workers (*29*, *132*) from $(C_5H_5)_2TiCl$ and $(C_2H_5)_3Al$ in boiling benzene, in which aluminum apparently bridges between titanium and the cyclopentadienyl ligand on the neighboring titanium atom as in (XVII).

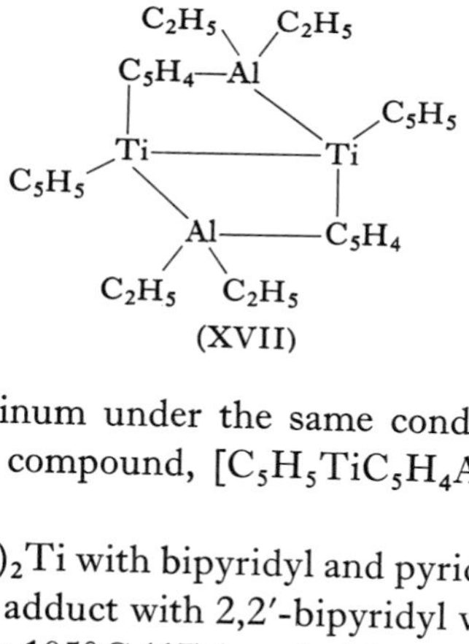

$$\begin{array}{ccccc} & C_2H_5 & & C_2H_5 & \\ & C_5H_4 & — & Al & \\ & | & & & C_5H_5 \\ & Ti & — & Ti & \\ C_5H_5 & & & | & \\ & & Al & — & C_5H_4 \\ & C_2H_5 & & C_2H_5 & \end{array}$$

(XVII)

With trimethylaluminum under the same conditions titanocene forms the analogous methyl compound, $[C_5H_5TiC_5H_4Al(CH_3)_2]_2$ with loss of methane (*184*).

Complexes of $(C_5H_5)_2Ti$ with bipyridyl and pyridine have been obtained in various ways. A 1:1 adduct with 2,2′-bipyridyl was obtained by heating the reactants together at 105° C (*17*) but the blue complex was too insoluble for molecular weight measurements to be made. Another adduct of the same stoichiometry was obtained (*17*) by reduction of the dichloride with dilithium bipyridyl. This compound is dark blue and monomeric, and

$$(C_5H_5)_2TiCl_2 + Li_2bipy \rightarrow (C_5H_5)_2Ti\cdot bipy + 2\,LiCl \tag{6}$$

is probably the same complex as was isolated by Fischer and Amtmann (*60*) from the action of 2,2′-bipyridyl on the dicarbonyl $(C_5H_5)_2Ti(CO)_2$.

Reduction of $(C_5H_5)_2TiCl_2$ with sodium pyridyl gave a complex of formula $[(C_5H_5)_2Ti]_2\cdot 3$ py (*184*). Oxidation followed by sublimation gave

TABLE VI

ORGANOMETALLIC COMPOUNDS OF TITANIUM(II)

Compound	Color	Visible spectra (kK)		μ_{eff} (BM, 20° C)	References
		Solid	Solution		
$(C_5H_5)_2Ti$	Dark green	—	—	Diamag.	*27, 59, 148, 158, 162, 186*
$(C_5H_5)_2Ti(CO)_2$	Red-brown	—	20.6 (277)	Diamag.	*17, 60, 61, 128*
$(C_5H_5)_2Ti \cdot NO$	Brown	—	—	0.43	*157*
$(C_5H_5)_2Ti \cdot bipy$	Blue-black	—	12.8 (2130)	0.6	*17, 60*
			17.4 (2530)	0.80	
$[(C_5H_5)_2Ti]_2 \cdot 3\ py$	Red-brown	—	—	0.96	*184*
$[(C_5H_5)_2Ti]_2 \cdot py$	Brown	—	—	—	*184*
$[C_5H_5Ti(C_5H_4)Al(C_2H_5)_2]_2$	Purple	—	9.3	Diamag.	*29, 132, 184*
$[C_5H_5Ti(C_5H_4)Al(CH_3)_2]_2$	Purple	—	—	Diamag.	*184*
$(C_5H_5)_2Ti[O{=}C{=}C(C_6H_5)_2]$	Orange-yellow	—	—	—	*97*
$C_5H_5TiC_6H_5 \cdot 2\ O(C_2H_5)_2$	Black	—	—	—	*147, 148*
$C_5H_5TiC_6H_5 \cdot 2\ NH_3$	Black	—	—	—	*147, 148*
$(C_6H_5)_2Ti$	Black	—	—	—	*111, 146*
$(C_6H_5)_2Ti \cdot THF$	Black	—	—	—	*111, 146*
$(C_6H_5)_2Ti \cdot NH_3$	Black	—	—	—	*111, 146*

a mixture of several bipyridyls so that it is not known whether the ligand is coordinated as pyridine or bipyridyl. Titanocene will dissolve on heating in pyridine and from the solution $[(C_5H_5)_2Ti]_2py$ has been isolated (*184*). Both of these complexes have been characterized by elemental analyses and molecular weight determinations.

The fact that complexing of "titanocene" with such donor ligands gives compounds which are not formed by reduction of $(C_5H_5)_2TiCl_2$ by alkali metal derivatives of the same ligands seems further proof that this reduction alters the bonding in the titanocene in some way. Comparison with the $(C_5H_5)_2Ti$ of Clauss and Bestian (*27*) or of Razuvaev and co-workers (*148*) would be of great interest.

3. *Bis(cyclopentadienyl)titanium dicarbonyl*

The only carbonyl of titanium is $(C_5H_5)_2Ti(CO)_2$, which was first prepared by Murray in 1959 (*128*) from titanium tetrachloride [or $(C_5H_5)_2TiCl_2$], excess sodium cyclopentadienide, and carbon monoxide under pressure. The carbonyl has been obtained also from the action of CO on $(C_5H_5)_3Ti$ at 80° C and 150 atm (*61*) and on $(C_5H_5)_2Ti$ at 20° C and atmospheric pressure (*17*). It is a red-brown readily sublimable solid which is pyrophoric in air and behaves as a monomer in benzene. Because of its diamagnetism, the NMR spectrum of the dicarbonyl shows a single sharp proton resonance peak at 5.42 τ in benzene-d_6, or 4.94 τ in acetone-d_6 (*17*).

As was mentioned above, $(C_5H_5)_2Ti(CO)_2$ expels carbon monoxide on treatment with substituted acetylenes and forms green titanium(IV) derivatives of type (XVIa) or (XVIb) (*124*, *164*), and with bipyridyl blue-black $(C_5H_5)_2Ti\cdot bipy$ is formed (*60*). When heated in solution to 160° C with phenanthroline or terpyridyl the Ti^0 complexes Ti·3 phen and Ti·2 terpy were obtained (*8*). These are violet to black in color and are diamagnetic. A similar reaction occurs with diphenylketene (*97*); carbon monoxide is expelled and the orange-yellow crystalline complex $(C_5H_5)_2Ti\cdot[O{=}C{=}C(C_6H_5)_2]$ is obtained.

The carbonyl also acts as a homogeneous catalyst for the hydrogenation of 1-alkynes to 1-alkenes (*164*).

B. *Mono(cyclopentadienyl)titanium(II) Compounds*

The only compound of this type is cyclopentadienylphenyltitanium which was isolated as an etherate, $C_5H_5TiC_6H_5\cdot 2\,O(C_2H_5)_2$, by Razuvaev and colleagues during their work on the pyrolysis of titanium(IV) derivatives of type $(C_5H_5)_nTiR_{(4-n)}$ (*147, 148*). At 20°C in ether $C_5H_5Ti(C_6H_5)_3$ decomposes with loss of two phenyl ligands, leaving the black etherate. With gaseous ammonia this is converted to a black ammoniate C_5H_5Ti-$C_6H_5 \cdot 2\ NH_3$.

C. Diphenyltitanium(II)

This is the only purely σ-bonded organotitanium(II) compound reported. Tetraphenyltitanium is thermally unstable above −20°C, eliminating two phenyl groups to form black diphenyltitanium. This compound complexes with tetrahydrofuran and also with anhydrous ammonia, giving 1:1 adducts (*111, 146*).

VIII

COMPLEXES OF TITANIUM IN VALENCIES LOWER THAN TWO

Under strongly reducing conditions in the presence of donor ligands titanium halides form a number of complexes in which the formal oxidation state of the metal is below 2. Breil and Wilke found that when titanium tetrabutoxide was reduced with triethylaluminum in the presence of cyclooctatetraene two complexes were formed depending on the ratio of reactants (*13*). These were $Ti(cot)_2$ and $Ti_2(cot)_3$, both formed in over 80% yield. The complexes are interconvertible and an X-ray crystal structure investigation of $Ti_2(cot)_3$ has shown it to have a double sandwich structure (*50*). The two outer rings are regular octahedrons whose planes are slightly inclined towards the axis of the molecule.

$Ti(cot)_2$ can also be prepared from $TiCl_4$ with 2 moles of disodium cyclooctatetraene. It is believed that the cyclooctatetraene molecules are bonded, at least partly, as quasi-aromatic planar 10 π-electron systems, i.e., as dianions (*13*).

When $(C_5H_5)_2Ti(CO)_2$ was heated to 160°C with phenanthroline or terpyridyl, carbon monoxide and cyclopentadienyl ligands were lost and the titanium(0) complexes $Ti(phen)_3$ and $Ti(terpy)_2$ were obtained (*8*).

TABLE VII

COMPLEXES OF TITANIUM IN VALENCIES LOWER THAN TWO

Compound	Color	μ_{eff} (BM, 20°C)	References
$Ti(cot)_2$	Violet-red	—	*13*
$Ti_2(cot)_3$	Yellow	—	*13, 50*
$Ti(phen)_3$	Violet-black	Diamag.	*8*
$Ti(terpy)_2$	Black	Diamag.	*8*
$Ti(bipy)_3$	Violet-black	Diamag.	*93, 94*
$Li[Ti(bipy)_3]3.7$ THF	Blue-violet	1.75	*93, 94*
$Li_2[Ti(bipy)_3]5.7$ THF	Green	Diamag.	*95*
$Li_3[Ti(bipy)_3]7$ THF	—	1.75	*92*

The dark violet to black compounds, formed in almost quantitative yield, are diamagnetic.

Herzog and co-workers have prepared a tris(bipyridyl) complex of titanium by reduction of titanium tetrachloride with dilithium bipyridyl in the presence of excess bipyridyl (*93, 94*). Further reduction of this complex with lithium or sodium in tetrahydrofuran or lithium aluminum hydride has given a series of complexes containing titanium in low oxidation states, and nonstoichiometric numbers of coordinated molecules of tetrahydrofuran (*92, 95*). These appear to be only weakly bonded.

$$\begin{array}{ccc} Ti(bipy)_3 & \underset{\text{Oxid}}{\overset{\text{Li}}{\rightleftarrows}} & Li[Ti(bipy)_3]\cdot 3.7\ \text{THF} \\ & & \text{Oxid}\uparrow\downarrow\text{Li} \\ Li_3[Ti(bipy)_3]\cdot 7\ \text{THF} & \rightleftarrows & Li_2[Ti(bipy)_3]\cdot 5.7\ \text{THF} \end{array} \qquad (7)$$

Although it would appear that the titanium reaches an oxidation number of −3, it is more probable that the ligands are being reduced and are functioning as anions (*92*), the electrons being delocalized into the ligand rings.

The bipyridyl complexes are interconvertible and by controlled oxidation the above reduction sequence may be reversed as shown in Eq. (7).

IX

LOWER-VALENT TITANIUM COMPLEXES IN CATALYSIS

A. Olefin Polymerization

It is not the purpose of this article to review the field of olefin polymerization (see *11*, *57*, *103*, for reviews) but any treatment of titanium(III) derivatives would not be complete without mention of some of the compounds which have been obtained during the search for new polymerization catalysts.

The Ziegler-type catalysts are in general composed of a transition metal compound and an organometallic reducing agent containing a Group I–III metal, the function of which is to alkylate and reduce the transition metal and to complex with it (*103*). Catalysts used in industry generally are prepared from $TiCl_4$ or $TiCl_3$ and triethylaluminum and undoubtedly contain alkyltitanium compounds, but their heterogeneous nature means that the structures and mechanism involved in the polymerization process are difficult to study and are not well understood.

Soluble catalysts for olefin polymerization have been prepared by reaction of $(\pi\text{-}C_5H_5)_2TiCl_2$ with alkylaluminums or alkylaluminum halides and several well-defined titanium complexes have been isolated as a result of this work. In addition, the mechanism of polymerization using these systems has been discussed (*84*) in terms of the theory proposed by Cossee (*30*) for heterogeneous catalysis.

With $(C_5H_5)_2TiCl_2$ and $(C_2H_5)_3Al$ reduction occurs extremely rapidly with evolution of ethane, giving the titanium(III) complex (XIX; X = Cl, R = C_2H_5). The fast reduction rate makes this mixture a poor catalyst for polymerization (*84*). With $(C_2H_5)_2AlCl$ or $C_2H_5AlCl_2$ the reduction is slower and the various steps in the reaction can be followed. It is believed that the first step is the rapid formation of a diamagnetic complex (*14*, *84*, *113*), e.g., $(C_5H_5)_2TiCl_2\cdot(C_2H_5)_2AlCl$, with bridging bonds between the two metals, in which some authors maintain (*84*, *150*), the titanium(IV) ion is in an octahedral environment with one vacant coordination site, e.g., (XVIII).

In the presence of olefins, π-bonding into the vacant site can occur, the double bond is weakened, and polymerization results. In the absence of olefins, hydrogen is transferred from one ethyl group to another on a second

$$\begin{array}{c} C_2H_5 \\ | \\ (C_5H_5)_2Ti\begin{array}{c}-Cl-\\ \\ -Cl-\end{array}Al\begin{array}{c}C_2H_5\\ \\ Cl\end{array} \end{array}$$

(XVIII)

molecule, probably via the vacant coordination site, giving ethylene and ethane (*84*). As a result the complex slowly loses its activity and changes to a stable paramagnetic complex in which the titanium has been reduced to the trivalent state and is now in a distorted tetrahedral environment. Methylaluminum compounds follow the same reaction course but reduction occurs less readily (*6, 117, 132*). An X-ray study of (XIX; $X = Cl$, $R = C_2H_5$) has been carried out by Natta, Corradini, and Bassi (*129*) and shows the distorted tetrahedral arrangement around titanium with the bond angles in the central four-membered ring close to 90°.

$$(C_5H_5)_2Ti\begin{array}{c}-X-\\ \\ -X-\end{array}Al\begin{array}{c}R\\ \\ R\end{array}$$

(XIX)

Complexes of type (XIX) have been prepared also from $(\pi\text{-}C_5H_5)_2TiCl$ and alkyls or halides of aluminum (*131*). By reduction of $(\pi\text{-}C_5H_5)_2Ti(C_3H_7)Cl$ with sodium or potassium in the presence of a Group III trichloride, similar complexes containing boron, gallium, or indium instead of aluminum were obtained (*87–89*). These complexes are tabulated in Table VIII; they are blue to green in color with one unpaired electron per titanium atom. The ESR spectra of some have been recorded (*6, 87–89, 117*) and show hyperfine interaction of the unpaired electron of the titanium (III) atom with the magnetic nuclei of the Group III elements.

The zinc complex $(\pi\text{-}C_5H_5)_2TiCl_2ZnCl_2Ti(\pi\text{-}C_5H_5)_2$, is readily prepared by reduction of $(\pi\text{-}C_5H_5)_2TiCl_2$ with metallic zinc and has been mentioned previously (Section IV,B,1).

From titanium tetrachloride, aluminum, and aluminum chloride in benzene an arene-titanium(II) complex, $C_6H_6 \cdot TiCl_2 \cdot 2\,AlCl_3$, was isolated (*122, 133, 176*). This has been formulated as the halogen-bridged complex (XX) in which benzene is coordinated to the central titanium ion (*176*); it is an active catalyst for the cyclooligomerization of butadiene (*176*) and is also useful in nitrogen fixation (*178, 179*),

TABLE VIII

BIMETALLIC COMPOUNDS WITH BRIDGING BONDS

Compound	Color	Visible spectra (kK)		μ_{eff} (BM, 20° C)	References
		Solid	Solution		
$(\pi\text{-}C_5H_5)_2TiCl_2ZnCl_2Ti(\pi\text{-}C_5H_5)_2$	Green	—	7.7 (33) 14.3 (96)	1.71^T	*155*
$(\pi\text{-}C_5H_5)_2TiCl_2Al(C_2H_5)_2$	Blue	—	—	1.70	*14, 129, 131, 134, 135*
$(\pi\text{-}C_5H_5)_2TiCl_2Al(C_2H_5)Cl$	Blue	—	—	1.56	*84, 130, 131, 132, 135*
$(\pi\text{-}C_5H_5)_2Ti(CH_3)ClAl(CH_3)_2$	—	—	—	—	*132*
$(\pi\text{-}C_5H_5)_2TiCl_2Al(CH_3)_2$	—	—	—	—	*6, 117*
$(\pi\text{-}C_5H_5)_2TiCl_2Al(iso\text{-}C_4H_9)_2$	—	—	—	—	*6, 117*
$(\pi\text{-}C_5H_5)_2TiCl_2MCl_2$ (M = B, Al, Ga, In)	Blue	—	—	1.7	*84, 87, 89, 130, 131, 135*
$[C_5H_5Ti(C_5H_4)\cdot Al(C_2H_5)_2]_2$	Purple	—	9.3	Diamag.	*29, 132, 184*
$[C_5H_5Ti(C_5H_4)\cdot Al(CH_3)_2]_2$	Purple	—	—	Diamag.	*184*
$Cl_2AlCl_2TiCl_2AlCl_2$ (with arene ring bonded to Ti, drawn as a structure)	—	—	—	—	*122, 133, 176, 178, 179*
$(C_9H_7)_2TiCl_2Al(C_2H_5)_2$	Dark green	—	—	—	*118*
$(C_9H_7)_2TiBr_2Al(C_2H_5)_2$	Green	—	—	1.68	*118*
$(C_9H_7)_2TiI_2Al(C_2H_5)_2$	Green	—	—	—	*118*

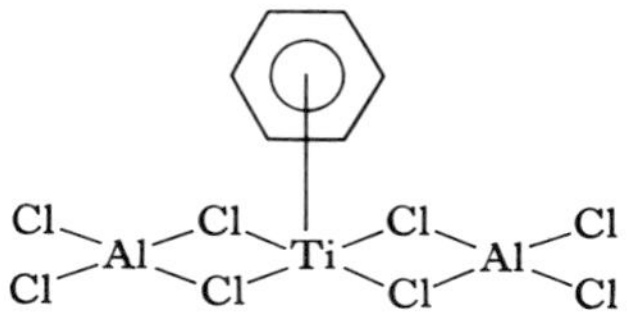

Cl Cl Cl Cl
Al Ti Al
Cl Cl Cl Cl

(XX)

The effectiveness of aryltitanium compounds as polymerization catalysts for vinyl chloride has been investigated by Razuvaev and co-workers (*149*). With the introduction of cyclopentadienyl ligands, the activity of the catalyst decreased.

From $(\pi\text{-}C_5H_5)_2TiCl$ and $(C_2H_5)_3Al$ in boiling benzene Natta and co-workers obtained the red complex $[(C_5H_5)Ti(C_5H_4)Al(C_2H_5)_2]_2$ (*156*) which is also active in polymerization. The same compound has been obtained by Wailes and Weigold (*184*) from titanocene and $(C_2H_5)_3Al$; its structure, determined from an X-ray study by Corradini and Sirigu (*29*), is discussed in Section VII,A,2. The methyl analog of this complex, $[(C_5H_5)Ti(C_5H_4)Al(CH_3)_2]_2$, has been obtained in a similar manner from titanocene and trimethylaluminum with liberation of methane (*184*).

The bis(indenyl) derivatives $(C_9H_7)_2TiX_2Al(C_2H_5)_2$ where X = Cl, Br, or I, have been isolated also (*118*) from $(C_9H_7)_2TiCl_2$ treated with triethylaluminum. With trimethylamine the complexes are split to give the corresponding bis(indenyl)titanium(III) halide. The olefin polymerization properties of the indenyl complexes have been explored by Marconi and collaborators (*118*).

B. Nitrogen Fixation

One of the most significant advances in metal-organic chemistry in recent years has been the realization that transition metals with unsaturated coordination sites can react with dinitrogen (N_2), either to form stable coordination complexes or intermediates capable of reacting with a proton source to give ammonia.

The stable dinitrogen complexes are generally found among the elements of higher atomic number and do not concern us here. For fixation of nitrogen the active systems consist of a complex or a salt of a transition metal reduced with Grignard reagents, alkyl or aryl lithiums, alkylaluminums, lithium aluminum hydride, or alkali metal naphthalide. Although chromium, molybdenum, tungsten, iron, cobalt, nickel, and zirconium are active in fixation, titanium is the most efficient (*178*, *179*), and most of the later experiments have been carried out using this metal.

The ligands around the metal influence its activity appreciably (*180*), as might be expected, but the extent of this influence has not been fully investigated. Most experiments have been carried out using halides, alkoxides, or cyclopentadienyl derivatives of titanium.

In a typical experiment of the type initiated by Vol'pin (*180*) excess ethylmagnesium bromide is added to bis(cyclopentadienyl)titanium dichloride in ether. Evolution of ethane and ethylene occurs immediately, the color changing from red to green to brown. The "reduced solution" will now absorb nitrogen, up to 1 gm atom per mole of titanium complex. High pressure hastens the absorption but does not increase the yield of nitrogen complex (*85*, *126*). The process has been studied by ESR spectroscopy both for Grignard reagents (*15*, *16*) and lithium naphthalide (*86*), and the kinetics of the reactions have been investigated (*125*, *126*). It seems to be agreed that these data indicate the presence of a monomeric titanium(III) hydride such as (XXI) in the "reduced solution," which is probably the intermediate in the fixation process.

$$\left[(C_5H_5)_2Ti(H)_2\right]^-$$

(XXI)

Although Nechiporenko maintains that the "reduced solution" loses its nitrogen-fixing ability with time (*136*), other authors found little loss of activity on aging (*126*), but fixation is inhibited by complexing agents which compete with nitrogen, e.g., carbon monoxide and acetylenes (*180*). The function of the Grignard reagent is merely to reduce the metal compound (*126*).

The mechanism of nitrogen complexation which follows formation of the reduced intermediate is not well understood. Since the molar ratio $NH_3:Ti$ does not exceed 1 in the system under discussion, then two titanium atoms must be involved in any dinitrogen complex. Whether these are contained in two separate molecules or in a dimeric intermediate has not been established. The nitrogen complex shows weak and complex ESR signals from which no conclusions could be drawn (*15*). The simplest explanation is the formation of a titanium nitride complex, as first suggested by Nechiporenko (*136*), which gives ammonia on hydrolysis (*125*). It is possible that the efficiency of titanium in nitrogen fixation experiments parallels its ready formation of nitrides (*126*).

In the system titanium trichloride and magnesium in tetrahydrofuran under nitrogen, Japanese workers have found nitrides of the type $[TiNMg_2Cl_2 \cdot THF]$ (*191*). Tetrahydrofuran and/or magnesium could be replaced without loss of nitrogen by treatment with pyridine, bipyridyl or benzoyl chloride. A hydrogen complex $[TiNMg_4Cl_{1.5}H_2 \cdot 2\,THF]$, was also observed. Although all of these complexes are noncrystalline they are believed to be homogeneous and all gave one equivalent of ammonia on hydrolysis

Russian workers found that $(C_5H_5)_2TiR_2$, where $R = CH_3$ or C_6H_5, added nitrogen on heating and the products gave ammonia on hydrolysis (*182*). Since the dimethyl- and diphenyltitanium(IV) compounds give $(C_5H_5)_2Ti$ on pyrolysis at 90° C (*148*), it would seem that titanocene is the active constituent. However, preformed titanocene reacted to a lesser degree, in line with the observations of van Tamelen (*175*).

In attempts to prepare a true catalytic system for nitrogen fixation Vol'pin and co-workers used $TiCl_4$ or $Ti(OR)_4$ reduced with aluminum powder and aluminum bromide at temperatures above 50° C in benzene or molten $AlBr_3$ (*178*, *179*). With ratios of $TiCl_4:Al:AlBr_3$ of 1:600:1000 at 130° C and 100 atm of nitrogen, yields of ammonia in the molar ratio $NH_3:Ti$ of 200 or more were obtained. In benzene the stable halogen-bridged complex $C_6H_6 \cdot TiCl_2 \cdot 2\,AlCl_3$ is formed (*122*, *133*, *176*; see Section IX,A) and this is believed to be the active compound. In the absence of aluminum and aluminum bromide the complex reacts with nitrogen at 130° C to give a compound whose analysis is close to that of $C_6H_6(TiCl_2 \cdot 2\,AlCl_3)_3N$ and which gives a stoichiometric yield of ammonia on hydrolysis (*178*).

Vol'pin has shown also that nitrogen can insert between an organic group and titanium (*181*). Thus in reactions of $(C_5H_5)_2TiCl_2$, $TiCl_4$, or $Ti(OR)_4$ with phenyllithium in ether under nitrogen at atmospheric pressure aniline as well as ammonia was obtained on hydrolysis.

Using systems based on titanium alkoxides reduced with alkali metals or alkali metal naphthalide, van Tamelen and co-workers have developed a system for fixation of nitrogen at atmospheric pressure which gives, after addition of a proton source, up to 1.1 for the molar ratio $NH_3:Ti$ per pass (*174*). A typical system consists of titanium tetraisopropoxide reduced with sodium naphthalide in diglyme in a stream of nitrogen. Two equivalents of alkali metal are required before nitrogen uptake commences, which means that a titanium(II) complex is the active species (*173*). If isopropanol is added as the proton source after nitrogen uptake is complete after 30–60 min, the process becomes a cyclic one provided the ammonia is removed and additional metallic sodium is added to regenerate sodium naphthalide. Over five such cycles a yield of ammonia corresponding to the molar ratio of 3.4 for $NH_3:Ti$ was obtained (*174*). The process may be represented by Eq. (8),

$$N_2 + 6\,e^- + 6\,ROH \rightarrow 2\,NH_3 + 6\,RO^- \qquad (8)$$

In addition a significant uptake of nitrogen from air has been observed by van Tamelen using such a system (*174*). Electrolytic reduction of molecular nitrogen to ammonia has been demonstrated using an electrolysis medium of $Ti(O\text{-iso-}C_3H_7)_4$ plus aluminum chloride (1:1.5) in 1,2-dimethoxyethane. Nitrogen was bubbled through the electrolysis cell and after 2 days about 10% yield of ammonia had been collected (*171*).

The authors claim that this system parallels the steps in the simplest biological nitrogen fixation system, namely, interaction of a transition metal in a low oxidation state with dinitrogen, subsequent reduction of the resulting coordinated nitrogen complex, followed by protonation and hydrolysis to give ammonia.

References

1. Adams, R. W., Bishop, E., Martin, R. L., and Winter, G., *Australian J. Chem.* **19**, 207 (1966).
2. Alyea, E. C., Bradley, D. C., Lappert, M. F., and Sanger, A. R., *Chem. Commun.* p. 1064 (1969).
3. Antler, M., and Laubengayer, A. W., *J. Am. Chem. Soc.* **77**, 5250 (1955).
4. Baker, K. L., and Fowles, G. W. A., *J. Chem. Soc., A* p. 801 (1968).
5. Barnum, D. W., *J. Inorg. & Nucl. Chem.* **21**, 221 (1961).
6. Bartelink, H. J. M., Bos, H., Smidt, J., Vrinssen, C. H., and Adema, E. H., *Rec. Trav. Chim.* **81**, 225 (1962).
7. Bartlett, P. D., and Seidel, B., *J. Am. Chem. Soc.* **83**, 581 (1961).
8. Behrens, H., and Brandl, H., *Z. Naturforsch.* **22b**, 1216 (1967).

8a. Bercaw, J. E., and Brintzinger, H., *J. Am. Chem. Soc.* **91**, 7301 (1969).

9. Birmingham, J. M., Fischer, A. K., and Wilkinson, G., *Naturwissenschaften* **42**, 96 (1955).
10. Blažeková, M., and Schläfer, H. L., *Z. Anorg. Allgem. Chem.* **360**, 169 (1968).
11. Boor, J., *Macromol. Rev.* **2**, 115 (1967).

12. Brauer, G., "Handbook of Preparative Inorganic Chemistry," 2nd ed., Vol. 2. Academic Press, New York, 1965.
13. Breil, H., and Wilke, G., *Angew. Chem. Intern. Ed. Engl.* **5**, 898 (1966).
14. Breslow, D. S., and Newburg, N. R., *J. Am. Chem. Soc.* **81**, 81 (1959).
15. Brintzinger, H., *J. Am. Chem. Soc.* **88**, 4305 (1966).
16. Brintzinger, H., *J. Am. Chem. Soc.* **89**, 6871 (1967).
17. Calderazzo, F., Salzmann, J. J., and Mosimann, P., *Inorg. Chim. Acta* **1**, 65 (1967).
18. Canty, A. J., Coutts, R. S. P., and Wailes, P. C., *Australian J. Chem.* **21**, 807 (1968).
19. Casey, A. T., and Clark, R. J. H., unpublished work (cited in Clark, 23).
20. Chakravarti, B. N., *Naturwissenschaften* **45**, 286 (1958).
21. Chatt, J., and Hayter, R. G., *J. Chem. Soc.* p. 1343 (1963).
22. Clark, R. J. H., *Spectrochim. Acta* **21**, 955 (1965).
23. Clark, R. J. H., "The Chemistry of Titanium and Vanadium." Elsevier, Amsterdam, 1968.
24. Clark, R. J. H., and Greenfield, M. L., *J. Chem. Soc.* p. 409 (1967).
25. Clark, R. J. H., Lewis, J., Machin, D. J., and Nyholm, R. S., *J. Chem. Soc.* p. 379 (1963).
26. Clauss, K., and Beerman, C., *Angew. Chem.* **71**, 627 (1959).
27. Clauss, K., and Bestian, H., *Ann. Chem.* **654**, 8 (1962).
28. Colton, R., and Martin, R. L., *Nature* **205**, 239 (1965); **207**, 141 (1965).
29. Corradini, P., and Sirigu, A., *Inorg. Chem.* **6**, 601 (1967).
30. Cossee, P., *J. Catalysis* **3**, 80 (1964); *Rec. Trav. Chim.* **85**, 1151 (1966).
31. Coutts, R. S. P., Kautzner, B., and Wailes, P. C., *Australian J. Chem.* **22**, 1137 (1969).
32. Coutts, R. S. P., and Surtees, J. R., *Australian J. Chem.* **19**, 387 (1966).
33. Coutts, R. S. P., Surtees, J. R., Swan, J. M., and Wailes, P. C., *Australian J. Chem.* **19**, 1377 (1966).
34. Coutts, R. S. P., and Wailes, P. C., *Inorg. Nucl. Chem. Letters* **3**, 1 (1967).
35. Coutts, R. S. P., and Wailes, P. C., *Australian J. Chem.* **20**, 1579 (1967).
36. Coutts, R. S. P., and Wailes, P. C., unpublished work (1969).
37. Coutts, R. S. P., and Wailes, P. C., *Chem. Commun.* p. 260 (1968).
38. Coutts, R. S. P., and Wailes, P. C., *Australian J. Chem.* **21**, 373 (1968).
39. Coutts, R. S. P., and Wailes, P. C., *Australian J. Chem.* **21**, 1181 (1968).
40. Coutts, R. S. P., and Wailes, P. C., *Australian J. Chem.* **21**, 2199 (1968).
41. Coutts, R. S. P., and Wailes, P. C., in preparation.
42. Coutts, R. S. P., and Wailes, P. C., *Australian J. Chem.* **22**, 1547 (1969).
43. Coutts, R. S. P., Wailes, P. C., and Kingston, J. V., *Chem. Commun.* p. 1170 (1968).
44. Coutts, R. S. P., Wailes, P. C., and Kingston, J. V., *Australian J. Chem.* **23**, 463 (1970).
45. Coutts, R. S. P., Wailes, P. C., and Kingston, J. V., *Australian J. Chem.* **23**, 469 (1970).
46. Coutts, R. S. P., and Wailes, P. C., *Australian J. Chem.* (1970) (in press).
47. Cox, M., personal communication to R. J. H. Clark (cited in Clark, 23); Ph.D. Thesis, London (1962).
48. Cox, M., Lewis, J., and Nyholm, R. S., *J. Chem. Soc.* p. 2480 (1965).
49. Crouch, P. C., Fowles, G. W. A., and Walton, R. A., *J. Chem. Soc., A* p. 2172 (1968).
50. Dierks, V., and Dietrich, H., *Acta Cryst.* **B24**, 58 (1968).
51. Doyle, G., Ph.D. Thesis, University of Minnesota (1968).
52. Drew, M. G. B., Fowles, G. W. A., and Lewis, D. F., *Chem. Commun.* p. 876 (1969).

53. Duckworth, M. W., Fowles, G. W. A., and Hoodless, R. A., *J. Chem. Soc.* p. 5665 (1963).
54. Edwards, D. A., Fowles, G. W. A., and Walton, R. A., *J. Inorg. & Nucl. Chem.* **27**, 1999 (1965).
55. Ehrlich, P., and Siebert, W., *Z. Anorg. Allgem. Chem.* **303**, 96 (1960).
56. Eve, D. J., and Fowles, G. W. A., *J. Chem. Soc., A* p. 1183 (1966).
57. Feld, R., and Cowe, P. L., "The Organic Chemistry of Titanium." Butterworth, London and Washington, D.C., 1965.
58. Figgis, B. N., Lewis, J., and Mabbs, F. E., *J. Chem. Soc.* p. 2473 (1963).
59. Fischer, A. K., and Wilkinson, G., *J. Inorg. & Nucl. Chem.* **2**, 149 (1956).
60. Fischer, E. O., and Amtmann, R., *J. Organometal. Chem.* (*Amsterdam*) **9**, 15 (1967).
61. Fischer, E. O., and Löchner, A., *Z. Naturforsch.* **15b**, 266 (1960).
62. Fischer, E. O., and Röhrscheid, F., *J. Organometal. Chem.* (*Amsterdam*) **6**, 53 (1966).
63. Fowles, G. W. A., Greene, P. T., and Lester, T. E., *J. Inorg. & Nucl. Chem.* **29**, 2365 (1967).
64. Fowles, G. W. A., and Hoodless, R. A., *J. Chem. Soc.* p. 33 (1963).
65. Fowles, G. W. A., Hoodless, R. A., and Walton, R. A., *J. Chem. Soc.* p. 5873 (1963).
66. Fowles, G. W. A., Hoodless, R. A., and Walton, R. A., *J. Inorg. & Nucl. Chem.* **27**, 391 (1965).
67. Fowles, G. W. A., and Lester, T. E., *Chem. Commun.* p. 47 (1967).
68. Fowles, G. W. A., and Lester, T. E., *J. Chem. Soc., A* p. 1180 (1968).
69. Fowles, G. W. A., Lester, T. E., and Russ, B. J., *J. Chem. Soc., A* p. 805 (1968).
70. Fowles, G. W. A., Lester, T. E., and Walton, R. A., *J. Chem. Soc., A* p. 198 (1968).
71. Fowles, G. W. A., Lester, T. E., and Walton, R. A., *J. Chem. Soc., A* p. 1081 (1968).
72. Fowles, G. W. A., and Walton, R. A., *J. Chem. Soc.* p. 4953 (1964).
73. Fowles, G. W. A., and Walton, R. A., *J. Less-Common Metals* **9**, 457 (1965).
74. Fry, F. H., and Watt, W. R., *J. Inorg. & Nucl. Chem.* **30**, 3115 (1968).
75. Garrasi, G., and Danielli, E., *Chim. Ind.* (*Milan*) **47**, 307 (1965).
76. Giddings, S. A., *Inorg. Chem.* **3**, 684 (1964).
77. Giggenbach, W., and Brubaker, C. H., Jr. *Inorg. Chem.* **7**, 129 (1968).
78. Giggenbach, W., and Brubaker, C. H., Jr. *Inorg. Chem.* **8**, 1131 (1969).
79. Gutmann, V., and Beer, G., *Inorg. Chim. Acta* **3**, 87 (1969).
80. Hartmann, H., Schläfer, H. L., and Hansen, K. H., *Z. Anorg. Allgem. Chem.* **284** 153 (1956).
81. Hartmann, H., Schläfer, H. L., and Hansen, K. H., *Z. Anorg. Allgem. Chem.* **289**, 40 (1956).
82. Hathaway, B. J., and Holah, D. G., *J. Chem. Soc.* p. 537 (1965).
83. Helmholdt, R. B., Jellinek, F., Martin, H. A., and Vos, A., *Rec. Trav. Chim.* **86**, 1263 (1967).
84. Henrici-Olivé, G., and Olivé, S., *Angew. Chem. Intern. Ed. Engl.* **6**, 790 (1967).
85. Henrici-Olivé, G., and Olivé, S., *Angew. Chem. Intern. Ed. Engl.* **6**, 873 (1967).
86. Henrici-Olivé, G., and Olivé, S., *Angew. Chem. Intern. Ed. Engl.* **7**, 386 (1968).
87. Henrici-Olivé, G., and Olivé, S., *Angew. Chem. Intern. Ed. Engl.* **7**, 821 and 822 (1968).
88. Henrici-Olivé, G., and Olivé, S., *Chem. Commun.* p. 113 (1969).
89. Henrici-Olivé, G., and Olivé, S., *J. Organometal. Chem.* (*Amsterdam*) **17**, 83 (1969).
90. Henrici-Olivé, G., and Olivé, S., *Angew. Chem. Intern. Ed. Engl.* **8**, 650 (1969).
91. Henrici-Olivé, G., and Olivé, S., *J. Organometal. Chem.* (*Amsterdam*) **19**, 309 (1969).
92. Herzog, S., and Grimm, U., *Z. Chem.* **8**, 186 (1968).
93. Herzog, S., and Taube, R., *Z. Anorg. Allgem. Chem.* **306**, 159 (1960).

94. Herzog, S., and Taube, R., *Z. Chem.* **2**, 208 (1962).
95. Herzog, S., and Zuhlke, H., *Z. Chem.* **6**, 434 (1966).
96. Hoekstra, H. R., and Katz, J. J., *J. Am. Chem. Soc.* **71**, 2488 (1949).
97. Hong, P., Sonogashira, K., and Hagihara, N., *Bull. Chem. Soc. Japan* **39**, 1821 (1966).
98. Issleib, K., and Häckert, H., *Z. Naturforsch.* **21b**, 519 (1966).
99. Issleib, K., and Wenschuh, E., *Chem. Ber.* **97**, 715 (1964).
100. James, B. D., Nanda, R. K., and Wallbridge, M. G. H., *Chem. Commun.* p. 849 (1966).
101. Jarrett, H. S., *J. Chem. Phys.* **27**, 1298 (1957).
102. Jeffery, E. A., and Mole, T., *J. Organometal. Chem.* (*Amsterdam*) **11**, 393 (1968).
103. Jordon, D. O., *in* "The Stereochemistry of Macromolecules" (A. D. Ketley, ed.), Vol. 1, p. 1. Marcel Dekker, New York, 1967.
104. Kautzner, B., and Wailes, P. C., unpublished results (1969).
105. Kenworthy, J. G., Myatt, J., and Todd, P. F., *Chem. Commun.* p. 263 (1969).
106. Kern, R. J., *J. Inorg. & Nucl. Chem.* **24**, 1105 (1962).
107. Kern, R. J., *J. Inorg. & Nucl. Chem.* **25**, 5 (1963).
108. Khan, M. M., and Ahmad, N., *Bull. Chem. Soc. Japan* **4**, 1254 (1967).
109. Köpf, H., and Block, B., *Z. Naturforsch.* **23b**, 1536 (1968).
110. Kühlein, K., and Clauss, K., *Angew. Chem. Intern. Ed. Engl.* **8**, 387 (1969).
111. Latyaeva, V. N., Razuvaev, G. A., and Kilyakova, G. A., *J. Gen. Chem. USSR* (*English Transl.*) **35**, 1500 (1965).
112. Línek, A., Šišková, J., and Jenšovský, L., *Collection Czech. Chem. Commun.* **31**, 4453 (1966).
113. Long, W. P., and Breslow, D. S., *J. Am. Chem. Soc.* **82**, 1953 (1960).
114. MacCorquodale, D. W., and Adkins, H., *J. Am. Chem. Soc.* **50**, 1938 (1928).
115. Machin, D. J., Murray, K. S., and Walton, R. A., *J. Chem. Soc., A* p. 195 (1968).
116. McDonald, G. D., Thompson, M. and Larsen, E. L., *Inorg. Chem.* **7**, 648 (1968).
117. Maki, A. H., and Randall, E. W., *J. Am. Chem. Soc.* **82**, 4109 (1960).
118. Marconi, W., Santostasi, M. L., and De Malde, M., *Chim. Ind.* (*Milan*) **44**, 229 (1962).
119. Martin, H. A., and Jellinek, F., *J. Organometal. Chem.* (*Amsterdam*) **6**, 293 (1966).
120. Martin, H. A., and Jellinek, F., *J. Organometal. Chem.* (*Amsterdam*) **8**, 115 (1967).
121. Martin, H. A., and Jellinek, F., *J. Organometal. Chem.* (*Amsterdam*) **12**, 149 (1968).
122. Martin, H., and Vohwinkel, F., *Chem. Ber.* **94**, 2416 (1961).
123. Martin, R. L., and Winter, G., *J. Chem. Soc.* p. 4709 (1965).
124. Masai, H., Sonogashira, K., and Hagihara, N., *Bull. Chem. Soc. Japan* **41**, 750 (1968).
125. Maskill, R., and Pratt, J. M., *Chem. Commun.* p. 950 (1967).
126. Maskill, R., and Pratt, J. M., *J. Chem. Soc., A* p. 1914 (1968).
127. Matsuzaki, K., and Yasukawa, T., *J. Organometal. Chem.* (*Amsterdam*) **10**, 9 (1967).
128. Murray, J. G., *J. Am. Chem. Soc.* **83**, 1287 (1961).
129. Natta, G., Corradini, P., and Bassi, I. W., *J. Am. Chem. Soc.* **80**, 755 (1958).
130. Natta, G., Dall'astra, G., Mazzanti, G., Giannini, U., and Cesca, S., *Angew. Chem.* **71**, 205 (1959).
131. Natta, G., and Mazzanti, G., *Tetrahedron* **8**, 86 (1960).
132. Natta, G., Mazzanti, G., Giannini, U., and Cesca, S., *Angew. Chem.* **72**, 39 (1960).
133. Natta, G., Mazzanti, G., and Pregaglia, G., *Gazz. Chim. Ital.* **89**, 2065 (1959).
134. Natta, G., Pino, P., Mazzanti, G., and Giannini, U., *J. Am. Chem. Soc.* **79**, 2975 (1957).
135. Natta, G., Pino, P., Mazzanti, G., and Giannini, U., *J. Inorg. & Nucl. Chem.* **8**, 612 (1958).

136. Nechiporenko, G. N., Tabrina, G. M., Shilova, A. K., and Shilov, A. E., *Dokl. Chem., Proc. Acad. Sci. USSR* (*English Transl.*) **164**, 1062 (1965).
137. Nesmeyanov, A. N., Nogina, O. V., and Freidlina, R. Kh., *Compt. Rend. Acad. Sci. URSS* **95**, 813 (1954).
138. Nöth, H., and Hartwimmer, R., *Chem. Ber.* **93**, 2238 (1960).
139. Pechiney Co., French Patent 1,157,159.
140. Pellizer, G., and De Alti, G., *J. Inorg. & Nucl. Chem.* **29**, 1565 (1967).
141. Pflugmacher, A., Carduck, H. J., and Zucketto, M., *Naturwissenschaften* **45**, 490 (1958).
142. Piper, T. S., and Carlin, R. L., *Inorg. Chem.* **2**, 260 (1963).
143. Podlahová, J., and Podlaha, J., *J. Inorg. & Nucl. Chem.* **28**, 2267 (1966).
144. Prasad, S., and Devi, K. S., *J. Indian Chem. Soc.* **43**, 495 (1966).
145. Pregaglia, G., Mazzanti, G., and Morero, D., *Ann. Chim.* (*Rome*) **49**, 1784 (1959).
146. Razuvaev, G. A., Latyaeva, V. N., Maysheva, A. V., and Kilyakova, G. A., *Dokl. Akad. Nauk SSSR* **150**, 566 (1963).
147. Razuvaev, G. A., Latyaeva, V. N., Vyshinskaya, L. I., and Vyshinskii, N. N., *Dokl. Akad. Nauk SSSR* **156**, 1211 (1964).
148. Razuvaev, G. A., Latyaeva, V. N., Vyshinskaya, L. I., and Kilyakova, G. A., *J. Gen. Chem. USSR* **36**, 1496 (1966).
149. Razuvaev, G. A., Minsker, K. S., Latyaeva, V. N., and Sangalov, Y. A., *Dokl. Akad. Nauk SSSR* **163**, 906 (1965).
150. Reichert, K. H., and Mallmann, M., *Angew. Chem. Intern. Ed. Engl.* **8**, 217 (1969).
151. Reid, A. F., and Wailes, P. C., *Australian J. Chem.* **18**, 9 (1965).
152. Russ, B. J., and Fowles, G. W. A., *Chem. Commun.* p. 19 (1966).
153. Russ, B. J., and Wood, J. S., *Chem. Commun.* p. 745 (1966).
154. Sabbana, V. V., Rao, G. S., and Bhattacharya, A. K., *J. Sci. Ind. Res.* (*India*) **18B**, 127 (1959).
155. Salzmann, J. J., *Helv. Chim. Acta* **51**, 526 (1968).
156. Salzmann, J. J., *Helv. Chim. Acta* **51**, 601 (1968).
157. Salzmann, J. J., *Helv. Chim. Acta* **51**, 903 (1968).
158. Salzmann, J. J., and Mosimann, P., *Helv. Chim. Acta* **50**, 1831 (1967).
159. Schläfer, H. L., and Götz, R., *Z. Anorg. Allgem. Chem.* **328**, 1 (1964).
160. Schläfer, H. L., and Götz, R., *Z. Physik. Chem.* (*Frankfurt*) [N.S.] **41**, 1 (1964).
161. Schmid, G., Petz, W., Arloth, W., and Nöth, H., *Angew. Chem.* **79**, 683 (1967).
162. Shikata, K., Yokogawa, K., Nakao, S., and Azuma, K., *J. Chem. Soc. Japan, Ind. Chem. Sect.* **68**, 1248 (1965).
163. Siddiqui, M. T., Ahmad, N., and Rahman, S. M. F., *Z. Anorg. Allgem. Chem.* **336**, 110 (1965).
164. Sonogashira, K., and Hagihara, N., *Bull. Chem. Soc. Japan* **39**, 1178 (1966).
165. Stähler, A., and Wirthwein, H., *Ber. Deut. Chem. Ges.* **38**, 2619 (1905).
166. Sutton, G. J., *Australian J. Chem.* **12**, 122 (1959).
167. Takashi, Y., *Bull. Chem. Soc. Japan* **40**, 999 (1967).
168. Takegami, Y., Ueno, T., Suzuki, T., and Fuchizaki, Y., *Bull. Chem. Soc. Japan* **41**, 2637 (1968).
169. Teuben, J. H., and De Liefde Meijer, H. J., *J. Organometal. Chem.* (*Amsterdam*) **17**, 87 (1969).
170. Van Oven, H. O., and De Liefde Meijer, H. J., *J. Organometal. Chem.* (*Amsterdam*) **19**, 373 (1969).
171. Van Tamelen, E. E., and Åkermark, B., *J. Am. Chem. Soc.* **90**, 4492 (1968).

172. Van Tamelen, E. E., Åkermark, B., and Sharpless, K. B., *J. Am. Chem. Soc.* **91**, 1552 (1969).
173. Van Tamelen, E. E., Boche, G., Ela, S. W., and Fechter, R. B., *J. Am. Chem. Soc.* **89**, 5707 (1967).
174. Van Tamelen, E. E., Boche, G., and Greeley, R., *J. Am. Chem. Soc.* **90**, 1677 (1968).
175. Van Tamelen, E. E., Fechter, R. B., Schneller, S. W., Boche, G., Greeley, R. H., and Åkermark, B., *J. Am. Chem. Soc.* **91**, 1551 (1969).
176. Vohwinkel, F., *Trans. N.Y. Acad. Sci.* [2] **26** No. 4, 446 (1964).
177. Vol'pin, M. E., Dubovitskii, V. A., Nogina, O. V., and Kursanov, D. N., *Dokl. Akad. Nauk SSSR* **151**, 623 (1963).
178. Vol'pin, M. E., Ilatovskaya, M. A., Kosyakova, L. V., and Shur, V. B., *Chem. Commun.* p. 1074 (1968).
179. Vol'pin, M. E., Ilatovskaya, M. A., Kosyakova, L. V., and Shur, V. B., *Dokl. Akad. Nauk SSSR* **180**, 103 (1968).
180. Vol'pin, M. E., and Shur, V. B., *Nature* **209**, 1236 (1966).
181. Vol'pin, M. E., Shur, V. B., Kudryavtsev, R. V., and Prodayko, L. A., *Chem. Commun.* p. 1038 (1968).
182. Vol'pin, M. E., Shur, V. B., Latyaeva, V. N., Vyshinskaya, L. I., and Shulgaitser, L. A. *Izv. Akad. Nauk SSSR, Ser. Khim.* **2**, 385 (1966).
183. Wailes, P. C., unpublished results (1965).
184. Wailes, P. C., and Weigold, H., unpublished results (1969).
185. Watt, G. W., and Baye, L. J., *J. Inorg. & Nucl. Chem.* **26**, 2099 (1964).
186. Watt, G. W., Baye, L. J., and Drummond, F. O., *J. Am. Chem. Soc.* **88**, 1138 (1966).
187. Weigold, H., unpublished work (1969).
188. Wilkinson, G., and Birmingham, J. M., *J. Am. Chem. Soc.* **76**, 4281 (1954).
189. Winter, G., *Inorg. Nucl. Chem. Letters* **2**, 161 (1966).
190. Winter, G., private communication (1969).
191. Yamamoto, A., Ookawa, M., and Ikeda, S., *Chem. Commun.* p. 841 (1969).
192. Yokokawa, K., and Azuma, K., *Bull. Chem. Soc. Japan* **38**, 859 (1965).

Organoberyllium Compounds

G. E. COATES and G. L. MORGAN

Chemistry Department
University of Wyoming
Laramie, Wyoming

I

INTRODUCTION

Though beryllium lies at the head of Group II of the Periodic Table, its chemical properties, which are well illustrated by its organic derivatives, are intermediate between those of magnesium and the heavier A subgroup elements (Ca, Sr, Ba) and those of the B subgroup (Zn, Cd, Hg). The organic chemistry of calcium, strontium, and barium is very inadequately developed but appears to be dominated by the ionic or at least very highly polarized nature of the bonds these elements form with carbon. The differences between the organometallic chemistry of magnesium and that of beryllium are due mainly to a combination of two factors: (a) magnesium is considerably more electropositive than beryllium, the Pauling electronegativity values being 1.2 and 1.5, resulting, by way of example, in the exchange

$$\text{Mg—C} + \text{Be—Cl} \rightarrow \text{Mg—Cl} + \text{Be—C}$$

being exothermic, and (b) the covalent radius of magnesium, 1.40 Å, is considerably greater than that of beryllium, 0.93 Å. The second effect allows a greater volume of ligand to be bound to magnesium than to beryllium, and many magnesium compounds are polymeric due to coordination polymerization or to polymerization caused by electron-deficient bonds, whose beryllium analogs are monomeric or oligomeric. For example, diethylmagnesium is polymeric whereas diethylberyllium is dimeric in benzene and in cyclohexane. Likewise magnesium *tert*-butoxide is insoluble in hydrocarbons, being a coordination polymer, whereas beryllium *tert*-butoxide is a soluble trimer $[Be(OBu\text{-}tert)_2]_3$.

Beryllium differs from zinc more in covalent radius (Be, 0.93; Zn, 1.2 Å) than in Pauling electronegativity (Be, 1.5; Zn, 1.6). Both elements have high tendencies to expand their coordination numbers to three or four and it is likely that the monomeric character of zinc alkyls, in contrast to the normally dimeric or polymeric beryllium alkyls, is due to the too short zinc–zinc distances that would result if R_2Zn were to associate (*132*). The heavier elements of the B subgroup, cadmium and mercury, are still more electronegative and also have a smaller tendency to increase the coordination number of the metal, particularly in organo derivatives R_2Cd and R_2Hg, from two.

Organoberyllium chemistry has been reviewed by Fetter (*84*), and by several Russian authors (*16*, *128*). It has also been reviewed by one of the authors of this article (*41*, *72*).

II

BERYLLIUM DIALKYLS

A. *Structural Considerations*

Dimethylberyllium is commonly quoted, along with diborane and the trimethylaluminum dimer, as an example to illustrate electron-deficient bonding. It is polymeric in the crystalline state (*133*, *141*) though the vapor consists largely of monomer along with amounts of dimer and trimer whose proportions depend on conditions of temperature and pressure (*53*).

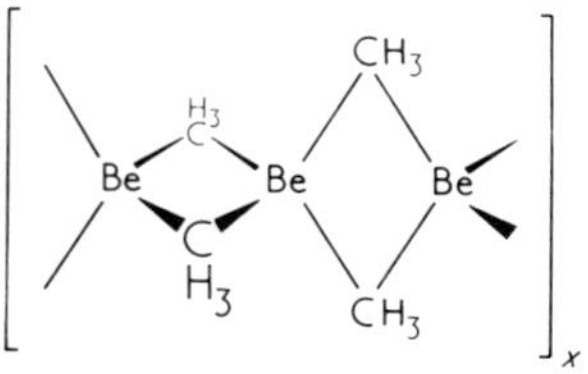

(I)

The distribution of carbon atoms about beryllium in the crystalline polymer is not far from tetrahedral, the internal C—Be—C angle being 114°. Each methyl carbon atom is regarded as bound to two beryllium atoms by means of a pair of electrons occupying a three-center molecular orbital derived from one carbon sp^3 and two beryllium sp^3 orbitals. The low Be—C—Be angle, 66°, results from a balance between the conflicting tendencies to maximize overlap and to minimize metal–metal repulsion. Nonbonding interactions are important in determining the stability of this type of compound. The metal–metal distance, 2.09 Å, is only 0.23 Å greater than twice the covalent radius of beryllium. The carbon–carbon distance within each four-membered ring is 3.15 Å, and the distance between a carbon atom belonging to one ring and either carbon atom belonging to the next ring in the chain is only 3.56 Å. In organic compounds nonbonded carbon atoms are normally at least 4.1 Å apart.

The Be—C distance in the dimethylberyllium polymer is 1.93 Å, which, as may be expected for what amounts to a half-bond, is considerably longer than that in the monomer in the gas phase, 1.70 Å (*8*).

Diethylberyllium is dimeric in benzene (*66*, *148*) and in cyclohexane, although differences between the ^{1}H NMR spectra in these two solvents may suggest two different types of dimers. Di-*n*-propylberyllium (*66*) and diisopropylberyllium (*51*), as well as the di-*n*-butyl (*66*), the diisobutyl (*66*), and the di(2-methyl)butyl (*107*) are all dimeric. The polymerization of these is prevented by steric interference, as has been shown by a crystal structure analysis of diethyl*magnesium* (*155*). Dimethylmagnesium is an electron-deficient polymer like dimethylberyllium, and the diethyl compound has a similar structure, but the distance between the methylene carbon of one bridge and one of the methyl groups belonging to a bridging ethyl group in the next four-membered ring is only 3.76 Å, which is less than the normal distance of closest approach between nonbonded carbon atoms by an amount which indicates some appreciable steric strain. If, in the diethylmagnesium polymer, the magnesium atoms were all replaced by the smaller beryllium atoms, then this nonbonding methylene–methyl distance would be reduced to 3.19 Å (even for a Be—C—Be bridge angle of 60°) and this is far too short. Hence, in diethylberyllium and the other beryllium dialkyls mentioned above, the degree of association is restricted by the condition that the coordination number of the metal cannot be four. Two possible structures for the diethyl, each involving three-coordinate beryllium, are (II) and (III).

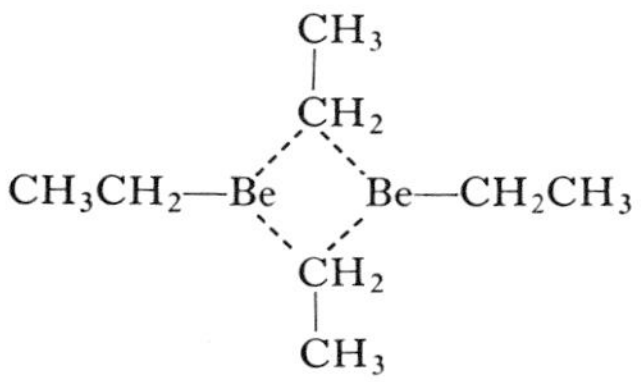

CH_3
CH_2
CH_3CH_2—Be Be—CH_2CH_3
CH_2
CH_3

(II)

CH_2CH_3
H_3C Be
H_2C CH_2—CH_3
Be Be
CH_3CH_2 CH_2 CH_2CH_3
CH_3

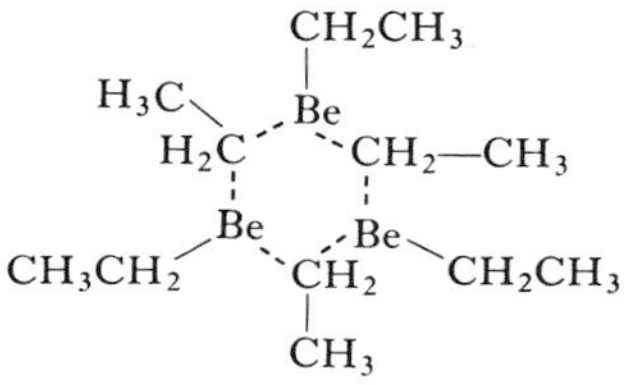

(III)

Similar structures can be considered, still involving three-coordinate beryllium, but corresponding to higher degrees of association. The dimeric structure (II) would be preferred to (III) both because the small Be—C—Be angle would allow better overlap of the atomic orbitals that form the bridging molecular orbital, and on account of the entropy factor which favors the lowest degree of association (most translational entropy per unit mass of material). Consequently the structure of all these dimeric alkyls is believed to correspond to (II).

Diisopropylberyllium has two alkyl groups bound to the α-carbon, but this still allows dimerization to occur. When there are *three* substituents on the α-carbon, as in di-*tert*-butylberyllium, then dimerization is prevented and the monomeric structure (IV) results. The C—Be—C angle is 180°

Me_3C—Be—CMe_3

(IV)

and the Be—C distance 1.70 Å (*9*). This and $[(Me_3Si)_2N]_2Be$ (*34*), which also has voluminous groups bound to beryllium, are the only known beryllium compounds which contain two-coordinate beryllium under ambient temperature conditions.

It is significant that the Be—C distances in *tert*-Bu_2Be and monomeric Me_2Be are essentially the same and not appreciably shorter than the sp^3-bonded Be—C distance of 1.71 Å in $(MeBeOSiMe_3)_4$ (*119*) [see (XLIX), Section VIII]. Dimethylberyllium had been considered an ideal candidate for hyperconjugative stabilization while *tert*-butyl groups do not manifest any of the attributes normally ascribed to hyperconjugation (*77*). The absence of bond shortening in dimethylberyllium thus provides evidence against the concept of ground state hyperconjugation. Similar evidence against hyperconjugation in trimethylborane has been presented (*19*, *36*). Indeed, charge-iterated extended Hückel MO calculations yield π-bond overlap populations of the M—C bonds that amount to less than 10% of the σ-bond populations in both of these molecules (*75*).

The mass spectra of R_2Be (R = Me, Et, *n*-Pr, iso-Pr, iso-Bu and *tert*-Bu) have been studied using a high-resolution instrument (*37*, *38*). Since beryllium has only one stable isotope high resolution is essential in order to distinguish hydrocarbon from organometallic ions, and several of the observed peaks are doublets consisting of the two kinds of ion $C_aH_b^+$ and $C_xH_yBe^+$.

Associated ions are abundant in the mass spectra of several alkyls, but their abundance decreases very rapidly as the source temperature increases. For example, ions containing two beryllium atoms constitute over 30% of the total ion current, and Be_3 ions over 0.4%, in the spectrum of Et_2Be when the source temperature is 50°–60° C, whereas at 100° C Be_2 ions are only about 2% of the total and Be_3 ions are negligible. Extensive and detailed fragmentation patterns have been established for all the beryllium alkyls studied, and have been in most cases confirmed by observation of the appropriate metastable peak. Ionization potentials decrease as the size of the organic group increases: Me_2Be 10.67, Et_2Be 9.46, *n*-Pr_2Be 8.71, iso-Pr_2Be 8.80, and iso-Bu_2Be 8.74 volts; that of Me_2Be is the highest measured for any organometallic compound. The bond dissociation energies $(RBe—R)^+ \rightarrow RBe^+ + R\cdot$ have been measured mass spectroscopically, and are in the range 29–49 kcal $mole^{-1}$. Since the positive ions must be formed by removal of a bonding electron (probably from a Be—C bond), the Be—C bond energies in neutral alkyls would be higher.

The hydrides BeH^+, BeH_2^+, BeH_3^+, and $Be_2H_3^+$ have been observed in the spectra of various alkyls. Dimethylberyllium is unique in giving a series of polynuclear ions. In addition to the two Be_2 ions, $C_2H_5Be_2^+$ and $C_3H_9Be_2^+$, the following have been observed:

$$C_{12}H_{33}Be_8^+ \xrightarrow{-C_2H_6Be} C_{10}H_{27}Be_7^+ \xrightarrow{-C_2H_6Be} C_8H_{21}Be_6^+ \longrightarrow C_6H_{15}Be_5^+$$

Two of the above steps are confirmed by the appropriate metastable peaks.

B. Preparative Methods

1. *Reactions between Beryllium Metal and Mercury Dialkyls*

The reaction between dimethylmercury and beryllium metal was used by Lavroff (*108*) in 1884, but the resulting dimethylberyllium was not characterized.

This method, which was further developed by Gilman and Schulze (*92*) and Burg and Schlesinger (*33*), is based on the relatively low dissociation

$$R_2Hg + Be \rightarrow R_2Be + Hg$$

energy of mercury–carbon bonds; for a further discussion of this, see Coates *et al.* (*57*). There is, in principle, no reason why alkyls of other heavy elements, such as lead and bismuth, which form relatively weak σ-bonds to carbon, should not similarly react with beryllium. But in practice, one would not use tetramethyllead, which is prone to explode when heated.

The very feature, namely, the relative weakness of the Hg—C bond, which makes the reaction proceed, is also the main limitation to its general application, since the rate of thermal decomposition can in many instances be faster than the reaction with beryllium.

$$R_2Hg \rightarrow RHg\cdot + R\cdot \rightarrow R\cdot + R\cdot + Hg$$

The method has found its main application for R = Me, Ph, and *p*-tolyl. It is useful for the preparation of ether-free dimethylberyllium, and has found application in the preparation of $(CD_3)_2Be$ (*28*). The separation of dimethylberyllium from mercury, which is also produced in the reaction, has caused some difficulty since sublimation results in a product that is usually grossly contaminated with mercury, and crystallization is not feasible since Me_2Be is only very sparingly soluble in inert solvents. The difficulty can be overcome by stirring the mixture with benzene, as the mercury then agglomerates and can easily be separated (*50*).

Diethylmercury undergoes thermal decomposition more readily than dimethylmercury; even so ether-free diethylberyllium can be prepared from it either using a little iodine or mercury(II) chloride as catalyst (*12, 35, 134*).

2. *Alkylation of Beryllium Halides*

This has been the most widely used method, and Grignard reagents have found more general application than organolithium reagents. These

$$BeCl_2 + 2\,RMgX \xrightarrow{\text{Ether}} R_2Be + MgX_2 + MgCl_2$$

preparations can go wrong in various ways. Not only must air and moisture be rigorously excluded, but care must be taken during the "work-up" stages to avoid overheating (preferably $< 70°$ C) in cases where the presence of hydrogen on a β-carbon allows olefin elimination. For example, Et_2Be,

$$—Be—CH_2—CHR_2 \rightarrow —Be—H + R_2C{=}CH_2$$

n-Pr_2Be, and particularly iso-Bu_2Be or *tert*-Bu_2Be are liable to decompose in this way, but Me_2Be, Ph_2Be, $(PhCH_2)_2Be$, and $(Me_3CCH_2)_2Be$ are considerably more stable to heat.

It is advantageous to decant the primary reaction product from as much magnesium halide as possible, since the subsequent distillation of the mixed $R_2Be + Et_2O$ product is then easier. For the same reason it is better to use alkyl chlorides rather than alkyl bromides in the preparation of the Grignard reagent, since magnesium chloride is much less soluble in ether than is magnesium bromide. Finally, the use of too concentrated solutions can result in the precipitation of magnesium chloride in a gel-like form which severely interferes with "work-up."

The recovery of dimethylberyllium makes use of the process of ether codistillation (*90*). An adaptation of this method has been devised for larger scale preparations (*160*). The first mention of the preparation of beryllium alkyls from $BeCl_2$ and Grignard reagents appears to be due to Krause and Wendt (*106*). The ether content of dimethylberyllium can easily be reduced to a few mole percent by evaporation at room temperature until only solid remains. The ether in the residue is doubtless present as chain-ending

$$Et_2O \rightarrow Be(Me)\left[(\mu\text{-}Me)_2Be\right]_x(\mu\text{-}Me)_2Be(Me) \leftarrow OEt_2$$

(V)

groups (V). By repeated sublimation at low pressure much of the residual ether can be removed, but the process becomes more difficult as the ether content diminishes. Alternatively, a concentrated solution of Me_2Be in ether can be added to an excess of toluene: as the mixture is boiled, Me_2Be crystallizes.

Dimethyl sulfide is a weaker base than diethyl ether towards Me_2Be, and it has been found (*103*) that methylation of beryllium chloride using a Grignard reagent prepared in dimethyl sulfide gives a product containing only traces of dimethyl sulfide. The use of ether-free organomagnesium halides in hydrocarbon solvents has been applied to the synthesis of *n*-Bu_2Be and to solutions of Et_2Be, $(n\text{-}C_5H_{11})_2Be$, Ph_2Be, and di-*p*-tolylberyllium (*93*).

Using the normal Grignard procedure, higher beryllium dialkyls (R_2Be, R = Et, *n*-Pr, iso-Pr, *n*-Bu, iso-Bu, *tert*-Bu, neopentyl) are generally recovered as approximately 1:1 R_2Be:ether mixtures, but the ratio can vary widely according to the distillation conditions. Most of these alkyls can be obtained free from ether by prolonged boiling with reflux at 10^{-3} to 10^{-2} mm, the process sometimes requiring up to 50 hours (*66*). This method fails for di-*tert*-butylberyllium, since the monomeric ether-free *tert*-Bu_2Be is more volatile than its ether complex. In this case, ether is removed by reaction with beryllium chloride (*98*). Some (*tert*-$BuBeCl \cdot OEt_2)_2$ is also formed. Ether does not separate from the 1:1 complexes

$$tert\text{-}Bu_2Be \cdot OEt_2 + BeCl_2 \rightarrow tert\text{-}Bu_2Be + BeCl_2 \cdot OEt_2$$

$(Me_3CCH_2)_2Be \cdot OEt_2$ and $(PhCH_2)_2Be \cdot OEt_2$, even on prolonged reflux at low pressure (*50*).

Taking advantage of the relatively great complexing properties of the fluoride ion toward light metal alkyls, Strohmeier and associates (*144*) have developed a procedure for preparing ether-free diethylberyllium. Potassium fluoride dissolves in a diethylberyllium–ether mixture, and most of the ether can then be removed under reduced pressure at room temperature. The remainder is liberated at ~60° C, leaving a solid complex, $KF \cdot 2\,Et_2Be$, m.p. 83° C. This material is decomposed either by stirring it with benzene,

$$KF \cdot 2\,Et_2Be \rightarrow KF \cdot Et_2Be + Et_2Be$$

or by heating to 100°–130° C under reduced pressure. The 1:1 complex $KF \cdot Et_2Be$ has m.p. 46°–48° C.

As might perhaps be expected from the "diagonal relationship" between beryllium and aluminum, aluminum alkyls are not very effective for the alkylation of beryllium halides since equilibria result (*118*):

$$BeCl_2 + R_3Al \rightleftharpoons RBeCl + R_2AlCl$$

$$RBeCl + R_3Al \rightleftharpoons R_2Be + R_2AlCl$$

It is claimed that, for example, diethylberyllium can be separated from such mixtures by addition of suitable amounts of a tertiary amine such as quinoline, which preferentially complexes with the aluminum compounds, thus allowing the beryllium dialkyl to be separated by distillation. A related device is to convert the EtBeCl produced into EtBeH, followed by reaction with ethylene (*117*).

$$EtBeCl + NaH \rightarrow EtBeH + NaCl$$

$$EtBeH + C_2H_4 \xrightarrow[65^{\circ}C]{8\ atm} Et_2Be$$

Some reactions have been reported resulting in the alkylation of beryllium chloride forming ether-free spiro complexes (*15*). These involve Grignard reagents containing a chelating basic group.

$$BeCl_2 \xrightarrow{MeO(CH_2)_4MgCl} [MeO(CH_2)_4]_2Be \text{ (spiro complex: two } CH_2\text{—}CH_2\text{—}CH_2\text{—}CH_2\text{—}OMe \rightarrow Be \text{ rings)}$$

$$BeCl_2 \xrightarrow{EtS(CH_2)_3MgCl} [EtS(CH_2)_3]_2Be \text{ (spiro complex: two } CH_2\text{—}CH_2\text{—}CH_2\text{—}EtS \rightarrow Be \text{ rings)}$$

3. *Other Preparative Methods*

The elimination of olefin, discussed in Section XI, is reversible:

$$\text{—}Be\text{—}CH_2\text{—}CHR_2 \rightleftharpoons \text{—}BeH + CH_2{=}CR_2$$

So far, however, the addition of olefin to beryllium–hydrogen bonds has not found extensive preparative application (*162*).

C. Chemical Properties

Most of the known reactions of beryllium alkyls are considered under other headings, e.g., their reactions with bases and with compounds containing protonic hydrogen. The elimination of olefin is considered in Section XI on hydride derivatives.

Beryllium–carbon bonds are rapidly attacked by water and by oxygen, unless access is sterically hindered. Most beryllium alkyls are hydrolyzed by water with explosive violence, and for analytical purposes it is advisable to moderate the reaction by using water vapor at room temperature, or an alcohol such as 2-methoxyethanol, or a tertiary amine followed by water and aqueous acid. Otherwise some thermal decomposition can occur as well as hydrolysis.

Most beryllium dialkyls inflame in the air, and the resulting toxic beryllium oxide, particularly when it appears as a smoke, is one of the major hazards in handling these compounds. Controlled oxidation of dimethylberyllium in diethyl ether gives mainly the insoluble dimethoxide, but this contains varying amounts of peroxidic oxygen (*112*).

Dimethylberyllium has been reported to inflame in carbon dioxide, but slow reaction in ether solution gives acetic acid after acid hydrolysis. It undergoes several other reactions which resemble those of Grignard reagents; thus it yields, after hydrolysis in each case, Ph_2MeCOH with benzophenone, $PhMe_2COH$ with benzoyl chloride, and PhNHCOMe with phenyl isocyanate (*91*, *136*). The addition of dimethylberyllium to azo-

$$Me_2Be + PhN{=}NPh \rightarrow (PhMeN{-}NPh)_2Be$$

benzene gives a hydrazine derivative (*95*), whose molecular complexity has not been studied.

The thermal stability of beryllium alkyls (or of their coordination complexes) depends on whether an olefin elimination process is feasible. Thus diisopropylberyllium eliminates propene slowly at 50° C (*51*), di-*tert*-butylberyllium undergoes slow isomerization to diisobutylberyllium even at room temperature, and the latter eliminates isobutene from about 80° C (*66*). In contrast, dimethylberyllium does not decompose rapidly below 200° C, when it forms beryllium carbide, Be_2C, through a polymeric intermediate $(BeCH_2)_x$ (*95*). The thermal decomposition of diethylberyllium at 190° C is complex (see Section XI). The ether complexes $(Me_3CCH_2)_2Be \cdot OEt_2$ and $(PhCH_2)_2Be \cdot OEt_2$ have considerable thermal stability; the latter, for example, distils at 170°–200° C (bath temp.)/10^{-3} mm, without decomposition (*50*).

III

BERYLLIUM DIARYLS

These have been less extensively studied than the dialkyls. Diphenylberyllium was first prepared by heating beryllium metal with diphenylmercury at ~200°–220° C (*92*, *147*). This method generally results in some decomposition. A more satisfactory procedure is to heat the reagents in xylene at 140° C for 72 hours, the metal having previously been activated by contact with a solution of a beryllium dialkyl or by addition of a trace of $HgCl_2$ (*70*). Diphenylberyllium (m.p. 248°–250° C, decomp.) may be crystallized better from benzene, in which it is only sparingly soluble, than from xylene. Di-*p*-tolylberyllium has also been described (*92*).

No crystal structure analysis of Ph_2Be has been carried out, but the substance is very likely to be an electron-deficient polymer like dimethylberyllium. The electron-deficient bridging properties of the phenyl group have been shown in the structure of Ph_6Al_2 (*110*).

IV

BIS(CYCLOPENTADIENYL)BERYLLIUM AND OTHER UNSATURATED DERIVATIVES

Bis(cyclopentadienyl)beryllium, $(C_5H_5)_2Be$, has been prepared from beryllium chloride and cyclopentadienylsodium (*86*). It forms colorless air-sensitive crystals, m.p. 59°–60° C, which can be sublimed under reduced pressure. An X-ray diffraction analysis (*135*) of the crystalline material indicated a structure similar to that of ferrocene, but this was difficult to reconcile with the appreciable dipole moment (over 2 D) of the compound both in benzene and in cyclohexane. The problem was resolved by an electron diffraction study of the vapor (*4*), which confirmed that the C_5H_5 rings are planar and parallel, but which also showed that the metal atom may occupy two alternative positions on the fivefold rotation axis, about 1.5 Å from the plane of one ring and about 2.0 Å from that of the other. The potential energy curve for the beryllium atom along the fivefold axis must therefore have two minima. The observed dipole moment would arise if the net charge on the metal atom (unsymmetrically placed between the rings) were only $+0.25e$. The charge on the metal is believed to be rather larger, and the bonding is considered to be mainly electrostatic. The apparently centrosymmetric structure indicated by the X-ray analysis is due to a random distribution of beryllium atoms between the two positions of minimum energy. This is equivalent to an element of disorder which was not detected in the X-ray analysis.

The infrared spectrum of the solid (*87, 114*) indeed indicates the presence of two different types of cyclopentadienide rings, one being more ionic than the other. The spectrum of the *vapor* is much simpler, consisting only of the bands expected for the D_{5h} cyclopentadienide anion (*114*). Its ionic constitution is further confirmed by the ultraviolet spectrum (*115*), which is consistent with the presence of cyclopentadienide anions and not at all similar to the calculated spectrum in which considerable covalent metal–ring interaction is assumed (*152*).

A recent study (*120*) of this interesting compound has shown that it is more nearly dimeric than monomeric in toluene solution. Its solutions in cyclohexane and other nonaromatic solvents are colorless and have no ESR spectra, but those in benzene, toluene, and fluorobenzene have a yellow color and are paramagnetic. Both the molecular weight data and the NMR spectra indicate that two $(C_5H_5)_2Be$ units are complexed with one benzene

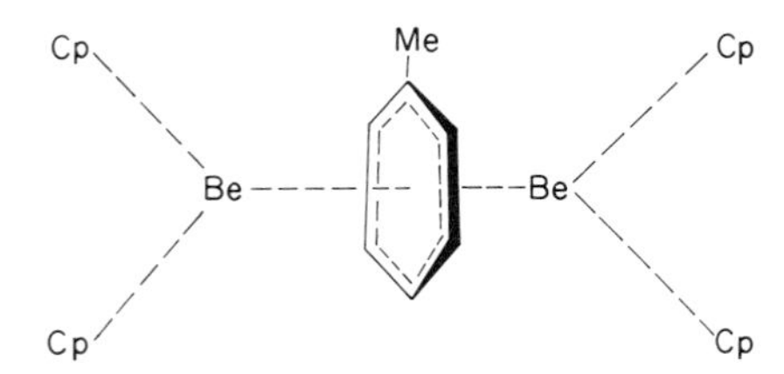

FIG. 1. Proposed structure of toluene-$BeCp_2$ complex.

ring. It is suggested that the beryllium atoms are sp^3-hybridized: two of the orbitals of each beryllium atom are believed to be used in bonding to the four C_5H_5 groups, the other two interacting with the normally vacant E_2 orbitals of the benzene (Fig. 1). In order to form a bond it is believed that electrons are promoted from the E_1 into the E_2 benzene orbitals, as qualitatively illustrated in Fig. 2.

Since the above complex is "electron-deficient," it represents a third major type of such metal–carbon compounds, the other two types employing hydrogen 1*s* and carbon σ-orbitals to form the delocalized molecular orbital bridging two or more metal atoms. The demonstration, in the ESR spectrum, that the signal due to one of the electrons is split by two equivalent beryllium atoms, is also verification of the validity of the molecular orbital model as first proposed for diborane. The paramagnetic $B_8H_8^-$ ion, whose structure is still not known, also confirms this model by having all equivalent boron and hydrogen atoms (*100*).

Some attempts at the preparation of beryllium bis alkenyls, e.g., from the halide and $Me_2C{=}CHLi$ (*43*), resulted in the formation of polymeric

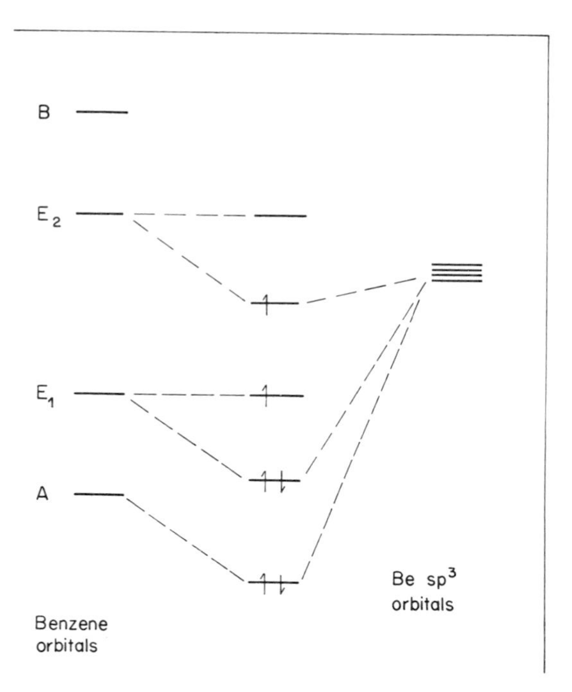

FIG. 2. Qualitative molecular orbital diagram for the bis(cyclopentadienyl)beryllium–benzene complex.

decomposition products. Ether solutions of bis(allyl)beryllium at room temperature have AX_4 patterns in their ^1H NMR spectra (*79*), analogous to the allyl derivatives of lithium and magnesium.

Though various coordination complexes of beryllium dialkynyls are described in Section V below, no uncomplexed dialkynyls have yet been obtained.

V

COORDINATION COMPLEXES OF THE DIALKYLS, DIARYLS, AND DIALKYNYLS

A. *With Monodentate Bases*

The electron-deficient character of organoberyllium compounds, R_2Be, normally resulting in association involving electron-deficient carbon bridges, has been discussed in Section II,A. It is thus to be expected that these compounds should react with donor molecules or bases.

1. *Amines and Phosphines*

For dimethylberyllium to form coordination complexes the heat of cooordination of the base to beryllium must be competitive with the heat of polymerization of Me_2Be (about 20 kcal mole^{-1} for each Me_2Be unit). The heat of coordination of trimethylamine to Me_2Be has been estimated (*60*) at 26 kcal mole^{-1} or more. Reaction between the amine and Me_2Be results in a stable 1:1 complex, $Me_2Be \cdot NMe_3$, m.p. 36° C. The deutero complex (*28*) has a higher melting point, 39°–40° C.

The monotrimethylamine complex is monomeric as vapor and in benzene solution (*56*) and must have the constitution (VI), in which the metal is

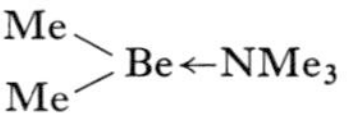

$$Me_2Be \leftarrow NMe_3$$

(VI)

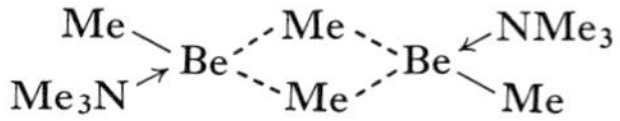

$$Me_3N \rightarrow Be(Me)(\mu\text{-}Me)_2Be(Me) \leftarrow NMe_3$$

(VII)

$$Me_2Be(\mu\text{-}NMe_3)_2BeMe_2$$

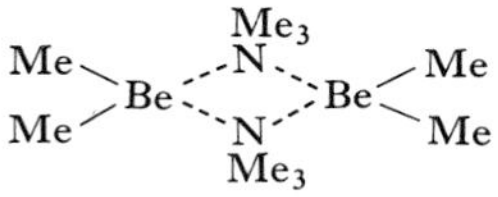

(VIII)

three-coordinate. Though (VI) is monomeric as vapor and in solution, the latent heat of vaporization of the liquid undergoes an unusually large change with temperature, decreasing from 12 kcal mole^{-1} at 50° C to about 8 kcal mole^{-1} at 130° C. This suggests the possibility that the constitution of the liquid may change with temperature, perhaps with increasing proportions of dimers such as (VII) or (VIII) at lower temperatures. A crystal structure analysis of the solid would thus be of interest. If a dimer containing four-cooordinate beryllium is formed, (VII) is a more likely structure than (VIII) because the tetrahedral orbitals of nitrogen are more compact than those of carbon in a methyl group, and thus less well adapted to form an electron-deficient bridge. The formation of two-coordinate bonds by oxygen atoms in alkoxides such as $(RBeOR)_4$ (see Section VIII) is quite a different matter since each oxygen atom has two lone pairs with which to form coordinate bonds.

The 1:1 complex adds a second molecule of trimethylamine, giving (IX),

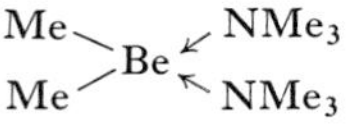

$$Me_2Be(\leftarrow NMe_3)_2$$

(IX)

m.p. 20° C, under 1 atm of trimethylamine. It loses 1 mole of amine very readily, its dissociation pressure being 22.7 mm at 0° C (*24*). The earlier description (*60*) of a complex $(Me_2Be)_2(NMe_3)_3$ is erroneous. The liquid triethylamine complex, $Me_2Be \cdot NEt_3$, is monomeric in benzene.

Diethylberyllium similarly forms two complexes, $Et_2Be \cdot NMe_3$ and $Et_2Be(NMe_3)_2$ (*129*), which are liquid at room temperature, like the isopropyl compound iso-$Pr_2Be \cdot NMe_3$ (*51*). Melting points are much influenced by symmetry, and the observation that *tert*-$Bu_2Be \cdot NMe_3$ (*66*), in which three symmetrical and nearly identical groups surround the metal atom, is a solid, m.p. 45°–46°C, is no surprise. Neither iso-$Pr_2Be \cdot NMe_3$ nor *tert*-$Bu_2Be \cdot NMe_3$ show any sign of adding a second molecule of trimethylamine.

The relatively high dissociation pressures of the known bis(trimethyl amine) complexes can reasonably be ascribed to steric interference. The nitrogen atom in pyridine is less hindered sterically than that in trimethylamine, and it is found that pyridine forms 2:1 complexes $Me_2Be\ py_2$, m.p. 91°–92° C (*56*), $Et_2Be\ py_2$, decomp. 140° C (*56*), and iso-$Bu_2Be\ py_2$, m.p. 65° C (*63*).

Diphenylberyllium (*70*) forms a bis(trimethylamine) complex, $Ph_2Be(NMe_3)_2$, which loses amine so readily that by the time the complex has been freed from solvent under reduced pressure by the usual methods applicable to air-sensitive compounds, the Be:amine ratio is about 1:1.3. The 1:1 complex has negligible dissociation pressure.

As would be expected if steric factors were of major importance in determining the relative stability of R_2Be complexes, the bis(trimethylamine) complex of bis(phenylethynyl)beryllium, $(PhC{\equiv}C)_2Be(NMe_3)_2$, m.p. 195–200° (decomp.) (*49*), has negligible dissociation pressure at room temperature and loses amine only at 90–100° C and 10^{-3} mm. The propynyl analog, $(MeC{\equiv}C)_2Be(NMe_3)_2$ is also known. Some interest attaches to the 1:1 complexes $(PhC{\equiv}C)_2Be \cdot NMe_3$, m.p. 186°–188°, and $(PhC{\equiv}C)_2Be \cdot NEt_3$, m.p. 102° C. Though the former is only sparingly soluble in benzene, the latter is readily soluble, is monomeric, and must contain three-coordinate beryllium. The possibility of dimerization in the crystalline state has to be considered, particularly in view of the strong bridging characteristics of the phenylethynyl group. The bis(pyridine) complex, $(PhC{\equiv}C)_2Be\ py_2$, is colorless, unlike most other $R_2Be\ py_2$ complexes, and is practically insoluble in benzene.

Ammonia and primary and secondary amines, all of which contain protonic hydrogen, commonly react with organoberyllium compounds forming aminoberyllium alkyls and related substances, considered in Section (VII). Coordination complexes are likely always to be formed as reaction intermediates, and in several instances these have been isolated. The rate of alkane elimination

$$R_2Be + R'NH_2 \rightarrow R_2Be \leftarrow NH_2R' \rightarrow (RBeNH'R)_x + RH$$

decreases in the order $NH_3 > RNH_2 > R_2NH$. For example, dimethylberyllium and ammonia react in ether at $-80°C$ forming the sparingly soluble complex Me_2BeNH_3, and Et_2Be gives the ether-soluble $Et_2Be \cdot NH_3$. The degrees of association of these complexes are not known, and the complexes decompose, with methane elimination and formation of insoluble polymeric material, between $-70°$ and $-50°C$. By 50°C the remaining methyl groups are also eliminated (*113*).

The methylamine adduct of dimethylberyllium also decomposes at low temperatures (from $-90°C$) and the 1:1 adduct $Me_2Be \cdot NH_2Me$ was not isolated. In this instance, methane elimination takes place in at least two distinct stages (*54*).

$$Me_2Be{\cdot}NH_2Me \xrightarrow{-90° \text{ to } 0°C} \frac{1}{x}(Me_3Be_2N_2H_3Me_2)_x + CH_4 \xrightarrow{10°–40°C} \frac{1}{y}(MeBeNHMe)_y + CH_4$$

In contrast, dimethylamine forms an adduct, $Me_2Be \cdot NHMe_2$, which decomposes only very slowly at room temperature, but rapidly when it melts at 44°C (*54*). The morpholine and piperidine complexes, $Me_2Be \cdot NH(CH_2)_4O$ and $Me_2Be \cdot NH(CH_2)_5$, have also been described (*88*), and they decompose at 20°C.

Acetylenic groups HC≡C— or RC≡C— bound to the more electropositive metals are less nucleophilic than methyl groups bound to the same metal. This is well illustrated by the isolation of various adducts of di(phenylethynyl)beryllium with primary and secondary amines: $(PhC{\equiv}C)_2Be(NHMe_2)_2$, m.p. 152°–158°C (decomp.); $(PhC{\equiv}C)_2Be(NH_2Me)_2$, m.p. 86°–87°C (decomp.); $(PhC{\equiv}C)_2Be(NH_2Ph)_2$, not melting $<300°C$. The methylamine complex begins to eliminate phenylacetylene in the range 60°–80°C. Ammonia does not yield a complex with di(phenylethynyl)beryllium which is stable at room temperature (*49*).

Trimethylphosphine is believed to be a weaker donor to dimethylberyllium than is trimethylamine (*60*), but instead of forming the two complexes Me_2BeL and Me_2BeL_2, it forms a series of complexes according to conditions of temperature and pressure, which probably differ in the number of Me_2Be units they contain. Thus, if a vessel containing Me_2Be with some

4–5 molar proportions of Me_3P was slowly heated from 0° to 150° C, the condensed phase could be seen alternately to melt and freeze, as many as 5–6 times, until solid Me_2Be was the only condensed phase present. Knowing the total amounts of Me_2Be and Me_3P present, and the pressure, temperature, and volume of gaseous Me_3P present, it was possible to calculate the composition of the condensed phases. These were (X), (XI), and compounds like (XI) but with more Me_2Be units. The latter can be

$Me_2Be(\leftarrow PMe_3)_2$

(X)

$(Me_3P \rightarrow)(Me)Be(\mu\text{-}Me)_2Be(Me)(\leftarrow PMe_3)$

(XI)

regarded as fragments of Me_2Be polymer in which Me_3P acts as a chain-ending group.

The only dialkylberyllium tertiary phosphine complex that has been isolated is $(\textit{tert}\text{-}Bu)_2Be \cdot PMe_3$, which, curiously, has the same melting point (within a degree) as its trimethylamine analog (*66*).

Though $Ph_2Be(NMe_3)_2$ is so unstable that much amine is normally lost during the isolation processes, there is no difficulty in obtaining the analogous phosphine complex $Ph_2Be(PMe_3)_2$. This apparent anomaly, i.e., that the bisphosphine has a lower dissociation pressure than the bis(amine) complex in spite of tertiary amines being more basic towards beryllium than tertiary phosphines, clearly is due to steric factors. Since phosphorus has a greater radius than nitrogen, the methyl groups of the phosphine are further away from the beryllium atom than are the methyl groups of the amine, and scale models show that in $Ph_2Be(PMe_3)_2$ the methyl groups interfere less with the phenyl hydrogen atoms than do the methyl groups in $Ph_2Be(NMe_3)_2$.

2. *Ethers and Sulfides*

Though the separation of ether from beryllium alkyls can be troublesome, or at least somewhat tedious, relatively few ether complexes of definite composition have been isolated. A vapor pressure study (*60*) of the Me_2Be–Me_2O system indicated the formation of $(Me_2Be)_2(Me_2O)_3$, $Me_2Be \cdot Me_2O$, $(Me_2Be)_2Me_2O$, and $(Me_2Be)_3Me_2O$. These were observed in the temperature range −3° to 63° C and in equilibrium with 65–410 mm pressure of dimethyl ether. They are likely to be oligomers of Me_2Be, with Me_2O acting as chain-ending groups.

Though solutions of most beryllium dialkyls in diethyl ether readily lose most of the ether by evaporation, the removal only of the last few percent being time consuming, there are some organoberyllium compounds which form rather stable ether complexes (see also Section II,B,2). Dineopentyl- and dibenzylberyllium form the 1:1 complexes $(Me_3CCH_2)_2Be \cdot OEt_2$, b.p. 30° C/$10^{-3}$ mm, and $(PhCH_2)_2Be \cdot OEt_2$, m.p. 50°–51° C (*50*), both being monomeric in benzene solution.

Diphenylberyllium forms a complex $Ph_2Be(OMe_2)_2$ whose dissociation pressure is negligible at room temperature, in contrast to $Ph_2Be(OEt_2)_2$, whose dissociation pressure is 16 mm at 0° C. Loss of ether from the latter proceeds readily until the composition $Ph_2Be \cdot OEt_2$ is reached (*70*). Di-(phenylethynyl)beryllium (*49*) crystallizes as a 1:1 (rather than the expected 1:2) ether complex $(PhC{\equiv}C)_2Be \cdot OEt_2$, m.p. 149°–151° C (decomp.), whose degree of association in benzene is between 1 and 2, indicating the possibility of an equilibrium between monomer and an electron-deficient

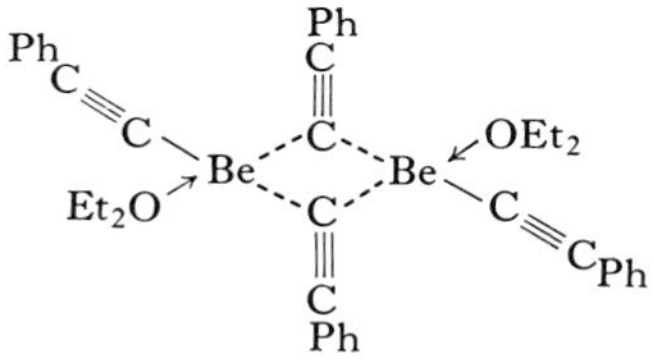

Ph, C, C, Be, C, Be, OEt₂, Et₂O, C, C, CPh, C, Ph, Ph

(XII)

bridged dimer (XII) in the crystalline state. Tetrahydrofuran, on the other hand, yields a monomeric 1:2 complex, $(PhC{\equiv}C)_2Be(THF)_2$, m.p. 138°–140° C (decomp.), and $(MeC{\equiv}C)_2Be(THF)_2$ (*49*).

In the early experiments on the interaction of dimethylberyllium with Me_3N, Me_3P, Me_2O, and Et_2O, the solid beryllium alkyl was exposed to the base in vapor form. Under these circumstances there was no indication of significant interaction with dimethyl sulfide. Following a suggestion that beryllium alkyls might be prepared with the use of Grignard reagents in dimethyl sulfide as solvent (*15*), the synthesis of dimethylberyllium was successfully accomplished by this method (*103*). The product, however, contained appreciable amounts of sulfide which required about six sub-limations for its removal (*104*). This suggested that the sulfide had greater coordination affinity for dimethylberyllium than had earlier been believed, and it was found that Me_2Be dissolved easily in Me_2S. The NMR spectra of the resulting solutions (*105*) were temperature-dependent and consistent with the equilibria,

$$Me_2Be \cdot SMe_2 + SMe_2 \rightleftharpoons Me_2Be(SMe_2)_2$$

$$n(Me_2Be)(SMe_2)_2 \rightleftharpoons (Me_2Be)_n(SMe_2)_2 + (2n-2)SMe_2$$

involving associated species resembling in constitution those discussed above in connection with Me_2Be–PMe_3 equilibria. Species such as (XIII; $n=7$) with as many as nine beryllium atoms in the polymer chain are

$$Me_2S \rightarrow Be(Me)\left[(\mu\text{-}Me)_2Be\right]_n(\mu\text{-}Me)_2Be(Me) \leftarrow SMe_2$$

(XIII)

believed to exist in solution. The assignment of proton magnetic resonance signals at 10.80 τ to the terminal, 10.41 τ to the bridging methyl groups at the end of the chain, and at 10.31 τ to those in the interior of the chain, is a particularly interesting feature of this study. It had previously been suggested (*115*) that the extremely weak ^1H NMR signals in the region of 10.3 τ for very dilute solutions of Me_2Be in aromatic solvents are probably due to internal methyl bridges of polymeric fragments.

As expected, dimethyl sulfide coordinates more strongly to beryllium when the metal is bound to groups which are more electronegative than methyl. Thus Ph_2Be gives the complex $Ph_2Be(SMe_2)_2$, m.p. 132°–134°C (decomp.), but this is partly dissociated in benzene as shown by cryoscopy. There is some evidence, from tensimetric measurements, that diethyl sulfide forms a complex $(Ph_2Be)_2(SEt_2)_3$, since the equilibrium pressure (at 0°C) rises rapidly when the Be:S ratio exceeds 1.5 (*70*). It is of some interest to note that the complex, $BeCl_2(SMe_2)_2$, in which the Lewis acid character of the metal is greater than in the phenyl complex, is not appreciably dissociated in benzene at its freezing point (*56*), though even this loses Me_2S when its solution in toluene is evaporated, giving (XIV).

$$Me_2S \rightarrow BeCl(\mu\text{-}Cl)_2BeCl \leftarrow SMe_2$$

(XIV)

B. Chelate Complexes

The stability increase, due to the entropy factor, of chelate relative to nonchelate complexes is well known, and is strikingly illustrated by the ether and the amine complexes of beryllium alkyls. Whereas no individual ether complex of dimethylberyllium has been isolated, the various complexes

$(Me_2Be)_m(OMe_2)_n$ having dissociation pressures in the range 10–200 mm at room temperature unless m ≫ n, the chelate complex (XV), m.p. 100°–101° C, may be sublimed unchanged at 60°–70° C and 0.2 mm (*56*).

$$Me_2Be \leftleftarrows \begin{matrix} OMe{-}CH_2 \\ | \\ OMe{-}CH_2 \end{matrix}$$

(XV)

$$Me_2Be \leftleftarrows \begin{matrix} NMe_2{-}CH_2 \\ | \\ NMe_2{-}CH_2 \end{matrix}$$

(XVI)

Similarly the tetramethylethylenediamine (TMED) complex (XVI), m.p. 81°–82°C (*56*), has negligible dissociation pressure of amine, though $Me_2Be(NMe_3)_2$ has a dissociation pressure of 23 mm at 0° C. A tetramethyl-*o*-phenylenediamine complex analogous to (XVI) is also known (*24*). Since the TMED molecule has nearly the same volume as two trimethylamine molecules, and since di-*tert*-butylberyllium forms only a 1:1 trimethylamine complex, *tert*-$Bu_2Be \cdot NMe_3$, it was of some interest to find that TMED formed a complex, *tert*-Bu_2Be(TMED), which is monomeric in benzene (*66*). This cannot be a true chelate complex, as (XVII), for steric reasons which at once become apparent when attempts are made to construct a molecular model. Clearly there is room for only one amine group to be complexed at a given instant of time, as in (XVIII). The ¹H NMR spectrum

$$(tert\text{-}Bu)_2Be \leftleftarrows \begin{matrix} NMe_2{-}CH_2 \\ | \\ NMe_2{-}CH_2 \end{matrix}$$

(XVII)

$$(tert\text{-}Bu)_2Be \leftarrow NMe_2{-}CH_2{-}CH_2{-}NMe_2$$

(XVIII)

$$(tert\text{-}Bu)_2Be \leftarrow NMe_2{-}CH_2{-}CH_2{-}NMe_2$$

(XIX)

(*41*) is consistent with a constitution in which only one nitrogen atom is coordinated at a time, but in which there is rapid exchange between free and complexed nitrogen, i.e., (XVIII) ⇌ (XIX). The spectrum is simple at room temperature, but a splitting of the resonances of the protons of the base is apparent below −20° C in C_7D_8 solution, as the rate of exchange becomes relatively slow. It is interesting to note that this effect is not observed for the magnesium analog (*59*), since the larger magnesium atom can accommodate all four groups. Nor is the ^{1}H NMR spectrum of the diisopropylberyllium TMED complex temperature–dependent, so both this and *tert*-$Bu_2Mg(TMED)$ are believed to have chelate structures analogous to (XVII).

Other chelate amine complexes are (XX; R=Me), m.p. 103°–104°C (*24*); (XX; R=Ph), m.p. 260°–261°C (decomp.) (*70*); and (XXI; R=

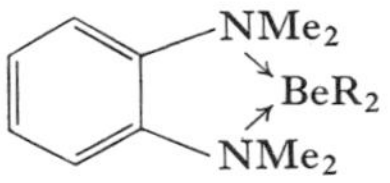

$C_6H_4(NMe_2)_2 \rightarrow BeR_2$

(XX)

$CH_2NMe_2{-}CH_2NMe_2 \rightarrow BeR_2$

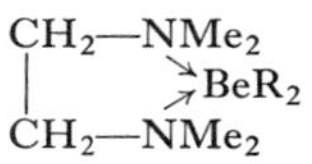

(XXI)

MeC≡C), m.p. 199°–201°C; (XXI; R=PhC≡C), m.p. 173°C (decomp.) (*49*). Tetramethyltetrazene forms two series of complexes $R_2Be(Me_2NN{=}NNMe_2)$ and $(R_2Be)_2(Me_2NN{=}NNMe_2)$ where R=Et, iso-Pr, and

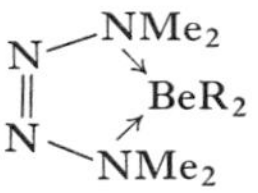

$N(NMe_2){=}N(NMe_2) \rightarrow BeR_2$

(XXII)

$R_2Be \leftarrow Me_2N{-}N{=}N{-}NMe_2 \rightarrow BeR_2$

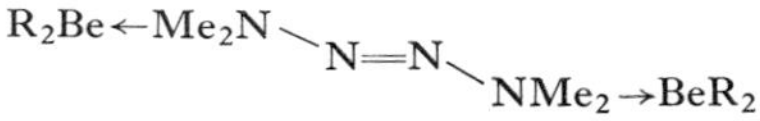

(XXIII)

tert-Bu (*83*). The former could have chelate structures (XXII) at least when R=Et. No splitting of the ^{1}H NMR signals of the N—Me protons of the diethylberyllium complex was observed at −75°C, but similar experiments on the isopropyl and tertiary butyl complexes do not appear to have been made. In the latter case, at least, the tetrazene is likely to behave as a monodentate ligand. The 2:1 complexes could well have the structure (XXIII). Though tetramethylhydrazine could conceivably behave as a chelating amine, it forms a 2:1 complex, $(Et_2Be)_2Me_2NNMe_2$ (*82*), even when diethylberyllium and the hydrazine are brought together in 1:1 molar proportions.

No chelate diphosphine complexes of beryllium alkyls have yet been described, though many could doubtless be prepared without difficulty.

The 1,2-dimethoxyethane complex of dimethylberyllium has already been mentioned. Other known 1,2-dimethoxyethane complexes are $Ph_2Be \cdot MeOC_2H_4OMe$, m.p. 143°–145°C (*70*), and $(PhC{\equiv}C)_2Be \cdot MeO$ C_2H_4OMe, m.p. 185°–190°C (decomp.) (*49*). The disulfide complex (XXIV), m.p. 127°–128°C, is not significantly dissociated in benzene solution (*70*).

$$\begin{array}{l} CH_2\text{—}SMe \searrow \\ \quad | \qquad\qquad BePh_2 \\ CH_2\text{—}SMe \nearrow \end{array}$$

(XXIV)

The color of some of the pyridine complexes of beryllium alkyls (e.g., Et_2py_2Be is orange-yellow) has already been mentioned. The colors of many of the complexes formed by 2,2′-bipyridyl (bipy) are commonly much more intense, and even some beryllium halides form colored bipyridyl complexes. The reactivities of the bipyridyl complexes of beryllium dialkyls are much lower than those of the dialkyls themselves, thus Me_2bipyBe is decomposed after about 15 minutes exposure to the air whereas Me_2Be inflames instantly. In Table I, λ_{max} refers to the long-wavelength absorption in or near the visible part of the spectrum. All bipyridyl compounds have very intense absorptions in the ultraviolet region.

TABLE I

2,2′-BIPYRIDYL COMPLEXES, R_2bipyBe AND bipyBeX_2

X in bipyBeX_2	Color	λ_{max} (mμ)	Molar extinction coefficient × 10^{-3}	References
Cl	White	352 infl.	1.2	(*56*)
Br	Pale cream	364	2.4	(*56*)
I	Yellow	368	7.0	(*56*)
Ph	Pale yellow	353 infl.	0.5	(*56*)
Me	Yellow	395	2.7	(*56*)
Et	Red	461	3.7	(*56*)
n-Pr	Red	—	—	(*66*)
PhC⋮C	White	—	—	(*49*)

The intensification of color in the sequence Cl < Br < I suggested that the light absorption is due to a charge-transfer process, which could be of the $n \rightarrow \pi^*$ type involving halogen nonbonding orbitals, and in which an electron is transferred into the lowest vacant π-molecular orbital of the heterocyclic system. The colors of the dialkyl complexes posed more of a problem, however. Again the depth of color increases with the electron-releasing characteristics of the organic group, and it has been suggested that the metal–carbon bond is the electron source in these compounds (*55, 56*). Recently it has been suggested that considering the two M—C bonds as being replaced by a symmetric $\psi(MC_1)+\psi(MC_2)$ and an asymmetric $\psi(MC_1) - \psi(MC_2)$ combination, the latter is of correct symmetry to interact with the bipyridyl π-orbitals (*78*). Thus the electron transfer would involve both M—C bonds equally, and would reduce the M—C bond order of both bonds to $\frac{3}{4}$ rather than that of one of them to $\frac{1}{2}$. Similar electronic transitions have been suggested as the origin of the colors of some decaborane complexes with heterocyclic bases (*96*). Sometimes a normally forbidden electronic transition becomes allowed, and thus of greater intensity, when a ligand is perturbed by coordination. The spectra of the R_2bipyBe complexes show not only that the λ_{max} but also the shape of the absorption changes with R, thus an effect such as charge transfer must be involved rather than the activation of a normally inactive transition.

Bipyridyl complexes with other main-group organometallic compounds, whose colors are similarly due to charge-transfer transitions, have been described, e.g., those of lithium (*154*), magnesium (*56, 154*), and aluminum (*32*). Some colored dialkylzinc complexes with 2,2′-bipyridyl and with *o*-phenanthroline are also known (*56*), and the range of these has been considerably extended (*125, 127*); in these instances the possibility of the 3*d* electron shell acting as electron source has also to be considered.

The complexes [$bipy_2Be$] and [$Libipy_2Be$] which are deep green and deep violet, respectively, in ethereal solvents, are not compounds of Be(0) and Be(−1), but should be regarded as complexes formed by the bipyridyl

$$\text{bipyBeCl}_2 + \text{Li}_2\text{bipy} \rightarrow [\text{bipy}_2\text{Be}] \xrightarrow{\text{Li}} [\text{Libipy}_2\text{Be}]$$

radical anion; they are paramagnetic (*56*). The neutral complex [$bipy_2Be$] has an electron spin resonance spectrum consistent with the above formulation (*30*).

C. NMR Spectra

It was predicted on the basis of the electronegativity of beryllium, that CH_3—Be proton resonances should occur in the region of about 11.2–11.4 τ, and such resonances were in fact reported over the range 11.06–11.52 (*28*). Later, in studies on alkylberyllium alkoxides (considered in Section VIII), CH_3—Be resonances were observed in the range 10.46–10.77 for the tetramers $(R'BeOR)_4$ containing four-coordinate metal, and in the range 11.06–11.53 for alkoxides containing three-coordinate metal (*45*). The range of resonances has more recently been extended down to 9.59. The lowest field resonances should occur for bridging methyl groups since, being bound to two metal atoms, they are the most "deshielded" (*157*). The resonances should move to higher field with increase in base strength of any coordinated ligand. Thus the 1:1 adduct $Me_2Be \cdot SMe_2$ with the rather weak base, Me_2S, has a CH_3—Be resonance at 10.77 while the adducts $Me_2Be \cdot OEt_2$ and $Me_2Be \cdot NMe_3$ have resonances at 11.16 and 11.19 τ, respectively. The resonance signals might also be expected to move to

TABLE II

^9Be AND ^1H MAGNETIC RESONANCES FOR SOME METHYLBERYLLIUM COMPLEXES

Species	Solvent	^9Be chemical shift[a]	^1H chemical shift of CH_3—Be (τ units)
$BeCl_2(SMe_2)_2$	SMe_2	−5.48	—
$MeBeCl(SMe_2)_2$	SMe_2	−4.24	11.17[b]
$Me_2Be(SMe_2)_2$	SMe_2	—	11.30[b]
$Me_2Be \cdot SMe_2$	SMe_2	−11.6	10.77[b]
$Me_2Be(NMe_3)_2$	NMe_3	−12.0	11.43[b]
$Me_2Be \cdot NMe_3$	Cyclohexane	−19.9	11.19[c]
$Me_2Be \cdot NMe_3$	Benzene	—	10.59[d]
$Me_2Be(Me_2NCH_2^-)_2$	Cyclohexane	—	11.52[c]
$Me_2Be(Me_2NCH_2^-)_2$	Benzene	—	10.80[d]
$Me_2Be \cdot OEt_2$	OEt_2	−20.8	11.16[c]
$BeCl_2(OEt_2)_2$	OEt_2	−3.14	—
$Me_2Be(PMe_3)_2$	PMe_3	−3.6	11.42[b]

[a] Ppm relative to Be^{2+} aq., Kovar and Morgan (*104*).
[b] Kovar and Morgan (*105*).
[c] Bell *et al.* (*28*).
[d] Coates and Francis (*49*).

higher field as the number of coordinated ligands increases: this is observed in some instances, e.g., $Me_2Be(Me_2S)_2$ (observed in dimethyl sulfide solutions at temperatures below −45°C), $Me_2Be(NMe_3)_2$ and Me_2Be (TMED) having CH_3—Be resonances at 11.17, 11.43, and 11.52, respectively. In other cases, however, such as the methylberyllium alkoxides mentioned above, the reverse is observed.

The still relatively narrow range of methylberyllium resonances precludes reliable generalizations, both for reasons quoted above, and also since solvent effects are sometimes unusually large (see Table II). Further, generalizations are unlikely to be useful for compounds in which groups other than methyl are bound to beryllium. The use of ^{9}Be resonance was thus considered as a possible means of elucidating the structural environment of beryllium in its chemical compounds.

The first studies of ^{9}Be resonance (*102*) showed a surprising intensitivity of the chemical shift to environment. All of the compounds studied, however, were inorganic complexes in which the beryllium atom was tetrahedrally coordinated either by oxygen or by fluorine. In contrast, the ^{9}Be resonances in organoberyllium compounds (*104*) occur over a relatively wide range (Table II). Clearly the coordination number of the beryllium, affecting the magnetic "shielding," is the dominant factor, local diamagnetic effects probably accounting for the remaining part of the chemical shift. For example, replacement of a group bound to beryllium by a more electronegative group should shift the resonance to lower field, thus the resonances in $MeBeCl(SMe_2)_2$ and $BeCl_2(SMe_2)_2$ are at -4.24 and -5.48 ppm, respectively. No evidence has been found for paramagnetic contributions.

One of the main conclusions so far drawn from ^{9}Be resonance data is that Me_2Be exists as the 1:1 adduct, $Me_2Be \cdot OEt_2$, in diethyl ether solution, not as the 1:2 adduct as previously supposed. At low temperatures some 1:2 adduct may also be present. No conclusion on this matter clearly emerges from ^{1}H NMR studies.

Unfortunately the only spin-coupled interactions observed so far have been for BeF_4^{2-} and BeF_2 aq. The ^{9}Be signal in $Me_2Be(PMe_3)_2$, in which there are Be—P bonds, does not reveal any spin-coupled interaction with the phosphorus nuclei.

VI

HALOBERYLLIUM ALKYLS, RBeX

The history of this class of organoberyllium compounds is rather long and confusing. As early as 1923 Gilman (*89*) tried without success to prepare various organoberyllium halides by heating beryllium metal with a range of halides (from methyl iodide to 1-bromonaphthalene) in several solvents and up to 250° C and 2 weeks' reaction time. Metallic beryllium was a very scarce commodity at that time, and unlikely to have been of adequate purity. A little later Durand (*80*) described the preparation of methylberyllium iodide from beryllium powder and methyl iodide in ether containing a little mercury(II) chloride. This claim was effectively disputed by Gilman and Schulze (*91*) (1927), who showed that Durand's product could not have been methylberyllium iodide, and who also succeeded in preparing ethereal solutions of MeBeI, EtBeBr, EtBeI, *n*-BuBeI, and PhBeI by heating the metal with the halide in ether at 80°–90° C for 15 hours in the presence of a little $HgCl_2$. No pure liquid or crystalline products were mentioned, but various reactions of the ether solutions were investigated. It is interesting to note that MeBeI was shown to disproportionate, giving Me_2Be when its solution was heated. About the same time (*92*) ether solutions of MeBeI were obtained by the reaction

$$Me_2Be + I_2 \xrightarrow{\text{Ether}} MeBeI + MeI$$

Gilman and Schulze also noted that RBeX is formed by reaction of R_2Be and BeX_2 (*91*). In this early work (*136*) it was also found that methylberyllium iodide could be obtained by heating beryllium with a trace of $HgCl_2$ and a large excess of methyl iodide, i.e., ether was not used.

In 1952 it was claimed (*140*) that $BeCl_2$ reacts with chloroform giving Cl_3CBeCl and $Be(CCl_3)_2$, and with bromoform giving Br_3CBeCl, HCl being the other product in both cases. None of these compounds were isolated and a reinvestigation of this reaction has shown that nothing happens if the $BeCl_2$ is pure and dry. Otherwise hydrogen chloride is formed but no evidence for $ClBeCCl_3$ was found. With CHF_3, $BeCl_2$ yields BeF_2 and $CHCl_3$ (*10*).

During the last fifteen years, since metallic beryllium became significant in nuclear reactor technology, methods for its commercial production in fairly pure form have been developed. It is now possible to achieve reactions with the metal that earlier could not be made to work. For example, beryllium has now been shown to react with various halides in the absence of ether and of any catalysts (*161*):

$$Be + RX \xrightarrow[12\text{–}60\ \text{hr}]{130°C} RBeX$$

$$(R = Et, X = I;\ R = n\text{-}Bu, X = Br, I;\ R = C_5H_{11}, C_8H_{17}, X = I)$$

The products, RBeX, are insoluble in the alkyl halides in which they are formed, and nothing is known of their molecular structure or complexity. However, it is quite likely that they are coordination polymers, perhaps like $(EtZnI)_x$ (*121*).

More is known about the coordination complexes of RBeX. In a recent careful study, Ashby and associates (*134*) have shown that methyl- and phenylberyllium bromide and chloride are all monomeric (or nearly so) in diethyl ether. The equilibrium

$$R_2Be + BeX_2 \rightleftharpoons 2\ RBeX$$

is believed to lie predominantly if not entirely to the right, contrary to an earlier report (*76*). The ^1H NMR spectra of solutions of Me_2Be in ether, to which various molar proportions of $BeCl_2$ (or $BeBr_2$) had been added, are entirely consistent with the only species present at room temperature

$$Me_2Be \leftarrow (OEt_2)_2 \qquad \text{(XXV)}$$

$$Me(Cl)Be \leftarrow (OEt_2)_2 \qquad \text{(XXVI)}$$

in significant concentration being solvent, (XXV)[1] and (XXVI). Solutions obtained by adding 1 mole of Me_2Be to 1 mole of $BeCl_2$ in ether are believed to consist predominantly of solvated MeBeCl also because addition of dioxane results only in slow precipitation. In contrast, addition of dioxane to $BeCl_2$ in ether results in immediate precipitation.

Several coordination complexes have been obtained in crystalline form, though no X-ray structure analyses have been carried out on them. *tert*-Butylberyllium chloride–ether complex (*98*) has been shown to be dimeric in benzene (*66*), and beyond reasonable doubt has the structure (XXVII).

$$tert\text{-}Bu(Et_2O\rightarrow)Be(\mu\text{-}Cl)_2Be(\leftarrow OEt_2)Bu\text{-}tert \qquad \text{(XXVII)}$$

$$tert\text{-}Bu(Cl)Be(\leftarrow OEt_2)_2 \qquad \text{(XXVIII)}$$

The chloride bridges in (XXVII) are cleaved by ether, and the complex is monomeric (XXVIII) in dilute solution in ether (*66*). The TMED complexes

$$R(Br)Be \leftarrow (NMe_2\text{—}CH_2)_2 \qquad \text{(XXIX)}$$

(XXIX, R = Et, m.p. 107°–109°C; $R = CH_2CMe_3$, m.p. 104°–106°) are monomeric in benzene ($BeBr_2 \cdot$TMED being practically insoluble in this solvent). In contrast, addition of trimethylamine to a benzene–ether solution of Me_3CCH_2BeBr results in disproportionation and precipitation of the trimethylamine complex of beryllium bromide. The constitution of (XXIX)

[1] More likely the monoether complex, see Section V,C.

is further supported by the fact that the CH_3—N ^{1}H NMR resonances are not equivalent at room temperature, but coalesce as the temperature is raised (*50*).

The products obtained when beryllium reacts with acyl chlorides,

$$\text{Be} + \text{RCOCl} \rightarrow \text{RCOBeCl} \qquad (\text{R} = \text{Me, Et, } n\text{-Pr})$$

bromides, and iodides, are haloberyllium acyls (rather than alkyls), but deserve mention here. They yield the corresponding aldehyde when hydrolyzed, and the expected reaction takes place with a ketone (*153*).

$$\text{MeCOBeBr} + \text{MeCOBu-}n \longrightarrow \text{MeCO}\underset{\text{Me}}{\overset{n\text{-Bu}}{\text{C}}}\text{OH} \quad \text{(after hydrolysis)}$$

Nothing is known of the constitution of RCOBeX; it is extremely unlikely that they are monomeric. Reaction between 2 moles of acyl chloride and one of beryllium gives 1,2-diketones, after hydrolysis. Presumably, one intermediate would be a diketone coordination complex of beryllium chloride.

$$\text{Be} + 2\,\text{RCOCl} \rightarrow \text{RCOCOR}\cdot\text{BeCl}_2$$

Hydrogen cyanide reacts with Me_2Be and with $Me_2Be \cdot NMe_3$ giving MeBeCN and $MeBeCN \cdot NMe_3$ respectively. Both are insoluble and are sure to be coordination polymers (*62, 111*).

VII

AMINOBERYLLIUM ALKYLS, R_2NBeR'

Most of these have been obtained by reactions between a beryllium dialkyl and a secondary amine (*44*). Unless restrained by steric hindrance, a

$$\text{R}'_2\text{Be} + \text{R}_2\text{NH} \rightarrow \text{R}'\text{H} + \text{R}_2\text{NBeR}'$$

second molecule of amine can react. For example, iso-Pr_2Be and 2 moles of

$$\text{R}_2\text{NBeR}' + \text{R}_2\text{NH} \rightarrow \text{R}'\text{H} + (\text{R}_2\text{N})_2\text{Be}$$

Me_2NH give $[(Me_2N)_2Be]_3$ (*51*). Bis(dimethylamino)beryllium was later prepared from Et_2Be and Me_2NH (*85*), and shown on the basis of its [1]H

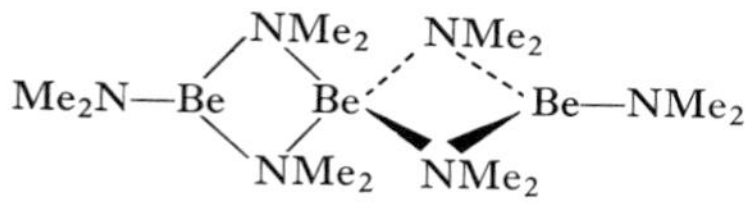

$$Me_2N{-}Be(\mu\text{-}NMe_2)_2Be(\mu\text{-}NMe_2)_2Be{-}NMe_2$$

(XXX)

NMR spectrum to have a linear structure (XXX) rather than the cyclic structure previously suggested. The structure (XXX) has been confirmed by X-ray analysis (*13*), an interesting feature of which is the indication of some p_π–p_π bonding between the terminal nitrogen and the three-coordinate beryllium atoms. The terminal Be—N distances (1.57 Å) are appreciably shorter than those of the four-membered rings (1.65 and 1.78 Å). Moreover, the terminal nitrogen atoms are coplanar with the carbon and beryllium atoms to which they are bound.

The ^9Be resonance spectrum of $[Be(NMe_2)_2]_3$ also strongly indicates that structure (XXX) persists in solution, as had earlier been suggested by its ^1H NMR spectrum. Its solutions in benzene have two ^9Be resonances at -2.95 and -9.8 ppm (relative to Be^{2+} aq.) in area ratio 1:2 corresponding to four- and three-coordinate beryllium, respectively (*104*; also see Table II). Some ketimino derivatives, e.g., $[p\text{-tolyl}_2C{=}N)_2Be]_3$, are also believed to contain some Be—N partial double bonds (*151*).

An aminoberyllium alkyl has also been prepared by the addition of BeH across an azomethine bond (*25*), but this method has not been applied further.

$$2\,MeBeH + 2\,PhCH{=}NPh \rightarrow [PhCH_2N(Ph)BeMe]_2$$

No monomeric aminoberyllium alkyls of the type R_2NBeR' are known. Such a compound, if monomeric, would have the metal two-coordinate and

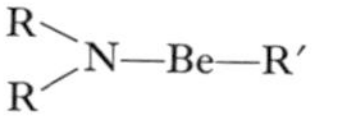

$$R_2N{-}Be{-}R' \qquad\qquad R_2N{=}Be{-}R'$$

(XXXI)  (XXXII)

the nitrogen three-coordinate, as in (XXXI). Nitrogen being more electronegative than carbon, the metal atom in (XXXI) would have greater Lewis acidity than the metal atom in a beryllium dialkyl. Conversely, the nitrogen in (XXXI) would be more basic than that in R_2NH, beryllium being more electropositive than hydrogen. The use of the nitrogen lone pair to increase the effective covalency of nitrogen to four and that of beryllium to three is therefore to be expected. This might be accomplished either by the forma-

$$\begin{array}{c} R' \\ \nearrow Be \searrow \\ R_2N \qquad NR_2 \\ \searrow Be \swarrow \\ R' \end{array}$$

(XXXIII)

$$\begin{array}{ccc} & R'Be—NR_2 & \\ \nearrow & & \searrow \\ R_2N & & BeR' \\ \searrow & & \swarrow \\ & R'Be \leftarrow NR_2 & \end{array}$$

(XXXIV)

tion of a p_π–p_π bond as in (XXXII), or by the formation of σ-bonds leading to associated species such as (XXXIII) and (XXXIV).

All of the compounds of the type R_2NBeR' so far studied have been found to be dimers or trimers, as (XXXIII) and (XXXIV), in solution. Higher degrees of association *in solution* have not been observed, though in some instances (one is mentioned below) there are indications of a polymeric constitution in the condensed state. The formation of π-bonds, as in (XXXII), appears to occur, leading to an unknown π-bond order only when the expansion of covalency by the formation of additional σ-bonds is sterically prevented. Instances where Be—N π-bonds are probably formed have been mentioned above, and other cases where beryllium may form a π-bond to nitrogen or to oxygen will be mentioned as they arise. The known amino-beryllium alkyls derived from secondary amines are listed in Table III.

TABLE III

AMINOBERYLLIUM DIMERS AND TRIMERS[a]

Dimers[b]	$(MeBeNPr_2\text{-}n)_2$	$(MeBeNPh_2)_2$	$(EtBeNEt_2)_2$
	$(PhBeNPh_2)_2$	$(EtBeNPh_2)_2$	$[MeBeN(CH_2Ph)Ph]_2$
Trimers[b]	$(MeBeNMe_2)_3$	$(MeBeNEt_2)_3$	$(PhBeNMe_2)_3$
	$(EtBeNMe_2)_3$	$(iso\text{-}PrBeNMe_2)_3$	

[a] Reference (*44*).

[b] In benzene solution, cryoscopically.

Since monomers would exist only if there were enough steric congestion about beryllium and nitrogen to prevent association (such a case might be, for example, *tert*-butylberyllium-2,2′,6,6′-tetramethylpiperidide), one has to consider what circumstances favor the formation of dimers and trimers. Low degrees of association in solution or in the gas phase are favored by the entropy factor, since the lower the degree of association the greater will be the number of independent molecules and the greater will be the translational entropy per unit mass of material. Thus, other things being equal dimers would be expected. However, the average internal ring angle in a dimer must be 90°, and this would result in appreciable angular valence strain. Nothing is known about strain energies involving beryllium, but by analogy with the strain energy in cyclobutane (about 6–7 kcal per gm atom of carbon) one might suppose the strain energy at the nitrogen atoms alone would amount to about 10–15 kcal per mole of dimer $(R_2NBeR')_2$. Since the entropy effect mentioned above is unlikely to favor dimers over trimers to an extent exceeding 3 kcal/mole, one concludes that the lowest degree of association, in the absence of other factors, should be three.

Inspection of Table III shows that all of the dimethylamino derivatives are trimers; also that with the exception of $(MeBeNEt_2)_3$ the complexes in which two groups larger than methyl are bound to nitrogen are all dimers. By constructing molecular models one can show that the steric interference between R and R′ groups is substantially less in the dimer than in the trimer. Summarizing, the entropy factor favors low rather than high degrees of association, the angular valence strain in a dimer results in trimers being preferred to dimers, unless the groups R′ and particularly R are big enough to cause significant steric interference, in which case this effect supervenes and dimers are then the preferred form.

In a few instances, some of which are mentioned in Section V,A,1, the complex formed when a secondary amine reacts with R'_2Be can be isolated before alkane elimination takes place, giving R_2NBeR'. For example, the complex $Me_2NH \cdot MeBe_2$ decomposes only slowly at room temperature, but when it melts at 44° C it evolves methane vigorously, forming MeBe-NMe_2. This compound has been shown to be trimeric, not only in solution, but also in the gas phase. The trimer (XXXIV; R = R′ = Me) cannot be planar, but the observed single ^1H NMR signal both for CH_3—Be and $(CH_3)_2N$ over the range −90° to +25° C, suggests a very rapid interconversion of conformations (*28*). When it was first prepared (*54*) MeBe-NMe_2 was described as forming white crystals, m.p. 55°–56° C. Since then, several dimethylamino, phosphino, and arsino derivatives of metals have been found to exist in a glassy state (*20*). A reexamination (*28*) of $MeBeNMe_2$ showed this too is isotropic when examined by polarized light, and in the condensed state it also gives no X-ray diffraction lines. Thus, in the condensed state it must be a liquid of very high viscosity. When heated in a sealed tube, as if for a melting point determination, it softens and turns into a clearly recognizable liquid over the range 51°–54° C, the process being reversible. Corresponding changes occur at 50°–53° C for $MeBeN(CD_3)_2$, and 48°–54° C for CD_3BeNMe_2. As in the examples considered in Beachley *et al.* (*20*) the "melting" process is believed to involve a rapid change of degree of polymerization. The glassy form probably consists of polymers and oligomers, $(MeBeNMe_2)_n$.

Reactions between beryllium dialkyls and ammonia (*113*) or primary amines have been less studied than those between R_2Be and secondary amines. The difficulty here is the relative ease with which insoluble polymeric products are formed. The reaction between Me_2Be and $MeNH_2$ has been mentioned in Section V,A,1; it proceeds in several stages and none of the products appears amenable to study of degree of association, etc. In contrast, *tert*-butylamine is sufficiently sterically hindered to give

$$tert\text{-}BuNH_2 + Me_2Be \xrightarrow{Et_2O} \tfrac{1}{3}(tert\text{-}BuNHBeMe)_3 + CH_4$$

$$\downarrow 40^\circ C,\ tert\text{-}BuNH_2$$

$$\tfrac{1}{2}[(tert\text{-}BuNH)_2Be]_2 + CH_4$$

relatively simple products (*69*). The steric requirements of hydrogen being small, the trimer $(tert\text{-}BuNHBeMe)_3$ can be compared with the trimer $(Et_2NBeMe)_3$, since in both cases the nitrogen is bound to a 4-carbon group. The bis amide $[(tert\text{-}BuNH)_2Be]_2$, m.p. 96°–97° C, is likely to have the structure (XXXV), and some π-bonding could occur here too.

NHBu-*tert*
tert-BuNH—Be ⇄ Be—NHBu-*tert*
NHBu-*tert*

(XXXV)

The even more sterically hindered silylamine derivative $(Me_3Si)_2N$—Be—$N(SiMe_3)_2$ is monomeric (*34*) and has a linear N—Be—N group in the vapor state, as indicated by electron diffraction. The Be—N bond lengths (1.566 Å) are similar to those of the terminal Be—N bonds (1.57 Å) in $[(Me_2N)_2Be]_3$, mentioned earlier in this section, and are consistent with some degree of p_π–p_π bonding. Thus the N—Be—N system in this compound has some formal resemblance to the allene system (*40*).

Reactions between diethylberyllium and several methylhydrazines have been studied by Fetter (*82*). Not surprisingly, hydrazines with two or more acidic hydrogen atoms tend to give insoluble (or poorly soluble) involatile and evidently polymeric materials. Trimethylhydrazine, however, contains only one acidic hydrogen, and this yielded both a coordination adduct, and the product resulting from ethane elimination:

$$Et_2Be + NHMeNMe_2 \rightarrow Et_2Be \cdot NHMeNMe_2 \rightarrow \tfrac{1}{4}(EtBeNMeNMe_2)_4$$

The structure of the tetramer $(EtBeNMeNMe_2)_4$, which is a viscous liquid, is not known. In the hypothetical monomeric form of this compound there are two available lone pairs, and two vacant coordination sites on the metal atom. It is quite likely that a cagelike structure is formed, consisting of fused five- and six-membered rings, as in the somewhat analogous compound $(MeZnON{=}CMe_2)_4$ (*72*, p. 139), which also contains an alkylated Group II metal bound to a pair of basic atoms.

Aminoberyllium alkyls, whether cyclic dimers or trimers, contain three-coordinate and therefore coordinatively unsaturated beryllium. Thus they react with bases unless prevented by steric hindrance. The dimethylamine compound, $MeBeNMe_2$, in the condensed phase does not react with gaseous trimethylamine (*54*), indicating that any adduct such as $(MeBeNMe_2 \cdot NMe_3)_n$ would have a considerable dissociation pressure. If, however, one of the hydrogen atoms of the dimethylamino group in $MeBeNMe_2$ is replaced by CH_2NMe_2 (a group which occupies nearly the same volume as NMe_3), giving $MeBeNMeCH_2NMe_2$, then a stable crystalline dimer (XXXVI; R=Me) m.p. 116°–118°C is formed, in which the metal atoms

```
CH2—Me2N↘    ↗R                 CH2—Me2N↘    ↗R
|         Be                    |          M
|      ↗      ↖                 |       ↗     ↖
CH2—MeN        NMe—CH2          CH2—MeN        NMe—CH2
       ↘      ↗     |                  ↘     ↗     |
          Be        |                     M        |
      ↗      ↖      |               R↗       ↖     |
    R          NMe2—CH2                        NMe2—CH2

     (XXXVI)                            (XXXVII)
```

are four-coordinate. Numerous analogous complexes, all prepared from the metal alkyl (or in one case the hydride) and *N,N,N'*-trimethylethylenediamine, have been described, the metals M being beryllium (*56*), magnesium (*58*), and zinc (*64*, *124*). The structure (XXXVII) has been confirmed by X-ray analysis in the case of two members of this group of compounds, M=Zn and R=H (*139*) and M=Mg, R=Me (*109*), the former having also been studied by neutron diffraction, which confirmed the positions of the hydridic hydrogen atoms.

Diphenylberyllium forms a similar dimer (XXXVI; R=Ph), but in the case of *tert*-Bu_2Be the bulky tertiary butyl group prevents the formation

```
               ↗NMe—CH2
tert-Bu—Be          |
               ↖NMe2—CH2

          (XXXVIII)
```

of a dimeric product. The *tert*-butyl complex (XXXVIII) not only is monomeric in benzene, but has a relatively low b.p. 45° C/1 mm. There could be significant p_π–p_π bonding between beryllium and the methylamino group. Though reaction between organoberyllium compounds, R_2Be, and 1 mole of trimethylethylenediamine gives products such as (XXXVI) and (XXXVIII), reaction with 2 moles gives a product (XXXIX) containing no

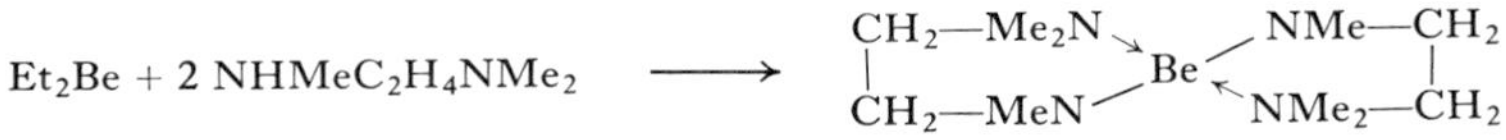

$$Et_2Be + 2\,NHMeC_2H_4NMe_2 \longrightarrow \begin{array}{l} CH_2\text{—}Me_2N \searrow \\ | \qquad\qquad\qquad\quad Be \\ CH_2\text{—}MeN \diagup \end{array} \begin{array}{l} \diagup NMe\text{—}CH_2 \\ \qquad\qquad\quad | \\ \nwarrow NMe_2\text{—}CH_2 \end{array}$$

(XXXIX)

Be—C bonds. There is some evidence that this complex may dissociate to the three-coordinate species (XL) in solution, since in benzene it reacts with methyl iodide much more rapidly than does any other dimethylamino complex examined, suggesting the presence of uncomplexed dimethylamino groups. Its infrared spectrum in solution is also very different from that of the solid, suggesting a major structural difference between solid and solution. Any such dissociation is to be attributed to the steric congestion resulting from the four amino groups being bound to one beryllium atom. In contrast, the analogous thio complex (XLI) has virtually the same infrared spectrum

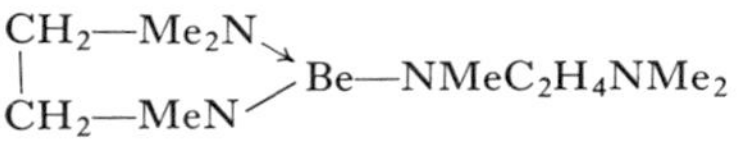

$$\begin{array}{l} CH_2\text{—}Me_2N \searrow \\ | \qquad\qquad\qquad\quad Be\text{—}NMeC_2H_4NMe_2 \\ CH_2\text{—}MeN \diagup \end{array}$$

(XL)

$$\begin{array}{l} CH_2\text{—}Me_2N \searrow \\ | \qquad\qquad\qquad\quad Be \\ CH_2\text{—}S \diagup \end{array} \begin{array}{l} \diagup S\text{—}CH_2 \\ \qquad\qquad | \\ \nwarrow NMe_2\text{—}CH_2 \end{array}$$

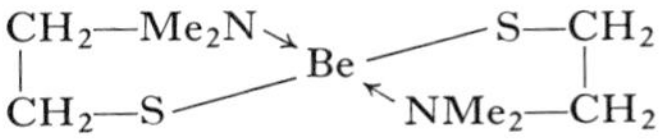

(XLI)

in solution and in the solid state; also, it reacts only very slowly with methyl iodide. A sulfur atom occupies less space than a methylamino group (*21*).

Reactions between dimethylberyllium and *N*-methylethylenediamines containing two or more acidic hydrogen atoms readily lead to condensed polymeric products, though the dimethylethylenediamines give isolable intermediates such as (XLII), which polymerize as they eliminate further methane (*56*).

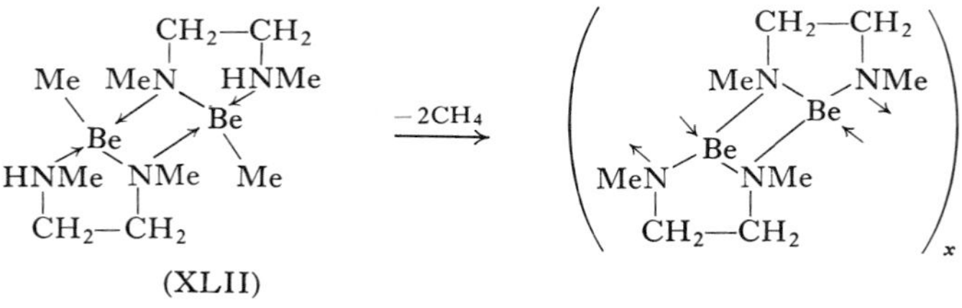

$$\begin{array}{c} CH_2\text{—}CH_2 \\ Me \quad MeN \quad HNMe \\ Be \quad\quad Be \\ HNMe \quad NMe \quad Me \\ CH_2\text{—}CH_2 \end{array} \xrightarrow{-2CH_4} \left(\begin{array}{c} CH_2\text{—}CH_2 \\ MeN \quad NMe \\ Be \\ Be \\ MeN \quad NMe \\ CH_2\text{—}CH_2 \end{array} \right)_x$$

(XLII)

The complexes, some of which are colored, formed by beryllium alkyls and the heterocyclic bases pyridine and 2,2′-bipyridyl, have been discussed in Section V. Both these bases are less sterically hindered than trimethylamine, and both form complexes with aminoberyllium alkyls (*44*). It is surprising that pyridine displaces the lone pair of a dimethylamino group,

$$\tfrac{2}{3}(MeBeNMe_2)_3 \xrightarrow{py} \text{Me(py)Be}(\mu\text{-NMe}_2)_2\text{Be(py)Me} \xrightarrow{py} \text{Me(Me}_2\text{N)Be}(py)_2$$

(XLIII) (XLIV)

as in the formation of (XLIV) from (XLIII). The complexes (XLIII) and (XLIV) are colorless and pale cream, but the diphenylamino analogs are pale and bright yellow, respectively. The complex $[Me(Ph_2N)Be\ py]_2$ is only sparingly soluble in benzene and is presumed dimeric; it was the first methylberyllium compound found not to be decomposed by cold water.

The addition of bases to amino-, alkoxy-, and alkylthioberyllium alkyls is sometimes complicated by disproportionation processes, for example, $Me_2Be\ py_2$ crystallizes, presumably being the least-soluble species present in the equilibrium, when pyridine reacts with di-*n*-propylamino(methyl)-beryllium:

$$(MeBeNPr_2\text{-}n)_2 + 2\ py \rightarrow Me_2Be\ py_2 + (n\text{-}Pr_2N)_2Be$$

2,2′-Bipyridyl, which forms colored complexes with beryllium dialkyls, also gives brightly colored complexes with aminoberyllium alkyls. Addition of the base to $MeBeNMe_2$ in ether gives a bright red precipitate, presumably of the adduct $Me(Me_2N)Be$ bipy, but this quickly decomposes. However, the brick red diphenylamino complexes $Me(Ph_2N)Be$ bipy and $Et(Ph_2N)Be$ bipy are stable at room temperature.

Finally, mention should be made of the chelate aminoberyllium alkyls that result from the reaction of R_2Be with pyridine-2-aldehyde phenylhydrazone:

$$C_5H_4N\text{-}CH{=}N\text{-}NHPh + R_2Be \longrightarrow C_5H_4N\text{-}CH{=}N\text{-}N(Ph)\text{-}BeR\ (\text{chelate}) + RH$$

(XLV)

The complexes (XLV; R = Me and R = Et) are yellow and red, respectively, and the latter is monomeric in benzene (the methyl compound is only sparingly soluble). There are just sufficient electrons available to allow the beryllium-containing ring to be aromatic (*69*).[2]

VIII

OXYBERYLLIUM ALKYLS, ROBeR′

Alcoholysis of beryllium dialkyls yields alkoxyberyllium alkyls and then beryllium dialkoxides.

$$R'_2Be + ROH \rightarrow R'H + ROBeR'$$

$$ROBeR' + ROH \rightarrow R'H + (RO)_2Be$$

For reasons similar to those discussed above in connection with aminoberyllium alkyls, the alkoxyberyllium alkyls ROBeR′ (which are also named alkylberyllium alkoxides) are associated. Each monomer unit has two lone pairs on each oxygen and at least two vacant acceptor sites on each beryllium atom. Cyclic dimers and trimers, (XLVI) and (XLVII), or any

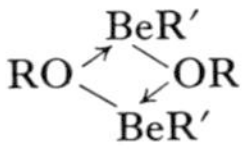

```
      BeR'                 R'Be—OR
   ↗     ↘                ↗      ↘
RO         OR           RO        BeR'
   ↖     ↙                \      /
      BeR'                 R'Be←OR

    (XLVI)                 (XLVII)
```

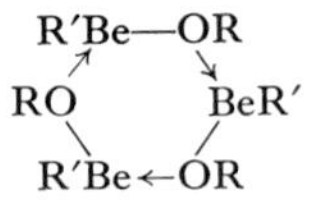

more associated open-ring structure involves three-coordinate beryllium, whereas there are enough lone pairs on each oxygen to allow an expansion of the valence shell of the metal. The combination Be_3O_3 being isoelectronic with B_3N_3, it may be suggested that alkylberyllium alkoxides could have

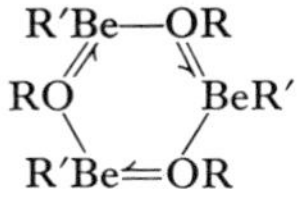

```
   R'Be—OR
   //↗   ⇘
 RO       BeR'
   \     /
   R'Be⇐OR
  (XLVIII)
```

significant aromatic character, as indicated in (XLVIII). However, a range of alkoxides, $(R'BeOR)_n$, is known, and this contains only two instances

[2] The authors are indebted to Dr. A. Haaland for suggestions leading to these experiments.

of trimers, viz., $(EtBeOCEt_3)_3$ and (iso-BuBeOBu-iso)$_3$. Beryllium–oxygen π-bonding could perhaps occur to a limited extent, but since the disparity between the radial parts of the Be $2p$ and O $2p$ wave functions would exceed that between Be $2p$ and N $2p$ it follows that π-bonding between Be and O should be weaker than that between Be and N. In the beryllium–nitrogen case it appears that valence expansion by π-bonding takes place only when valence expansion by σ-bonding is prevented by steric hindrance. It is likely that this is also true for the beryllium–oxygen case.

Most of the alkyl alkoxides of beryllium (*45*) are tetrameric in solution, as are many of those of several other second group elements, e.g, Mg (*65*) Zn (*64, 138*), and Cd (*61*). The preponderance of tetramers (see Table IV

TABLE IV

ALKYLBERYLLIUM ALKOXIDES

		References
Dimers [a]	(*tert*-BuBeOBu-*tert*)$_2$	*45*
	$(MeBeOCHPh_2)_2$	*45*
	$(MeBeOCPh_3)_2$	*45*
Trimers [a]	$(EtBeOCEt_3)_3$	*45*
	(iso-BuBeOBu-iso)$_3$	*50*
Tetramers [a]	$(MeBeOR)_4$, R = Me, Et, *n*-Pr, iso-Pr, *tert*-Bu	*45*
	$(MeBeOCH_2Ph)_4$	*25*
	(iso-PrBeOMe)$_4$, (*tert*-BuBeOMe)$_4$	*45*
	$(PhBeOMe)_4$	*70*
	$(MeBeOSiMe_3)_4$	*48, 119*

[a] Cryoscopically in benzene.

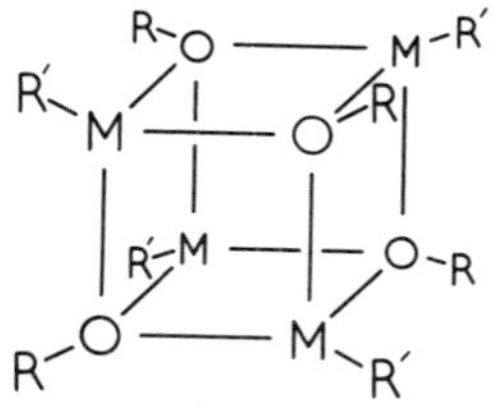

for the alkylberyllium alkoxides) is due to the fact that the lowest degree of association consistent with the attainment of four-coordination both for beryllium and oxygen is four, with the cubic arrangement (XLIX).

(XLIX)

This cubic or near-cubic structure has been confirmed by X-ray analysis for the cases M = Zn, R = R′ = Me (*138*) and M = Be, R = $SiMe_3$, R′ = Me (*119*). The formation of tetrameric R′BeOR is prevented when one or both of the groups R and R′ are voluminous, as in the examples $(tert\text{-}BuBeOBu\text{-}tert)_2$ and $(MeBeOCPh_3)_2$.

Nearly all the alkoxides listed in Table IV were prepared by alcoholysis of the appropriate beryllium dialkyl, but other syntheses are summarized as follows:

$$Me_2Be + Me_2CO \rightarrow \tfrac{1}{4}(MeBeOBu\text{-}tert)_4 \quad (45)$$

$$Me_2Be + tert\text{-}BuOOBu\text{-}tert \rightarrow \tfrac{1}{4}(MeBeOBu\text{-}tert)_4 + tert\text{-}BuOMe \quad (45)$$

$$3\,Me_2Be + [(tert\text{-}BuO)_2Be]_3 \rightarrow \tfrac{3}{2}(MeBeOBu\text{-}tert)_4 \quad (45)$$

$$Me_2Be + \underset{\text{O}}{CH_2\text{—}CH_2} \rightarrow \tfrac{1}{4}(MeBeOPr\text{-}n)_4 \quad (45)$$

$$MeBeH + PhCHO \rightarrow \tfrac{1}{4}(MeBeOCH_2Ph)_4 \quad (25)$$

$$4\,Me_2Be + (Me_2SiO)_4 \rightarrow (MeBeOSiMe_3)_4 \quad (48)$$

Careful studies on methylzinc methoxide (*3, 31, 81*) largely by ^1H NMR methods have shown that relatively complex disproportionation equilibria obtain in solution. The ^1H NMR spectra of some of the alkylberyllium alkoxides have perplexing features (*45*) which are also suggestive of disproportionation equilibria. For example, the spectrum of $(MeBeOMe)_4$ in benzene consists of a singlet due to the methylberyllium protons and a doublet due to the methoxy protons, and is not temperature-dependent between $-90°$ and $+100°$C.

As the oxygen atoms in the tetramers (XLIX) make use of both lone pairs it is of some interest to inquire how readily these lone pairs are displaced from coordination positions about beryllium by reaction with other bases. In several instances, e.g. $(MeBeOPr\text{-}iso)_4$ and $(MeBeOBu\text{-}tert)_4$, the alkoxides may conveniently be prepared in diethyl ether and crystallize solvent-free. The degree of association of MeBeOBu-*tert* in ether has been measured isopiestically at a concentration of 0.088 *M* (calculated as monomer), and was 3.8. By ebullioscopic measurements, also in ether, but at much lower concentrations (0.004–0.015 *M*, calculated as monomer) the degree of association is only two, and similar results were obtained for various other methylberyllium alkoxides. Therefore an equilibrium must obtain:

$$\tfrac{1}{2}(\text{MeBeOBu-}tert)_4 + 2\,\text{Et}_2\text{O} \rightleftharpoons \begin{matrix} \text{Et}_2\text{O} \rightarrow \text{Be}(\text{Me})(\mu\text{-OBu-}tert)_2\text{Be}(\text{Me}) \leftarrow \text{OEt}_2 \end{matrix}$$

In relatively concentrated solution the equilibrium lies to the left, and in dilute solution to the right. Thus, even in the presence of a great excess of ether, one lone pair of each alkoxy oxygen is still being used for coordination to beryllium. The acetylenic complex ($PhC{\equiv}CBeOBu$-*tert*·THF) (*49*) has a degree of association between 1 and 2 (in benzene).

When relatively voluminous groups are bound to the alkoxy oxygen, the coordinate link is readily split. For example, methylberyllium hydride adds to benzophenone in ether, giving a crystalline product (L) which is

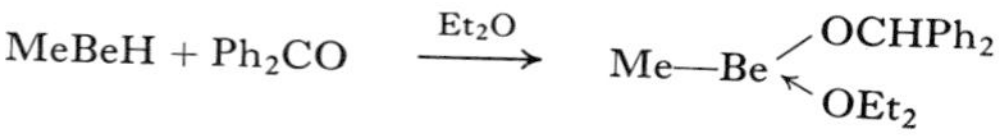

$$\text{MeBeH} + \text{Ph}_2\text{CO} \xrightarrow{\text{Et}_2\text{O}} \text{Me—Be}(\text{OCHPh}_2)(\leftarrow\text{OEt}_2)$$

(L)

monomeric in benzene (*25*). Reaction of Me_2Be with Ph_2CHOH in the absence of ether gives the dimeric alkoxide (LI), which is immediately

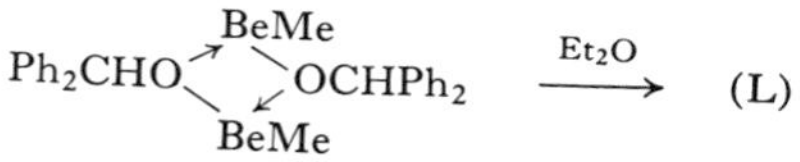

$$\text{Ph}_2\text{CHO}(\text{BeMe})_2\text{OCHPh}_2 \xrightarrow{\text{Et}_2\text{O}} (\text{L})$$

(LI)

and completely converted to (L) on reaction with ether. Triphenylcarbinol similarly yields products analogous to (LI) and (L) on reaction with dimethylberyllium in the absence and presence of ether, respectively (*45*).

Pyridine not only reacts with the tetramers, sometimes reversibly, but is liable to cause disproportionation. For example, if 1 mole of pyridine is added per gram atom of beryllium as $(MeBeOMe)_4$, the following reaction takes place:

$$(\text{MeBeOMe})_4 + 4\,\text{py} \rightarrow 2\,\text{Me}_2\text{Be py}_2 + 2\,\text{Be(OMe)}_2$$

2,2′-Bipyridyl produces a similar result. In contrast, the addition of pyridine in excess yields a simple adduct (LII), monomeric in benzene,

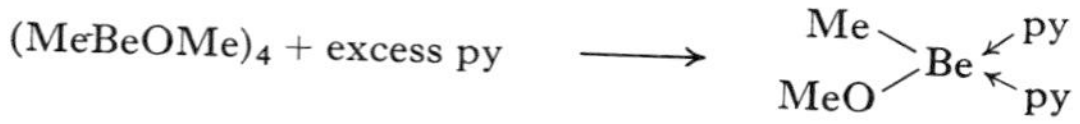

$$(\text{MeBeOMe})_4 + \text{excess py} \longrightarrow (\text{Me})(\text{MeO})\text{Be}(\leftarrow\text{py})_2$$

(LII)

in which all of the Be—O coordinate bonds have been broken. The *tert*-butoxide, (MeBeOBu-*tert*)$_4$, adds 4 moles of pyridine, giving a crystalline complex Me(*tert*-BuO)Be py whose degree of association in benzene is in the range 1.2–1.4 (0.3–0.7 wt %) and whose solutions contain free pyridine. These observations are consistent with the following equilibrium (*45*):

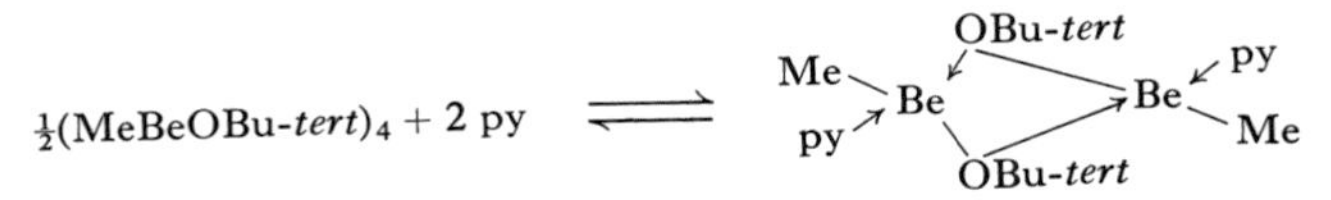

$$\tfrac{1}{2}(\text{MeBeOBu-}tert)_4 + 2\ \text{py} \rightleftharpoons \text{Me(py)Be}(\mu\text{-OBu-}tert)_2\text{Be(py)Me}$$

Few complexes between tetramethylethylenediamine (TMED) and R′BeOR have been investigated. Though reaction between $Me_2BeTMED$ and methanol gives only unreacted $Me_2BeTMED$ and insoluble Be-$(OMe)_2$, (iso-BuBeOBu-iso)$_3$ yields the bridged complex (LIII) (*49*) analogous to the zinc compound (LIV) (*126*).

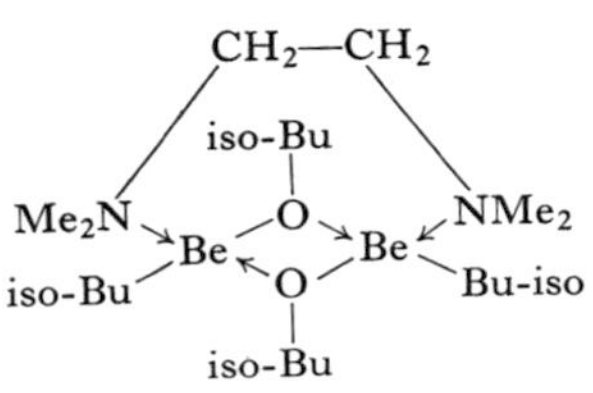

CH_2—CH_2 / $Me_2N \rightarrow$ Be(iso-Bu)(μ-O-iso-Bu)$_2$Be(Bu-iso) $\leftarrow NMe_2$

(LIII)

CH_2—CH_2 / $Me_2N \rightarrow$ Zn(Et)(μ-OPh)$_2$Zn(Et) $\leftarrow NMe_2$

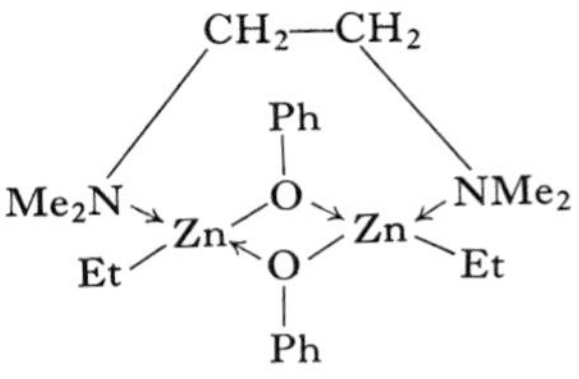

(LIV)

Several examples are known of alkoxides in which a basic group is incorporated in the alkoxy part of the molecule. Though this commonly leads to chelate structures [compare (XXXVI), Section VII], both (MeBe $OCH_2CH_2OMe)_4$ and $(EtBeOCH_2CH_2OMe)_4$ are tetrameric in benzene

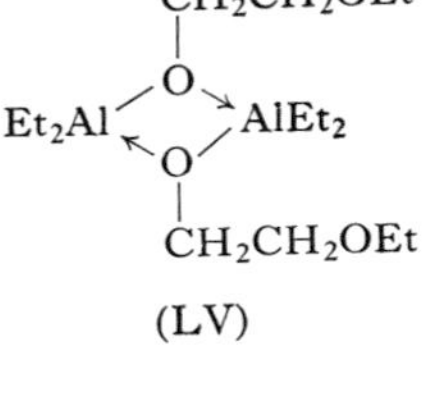

Et_2Al(μ-$OCH_2CH_2OEt)_2AlEt_2$

(LV)

$Et_2Al \leftarrow O(C_2H_5)$—$CH_2$—$CH_2$—O—$AlEt_2$ (chelate)

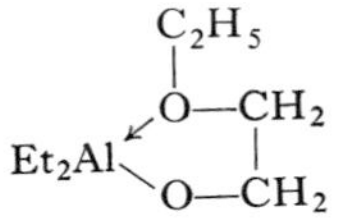

(LVI)

and the ether oxygen atoms are likely to take no part in the internal co-ordination. In this connection it may be recalled that $Et_2AlOC_2H_4OEt$ (*99*) is a dimer (LV) rather than the chelate monomer (LVI). Incorporation of the more basic dimethylamino instead of the methoxy group in the alkoxy side chain leads to participation of nitrogen in the coordination structure, since the complex is oligomeric ($n = \sim 7$) in benzene, $(MeBeOCH_2CH_2NMe_2)_{\sim 7}$ and may be polymeric in the crystalline state. This complex is stable to cold water.

Reaction between dimethylberyllium and acetoxime yields a tetramer $(MeBeON{=}CMe_2)_4$. The monomer $MeBeON{=}CMe_2$ has two available lone pairs on the oxygen and one on the nitrogen, more than enough to raise the coordination number of the metal to four. The structure of the analogous zinc compound $(MeZnON{=}CMe_2)_4$ has been determined (*72*, p. 139), and is a cage made up of fused five- and six-membered zinc–oxygen–nitrogen rings, all nitrogen and oxygen atoms being three-co-ordinate. Though all zinc atoms are four-coordinate, three different coordination environments can be distinguished: two zinc atoms are each bound to two oxygens and one nitrogen, another is bound to one oxygen and to two nitrogens, and the fourth is bound to three oxygens. However, the methylzinc complex gives only one ^{1}H NMR signal due to CH_3Zn, probably on account of exchange processes. In contrast, the beryllium complex has three CH_3Be resonances in area ratio 2:1:1, as would be expected if the beryllium and zinc complexes have similar structures, and if exchange processes were slow in the case of the beryllium complex.

The 8-hydroxyquinoline complex $(MeBeOC_9H_6N)_4$ is also tetrameric, and it is believed the structure could consist of two nonplanar dimeric units (LVII) parallel to each other, with coordination between each oxygen in one dimer and a beryllium atom in the other, giving a tetramer containing three-coordinate oxygen and four-coordinate beryllium (*47*).

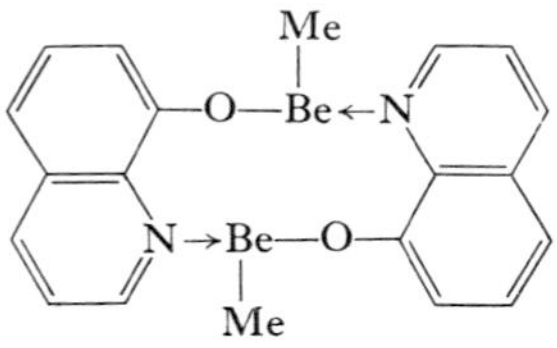

Me
O—Be←N
N→Be—O
Me

(LVII)

IX

THIOBERYLLIUM ALKYLS, RSBeR′

Thiols, RSH, react with beryllium alkyls in two stages:

$$R'_2Be + RSH \rightarrow RSBeR'$$

$$RSBeR' + RSH \rightarrow (RS)_2Be$$

The thioberyllium alkyls (*46*), RSBeR′, are analogous to the alkoxides, ROBeR′, and those that have been prepared are tetrameric. The tetramers are likely to have structures analogous to (XLIX). The sulfur compounds, however, are more liable to disproportionate than their oxygen analogs, and their behavior is strongly dependent on steric factors. Though numerous methylberyllium alkoxides have been prepared, the only sulfur analog that has been described is $(MeBeSBu\text{-}tert)_4$. Both this and $(EtBeSBu\text{-}tert)_4$ disproportionate in solution in hydrocarbons, the former more readily. This effect is likely to be associated both with the good bridging properties of methylberyllium groups and with the less basic character of sulfur (relative to oxygen) towards beryllium. Any disproportionation

$$(RSBeR')_4 \rightleftharpoons 2\,(RS)_2Be + 2\,R'_2Be$$

process must involve the displacement of sulfur by methyl from a coordination position about the beryllium. Since sulfur is a weaker base to beryllium than is oxygen, it follows that disproportionation is more likely to take place with $(MeBeSR)_4$ than with $(MeBeOR)_4$.

Unlike $(MeBeSBu\text{-}tert)_4$, whose solutions in benzene deposit Me_2Be and $Be(SBu\text{-}tert)_2$ at room temperature, solutions of $(EtBeSBu\text{-}tert)_4$ are stable at room temperature but deposit insoluble $Be(SBu\text{-}tert)_2$ (contrast the soluble beryllium *tert*-butoxide) at 50° C.

The thioberyllium alkyls show a range of behavior in reaction with bases. The sulfur bridges in $(EtBeSBu\text{-}tert)_4$ are broken by tetrahydrofuran, pyridine, and 2,2′-bipyridyl. Tetrahydrofuran, even in excess, yields a mono adduct, EtBeSBu-*tert*(THF), which has an apparent degree of association in benzene only slightly exceeding one, and its solutions contain free tetrahydrofuran. Reaction of 1 mole of pyridine per beryllium atom yields a similar complex, EtBeSBu-*tert*(py), but the apparent degree of association in this instance is slightly less than two. These data are consistent with the following equilibria:

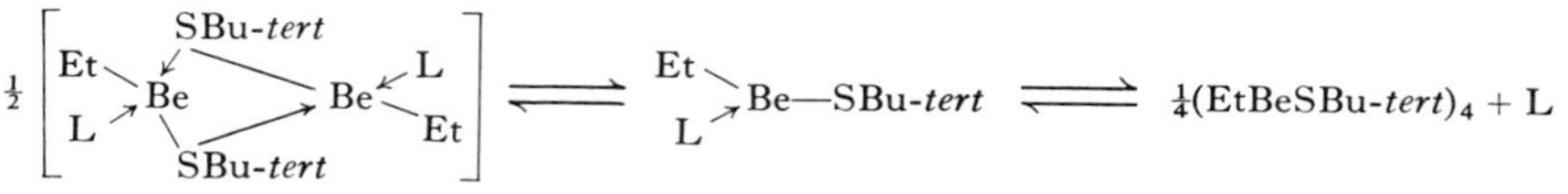

$$\tfrac{1}{2}\left[\begin{matrix} & \text{SBu-}tert & \\ \text{Et}\diagdown & & \diagup\text{L} \\ \text{Be} & & \text{Be} \\ \text{L}\diagup & & \diagdown\text{Et} \\ & \text{SBu-}tert & \end{matrix}\right] \rightleftharpoons \begin{matrix}\text{Et}\diagdown \\ \text{L}\diagup\end{matrix}\text{Be—SBu-}tert \rightleftharpoons \tfrac{1}{4}(\text{EtBeSBu-}tert)_4 + \text{L}$$

with the equilibrium lying mainly to the right when L is tetrahydrofuran (the weaker base), and to the left when it is pyridine. Reaction of (EtBeSBu-*tert*)$_4$ with an excess of pyridine results in the fission of all the beryllium–sulfur coordinate bonds, giving the yellow monomer EtBeSBu-*tert* py$_2$. 2,2′-Bipyridyl gives a similar complex, but more deeply colored, EtBeSBu-*tert* bipy being bright orange-red.

The ethylberyllium complexes (EtBeSEt)$_4$ and (EtBeSPr-iso) not only are stable with respect to disproportionation [in fact EtBeSEt can be prepared from Et$_2$Be and Be(SEt)$_2$], but they do not yield isolable ether nor pyridine adducts. Though (EtBeSEt)$_4$ dissolves in pyridine giving a yellow solution, indicative of the formation of a complex, evaporation of solvent results in crystallization of the pyridine-free tetramer. Similarly, EtBeSPr-iso, which is tetrameric in benzene, is dimeric in dilute solution

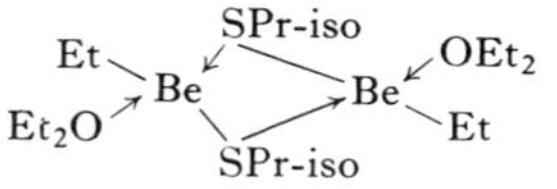

$$\begin{matrix} & \text{SPr-iso} & \\ \text{Et}\diagdown & & \diagup\text{OEt}_2 \\ \text{Be} & & \text{Be} \\ \text{Et}_2\text{O}\diagup & & \diagdown\text{Et} \\ & \text{SPr-iso} & \end{matrix}$$

(LVIII)

in ether, in which it would have the constitution (LVIII). When the solvent is evaporated, the tetramer (EtBeSPr-iso)$_4$ crystallizes. The effect of interchanging ethyl and isopropyl groups is remarkable, since the reaction

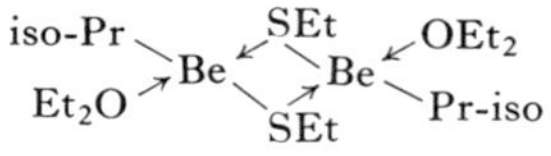

$$\begin{matrix} & \text{SEt} & \\ \text{iso-Pr}\diagdown & & \diagup\text{OEt}_2 \\ \text{Be} & & \text{Be} \\ \text{Et}_2\text{O}\diagup & & \diagdown\text{Pr-iso} \\ & \text{SEt} & \end{matrix} \qquad \begin{matrix} & \text{SEt} & \\ \text{iso-Pr}\diagdown & & \diagup\text{py} \\ \text{Be} & & \text{Be} \\ \text{py}\diagup & & \diagdown\text{Pr-iso} \\ & \text{SEt} & \end{matrix}$$

(LIX) 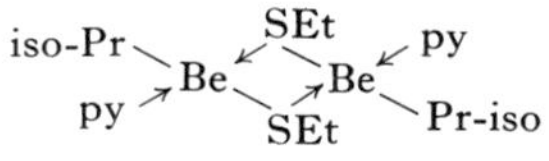 (LX)

between iso-Pr$_2$Be and EtSH in ether produces (LIX) which has no significant dissociation pressure. The ether is quantitatively displaced by pyridine, giving (LX). These differences are to be ascribed to increasing steric congestion about the metal atom. With isopropyl groups both on beryllium and sulfur, the only product that could be isolated was the yellow monomeric bis pyridine adduct, iso-PrBeSPr-iso py$_2$, i.e., neither (iso-PrBeSPr-iso)$_4$ nor (iso-PrBeSPr-iso,L)$_2$ where L is ether or pyridine could be obtained.

Increasing the steric congestion still further, the reaction between iso-Pr_2Be and *tert*-BuSH gives disproportionation products:

$$\text{iso-}Pr_2Be + \textit{tert}\text{-BuSH} \rightarrow [\text{iso-PrBeSBu-}\textit{tert}] \rightarrow \tfrac{1}{2}\,\text{iso-}Pr_2Be + \tfrac{1}{2}\,Be(SBu\text{-}\textit{tert})_2$$

The reverse type of reaction takes place when $Be(SEt)_2$ dissolves in ether solutions of Et_2Be, giving $(EtBeSEt)_4$ which can be obtained by three routes:

Et_2Be (in Et_2O) → $(EtBeSEt)_4$ via EtSH; via $Be(SEt)_2$; via EtSSEt

The acetylenic complex (Ph≡CBeSBu-*tert*,THF)$_2$ is a dimer, probably containing sulfur bridges (*49*).

Thiophenol and selenophenol have yielded the dimeric complexes (LXI) and (LXII), which do not dissociate significantly in benzene, unlike

(LXI): Me(Et$_2$O→)Be(μ-SPh)$_2$Be(←OEt)Me

(LXII): Et(Et$_2$O→)Be(μ-SePh)$_2$Be(←OEt$_2$)Et

$(MeBeOPh \cdot OEt_2)_2$, which in solution is in equilibrium with free ether and, mainly, the tetramer $(MeBeOPh)_4$.

Attempts to prepare the selenium analog of $(EtBeSEt)_4$ from Et_2Be and $(EtSe)_2$ have not been successful, since $Be(SeEt)_2$ was formed instead by a disproportionation reaction. However, an ethylberyllium ethylselenide can be isolated as a yellow bispyridine adduct, EtBeSeEt py_2.

The chelating thiol, $Me_2NC_2H_4SH$, yields the trimer (LXIII) on reaction

(LXIII): cyclic trimer [MeBe(μ-SCH$_2$CH$_2$NMe$_2$→)]$_3$ with Be–S ring, each Me_2N coordinated to Be

with dimethylberyllium (*47*). This is the only known beryllium–sulfur trimer. Reaction with a second molecule of the thiol yields the aminosulfide (XLI), which has no beryllium carbon bonds.

It should be noted that $Be(SBu\text{-}tert)_2$ is insoluble in ether and in hydrocarbons, and is thus likely to be a coordination polymer unlike $[Be(OBu\text{-}tert)_2]_3$. However, it yields a pyridine complex $(tert\text{-}BuS)_2Be\ py_2$ which

$$2\ (tert\text{-}BuS)_2Be\ py_2 \rightleftharpoons \begin{matrix} & & SBu\text{-}tert & & \\ tert\text{-}BuS & \searrow & & & \swarrow\ py \\ & Be & & Be & \\ py & \nearrow & & & \searrow\ SBu\text{-}tert \\ & & SBu\text{-}tert & & \end{matrix} + 2\ py$$

dissociates in benzene. It also gives an ochre-colored bipyridyl complex, $(tert\text{-}BuS)_2Be$ bipy (*46*).

X

ANIONIC ORGANOBERYLLIUM COMPLEXES

In this review, only anionic complexes containing beryllium–carbon bonds are considered. They are formed by reactions between beryllium alkyls and (a) halides and cyanides, a typical product being $KF(Et_2Be)_2$, (b) other metal alkyls, e.g., forming Li_2Me_4Be, and (c) alkali metal hydrides, e.g., forming $NaMe_2BeH$.

A. Halide Complexes

The chemistry of the halide complexes has been developed largely by W. Strohmeier and his colleagues. The formation of complexes such as $NaMe_2AlCl_2$ by reactions of organoaluminum compounds and halides, has been more extensively studied and the factors (involving lattice and bond energies) conducive to complex formation have been established (*165*). In general, complexes are most readily formed when the anion of the reacting salt is small, and when the cation is large. Similar considerations apply to reactions between beryllium alkyls and metal (or other) halides. Thus, in the case of the chloride anion, only the relatively large quaternary ammonium cations react, e.g., Et_4NCl, whereas even CsCl does not (*146*). These complexes are exemplified by $Me_4NCl(Et_2Be)_2$, $Et_4NCl(Et_2Be)_2$, and $PhCH_2NMe_3Cl(Et_2Be)_2$.

Potassium fluoride dissolves in a diethylberyllium–ether mixture, when stirred at room temperature. Removal of ether at 60°C under reduced pressure then yields $KF(Et_2Be)_2$, m.p. 83°C (*97, 142*). Similar complexes are formed by RbF and CsF (*143*), and, as might be expected, the large quaternary ammonium cations also give fluoride complexes such as $Me_4NF(Et_2Be)_2$ (*146*). The preparation of ether-free Et_2Be taking advantage of the decomposition,

$$KF(Et_2Be)_2 \rightarrow KF(Et_2Be) + Et_2Be$$

has been mentioned earlier (Section II,B,2).

Potassium cyanide and diethylberyllium yield the remarkable complex $KCN(Et_2Be)_4$, m.p. 52°–53° C, which also decomposes when heated (*146*). No structural information is available concerning this compound.

It is likely that the fluoride complexes of the type $KF(Et_2Be)_2$ have linear Be---F---Be bonds analogous to the linear Al---F---Al bonds in $KF(Et_3Al)_2$ (*2*).

Strohmeier and his colleagues have studied the electrolysis of $KF(Et_2Be)_2$ and related complexes. An early report (*145*) referred to the deposition of beryllium at the cathode, which would be analogous to the electrodeposition of aluminum from $KF(Et_3Al)_2$, but later it was found (*150*) that potassium is the primary cathode product. The potassium reacts with the electrolyte, perhaps with free Et_2Be, giving various products including beryllium metal. In separate experiments potassium was found to react with diethylberyllium, precipitating beryllium metal containing 14–20% carbide, Be_2C. Electrolysis of a solution of Et_2Be in pyridine gives a deep blue paramagnetic solution around the cathode, and the pyridine-stabilized radical EtBe py· could be isolated as a black material which gave a paramagnetic solution in benzene (*149*).

B. *Alkali Metal Beryllium Alkyls and Aryls*

Few of these are known and structural data are available only for one (Li_2BeMe_4). The first to be described was the phenyl complex $LiBePh_3$, which crystallizes on addition of xylene to the product of the exothermic reaction between ethereal PhLi and Ph_2Be (*159*). Particularly since phenyl is a good electron-deficient bridging group, $LiBePh_3$ may have an electron-deficient constitution:

$$Li\genfrac{}{}{0pt}{}{\cdot\cdot Ph \cdot\cdot}{\cdot\cdot Ph \cdot\cdot}Be\genfrac{}{}{0pt}{}{\cdot\cdot Ph \cdot\cdot}{\cdot\cdot Ph \cdot\cdot}Be\genfrac{}{}{0pt}{}{\cdot\cdot Ph \cdot\cdot}{\cdot\cdot Ph \cdot\cdot}Li$$

It forms a dioxanate which is likely to be a salt $[Li(dioxane)_4]^+[BePh_3]^-$ or $[Li(dioxane)_4]_2{}^+[Be_2Ph_6]^{2-}$.

Twenty-one years later the first alkyl complex was prepared and its structure determined by X-ray diffraction. When methyllithium is added to dimethylberyllium in ether, the sparingly soluble Li_2BeMe_4 crystallizes (*156*). The methyl groups are primarily bound to beryllium in a somewhat distorted tetrahedral arrangement (C—Be—C angles 102° and 113°). The Be—C distance, 1.84 Å, is greater than in Me_2Be and *tert*-Bu_2Be (1.70 Å), as would be expected if the $BeMe_4$ units carried appreciable negative charge. The shortest Li—C distance is 2.52 Å, which is appreciably longer than the Li—C distances (~2.3 Å) in Me_4Li_4.

The sodium beryllium ethyl complex $NaBeEt_3$ has been mentioned as a propene dimerization catalyst (*163*), and was later prepared in crystalline form as a product of the reaction of sodium with diethylberyllium (*150*). Reaction between $(PhC{\equiv}C)_2Be$ and $PhC{\equiv}CLi$ in ether gives $Li_2Be(C{\equiv}CPh)_4$, which is insoluble in benzene (*49*). Though not an alkali metal compound, the mixed Be—Al complex $BeAl_2Me_8$ should be mentioned here. It exists in solution at low temperature and is believed to be $Me_2AlMe_2BeMe_2AlMe_2$ like the well-established magnesium analog $MgAl_2Me_8$. Attempts to isolate the solid complex yielded only Me_2Be (*14*).

C. Hydride Complexes

The first of these to be described was the phenyl complex $LiBePh_2H \cdot OEt_2$, prepared by heating lithium hydride with diphenylberyllium ether complex (*158*). No further addition to this class of complex was made until ten years later, when sodium diethylberyllium hydride was prepared (*42*) and used as an intermediate for the preparation of ethylberyllium hydride complexes (e.g., $EtBeH \cdot NMe_3$), see Section XI.

The sodium dialkylberyllium hydrides NaR_2BeH, R = Me (*23, 28*), Et (*23, 42*), *n*-Pr, iso-Pr, and iso-Bu (*63*) have been prepared from sodium hydride and ether solutions of R_2Be. The methyl derivative is only sparingly soluble, the ethyl moderately, and the others easily soluble in ether. Most of these compounds crystallize from ether with one molecule of ether for each sodium atom, but the ether dissociation pressure is high ($NaEt_2BeH \cdot OEt_2$ 17 mm at 20° C) and the ether-free complexes are readily obtained.

The crystal structure of $NaEt_2BeH \cdot OEt_2$ (*1*) is shown in part in Fig. 3. The dimeric $Et_4Be_2H_2$ unit is easily discerned, and it is likely that the other salts have similar $R_4Be_2H_2$ units containing a BeH_2Be bridge. The ether molecules are coordinated to the sodium, and the ethyl groups of the ether can occupy two alternative positions, as indicated by the four (instead of two) thin lines from O in Fig. 3. The positions of the hydridic hydrogen atoms were revealed by the crystallographic analysis.

Lithium hydride reacts more slowly than sodium hydride with beryllium alkyls, but the complexes $LiEt_2BeH$ (*26*) and Li[iso-Bu_2BeH] (*63*) (and their monoether solvates) are known. Whereas $LiEt_2BeH \cdot OEt_2$ (m.p. 33°–35° C) is readily soluble in benzene, in which its apparent degree of

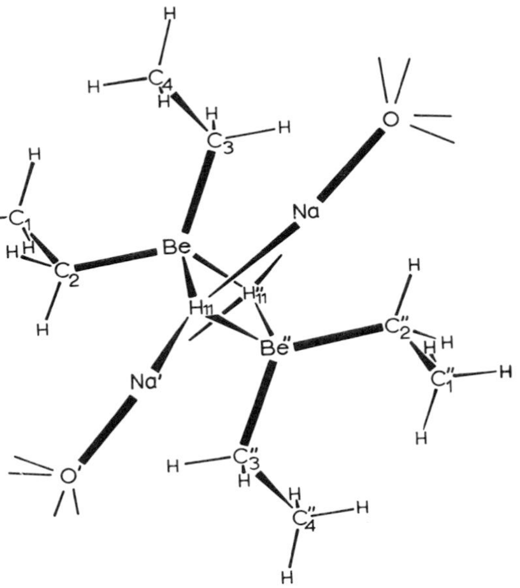

FIG. 3. Structure of $(NaOEt_2)_2(Et_4Be_2H_2)$, after Adamson and Shearer (*1*).

association, measured cryoscopically, is between one and two, the ether-free compound is insoluble in hydrocarbons. The sodium salts are insoluble in hydrocarbons, but Na[iso-Bu_2BeH] dissolves in a solution of iso-Bu_2Be in hexane until the material in solution has a composition close to Na_2iso-$Bu_6Be_3H_2$. That is, 1 mole of iso-Bu_2Be (reckoned as monomer) dissolves two of Na[iso-Bu_2BeH]. Nothing is known of the structure of the species in solution, and attempted crystallization results in deposition of Na[iso-Bu_2BeH]. The reaction between Et_2Be (in benzene) and $NaEt_2BeH$ takes a different course and the product is insoluble. The sodium salt, when shaken with Et_2Be in benzene, removes the diethylberyllium from solution until the composition of the solid is $NaEt_6Be_3H$, or $NaEt_2BeH$ 2 Et_2Be. Again, nothing is known about the structure of this material, whose X-ray powder pattern is quite different from that of $NaEt_2BeH$ (*63*).

In contrast to $NaEt_2BeH$, which melts undecomposed at 198° C, the lithium analog eliminates diethylberyllium when it is heated, leaving a residue of lithium hydride. Since beryllium alkyls in which there is chain branching at the β-carbon readily eliminate olefin giving beryllium hydride derivatives, it might be anticipated that, for example, Na[iso-Bu_2BeH] would decompose thermally to isobutene and $NaBeH_3$. However, its thermal decomposition is more complex and is dependent on reaction conditions, but approximates to the reaction:

$$\text{Na-iso-Bu}_2\text{BeH} \rightarrow \tfrac{1}{2}\,\text{iso-Bu}_2\text{Be} + \tfrac{1}{2}\,\text{Na}_2\text{BeH}_4$$

The isopropyl compound Na[iso-Pr_2BeH] behaves similarly, but the lithium derivative Li[iso-Bu_2BeH] is thermally more stable than the sodium analog and at 208° C, for example, gives mainly isobutene and a mixture of BeH_2 and Li_2BeH_4.

Di-*tert*-butylberyllium yields, on reaction with sodium hydride, a complex of different stoichiometry, viz., $Na(OEt_2)_4$-*tert*-Bu_4Be_2H, from the compounds previously considered. It is possible that the bulky *tert*-butyl groups prevent the formation of structures containing BeH_2Be bridges and four-coordinate beryllium. The *tert*-butyl product could well have a single hydrogen bridge [*tert*-$Bu_2Be \cdot H \cdot BeBu$-*tert*$_2$]$^-$, and only three-coordinate beryllium (*63*).

XI

BERYLLIUM HYDRIDE DERIVATIVES

A. Organoberyllium Hydrides, RBeH

1. *Preparative Methods*

The first reference to organoberyllium hydrides was the description of the pyrolysis at 190°–200° C of Et_2Be containing a trace of ether (*94*). This complex decomposition gave ethane, ethylene, and some butene, along with traces of hexene, cyclohexadiene, and benzene. The residue was a viscous oil which must have contained beryllium–hydrogen bonds, and it yielded hydrogen as well as hydrocarbons when hydrolyzed. A few years later (*51*) iso-Pr_2Be was found to decompose at 200° C in a less complex way, since only propene was evolved, leaving a glassy residue of propylberyllium hydride. In the light of recent work (*67*) on the pyrolysis of *tert*-Bu_2Be, the product was very probably a mixture of *n*-PrBeH and iso-PrBeH rather than the latter only.

Di-*tert*-butylberyllium (*98*) and its ether complex (*52*) evolve isobutene when heated and at 200° C leave a residue consisting largely of beryllium hydride, which is an involatile polymeric material whose main characteristic is a broad infrared absorption centered at 1760 cm^{-1}, width 300 cm^{-1} at half-height (*17*). When *tert*-Bu_2Be is heated at 105°–110° C, elimination of isobutene is rapid but does not go beyond the half-hydride, RBeH, stage (*67*). The glassy residue, which is soluble in aromatic hydrocarbons, is a mixture of $\sim\frac{1}{3}$ *tert*-BuBeH and $\frac{2}{3}$ iso-BuBeH, on account of the isomerization:

$$—BeCMe_3 \rightarrow CH_2{=}CMe_2 + —BeH \rightarrow —BeCH_2CHMe_2$$

Di-*tert*-butylberyllium slowly isomerizes to iso-Bu_2Be even at room temperature. Rapid pyrolysis of iso-$Bu_2Be \cdot OEt_2$ at 150° C results in elimination of the ether and of only 1 mole of isobutene, yielding isobutylberyllium hydride as a colorless glass which is ~15–20-fold associated in benzene (*67*). No other alkylberyllium hydrides have yet been isolated, though several coordination complexes RBeH · L have been described.

Dimethylberyllium was found to dissolve in a solution of dimethylaluminum hydride in pentane but methylberyllium hydride could not be

$$Me_2Be + Me_2AlH \rightarrow MeBeH + Me_3Al$$

separated from the reaction product (*18*).

Exchange reactions with tin hydrides have been used to prepare alkylberyllium hydrides, but since ether was present the products were ether complexes. It should be noted that alkyl–hydrogen, but not alkyl–alkyl

$$Me_2Be + Et_3SnH + Et_2O \rightarrow MeBeH \cdot OEt_2 + Et_3MeSn$$

exchange takes place (*23*, *71*). This reaction is not satisfactory for the preparation of phenylberyllium hydride complexes (*71*).

Complexes of MeBeH and EtBeH have been obtained from the anionic hydride complexes, NaR_2BeH, using the following sequence (*22*, *23*):

$$NaH + R_2Be \rightarrow NaR_2BeH$$

$$2\ NaR_2BeH + BeCl_2 \rightarrow 2\ NaCl + R_2Be + 2\ RBeH$$

$$R_2Be + 2\ RBeH + 3\ NMe_3 \rightarrow R_2Be \cdot NMe_3 + (RBeH \cdot NMe_3)_2$$

The products have been separated by crystallization and by fractional condensation.

The reaction between lithium hydride and RBeBr is one of the most convenient preparative methods for methyl- and ethylberyllium hydride ether complexes (*25*), e.g.,

$$Me_2Be + BeBr_2 \xrightarrow{Et_2O} 2\ MeBeBr$$

$$2\ MeBeBr + 2\ LiH \xrightarrow{Et_2O} (MeBeH \cdot OEt_2)_2 + 2\ LiBr$$

The LiBr may be removed by replacing the ether by benzene, in which it is insoluble.

Sodium triethylborohydride may also be used as the source of hydride (*71*).

$$Et_2Be + BeCl_2 + 2\ NaEt_3BH \xrightarrow{Et_2O} (EtBeH \cdot OEt_2)_2 + 2\ Et_3B + 2\ NaCl$$

2. *Properties*

Little is known about the base-free alkylberyllium hydrides. The only one to have been described so far as an individual compound, iso-BuBeH, is a glassy substance that is extensively associated in benzene. Various reactions that have given mixtures of base-free hydrides have also yielded glassy products. The isolation of a crystalline base-free hydride would be of considerable interest.

The ether complexes, $(RBeH \cdot OEt_2)_2$, are all dimers in benzene and are liquids at room temperature. All of the complexes $(RBeH \cdot L)_2$ are believed to contain a BeH_2Be bridge analogous to that found crystallographically in $(NaOEt_2)_2(Et_4Be_2H_2)$ (see Section X). Most of the trimethylamine complexes are solids, e.g., $(MeBeH \cdot NMe_3)_2$, m.p. 73.0°–73.2° C (*23*); $(MeBeD \cdot NMe_3)_2$, m.p. 75°–76° C (*23*); $[MeBeH \cdot N(CD_3)_3]_2$, m.p. 74°–75° C (*29*); $(EtBeH \cdot NMe_3)_2$, m.p. 90°–91° (*23*); $(PhBeH \cdot NMe_3)_2$, 180°–230° (decomp.) (*71*). Evidence for temperature-dependent equilibria between the cis (LXIV) and trans (LXV) isomers have been obtained from ^1H NMR

Me, $Me_3N \rightarrow$ Be(μ-H)₂Be, Me, $\leftarrow NMe_3$

(LXIV)

Me, $Me_3N \rightarrow$ Be(μ-H)₂Be, $\leftarrow NMe_3$, Me

(LXV)

spectra (*29*). The enthalpy change is only 3.1 ± 0.2 kcal $mole^{-1}$, the cis form being the more stable isomer at low, and the trans at high temperature. The relatively large value of ΔS (13 ± 2 cal deg^{-1} $mole^{-1}$) is particularly significant, since the intramolecular contributions to the entropy of each isomer should be nearly the same. Thus the main origin of ΔS is the greater ordering of solvent molecules by the highly polar cis form relative to the nonpolar trans form. The entropy change for the cis–trans interconversion of $(PEt_3)_2PtCl_2$ in benzene is also 13 cal deg^{-1} $mole^{-1}$, and is believed to have a similar origin (*39*). Evidence for cis–trans isomerism has not been found in the ^1H NMR spectra of other complexes of the type $(RBeH \cdot L)_2$, though the resonances do broaden somewhat as the temperature is reduced.

The proton resonances due to bridging hydrogen atoms have been observed only in two compounds, $(MeBeH \cdot OEt_2)_2$ at τ 8.42 and $(MeBeH \cdot pyridine)_2$ at τ 6.72. These are broad resonances, the width at half-height being 6 and 36 cycles per second, respectively, on account of the quadrupole moment of the beryllium nucleus and the unsymmetrical environment of the hydridic protons.

In contrast to the BH_2B bridge in diborane and substituted diboranes, the BeH_2Be bridge in the complexes $(RBeH \cdot L)_2$, as in (LXIV) or (LXV) resist fission by reaction with an excess of base. Reaction of $(MeBeH \cdot OEt_2)_2$ with tetramethylethylenediamine (*23*) does not yield (LXVI), but instead gives a very sparingly soluble complex in which the BeH_2Be bridge is retained (as shown spectroscopically) and believed to have the polymeric

CH_2—Me_2N→Be(H)(Me) ← Me_2N—CH_2 (chelate ring: CH_2—CH_2)

(LXVI)

[—CH_2—Me_2N→Be(Me)(μ-H)₂Be(Me)←NMe_2—CH_2—]$_x$

(LXVII)

constitution (LXVII). Ethylberyllium hydride yields a complex similar to (LXVII), but isobutylberyllium hydride in contrast gives the soluble monomeric complex (LXVIII).

CH_2—CH_2 bridging Me_2N→Be(iso-Bu)(μ-H)₂Be(Bu-iso)←NMe_2

(LXVIII)

Infrared absorptions due to the BeH_2Be unit occur in the ranges 1294–1344 and 1065–1165 cm^{-1}, there being two infrared-active vibrations. These assignments have been confirmed by the study of deuterated analogs (*23*). The infrared stretching frequencies of terminal Be—H bonds are considerably higher, being at 1740 and 1780 cm^{-1} in (LXIX) (*139a*) and at 1787 and 1807 cm^{-1} in (LXX) (*67*).

$$\begin{matrix} Me_3N \searrow & & H & & \nearrow H \\ & Be & & Be & \\ H \nearrow & & H & & \nwarrow NMe_3 \end{matrix}$$

(LXIX)

$$\left[\begin{matrix} -CH_2-Me_2N \searrow & & H & & \nearrow H \\ & Be & & Be & \\ H \nearrow & & H & & \nwarrow NMe_2-CH_2- \end{matrix} \right]_x$$

(LXX)

The spectra of these complexes also contain the absorptions characteristic of the bridging BeH_2Be units.

3. *Reactions*

Both the alkyl group and the hydridic hydrogen are readily displaced from RBeH by reaction with protonic acids. Whereas the dialkyls, R_2Be, generally react with 1 mole of acid, e.g., R'_2NH or R'OH, giving $RBeNR'_2$ or RBeOR', the displacement of R and H from RBeH by R'_2NH takes place at comparable rates, resulting in mixtures of $RBeNR'_2$ and $HBeNR'_2$. For example, equimolar amounts of propylberyllium hydride and dimethylamine gave propane and hydrogen in 2.5:1 ratio (*51*). In contrast, only hydrogen is normally eliminated from R_2AlH in similar reactions (*164*).

Alkylberyllium hydride complexes also differ from aluminum hydride complexes in reaction with diethylmercury. The ethylberyllium hydride–trimethylamine complex reacts quantitatively at 60° C giving ethane as the only gaseous product (*71*)

$$(EtBeH \cdot NMe_3)_2 + 2\ Et_2Hg \rightarrow 2\ Hg + 2\ C_2H_6 + 2\ Me_3N \cdot BeEt_2$$

whereas a typical aluminum hydride reaction is (*131*)

$$Me_3N \cdot AlH_3 + \tfrac{3}{2}\ Et_2Hg \rightarrow \tfrac{3}{2}\ Hg + \tfrac{3}{2}\ H_2 + Me_3N \cdot AlEt_3$$

The reduction of carbon–halogen bonds by RBeH has not been studied appreciably, but ethylberyllium hydride reduces methyl iodide quantitatively to methane (*25*). The reaction is much slower than the reduction with $LiAlH_4$.

The reduction of polar multiple bonds by RBeH is fast at room temperature, in contrast to the reduction of C=C or C≡C bonds. Methylberyllium hydride reduces benzaldehyde to $(PhCH_2OBeMe)_4$ and, in ether solution, reduces benzophenone to $Ph_2CHOBeMe \cdot OEt_2$ (*25*). The reduction of an azomethine group is illustrated by

$$2\ PhCH{=}NPh + 2\ MeBeH \rightarrow (PhCH_2NPhBeMe)_2$$

Pyridine is immediately reduced to an orange dihydropyridine derivative.

$$EtBeH + 3\ C_5H_5N \rightarrow C_5H_6NBeEt \cdot py_2$$

Thus the preparation of pyridine complexes of alkylberyllium hydrides requires care: not more than 1 mole of pyridine must be added *to* the alkylberyllium hydride (*25*).

As expected on the basis of reactions of olefins with boron and aluminum hydrides, terminal olefins react much faster than internal olefins. For example, under comparable conditions 1-pentene reacts over 200 times faster with ethylberyllium hydride than does 2-pentene (95% cis isomer). Since bromination of the product from the EtBeH + 2-pentene reaction gave 82% 1-bromo-, 12% 2-bromo-, and 6% 3-bromopentane, it follows that beryllium (like boron) migrates to the end of the carbon chain (*25*).

The rate of addition of Be—H to olefins is strongly influenced by the presence of base and boron hydride complexes [cf. addition of B—H to olefins (*101*)]. The half-lives of the reactions between 1-pentene and isobutylberyllium hydride, its ether complex, and its trimethylamine complex, have been compared under the same experimental conditions (4–5 mmoles of each reactant in 0.4 cc benzene at 33.5° C) and were 10–15 minutes, 7–9 hours, and 20–25 hours, respectively, these being about in 1:40:110 ratio (*67*). Recent kinetic studies (*122*) of the reaction between $(MeBeH \cdot NMe_3)_2$ and 1-decene indicate that the reaction proceeds by a mechanism involving a dimer–monomer equilibrium followed by addition of monomeric $MeBeH \cdot NMe_3$ to the olefin. The Arrhenius activation energy was found to be 16 ± 2 kcal mole^{-1}. During these studies it emerged from ^1H NMR evidence that solutions of $(MeBeH \cdot NMe_3)_2$ in benzene slowly decompose over a period of weeks at room temperature; thus freshly prepared solutions are needed for kinetic work.

The reaction of alkylberyllium hydrides with internal acetylenes RC≡CR is complex in that both Be—C and Be—H add to the carbon–carbon bond, and mixtures of many products result (*49*).

B. Amino and Oxy Beryllium Hydrides

Few examples of these are known, and no satisfactory general methods have yet been developed for their preparation. The first aminoberyllium hydride mentioned in the literature was Me_2NBeH, obtained (*51*) by the reaction

$$\text{iso-PrBeNMe}_2 \xrightarrow{100°\text{–}200°C} Me_2NBeH + C_3H_6$$

The product, which was not obtained pure since the iso-$PrBeNMe_2$ itself was not pure [this compound was studied again much later (*44*) when it was prepared in a purer state], is vigorously hydrolyzed and is an evidently polymeric glass. It does not absorb trimethylamine at room temperature. Since both nitrogen and the hydridic hydrogen in $(Me_2NBeH)_x$ can act as strong bridging groups, the metal is likely to be four-coordinate.

Attempts to prepare aminoberyllium hydrides by the reaction of beryllium hydride with various secondary amines have not been successful, but reaction with trimethylethylenediamine gives a crystalline product (*27*), m.p. 132°–133° C.

$$Me_2NCH_2CH_2NHMe + BeH_2 \rightarrow Me_2NCH_2CH_2NMeBeH$$

A similar compound is formed from trimethylethylenediamine and zinc hydride, which yield $(Me_2NC_2H_4NMeZnH)_2$, m.p. 128°–129° C. This is dimeric both in benzene solution and in the crystal, whose structure has been shown to be (LXXI; M = Zn) (*139*) both by X-ray and by neutron

```
CH2—Me2N↘    ↗H
|         M
|        ↗ ↖NMe—CH2
CH2—MeN         |
       ↘ M      |
    H↗    ↖NMe2—CH2
```

(LXXI)

diffraction. The infrared spectrum of (LXXI; M = Zn) as a Nujol mull contains an absorption at 1825 cm^{-1} which beyond reasonable doubt is due to Zn—H stretching vibrations. However, its breadth, 120 cm^{-1} at half-height, is suggestive of bridging hydrogen as in several alkylaluminum hydrides. The beryllium complex is trimeric in benzene but dimeric in the crystalline state, its crystal structure (*137*) being (LXXI; M = Be). This is an interesting compound since the hypothetical monomer $Me_2NC_2H_4$-NMeBeH contains three donor sites, viz., both nitrogen atoms and the hydridic hydrogen. In view of the resistance of the BeH_2Be bridge in complexes such as $(MeBeH \cdot NMe_3)_2$ to fission by tertiary amines, it is surprising that (LXXI; M = Be) contains terminal Be—H bonds. The infrared spectrum of this compound (as a Nujol mull, i.e., as crystalline solid) contains a strong and rather broad absorption with sharp peaks at 1536, 1634, and 1715 cm^{-1}. Though lower than other absorptions known to be due to terminal Be—H stretching vibrations (Section XI,A), perhaps some or all of these are due to ν Be—H in (LXXI; M = Be).

An aminoberyllium hydride has been obtained from an azomethine (*25*):

$$PhCH{=}NPh + BeH_2 \xrightarrow{THF} HBeNPhCH_2Ph \cdot THF$$

This complex has an apparent degree of association of 1.2–1.3 in benzene, cryoscopically, so it is likely that it forms an associated species, possibly a dimer like (LXXI; M = Be) which dissociates. The crystalline complex

$$(HBeNPhCH_2Ph \cdot THF)_2 \rightleftharpoons (HBeNPhCH_2Ph)_n + 2\,THF$$

slowly loses tetrahydrofuran under reduced pressure, and the tetrahydrofuran can be displaced by 4-dimethylaminopyridine, giving the sparingly soluble complex $HBe(NPhCH_2Ph) \cdot NC_5H_4NMe_2$.

Still less is known about oxyberyllium hydrides. Beryllium hydride in suspension in tetrahydrofuran adds to benzophenone. The resulting

$$Ph_2CO + BeH_2 \xrightarrow{THF} (HBeOCHPh_2)_x \xrightarrow{H_2O} Ph_2CHOH$$

diphenylmethoxyberyllium hydride is an amorphous (by X-ray diffraction) solid, which is soluble in benzene in which it is some seven- to eightfold associated. Evidence for the formation of an oxyberyllium hydride is also to be found in the reaction

$$\text{iso-}Bu_2AlH + Be(OBu\text{-}tert)_2 \rightarrow \text{iso-}Bu_2AlOBu\text{-}tert + HBeOBu\text{-}tert$$

The ^1H NMR spectrum of a benzene solution shows only the presence of starting materials when the solution is freshly prepared, but after 3 hours at 70°–80° C. the spectrum becomes identical with that of iso-Bu_2AlOBu-*tert* and some glassy material is deposited. Hydrolysis of the latter yields hydrogen, beryllium hydroxide, and a small amount of butane. The product is likely to have been an impure butoxyberyllium hydride, since some butyl groups as well as hydridic hydrogen were transferred to the beryllium (*27*).

C. *Beryllium Boron Hydrides*

The structure of beryllium borohydride, long believed to be as shown in

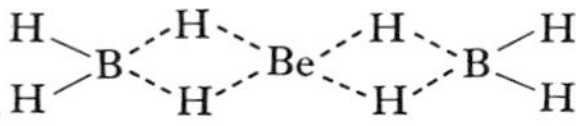

$$\begin{matrix} H & & H & & H & & H \\ & B & & Be & & B & \\ H & & H & & H & & H \end{matrix}$$

(LXXII)

(LXXII), has become the subject of recent controversy following the reinvestigation of its electron diffraction pattern (*5*, *6*). These data are inconsistent with (LXXII) as they demand a triangular arrangement of the metal atoms. Accordingly the authors proposed a new structure which was immediately challenged as having a total higher energy than (LXXII) (*11*) as well as being inconsistent with the infrared and mass spectra (*73*). A dipole moment has been reported (*123*) although no microwave spectrum could be observed (*116*). In these latter two experiments serious decomposition problems were encountered. Attempts to reproduce the electron diffraction data have subsequently failed (*7*) and again serious decomposition problems were encountered. The gas-phase infrared spectrum (*74*) has group frequencies consistent with (LXXII), although the band shapes (PR separations) indicate the molecule must be bent. Thus the most acceptable structure should have bonding as in (LXXII) but with C_{2v} symmetry, the bridging hydrogens being coplanar.

Dimethylberyllium reacts with diborane to produce beryllium borohydride (*33*). Initially polymeric materials are formed which indicate the presence of both bridging methyl and bridging hydride groups (*74*). The controlled action of diborane on dimethylberyllium at 100°C produces methylberyllium borohydride (*33*).

The vapor pressure of methylberyllium borohydride (*74*) is about double that of beryllium borohydride, about 10 mm at 20°C. It is accordingly purified by passing the vapors slowly through a trap at −45°C and collecting the purified product in a trap at −80°C. Beryllium borohydride is retained in the −45°C trap.

Methylberyllium borohydride is quite soluble in benzene, where it is (cryoscopically) dimeric. The extreme low field methyl resonance signal for its solutions in benzene, 10.14 τ, and even lower field resonance in cyclopentane solution, 9.59 τ, strongly argue for dimerization via bridging methyl groups. The ^{9}Be resonance signal at −11.0 ppm is consistent with a rather deshielded environment for the beryllium atom.

Infrared studies of the unsaturated vapors at about 3 mm pressure show that the compound exists as about 95% dimer (LXXIII) and 5% monomer (LXXIII) with a small amount of methane as a decomposition product.

```
                    H H H
                     \|/
H     H       .C.       H     H
 >B<     >Be<     >Be<     >B<
H     H       'C'       H     H
                     /|\
                    H H H
```

(LXXIII)

```
H              H       H
H—C—Be<     >B<
H              H       H
```

(LXXIV)

These spectra were assigned with the aid of deuterium and ^{10}B substitution and comparison with the assigned spectra of dimethylberyllium (*103*) and beryllium borohydride (*74*). The beryllium–carbon stretching frequencies are quite informative. The Be—CH_3—Be bridge asymmetric stretching frequency in (LXXIII) occurs at 587 cm^{-1} compared with the similar mode in solid, polymeric, dimethylberyllium which appears at

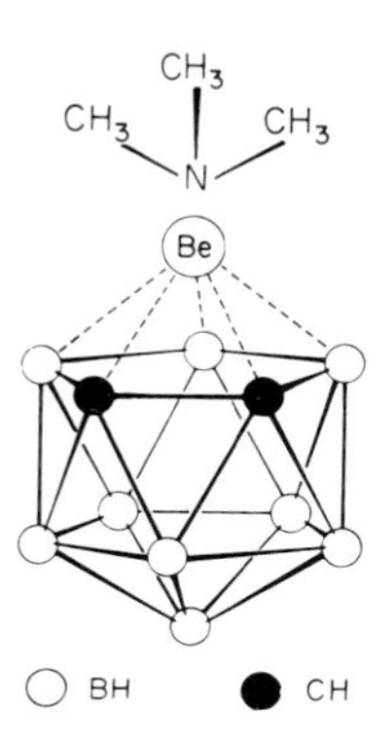

FIG. 4. Proposed schematic structureof $B_9BeC_2H_{11}\cdot NMe_3$, after Popp and Hawthorne (*130*).

565 and 534 cm^{-1} (*95*). One is tempted to conclude that the higher frequency for (LXXII) reflects a stronger bond energy since this is also suggested by the very preference of methyl bridges in this molecule over the generally more stable hydride bridges.

The Be—CH_3 terminal asym. stretching frequency in the monomer (LXXIV) occurs at 1108 cm^{-1} compared to 1081 cm^{-1} in monomeric dimethylberyllium (*103*). Both of these frequencies are much higher than those in basic adducts of dimethylberyllium (*28*) which generally occur in the range 700–900 cm^{-1}. The extremely low Be—C frequency, 450 cm^{-1}, extracted from the complete Raman-infrared study of di-*tert*-butylberyllium (*68*) most probably reflects a high degree of vibronic coupling. Since the masses of $^{11}BH_4$ and CH_3 are about the same and coupling is not expected through bridging hydrogens, the 1108 and 1081 cm^{-1} frequencies may be directly compared, with the conclusion that the Be—C bond in (LXXIII) is stronger than that in dimethylberyllium.

The reaction of dimethylberyllium with boranes has been further extended to exploit the fact that a beryllium plus a carbon atom are isoelectronic with two boron atoms (*130*). (3)-1,2-$B_9C_2H_{13}$ reacts with dimethylberyllium according to the equation

$$B_9C_2H_{13} + Be(CH_3)_2 \cdot x(C_2H_5)_2O \rightarrow B_9BeC_2H_{11} \cdot O(C_2H_5)_2 + 2\ CH_4$$

The resulting etherate (m.p. 120°–121° C) is isoelectronic with $B_{11}CH_{12}^-$ and is analogous to $B_9BeC_2H_{12}^-$, in which an ether molecule replaces a hydride ion. The ether may be displaced by trimethylamine in methylene chloride solution, producing $B_9BeC_2H_{11} \cdot N(CH_3)_3$ (m.p. 221°–223° C decomp.), the proposed structure of which is shown in Fig. 4. This proposed icosohedral structure, with the beryllium atom in a coordination sphere of two carbons, three borons, and one nitrogen, is a novel and unique example of electron-deficient beryllium–carbon bonding.

References

1. Adamson, G. W., and Shearer, H. M. M., *Chem. Commun.* p. 240 (1965).
2. Allegra, G., and Perego, G., *Acta Cryst.* **16**, 185 (1963).
3. Allen, G., Bruce, J. M., Farren, D. W., and Hutchinson, F. G., *J. Chem. Soc., B* p. 799 (1966).
4. Almenningen, A., Bastiansen, O., and Haaland, A., *J. Chem. Phys.* **40**, 3434 (1964).
5. Almenningen, A., Gundersen, G., and Haaland, A., *Chem. Commun.* p. 557 (1967).
6. Almenningen, A., Gundersen, G., and Haaland, A., *Acta Chem. Scand.* **22**, 859 (1968).
7. Almenningen, A., Haaland, A., and Morgan, G. L., unpublished observations (1969).
8. Almenningen, A., Haaland, A., and Morgan, G. L., *Acta Chem. Scand.* **23**, 2921 (1969).
9. Almenningen, A., Haaland, A., and Nilson, J. E., *Acta Chem. Scand.* **22**, 972 (1968).
10. Andersen, R. A., Kovar, R. A., and Morgan, G. L., unpublished observations (1968).
11. Armstrong, D. R., and Perkins, P. G., *Chem. Commun.* p. 353 (1968).
12. Ashby, E. C., and Arnott, R. C., *J. Organometal. Chem.* (*Amsterdam*) **14**, 1 (1968).
13. Atwood, J. L., and Stucky, G. D., *Chem. Commun.* p. 1169 (1967); *J. Am. Chem. Soc.* **91**, 4426 (1969).
14. Atwood, J. L., and Stucky, G. D., *J. Am. Chem. Soc.* **91**, 2538 (1969).
15. Bähr, G., and Thiele, K. H., *Chem. Ber.* **90**, 1578 (1957).
16. Balueva, G. A., and Ioffe, S. T., *Russ. Chem. Rev.* (*English Transl.*) **31**, 439 (1962).
17. Banford, L., and Coates, G. E., *J. Chem. Soc.* p. 5591 (1964).
18. Barbaras, G. D., Dillard, C., Finholt, A. E., Wartik, T., Wilzbach, K. E., and Schlesinger, H. I., *J. Am. Chem. Soc.* **73**, 4585 (1951).
19. Bartell, L. S., and Caroll, B. L., *J. Chem. Phys.* **42**, 3076 (1965).
20. Beachley, O. T., and Coates, G. E., *J. Chem. Soc., A* p. 3241 (1965); Beachley, O. T., Coates, G. E., and Kohnstam, G., *ibid.* p. 3248.
21. Bell, N. A., *J. Chem. Soc., A* p. 542 (1966).
22. Bell, N. A., and Coates, G. E., *Proc. Chem. Soc.* p. 59 (1964).
23. Bell, N. A., and Coates, G. E., *J. Chem. Soc.* p. 692 (1965).
24. Bell, N. A., and Coates, G. E., *Can. J. Chem.* **44**, 744 (1966).
25. Bell, N. A., and Coates, G. E., *J. Chem. Soc., A* p. 1069 (1966).
26. Bell, N. A., and Coates, G. E., *J. Chem. Soc., A* p. 628 (1968).

27. Bell, N. A., and Coates, G. E., *J. Chem. Soc., A* p. 823 (1968).
28. Bell, N. A., Coates, G. E., and Emsley, J. W., *J. Chem. Soc., A* p. 49 (1966).
29. Bell, N. A., Coates, G. E., and Emsley, J. W., *J. Chem. Soc., A* p. 1360 (1966).
30. Brown, I. M., and Weissman, S. I., *J. Am. Chem. Soc.* **85**, 2528 (1963).
31. Bruce, J. M., Cutsforth, B. C., Farren, D. W., Hutchinson, F. G., Rabagliati, F. M., and Reed, D. R., *J. Chem. Soc., B* p. 1020 (1966).
32. Brüser, W., Thiele, K. H., and Müller, H. K., *Z. Chem.* **2**, 342 (1962).
33. Burg, A. B., and Schlesinger, H. I., *J. Am. Chem. Soc.* **62**, 3425 (1940).
34. Bürger, H., Forker, C., and Goubeau, J., *Monatsh. Chem.* **96**, 597 (1965).
35. Campbell, D. H., and Lowrance, B. R., U.S. Patent 3,202,722 (1965).
36. Caroll, B. L., and Bartell, L. S., *Inorg. Chem.* **7**, 219 (1968).
37. Chambers, D. B., Coates, G. E., and Glockling, F., *Discussions Faraday Soc.* **47**, 157 (1969).
38. Chambers, D. B., Coates, G. E., and Glockling, F., *J. Chem. Soc., A* p. 741 (1970).
39. Chatt, J., and Wilkins, R. G., *J. Chem. Soc.* pp. 273 and 4300 (1952); p. 525 (1956).
40. Clark, A. H., and Haaland, A., *J. Chem. Soc., D* p. 912 (1969).
41. Coates, G. E., *Record Chem. Progr.* (*Kresge-Hooker Sci. Lib.*) **28**, 3 (1967).
42. Coates, G. E., and Cox, G. F., *Chem. & Ind.* (*London*) p. 269 (1962).
43. Coates, G. E., and Cox, G. F., unpublished observations (1961).
44. Coates, G. E., and Fishwick, A. H., *J. Chem. Soc., A* p. 1199 (1967).
45. Coates, G. E., and Fishwick, A. H., *J. Chem. Soc., A* p. 477 (1968).
46. Coates, G. E., and Fishwick, A. H., *J. Chem. Soc., A* p. 635 (1968).
47. Coates, G. E., and Fishwick, A. H., *J. Chem. Soc., A* p. 640 (1968).
48. Coates, G. E., and Fishwick, A. H., unpublished observations (1968).
49. Coates, G. E., and Francis, B. R., unpublished observations (1969).
50. Coates, G. E., Francis, B. R., and Murrell, L. L., unpublished observations (1969).
51. Coates, G. E., and Glockling, F., *J. Chem. Soc.* p. 22 (1954).
52. Coates, G. E., and Glockling, F., *J. Chem. Soc.* p. 2526 (1954).
53. Coates, G. E., Glockling, F., and Huck, N. D., *J. Chem. Soc.* p. 4496 (1952).
54. Coates, G. E., Glockling, F., and Huck, N. D., *J. Chem. Soc.* p. 4512 (1952).
55. Coates, G. E., and Green, S. I. E., *Proc. Chem. Soc.* p. 376 (1961).
56. Coates, G. E., and Green, S. I. E., *J. Chem. Soc.* p. 3340 (1962).
57. Coates, G. E., Green, M. L. H., Powell, P., and Wade, K., "Principles of Organometallic Chemistry," Chapters 1 and 2. Methuen, London, 1968.
58. Coates, G. E., and Heslop, J. A., *J. Chem. Soc., A* p. 26 (1966).
59. Coates, G. E., and Heslop, J. A., *J. Chem. Soc., A* p. 514 (1968).
60. Coates, G. E., and Huck, N. D., *J. Chem. Soc.* p. 4501 (1952).
61. Coates, G. E., and Lauder, A., *J. Chem. Soc., A* p. 264 (1966).
62. Coates, G. E., and Mukherjee, R. N., *J. Chem. Soc.* p. 229 (1963).
63. Coates, G. E., and Pendlebury, R. E., *J. Chem. Soc., A* p. 156 (1970).
64. Coates, G. E., and Ridley, D., *J. Chem. Soc.* p. 1870 (1965).
65. Coates, G. E., and Ridley, D., *Chem. Commun.* p. 560 (1966); Coates, G. E., Heslop, J. A., Redwood, M. E., and Ridley, D., *J. Chem. Soc., A* p. 1118 (1968).
66. Coates, G. E., and Roberts, P. D., *J. Chem. Soc., A* p. 2651 (1968).
67. Coates, G. E., and Roberts, P. D., *J. Chem. Soc., A* p. 1008 (1969).
68. Coates, G. E., Roberts, P. D., and Downs, A. J., *J. Chem. Soc., A* p. 1085 (1967).
69. Coates, G. E., and Strafford, R. G., unpublished observations (1968).
70. Coates, G. E., and Tranah, M., *J. Chem. Soc., A* p. 236 (1967).
71. Coates, G. E., and Tranah, M., *J. Chem. Soc., A* p. 615 (1967).

72. Coates, G. E., and Wade, K., *in* "Organometallic Compounds," 3rd ed., Vol. I, Chapter 2, pp. 103–121. Methuen, London, 1967.
73. Cook, T. H., and Morgan, G. L., *J. Am. Chem. Soc.* **91**, 774 (1969).
74. Cook, T. H., and Morgan, G. L., *J. Am. Chem. Soc.* **92** (1970) in press.
75. Cowley, A. H., and White, W. D., *J. Am. Chem. Soc.* **91**, 34 (1969).
76. Dessy, R. E., *J. Am. Chem. Soc.* **82**, 1580 (1960).
77. Dewar, M. J. S., "Hyperconjugation." Ronald Press, New York, 1962.
78. Drenth, W., communicated to J. Boersma and J. G. Noltes, "Organozinc Co-ordination Chemistry," p. 24. Intern. Lead Zinc Res. Organ., Inc., Utrecht, 1968.
79. Drew, D., and Morgan, G. L., unpublished observations (1969).
80. Durand, J. F., *Compt. Rend.* **182**, 1162 (1926).
81. Eisenhuth, W. H., and Van Wazer, J. R., *J. Am. Chem. Soc.* **90**, 5397 (1968).
82. Fetter, N. R., *Can. J. Chem.* **42**, 861 (1964).
83. Fetter, N. R., *J. Chem. Soc., A* p. 711 (1966).
84. Fetter, N. R., *Organometal. Chem. Rev.* **3**, 1 (1968).
85. Fetter, N. R., and Peters, F. M., *Can. J. Chem.* **43**, 1884 (1965).
86. Fischer, E. O., and Hofmann, H. P., *Chem. Ber.* **92**, 482 (1959); Fritz, H. P., and Schneider, S., *ibid.* **93**, 1171 (1960).
87. Fritz, H. P., and Sellman, D., *J. Organometal. Chem.* (*Amsterdam*) **5**, 501 (1966).
88. Funk, H., and Masthoff, R., *J. Prakt. Chem.* [4] **22**, 255 (1963).
89. Gilman, H., *J. Am. Chem. Soc.* **45**, 2693 (1923).
90. Gilman, H., and Brown, R. E., *J. Am. Chem. Soc.* **52**, 4480 (1930).
91. Gilman, H., and Schulze, F., *J. Am. Chem. Soc.* **49**, 2904 (1927).
92. Gilman, H., and Schulze, F., *J. Chem. Soc.* p. 2663 (1927).
93. Glaze, W. H., Selman, C. M., and Freeman, C. H., *Chem. Commun.* p. 474 (1966).
94. Goubeau, J., and Rodewald, B., *Z. Anorg. Allgem. Chem.* **258**, 1962 (1949).
95. Goubeau, J., and Walter, K., *Z. Anorg. Allgem. Chem.* **322**, 58 (1963).
96. Graybill, B. M., and Hawthorne, M. F., *J. Am. Chem. Soc.* **83**, 2673 (1961).
97. Hans, G., German Patent 1,102,736 (1962).
98. Head, E. L., Holley, C. E., and Rabideau, S. W., *J. Am. Chem. Soc.* **79**, 3687 (1957).
99. Hoffmann, E. G., *Ann. Chem.* **629**, 104 (1960).
100. Klanberg, F., Eaton, D. R., Guggenberger, L. J., and Muetterties, E. L., *Inorg. Chem.* **6**, 1271 (1967).
101. Köster, R., Griasnow, G., Larbig, W., and Binger, P., *Ann. Chem.* **672**, 1 (1964).
102. Kotz, J. C., Schaeffer, R., and Clouse, A., *Inorg. Chem.* **6**, 620 (1967).
103. Kovar, R. A., and Morgan, G. L., *Inorg. Chem.* **8**, 1099 (1969).
104. Kovar, R. A., and Morgan, G. L., *J. Am. Chem. Soc.* **92**, 5067 (1970).
105. Kovar, R. A., and Morgan, G. L., *J. Am. Chem. Soc.* **91**, 7269 (1969).
106. Krause, E., and Wendt, B., *Chem. Ber.* **56**, 467, footnote 2 (1923).
107. Lardicci, L., Lucarini, L., Palagi, P., and Pino, P., *J. Organometal. Chem.* (*Amsterdam*) **4**, 341 (1965).
108. Lavroff, D., *J. Russ. Phys.-Chem. Soc.* **16**, 93 (1884); *Bull. Soc. Chim.* **41**, 548 (1884).
109. Magnuson, V. R., and Stucky, G. D., *Inorg. Chem.* **8**, 1427 (1969).
110. Malone, J. F., and McDonald, W. S., *Chem. Commun.* p. 444 (1967).
111. Masthoff, R., *Z. Chem.* **3**, 269 (1963).
112. Masthoff, R., *Z. Anorg. Allgem. Chem.* **336**, 252 (1965).
113. Masthoff, R., and Vieroth, C., *Z. Chem.* **5**, 142 (1965).
114. McVicker, G. B., and Morgan, G. L., *Spectrochim Acta* **26A**, 23 (1970).
115. McVicker, G. B., Ph.D. Thesis, University of Wyoming (1968).

116. Møllendal, H., personal communication (1969).
117. Montecatini, British Patent 921,806 (1961).
118. Montecatini, British Patent 928,716 (1962).
119. Mootz, D., Zinnius, A., and Böttcher, B., *Angew. Chem.* **81**, 398 (1969).
120. Morgan, G. L., and McVicker, G. B., *J. Am. Chem. Soc.* **90**, 2789 (1968).
121. Moseley, P. T., and Shearer, H. M. M., *Chem. Commun.* p. 876 (1966).
122. Murrell, L. L., unpublished observations (1969).
123. Nibler, J. W., and McNabb, J., *J. Chem. Soc., D* p. 134 (1969).
124. Noltes, J. G., *Rec. Trav. Chim.* **84**, 126 (1965).
125. Noltes, J. G., and Boersma, J., *J. Organometal. Chem. (Amsterdam)* **9**, 1 (1967).
126. Noltes, J. G., and Boersma, J., *J. Organometal. Chem. (Amsterdam)* **12**, 425 (1968).
127. Noltes, J. G., and van den Hurk, J. W. G., *J. Organometal. Chem. (Amsterdam)* **3**, 222 (1965).
128. Novoselova, A. V., Semenenko, K. N., and Turova, A. Y., *Vestn. Mosk. Univ., Ser. II: Khim.* **13**, 139 (1958).
129. Peters, F. M., *J. Organometal. Chem. (Amsterdam)* **3**, 334 (1965).
130. Popp, G., and Hawthorne, M. F., *J. Am. Chem. Soc.* **90**, 6553 (1968).
131. Ruff, J. K., *J. Am. Chem. Soc.* **83**, 1798 (1961).
132. Rundle, R. E., *Surv. Progr. Chem.* **1**, 81 (1963).
133. Rundle, R. E., and Snow, A. I., *J. Chem. Phys.* **18**, 1125 (1950).
134. Sanders, J. R., Ashby, E. C., and Carter, J. H., *J. Am. Chem. Soc.* **90**, 6385 (1968); *Chem. Commun.* p. 997 (1967).
135. Schneider, R., and Fischer, E. O., *Naturwissenshaften* **50**, 349 (1963).
136. Schulze, F., *Iowa State Coll. J. Sci.* **8**, 225 (1933).
137. Shearer, H. M. M., and Schneider, M. L., personal communication (1969).
138. Shearer, H. M. M., and Spencer, C. B., *Chem. Commun.* p. 194 (1966).
139. Shearer, H. M. M., and Spencer, C. B., personal communication (1969).
139a. Shepherd, L. H., Ter Haar, G. L., and Marlett, E. M., *Inorg. Chem.* **8**, 976 (1969).
140. Silber, P., *Ann. Chim. (Paris)* [12] **7**, 182 (1952).
141. Snow, A. I., and Rundle, R. E., *Acta Cryst.* **4**, 348 (1951).
142. Strohmeier, W., and Gernert, F., *Z. Naturforsch.* **16b**, 760 (1961).
143. Strohmeier, W., and Gernert, F., *Z. Naturforsch.* **17b**, 128 (1961).
144. Strohmeier, W., and Gernert, F., *Chem. Ber.* **95**, 1420 (1962); Hans, G., German Patent 1,102,736 (1962); *Chem. Abstr.* **57**, 13800 (1962); Strohmeier, W., Haecker, W., and Popp, G., *Chem. Ber.* **100**, 405 (1967).
145. Strohmeier, W., and Gernert, F., *Z. Naturforsch.* **20b** 829 (1965).
146. Strohmeier, W., Haecker, W., and Popp, G., *Chem. Ber.* **100**, 405 (1967).
147. Strohmeier, W., and Hümpfner, K., *Z. Elektrochem.* **60**, 1111 (1956); Wittig, G., and Wittenberg, D., *Ann. Chem.* **606**, 15 (1957).
148. Strohmeier, W., Hümpfner, K., Miltenberger, K., and Seifert, F., *Z. Elektrochem.* **63**, 537 (1959).
149. Strohmeier, W., and Popp, G., *Z. Naturforsch.* **22b**, 891 (1967).
150. Strohmeier, W., and Popp, G., *Z. Naturforsch.* **23b**, 38 (1968).
151. Summerford, C., Wade, K., and Wyatt, B. K., *J. Chem. Soc., D* p. 61 (1969).
152. Sundbom, M., *Acta Chem. Scand.* **20**, 1608 (1966).
153. Topkin, I. I., Anvarova, G. Y., and Povarnitsyan, T. Y., *Zh. Obshch. Khim.* **36**, 1952 (1956).
154. Watson, S. C., and Eastham, J. F., *J. Organometal. Chem. (Amsterdam)* **9**, 165 (1967).
155. Weiss, E., *J. Organometal. Chem. (Amsterdam)* **4**, 101 (1965).

156. Weiss, E., and Wolfrum, R., *J. Organometal. Chem. (Amsterdam)* **12**, 257 (1968).
157. Williams, K. C., and Brown, T. L., *J. Am. Chem. Soc.* **88**, 5460 (1966).
158. Wittig, G., and Hornberger, P., *Ann. Chem.* **577**, 11 (1952).
159. Wittig, G., and Keicher, G., *Naturwissenschaften* **34**, 216 (1947).
160. Wood, G. B., and Brenner, A., *J. Electrochem. Soc.* **104**, 29 (1957).
161. Zakharkin, L. I., Okhlobystin, O. Y., and Strunik, B. N., *Bull. Acad. Sci. USSR, Div. Chem. Sci. (English Transl.)* p. 2114 (1961).
162. Ziegler, K., British Patent 763,824 (1956).
163. Ziegler, K., British Patent 775,384 (1958).
164. Ziegler, K., *in* "Organometallic Chemistry" (H. Zeiss, ed.), Chapter 5, p. 206. Reinhold, New York, 1960.
165. Ziegler, K., Köster, R., Lehmkuhl, H., and Reinert, K., *Ann. Chem.* **629**, 33 (1960).

Isoelectronic Species in the Organophosphorus, Organosilicon, and Organoaluminum Series

HUBERT SCHMIDBAUR

Institut für Anorganische Chemie
Universität Würzburg
Würzburg, Germany

I

INTRODUCTION

Organosilicon chemistry in many ways has a unique position in organometallic chemistry. This is immediately obvious not only from the exceedingly high number of compounds known to date, but also from their unusual chemical and thermal stability (*36*, *119*, *258*). This position has often been related to the special role played by the lighter homolog of silicon, carbon, in the family of the elements. Such a relation, however, can at best account for the great variety of compounds, but not for their typical and often extraordinary properties.

The latter result from special types of chemical bonding with silicon, which are found neither for carbon nor for other Group IV elements. A theoretical evaluation of this bonding mechanism is in principle very difficult (*121*, *424*). At present it is made most plausible by the concept of a separate treatment of σ- and π-interactions, of which the latter are referred to as the $(p\rightarrow d)\pi$ interactions or, less frequently, $(d\rightarrow d)\pi$ interactions. This, of course, is by no means the only approach to this problem, but it is the one easiest to apply qualitatively.

Among the various classes of organosilicon compounds the *organosiloxane* species are of special interest. These compounds have great practical value as large-scale industrial products. Theoretical considerations have often focused on the principles of chemical bonding in the siloxanes. The Si—O—Si moieties occurring in all modifications of silicon dioxide, in numerous silicates, and in organosiloxane oligomers and polymers seem to represent a relative optimum in chemical and thermal stability (*331*).

The special properties of such bonds as SiF, SiO, SiN, and others must be related to the number of atoms and electrons present in these moieties. In order to detect similar characteristics it therefore seems reasonable to investigate the structure and bonding in classes of compounds which are *isosteres* of or *isoelectronic* with the fluorosilanes, siloxanes, etc. The "principle of isosterism," first proposed by I. Langmuir (*211–214*) more than half a century ago in 1919, has turned out to be an extremely useful concept in many areas of chemistry (*41*, *57*, *66*, *140*, *147*, *332*, *333*, *421*, *437*).

This chapter is an attempt to summarize work from this point of view which has been done during the last 10–15 years. Starting from the chemistry of fluorosilanes, silanols, siloxanes, and heterosiloxanes the lines drawn by isoelectronic relations will be followed into areas of organophosphorus and organoaluminum chemistry. Often the new classes of compounds considered have little in common with the silicon compounds chemically, but are, in fact, true isoelectronic systems. Many of the series of compounds had been known in principle for a long time, but had never been considered from this point of view. The earlier literature on their chemistry and on the theory of isosterism itself cannot be discussed in this chapter. Some key references will be given, however, to provide a basis for further reading. Where a special topic has been the subject of earlier reviews the treatment will be brief and the selection of material arbitrary. Other areas with more recent major achievements will be dealt with in greater detail.

II

FLUORO, HYDROXY, AMINO, AND METHYL SILANES

A. Fluoro Silanes, Germanes, and Stannanes

1. General Properties

According to rules established by *Grimm* (*154–156*) in 1929 and later by others the fluoride ion is isoelectronic with the hydroxyl and amide ions. It is therefore not too surprising that relations are to be detected in the organometallic fluoride series of Group IVb elements which are similar to those in the isoelectronic series of the hydroxyl and amino analogs to be discussed later in this article. Even the methyl derivatives should be included:

R_3SiF	R_3SiOH	R_3SiNH_2	R_3SiCH_3
R_3GeF	R_3GeOH	R_3GeNH_2	R_3GeCH_3
R_3SnF	R_3SnOH	R_3SnNH_2	R_3SnCH_3

Organofluorosilanes are somewhat exceptional in particular with respect to the high *bond energy* of their Si—F linkage. This has been ascribed to a special type of bonding in these molecules, often exclusively referred to as the $(p \rightarrow d)\pi$-bonding interactions. However, contributions from the inherent polarity of the Si—F bonds are also sufficient to account for the anomalies in bond energies and distances observed (Table I). Thus, there is no reason for the assumption that a dipolar resonance form contributes significantly to the ground state of the molecules, on the basis of a high bond energy alone. The same is true for the *bond orders* derived from

$$R_3Si{-}\underline{\overline{F}}| \leftrightarrow R_3\overset{-}{Si}{=}\overset{+}{\underline{\overline{F}}}$$

vibrational spectroscopy via force constant evaluations, and other physicochemical measurements, such as NMR, NQR, and Mössbauer spectroscopy, or from dipole moment studies (Table I).

A further complication arises from the destabilizing contribution of fluorine lone-pair versus element bond-pair repulsions. These contributions are to be expected to be most pronounced in the carbon compounds, where the shortest element–fluorine distance is encountered. A consideration of these interactions, best known from arguments about the bonding in the fluorine molecule F_2 (*67*, *77*, *251*, *269*, *277–279*, *303*), could possibly help

TABLE I

BONDING CHARACTERISTICS IN ORGANOFLUOROSILANES AND RELATED COMPOUNDS

	M—F Bond				References	
	Energy (kcal/mole)		Distance (Å)			
	Found	Calc.	Found	Calc.	IR/R	NMR
SiF_4	142 ± 2 (*411, 428*)	152 (*121, 269*)	1.54 (*63, 271*)	1.69 (*269*)	*117, 186, 241, 405, 406, 430*	*159*
		120 (*302*)	1.55 (*61*)	1.83 (*302*)	—	—
		129.3 (*269*)	1.56 (*28*)	—	—	—
$(CH_3)_3SiF$	193 ± 10 (*168*)	—	1.55 (*158*)	1.69 (*207, 208, 269, 302*)	—	*321, 431*
GeF_4	113 (*105*)	148 (*269, 302*)	1.63 (*87*)	1.94 (*88, 269, 302*)	—	*159*
$(CH_3)_3GeF$	—	—	—	—	*122, 223*	*360*[a]
SnF_4	—	—	1.88 (*171*)	2.10 (*269*)	—	—
			2.02 (*171*)			
$(CH_3)_3SnF$	—	—	2.10 (*94*)	2.10 (*269*)	*65*	*145, 167* (Möss.)
			2.2–2.6 (*94*)			

[a] Dipole moment, 2.51 D (*189*).

to explain the variation in bond energies (kcal/mole) of C—F and Si—F linkages:

C—F	116
Si—F	142
Ge—F	113

Organofluorosilanes generally are true molecular compounds showing no unusual intermolecular interactions in a condensed phase (*223*). With *fluorogermanes*, however, some anomalies occur which are related to coordination phenomena and corresponding exchange processes. Fluorogermanes are less volatile than could be extrapolated from fluorosilane chemistry; furthermore considerable bathochromic shifts of Ge—F stretching frequencies in the IR spectra are observed upon condensation of gaseous fluorogermanes (*223*); and proton magnetic resonance finally shows rapid intermolecular fluorine exchange, which leads to a vanishing of the HCGeF coupling at higher temperatures and concentrations (*351*).

Most *fluorostannanes* are true coordination polymers (*299*), if the steric requirements of the organic ligands permit the appropriate intermolecular interactions. The bridging of tin atoms by fluoride ligands is clearly analogous to the principle of structure in *stannols*, i.e., hydroxystannanes, as is the behavior of fluorogermanes to what is found in germanols, i.e., hydroxygermanes (see below). Formulas may therefore be drawn for the basic members of the series, which are as follows:

$(CH_3)_3SiF$ — B.p. 16.4°C, M.p. −74.3°C

$[(CH_3)_3GeF]_2$ (fluorine-bridged dimer) — B.p. 76°C, M.p. 1.9°C

$[(CH_3)_3SnF]_n$ (fluorine-bridged chain polymer) — M.p. 375°C (dec) (*94*)

$(CH_3)_3Pb^+F^-$
dec.

The structure of the tin compound has been verified by an X-ray structural investigation (*94*); the fluorosilane structure is inferred from spectroscopic data of various kinds, whereas the germanium species is depicted so as to account for the associative phenomena detected in the condensed phases (*223, 351*).

The structure of *organolead fluorides* is not shown, but the general properties of these compounds are best interpreted as being due to a coordinative type of bonding with highly polar or saltlike features (*299*). Generally, the exceptional behavior of fluorosilanes thus is not only a consequence of the nature of the element–fluorine bond but also of the coordinative features of the element involved. The same situation will be met in the chemistry of all the isosteres.

TABLE II

PHYSICAL PROPERTIES OF DIALKYLELEMENT(IVb) DIFLUORIDES

	M.p.(°C)	B.p.(°C)	References
$(CH_3)_2SiF_2$	−87.5°	2.7°	*258*
$(CH_3)_2GeF_2$	—	112°	*122, 280*
$(CH_3)_2SnF_2$	360°(dec)	—	*318*
$(CH_3)_2PbF_2$	dec	—	*203*

Table II gives some properties for a complete homologous series of simple representative compounds, and Fig. 1 shows the crystal structure of $(CH_3)_2SnF_2$ (*318*).

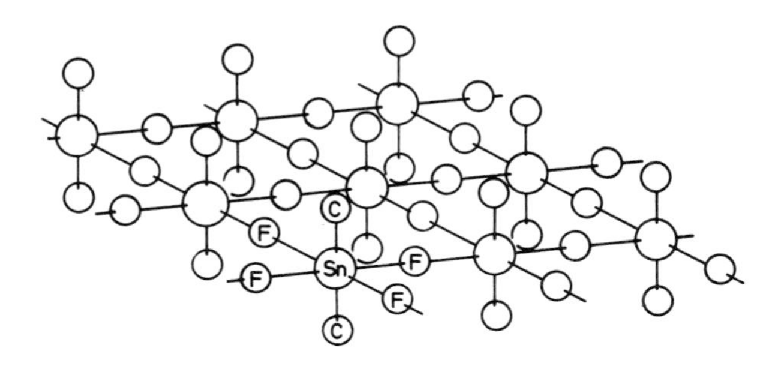

FIG. 1. The crystal structure of dimethyltin difluoride.

2. *Coordination at Fluorine*

Results of experiments designed to test the donor properties of fluorosilanes make it seem unlikely, that back-donation of fluorine lone pairs of electrons to silicon and its homologs is significant for the overall stability of the element–fluorine linkage. It was found that fluorosilanes—contrary to expectations—are able to function as donors towards strong acceptor molecules (*349*).

At low temperatures trimethyl- and triethylfluorosilane add equimolar amounts of trimethyl- or triethylaluminum with formation of well-defined 1:1 complexes. These addition compounds are stable up to room temperature, where secondary reactions occur leading to tetraalkylsilanes and

$$2\,R_3Si{-}\overline{\underline{F}}| + [AlR_3']_2 \rightarrow 2\,R_3Si{-}\overset{+}{\underline{\overline{F}}}{-}\overset{-}{Al}R_3'$$

$$4\,R_3SiFAlR_3' \xrightarrow{\text{Heat}} 4\,R_3SiR' + [R_2'AlF]_4$$

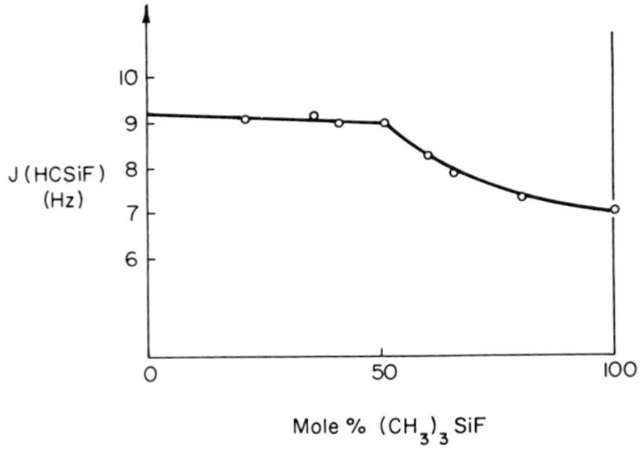

FIG. 2. Spin–spin coupling constant $\mathcal{J}(^1HCSi^{19}F)$ as a function of the mole fraction of $(CH_3)_3SiF$ in mixtures with $(C_2H_5)_3Al$ of various ratios.

dialkylaluminum fluorides (*349*, *351*). In NMR experiments using R_3SiF/AlR_3 mixtures of various ratios of reactants and their relation to chemical shifts and coupling constants, it was demonstrated that only a 1:1 complex is detectable. Figure 2 is a plot of the ratios of reactants versus coupling constant $\mathcal{J}(^1HCSi^{19}F)$. The latter is seen to increase steadily until all of the fluorosilane is trapped by AlR_3 molecules (1:1). The drastic increase of this J value upon coordination (by about 30%) points to a change of bonding at the *fluorine* atom, as $J(^1H^{13}C)$ and $J(^1HC^{29}Si)$ show no significant alterations for silicon or carbon.

This to our knowledge is the first example of a coordination compound wherein a fluorine atom engaged in a basically covalent bond can act as a donor site.[1] A spectacular type of complex salt (*460*) synthesized several years ago, however, offers a true analogy, which makes the existence of the new compounds less surprising (*332*, *333*). Aluminum alkyls are known to form coordination compounds with alkali fluorides not only in the ratio 1:1, but also *2:1*. These complexes have been formulated as

$$M^+[R_3Al—\underline{\overline{F}}—AlR_3]^-$$

and this structure was confirmed by single-crystal X-ray analysis of the hexaethyl-substituted homolog (Fig. 3A) (*5*, *253*).

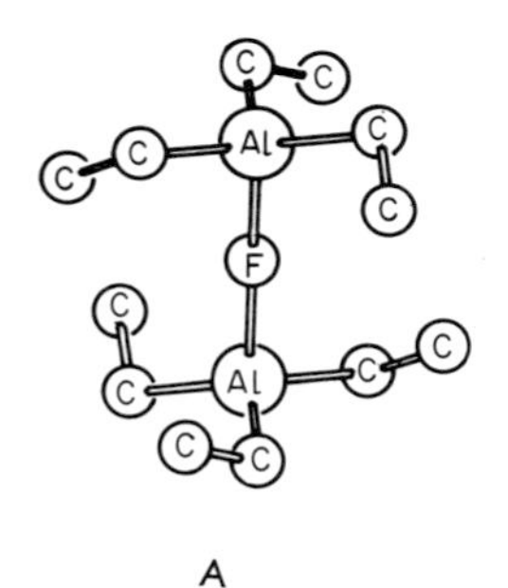

FIG. 3A. Crystal structure of the bis(triethylaluminum) fluoride anion $[(C_2H_5)_3Al—F—Al(C_2H_5)_3]^-$ (*5*).

The most interesting detail of the molecular geometry is the linear arrangement of the triatomic Al—F—Al bridge. There are other linear fluorine bridges in inorganic fluorine compounds of quite different composition and nature (*318*, *440*), and thus an interpretation on the grounds of $(p \rightarrow d)\pi$ interactions is doubtful. This description is even less attractive,

[1] None of the alkyl fluorides, e.g., has been observed to act as a donor.

as the fluorine atom would be loaded with a considerable positive charge in corresponding resonance forms:

$$R_3\overset{-}{Al}-\overset{+}{\underline{F}}-\overset{-}{Al}R_3 \leftrightarrow R_3\overset{2-}{Al}=\overset{2+}{\underline{F}}-\overset{-}{Al}R_3 \leftrightarrow R_3\overset{-}{Al}-\overset{2+}{\underline{F}}=\overset{2-}{Al}F_3$$

A simple electrostatic description therefore appears to be justified. The valence angle at the fluorine atoms in the polymeric tin fluorides, being 180° in $(CH_3)_2SnF_2$ (*318*), but less in $(CH_3)_3SnF$ (*94*), is consistent (Fig. 1).

The $R_3AlFAlR_3^-$ anions as well as the $R_3SiFAlR_3$ complexes are easily recognized as isoelectronic with disiloxanes $R_3SiOSiR_3$ and related compounds, for which the valency angle at the bridging atom is also a critical value, which will often be referred to again in later sections.

TABLE III

PROPERTIES OF $R_3SiFAlR_3$ COMPLEXES

	M.p.(°C)	dec.	$J(^1HCSi^{19}F)$	References
$(CH_3)_3SiFAl(CH_3)_3$	−25° to −24°	+21°	9.10	*349, 351*
$(CH_3)_3SiFAl(C_2H_5)_3$	−81° to −79°	+15°	9.40	*349, 351*
$(C_2H_5)_3SiFAl(C_2H_5)_3$	−75° to −73°	+20°	—	*349, 351*
$(CH_3)_3SiFAl(C_6H_5)_3$	—	—	10.01	*349, 351*
$(CH_3)_2C_6H_5SiFAl(C_2H_5)_3$	—	—	8.83	*349, 351*
$CH_3(C_6H_5)_2SiFAl(C_2H_5)_3$	—	—	8.20	*349, 351*
$(CH_3)_3SiF$	−74.3°	—	7.28	*321*
$(CH_3)_2SiF(C_6H_5)$	—	—	7.32	*118*
$CH_3SiF(C_6H_5)_2$	—	—	7.35	*118*

Weaker acceptor molecules like trimethylgallium or trimethylindium, unlike R_3Al compounds, do *not* form addition compounds with fluorosilanes. With *fluorogermanes* and *-stannanes* the rearrangement reactions are too fast even at low temperatures, and no complex intermediates can be detected (*349, 351*). Alkylaluminum fluorides or alkylgallium fluorides are

$$3(CH_3)_3GeF + 3(CH_3)_3Ga \rightarrow 3(CH_3)_4Ge + [(CH_3)_2GaF]_3$$

formed almost instantaneously. The trimeric or tetrameric products of composition R_2MF are the subject of a later section on six- and eight-membered ring compounds. Table III lists some compounds taken from the $R_3SiFAlR_3$ series with their physical properties.

B. *Silanols, Germanols, and Stannols*

1. *General Properties*

Silanols are the alcohols of organosilicon chemistry. They differ from their carbon analogs by an enhanced *acidity*, unexpected from simple electronegativity considerations. Their exceptional behavior is also evident from a comparison with germanols, stannols, or plumbols, which are again weaker acids. This appears from titration curves, IR shifts of the OH stretching frequencies in the presence of basic solvents, and from NMR spectra. The latter also prove the silanols to be the molecules with the relatively *strongest hydrogen bonding* (Table IV).

The increase in acidity of silanols can be related to $(p \rightarrow d)\pi$ *bonding* without encountering serious difficulties. The obvious stabilization of the silanolate anions R_3SiO^- may also be a consequence of the reduced lone pair–bond pair repulsions resulting from the increase of Si—O bond lengths as compared with C—O in carbinols. Such a consideration of a *reduced charge density* in a given volume element we may infer frequently throughout this text, whenever it might offer an alternative to the $(p \rightarrow d)\pi$ argument. Here the idea is that the negative charge produced at the oxygen atom of a silanol upon deprotonation causes less electrostatic difficulties with respect to the bonding pairs of the neighboring silicon atom, because of the bigger radius of the latter, than in carbinolate anions. For the same reason solvation of a silanolate anion is easier (sterically) than for a carbinolate anion. This effect might even outweigh the unfavorable polarity of the SiO bonds, due to the greater electronegativity difference as compared with CO bonds (Table IV).

With *germanols* and *stannols* the situation is not clear, as far fewer reliable data are available and because of additional coordination phenomena. To give a typical example, trimethylstannol $(CH_3)_3SnOH$ prefers *oxygen* bridging between tin atoms over *hydrogen* bonds between hydroxyl oxygen atoms in the solid state and probably also in the melt and in solution. It is likely that germanols are in an intermediate position, where metal–oxygen coordination as well as hydrogen bonding are feasible. This situation probably is responsible for the very mobile germanol–germoxane/water equilibria found in several cases. For this reason, no pure trialkylgermanol has ever been prepared! (See Table IV).

In silanol chemistry the condensation equilibrium for typical compounds

TABLE IV

PHYSICAL CHARACTERISTICS OF SOME SELECTED SILANOLS, GERMANOLS, AND STANNOLS

	M.p. (°C)	B.p. (°C)	References		
			IR/R	NMR	Acidity
$(CH_3)_3SiOH$	−4.5° (*33*)	98.9° (*157*)	*110, 190, 191, 295, 425, 442*	*6, 327*	*238, 327, 413, 414, 442*
$(C_2H_5)_3SiOH$	—	63°/12 mm (*157*)	*442*	—	*188, 442*
$(C_6H_5)_3SiOH$	155° (*112*)	—	*442*	—	*33, 187, 193, 238, 441, 442*
$(C_6H_5)_3GeOH$	134.2° (*64, 141, 201, 443*)	—	*443*	—	*443*
$(C_6F_5)_3GeOH$	115°–117° (*125*)	—	—	—	
$(CH_3)_3SnOH$	118°–119° (*196, 200, 209, 231*)	subl. 80°	*192, 209, 261*	—	*206, 209*
$(C_2H_5)_3SnOH$	56° (*196*)	—	—	—	—
$(C_6H_5)_3SnOH$	119°–120° (*393, 443*)	—	*443*	—	*443*
$(C_6H_5)_3PbOH$	300°–310° (dec) (*443*)	—	*443*	—	*443*

lies completely to the right, whereas with stannols the opposite is true, if the product does not experience a further stabilization.

$$2\ R_3SiOH \rightleftharpoons R_3Si{-}O{-}SiR_3 + H_2O$$

$$2\ R_3GeOH \rightleftharpoons R_3Ge{-}O{-}GeR_3 + H_2O$$

$$2\ R_3SnOH \rightleftharpoons R_3Sn{-}O{-}SnR_3 + H_2O$$

This, however, is often warranted by intra- and intermolecular coordination phenomena. Possible transition states for the equilibria are represented by tentative formulas that enable us to account for the experimental observations.

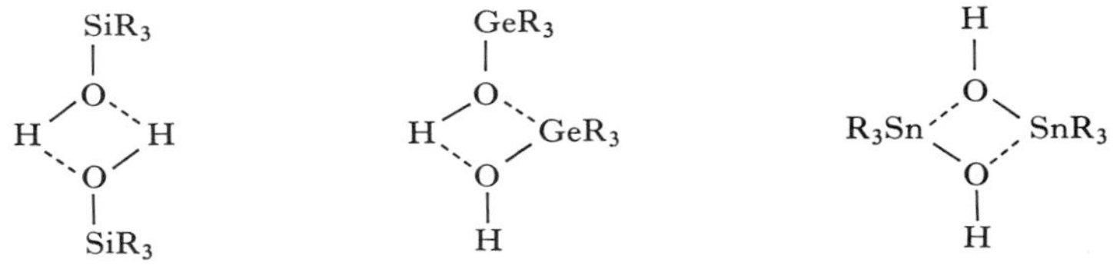

Of the various possible coordination interactions indicated by these formulas the one drawn for germanols is most illuminating. A structure of this type is likely to be the transition state for the dehydration of the hydroxy compounds or the hydration of the oxides (*327*).

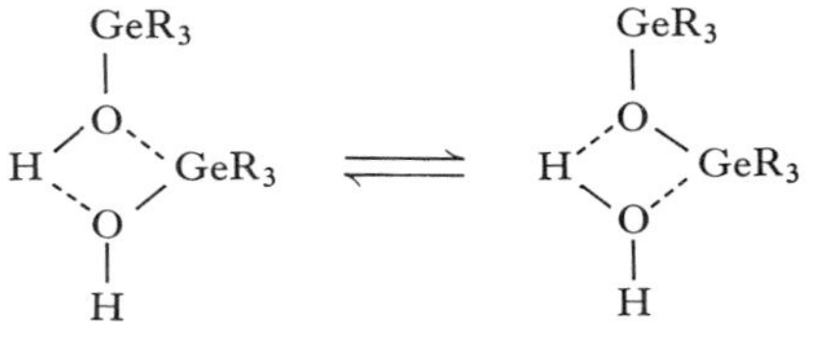

The reader again is referred to the formulas for the isoelectronic organometallic *fluorides*, in Section II,A, from which the validity of the isoelectronic principle obtains new support.

Table IV quotes physical properties of some selected silanols, germanols, and stannols.

2. *Metal and Organometal Silanolates*

Silanols form numerous classes of derivatives, some of which are of great interest both practically and theoretically. Only those derived from Groups I–IIIa metals will be described here, as these serve well for a comparative discussion and for the characterization of the coordinative properties of the silanolate anion R_3SiO^-, the isostere of the fluorosilane unit R_3SiF.

a. *Alkali Silanolates.* Silanolates have been prepared from all elements of the alkali group (*359*) and some of these are widely used in synthetic chemistry (*36*, *119*, *258*). These compounds appear to be oligomers of various molecular sizes in organic solvents and probably also in the solid state, though no structural details are available.[2] Some of them are volatile

TABLE V

ALKALI SILANOLATES, DOUBLE SILANOLATES, AND PHOSPHINE IMIDES

	M.p. (°C)	Subl. °C(mm)	IR ν(SiO) (cm^{-1})	References
$(CH_3)_3SiOLi$	120°	115°/1	948/966	*359, 397, 425*
$(CH_3)_3SiONa$	147°–150°	145°/1	941/975	*137, 176, 359, 414*
$(CH_3)_3SiOK$	135°	170°/1	980/990	*176, 359, 425*
$(CH_3)_3SiORb$	140°–150°	—	980/996	*359*
$(CH_3)_3SiOCs$	200°	—	986/1000	*359*
$[(CH_3)_3SiO]_2LiNa$	232°–235°	—	967/977	*383*
$[(CH_3)_3SiO]_2LiK$	258°–260°	—	945/1014	*383*
$[(CH_3)_3SiO]_2NaK$	235°–237°	—	984	*383*
$(CH_3)_2C_6H_5SiONa$	87°–94°	—	—	*176*
$CH_3(C_6H_5)_2SiONa$	—	—	—	*176*
$(C_6H_5)_3SiONa$	300°–350° (dec)	—	—	*176, 425*
$(CH_3)_3GeOLi$	—	—	—	*300, 397*
$(C_6H_5)_3GeONa$	250°	—	—	*201*
$(CH_3)_3SnOLi$	200° (dec)	—	—	*338*
$(CH_3)_3PNLi$	(dec)	—	—	*290, 343–345*
$(C_2H_5)_3PNLi$	134°–137°	—	—	*344*
$(C_6H_5)_3PNLi$	214°–219°	—	—	*344*
$(CH_3)_2(C_2H_5)PNLi$	—	—	—	*290*

in a vacuum, whereas others, as derived from rubidium or cesium, are not (Table V). From IR studies it was concluded that the Si—O bonds of the silanolates are changed considerably upon coordination interaction of the oxygen atoms with the metals (*268*, *359*, *425*). The Si—O stretching

[2] Very recent X-ray and mass spectroscopic work has now provided this information (439*a*).

frequencies are shifted to smaller values with increasing acceptor properties (i.e., polarizing properties) of the alkali metal, Cs → Li. As with analogous alkali carbinolates, a more or less saltlike description of bonding seems appropriate for the Rb and Cs derivatives. Well-defined alkali silanolates are also formed from mixtures of two different metal silanolates (*383*). These "double silanolates" exhibit spectroscopic characteristics intermediate between those of the pure parent silanolates. This result shows that mixed coordination interactions with both types of metals determine the nature of the Si—O bonds in the double silanolates. It clearly confirms the assumption that the siloxy anions serve as polyfunctional ligands in their alkali metal complexes, thus making use of at least two of the three oxygen "lone pairs" for chemical bonding. Unfortunately no structural details have been provided to date for alkali silanolates, but some analogies may be drawn from alkali carbinolates. For example, results of studies on alkali *tert*-butoxides, generally appear to support the above structural suggestions (*439*).[2]

b. *Silanolates of Boron, Aluminum, and Gallium.* No alkaline earth silanolates have been prepared, except for some somewhat ill-defined products containing beryllium or magnesium. (An *organo*beryllium compound will be discussed in a later section.) However, boron as well as aluminum and gallium form many siloxides, some of which have been studied in great detail.

Known for several years (*1, 54, 369, 457, 458*) and accessible by several synthetic routes, *boron-tris(trimethylsilanolate)* $[(CH_3)_3SiO]_3B$ is a suitable reference compound for our purposes. This compound is a *monomer* having three equivalent singly coordinate siloxide groups attached to boron. From IR and NMR studies it was suggested that the boron–oxygen bonds are stabilized by a $(p_B$–$p_O)\pi$ multiple bonding usually inferred for boron–oxygen compounds (*54*). This might lead to a change in the Si—O bond character, which may be assumed to possess its own $(d_{Si}$–$p_O)\pi$ system.

SiR_3
O
B — O — SiR_3
O
R_3Si

This σ/π separation, as in many other cases, is a crude treatment of the state of affairs, but it is at least in qualitative agreement with most observations, and the spectroscopic data pertinent to the Si—O bonds can be interpreted on these lines. Properties for some borosiloxane compounds appear in Table VI.

TABLE VI

SOME BORO-, ALUMINO-, AND GALLOSILOXANES, $(R_3SiO)_3M$; M = B, Al, Ga

	M.p. (°C)	B.p. (°C/torr)	Ref.	References	
				IR/R	NMR
$[(CH_3)_3SiO]_3B$	—	48°/5	(*369, 458*)	*1, 457*	*369*
		184.5°/776			
	35°	186°/760	(*54*)		
		84°/20	(*1*)		
$[(C_2H_5)_3SiO]_3B$	—	120°–130°/1	(*458*)	—	—
		178°–179°/13	(*458*)		
		139°–142°/2	(*458*)		
$[(C_6H_5)_3SiO]_3B$	150°	—	(*54*)	—	—
$\{[(CH_3)_3SiO]_3Al\}_2$	238°	155°/1 subl.	(*9, 242, 325, 369*)	*325, 369*	*322, 325, 369*
$\{[(C_2H_5)_3SiO]_3Al\}_2$	159°	—	(*10, 11, 30*)	*30*	—
$[(C_6H_5)_3SiO]_3Al$	485°	—	(*54, 205*)	—	—
$\{[(CH_3)_3SiO]_3Ga\}_2$	208°	135°/1	(*325, 369*)	*325, 369*	*322, 325, 369*

Tris(trimethylsiloxy)aluminum and -gallium, though belonging to the same analytical formula type, $(R_3SiO)_3M$, differ greatly from their boron analogs in being *dimers* with a more complicated structure. From NMR and IR studies (*30*, *322*, *369*, *457*) it was found that two types of siloxide ligands are present in these dimeric molecules, four of the six serving as terminal, the other two as bridging units.

Here again the siloxide groups prove their capability to function as polycoordinate ligands, which had not been anticipated (*8–11*). Si—O

```
                    SiR3
                     |
R3Si—O             O             O—SiR3
        >Al<            >Al<
R3Si—O             O             O—SiR3
                     |
                    SiR3
```

stretching absorptions are shifted towards longer wavelengths upon coordination, and the proton shielding in bridging siloxy groups is reduced, compared with findings for terminal groups.

X-Ray investigations (*51, 53*) on the *dihalogen aluminum compound* $[Br_2AlOSi(CH_3)_3]_2$ afforded a final proof for the structures proposed earlier (*342*) and gave further information on this metal–siloxide coordination interaction. The Si—O bonds were found to be somewhat lengthened, as expected from the above considerations, and the geometry of the oxygen ligands turned out to be *planar*. This result confirmed an observation of an earlier more qualitative X-ray study of a dialkylaluminumsiloxide analog (*323, 363, 371*), which had used the isomorphism of the unit cell, the space group, and striking similarities in the diffraction pattern as an indication of this molecular geometry (*446*). The isoelectronic and isomorphous silazane reference compound had been completely X-ray analyzed beforehand, and thus the pertinent conclusion was highly justified (*445*).

CH_3 Br Br
CH_3 Al CH_3
Si—O O—Si
CH_3 Al CH_3
Br Br CH_3

The planarity of the oxygen ligands was a most surprising feature of this structure (*100*). More recently, however, other examples of such an arrangement have been recognized and the alumosiloxanes have lost their exceptional position (*25, 52, 233*). It now would seem rather striking if they had *not* this trigonal planar arrangement of the oxonium moiety. In this they differ only from the corresponding sulfonium structures, which are reported to have a pyramidal, nonplanar geometry at sulfur (*34, 461*).

It seems unlikely then, that earlier suggestions ascribing the planar oxonium structure in aluminosiloxanes to the $(p_O \rightarrow d_{Si,Al})\pi$ effect (*100, 323, 363, 371, 445, 446*) are fully justified, as other examples with this geometry become known.

Initially it was the structural relation to the (planar) trisilylamines which had prompted this explanation. The trisilylamine structure is one of the few exceptions left that require explanation in terms of a *d*-orbital effect.[3] For oxonium structures this probably is no longer the case. The lengthening of bonds upon further coordination of an atom is also quite common in coordination chemistry and this phenomenon is therefore not restricted to possible *d*-orbital contribution (*246, 440*).

Mention should be made here of an isoelectronic species from the phosphine imide series (*390*) which will be the subject of a later section. *Dibromo-*

[3] See, however, a recent paper by Lehn, J. W., and Munsch, B., for a theoretical treatment [*Chem. Commun.* p. 994 (1970)].

aluminum-trimethylphosphinimide, $[Br_2AlNP(CH_3)_3]_2$, has also been shown to exist as a dimer. Spectroscopic characteristics are typical here for a two-coordinate phosphinimino group. The following structure has been assigned to the molecule.

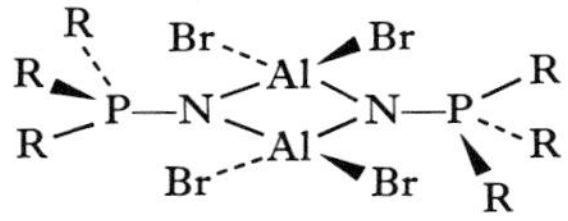

Though a detailed structure analysis has not yet been conducted, it is highly likely that this compound is isostructural with its siloxane analog. This then would be a further example (*233*, *343*, *403*) of a planar arrangement of ligands at a nitrogen atom which is not engaged in true $(p_N\text{–}p_X)\pi$ bonding, as in pyridine and its complexes.

Alkali phosphinimides $MNPR_3$, like alkali siloxides $MOSiR_3$ (*343*, *345*), are coordination oligomers or polymers, probably resembling their isosteres in having multicoordinate phosphinimino nitrogen atoms. Both classes of compounds are useful reactants in chemical synthesis. Some of the compounds known to date are also shown in Table V.

C. Amino Silanes, Germanes, and Stannanes

A discussion of the chemistry of silylamines, $R_3Si{—}NH_2$, is restricted by the limited information on the properties of these species. Some characteristic compounds among the few known to date are listed in Table VII.

TABLE VII

AMINOSILANES

	M.p. (°C)	References
$(C_2H_5)_3SiNH_2$	—	*219, 415*
$(C_3H_7)_3SiNH_2$	—	*218*
$(C_4H_9)_3SiNH_2$	—	*216*
$(C_6H_5)_3SiNH_2$	55°–56°	*202*

Attention should be drawn to the obvious nonexistence of aminotrimethylsilane, -germane, and -stannane. These compounds have been the goal of many synthetic attempts that have repeatedly failed to yield the desired products; in all cases only the products of a condensation reaction could be isolated.

D. Methyl Silanes and Related Compounds

It may seem to be arbitrary, not to say formalistic, to include methylsilyl compounds in the present discussion. Observations at the Si—CH_3 linkage have seldom caused theoretical difficulties and the principles of structure and bonding may be taken as understood on a preliminary basis. The same could be said about methylgermanyl, -stannyl, and even -plumbyl species; and, of course, of CH_3 groups bound to carbon. Nowhere in chemistry are the analogies with the principles of organic chemistry in the narrowest sense so pronounced as in alkyl silicon chemistry. What may be the properties then, that are of interest to us in our discussion of isosterism? Above other properties, it is the acid–base behavior of methyl groups bound to silicon and the reactivity in radical reactions.

1. *The Acidity of Methyl Silicon Compounds*

Recent experiments have shown that methylsilicon compounds may act as protic acids towards organoalkali reagents (*142*, *275*). Tetramethylsilane when treated with butyllithium in the presence of chelating amines is transformed into lithiomethyltrimethylsilane (*275*) with liberation of *n*-butane. Alkanes under similar conditions do *not* give this reaction and therefore the

$$RLi + (CH_3)_4Si \rightarrow RH + (CH_3)_3SiCH_2Li$$

silicon atom again allows the introduction of a negative charge in its vicinity, whereas carbon does not. This, however, is contrary to expectations from electronegativity considerations.

Possible explanations for this anomaly stem from a $(p \rightarrow d)\pi$ stabilization of the anion according to

$$(CH_3)_3Si—\overline{C}H_2^- \leftrightarrow (CH_3)_3\bar{Si}{=}CH_2$$

or from relief of electrostatic repulsions due to the increased Si—C distance when compared to C—C, and the better solvation or coordination by solvent or metal, due to lower steric strain in the silicon compound. In this latter argument we follow the thoughts presented for $(CH_3)_3SiF$, $(CH_3)_3SiO^-$, or $(CH_3)_3PCH_2$ (see below).

Other parallels are to be detected with the tetramethylphosphonium cation $(CH_3)_4P^+$ (*114*, *185*), which is more acidic than tetramethylammonium $(CH_3)_4N^+$, and with trialkylphosphineboranes $(CH_3)_3PBH_3$ (Section III, D).

2. *Silylmethyl Radicals, $R_3SiCH_2\cdot$*

ESR spectroscopy has recently been used to follow the reactions of *tert*-butoxy radicals with organometallics and to detect the radical species formed therein (*210*). In these studies silylmethyl radicals were detected as primary products of suprising stability. Thus, from tetramethylsilane the radical $(CH_3)_3SiCH_2\cdot$ was formed in a reasonable concentration, allowing its ESR spectrum to be recorded with an excellent signal-to-noise ratio. From $(CH_3)_4Ge$ and $(CH_3)_4Sn$ the corresponding radicals could also be obtained.

This formation of radicals $R_3MCH_2\cdot$ is quite noteworthy since the carbon analog neopentane $(CH_3)_4C$ did not afford an ESR spectrum of comparable quality under the same conditions. From this behavior it was deduced (*210*) that the presence of Si, Ge, and Sn either enhances the reactivity of the methyl groups toward hydrogen abstraction, or stabilizes the resultant radical. The latter is in accord with the known reluctance of α-silyl radicals to undergo rearrangement and can be attributed to stabilization of such species by $(p\rightarrow d)\pi$ electron delocalization.

III

ORGANOPHOSPHINE OXIDES, IMINES, METHYLENES, BORANES, AND RELATED COMPOUNDS

It is immediately obvious from the following columns of formulas that organophosphine oxides, imines, methylenes, and boranes are true isosteres of fluoro, hydroxy, amino, and methyl silanes. It therefore seems promising to turn to a comparative study of the most closely related species of this series. The chemistry of some of these compounds is well known and has previously been summarized. Where this is true, the discussion will be cut to a minimum to provide more space for more recent developments.

R_3PO	R_3SiF
R_3PNH	R_3SiOH
R_3PCH_2	R_3SiNH_2
R_3PBH_3	R_3SiCH_3

A. Phosphine Oxides, $R_3P{=}O$, and Related Compounds

1. *Physical Properties and Structure*

Trimethylphosphine oxide, a suitable model compound for our discussion, has been studied in considerable detail (*35, 148, 149*). It is a monomer in the gas phase and in solution, but is subject to *association* processes in the melt and in the solid (*99*). This is obvious from IR results published by Goubeau *et al.* (*35, 148, 149*) and later investigators (*3, 4, 98, 99, 108, 109, 124, 138*). The findings are of relevance for the description of bonding in this molecule, usually given by the following resonance forms:

$$R_3\overset{+}{P}{-}\overline{\underline{O}}|^- \leftrightarrow R_3P{=}\overline{\underline{O}}$$

The latter of these implies $(p\rightarrow d)\pi$ bonding. The dipolar ylidic formula accounts better for the high melting point, the low volatility, and the tendency (of many phosphine oxides) to associate.

P—O bond distances and energies known for some homologs (*58–60, 98, 99, 224*) have to be interpreted on the basis of polar bond contributions to the underlying σ-bonding, if the π-bonding concept is to be ignored or rejected. It is, in fact, possible to rationalize the experimental values on an electrostatic basis alone (*162, 454*), as was the case with the fluorosilanes in the silicon series (*270*).

The bond order obtained from *infrared studies* on trimethylphosphine oxide is 1.96, as calculated from a force constant of 9.19 mdyne/A (*35*). This value is perhaps higher than expected for a merely semipolar double bond, but the basis to start from in theoretical calculations, that is, the P—O single bond, is not well enough defined in phosphorus chemistry generally.

NMR data for trimethylphosphine oxide (*166*) do not differ significantly from what is observed for tetramethylphosphonium salts in the same solvent, as far as the shielding of the hydrogen and phosphorus nuclei and their coupling constants $J(^1H^{13}C)$ and $J(^1HC^{31}P)$ are concerned (*160, 314*). From this result it may be concluded that the state of bonding of the hydrogen and phosphorus atoms does ***not*** differ significantly in these species. The same is true for other homologs. The phosphorus and carbon atoms may then be taken as sp^3-hybridized, as suggested from the geometry found in *X-ray work* (*99, 224*). Dipole moments for trimethylphosphine oxide have invariably been found to be as high as 4.35 D (*27, 144*). In this it differs little from trimethyl*amine* oxide and trimethyl*arsine* oxide. A detailed evaluation, of course, is difficult.

Trimethylamine oxide and its homologs in principle do not present the "π-problem," as the ylenic formula is excluded by the octet rule. The

TABLE VIII

STRUCTURAL CHARACTERISTICS OF TRIORGANOAMINE-, -PHOSPHINE, -ARSINE, AND -STIBINE OXIDES

	d(MO) (Å)	References for IR/R/NMR	References for Dipole moment
$(CH_3)_3NO$	1.388(X-ray) (*86*) 1.36 (ED) (*139*)	*175, 225*	*27, 144*
$(CH_3)_3NO \cdot M$		*175*	—
$(CH_3)_3PO$	1.48 (*99*)	*4, 35, 98, 99, 138, 148, 149, 166, 175*	*27, 144*
$[(CH_3)_3PO]_2ZnI_2$	—	*98*	—
$[(CH_3)_3PO]_2CoCl_2$	—	*98*	—
$[(CH_3)_3PO]_2Co(NO_3)_2$	1.540 (*99*)	*98*	—
$[(CH_3)_3PO]_2UCl_2$	—	*138*	—
$(C_6H_5)_3PO$	—	*162*	—
$(C_6H_5)_3PO \cdot Fe[S_2C_2(CF_3)_2]_2^-$	— (*123*)	—	—
$[(C_6H_5)_3PO]_4Cu_4OCl_6$	— (*42*)	—	—
$[(C_6H_5)_3PO]_5LiI$	1.465 (*82*)	—	—
$(C_6H_5)_3PO \cdot M$	—	*95*	—
R_3AsO	—	*95, 243*	*27, 144*
$[(CH_3)_3AsO]_5Ni^{2+}$	— (*174*)	—	—
$[(C_6H_5)_3AsO \cdot H_2O]_2$	1.644 (*126*)	*163*	*184*
$[(C_6H_5)_2CH_3AsO]_4Co^{3+}$	— (*272*)	—	—
$[(C_6H_5)_3AsO]HgCl_2$	1.66 (*58–60*)	—	—
$(CH_3)_3SbO$	—	*358*	—
$(C_6H_5)_3SbO$	—	*92, 335, 429*	—

reduced thermal and chemical stability of the amine oxides may thus be simply related to the lack of such an ylenic resonance form. On the other hand relative instability of N—O bonds, as in hydroxylamines, is by no means uncommon and is usually attributed to lone-pair versus bond-pair or lone-pair repulsions. These repulsive interactions should also be of significance in the amine oxides, of course. They should be reduced, however, in the phosphine oxides, and thus we may perhaps again ignore any *d*-orbital contributions in the latter. Similar arguments may be inferred for the pairs R_3CF/R_3SiF, where the relatively high Si—F bond energies give rise to similar speculative considerations. The NO *bond distance* found for trimethylamine oxide (*86*) in *single-crystal X-ray* work is not appreciably shorter than other so-called "true" NO single bonds. It is interesting to note the data reported on the *1:1 addition compound* of trimethylamine oxide with hydrogen chloride (*85, 294*). In this adduct the NO bond distance is increased by 0.36 Å, indicating that the NO bond order is lowered considerably upon protonation, probably even below unity. (Phosphine oxides do not form HCl adducts of comparable stability.)

TABLE IX

PHYSICAL PROPERTIES OF TRIMETHYLAMINE, -PHOSPHINE, -ARSINE, AND -STIBINE OXIDES

	M.p. (°C)	Subl. (°C/torr)	References
$(CH_3)_3NO$	213°–214°	180°–200°/15 (subl.)	*249*
$(CH_3)_3PO$	141.5°	b.p. 216.5 (extrap.)	*148, 149*
$(CH_3)_3AsO$	191.2°–195.2°	—	*243*
$(CH_3)_3SbO$	297°–280° (dec)	150°/1	*358*

Trimethylamine oxide molecules are not associated in the solid, but the molecular dipoles are oriented in a common direction. The reluctance of nitrogen atoms to increase their coordination number beyond four in this case precludes a true intermolecular coordination interaction. Table VIII gives structural details for some trialkylphosphine and amine oxides and quotes literature on the application of other physical methods to these compounds (*27, 139, 144, 225*). Some physical properties of selected members of the series are summarized in Table IX.

Trialkylarsine oxides have been investigated only very recently (*243*), but some work on *trialkylstibine oxides* has shown interesting parallels to the isoelectronic fluorostannane series: $(CH_3)_3SnF/(CH_3)_3SbO$. All results (*92, 174, 224, 272, 314, 335, 358, 364, 429*) lead to the conclusion that compounds like trimethylstibine oxide are coordination polymers, in which oxygen atoms form bridges between trimethylantimony groups. Only in solvents of high donor strength, like dimethyl sulfoxide, are these compounds soluble (as monomers). In solution the antimony atoms probably are not four-coordinate, but increase their coordination number through addition of solvent molecules. The same should be true for the tin atoms in fluorostannanes.

CH_3
—O Sb CH_3 CH_3 Sb O Sb CH_3 CH_3 Sb
CH_3 O CH_3 CH_3 O CH_3
CH_3 CH_3 CH_3

Higher coordination numbers at antimony in a similar state of bonding are well documented. Trialkylantimony alkoxides and siloxides are all molecular compounds with five-coordinate antimony atoms, two of the ligands being oxygen atoms (*335*, *358*). The triorganoarsenic oxides seem to be in an intermediate position between the phosphorus and antimony extremes, as were the fluorogermane isosteres in the fluoride series R_3MF.

2. *Coordination Compounds*

Of the chemical reactivities of phosphine oxides the donor properties are of special interest. As expected from the dipolar ylidic formula these compounds are very powerful donor molecules, which form numerous complexes with various kinds of Lewis acids (*98*, *99*, *224*). Fluorosilanes, as explained above, are much poorer donors, though some examples are known.

The coordination compounds of phosphine oxides with metal alkyls of the Group IIIb elements (*314*, *316*, *364*) are truly isoelectronic with the disiloxanes, and so are of particular interest. Compounds of the type $R_3\overset{+}{P}—O—\overset{-}{Al}R_3$ are obtained quite readily from the formula components, R_3PO and R_3Al, in 1:1 ratio (*260*, *314*, *316*, *364*). The products show surprising thermal stability. In this they differ markedly from the complexes of amine oxides as well as from those of phosphine oxides with other organometallics, such as R_3B, Ga, and In. Though phosphine oxides would be expected to be reduced by the strongly reducing metal alkyls, no redox reaction takes place up to about 200°C. Under similar conditions amine and phosphine oxides are reduced by boron alkyls with formation of amine or phosphine (*198*, *199*).

The compounds R_3POAlR_3 are monomers in solution and may be sublimed in a vacuum. The dipolar formula

$$R_3\overset{+}{P}—\overline{\underline{O}}—\overset{-}{Al}R_3$$

is proposed as a description of the bonding in these molecules (*260, 314, 316, 364*). The corresponding amine oxide–borane complexes are supposed to belong to a similar type:

$$R_3\overset{+}{N}—\overline{\underline{O}}—\overset{-}{B}R_3$$

In this formula, however, due to shorter bond distances NOB, repulsive interactions with nonbonding lone pairs should weaken the bonding interactions leading to the lower overall stability which is observed (*199*).

Bond distances and angles in the aluminophosphoxanes are not yet known, but there is good reason to believe that they are similar to those in their isoelectronics, the disiloxanes.

Structural details are known for several other phosphine oxide complexes (*58–60, 82, 99, 123, 224*). With one exception (*42*) all of those show a geometry *bent at oxygen* with the expected *d*(PO) bond, lengthened upon

TABLE X

METALALKYL COMPLEXES OF AMINE, PHOSPHINE, AND ARSINE OXIDES

	M.p. (°C)	B.p. (°C/1 torr)	References
$(CH_3)_3NOAl(CH_3)_3$	102°	142°	*314*
$(CH_3)_3NOGa(CH_3)_3$	77°	120°	*314*
$(CH_3)_3NOIn(CH_3)_3$	66°	124°	*314*
$(CH_3)_3POAl(CH_3)_3$[a]	89°	117°	*260, 314, 316, 364*
$(CH_3)_3POGa(CH_3)_3$	19°	95°	*314*
$(CH_3)_3POIn(CH_3)_3$	34°	88°	*314*
$(CH_3)_3POAl(C_2H_5)_3$	−23°	121°	*316, 364*
$(C_2H_5)_3POAl(CH_3)_3$	7°	123°	*316, 364*
$(C_2H_5)_3POAl(C_2H_5)_3$	−13°	142°	*316, 364*
$(C_6H_5)_3POAl(CH_3)_3$[b]	—	—	*260*
$(CH_3)_3AsOGa(CH_3)_3$	+54°	dec	*316*

[a] $\Delta H_f = -32$ kcal/mole (*260*).
[b] $\Delta H_f = -28.7$ kcal/mole (*260*).

coordination. One example taken from the literature (*224*) is depicted in the following figure:

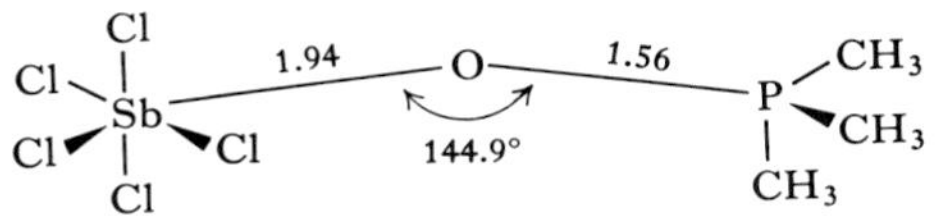

$$Cl_4Sb(Cl)\overset{1.94}{—}O\overset{1.56}{—}P(CH_3)_3 \qquad \angle Sb\text{–}O\text{–}P = 144.9^\circ$$

Similar structural characteristics are to be expected for the metal alkyl complexes of phosphine oxides.

Arsine oxides are also known to form many coordination compounds (*95, 126, 174, 243, 272*), but little information is available about complexes with simple organometallics. 1:1-Complexes with aluminum and gallium alkyls have recently been obtained and characterized (Table X) (*316*). No special features were evident from the properties reported. Recent X-ray work on metal complexes of *trimethylarsine oxide* provided values for bond distances and angles, which give a rough idea of what is to be expected from the metal alkyl complexes (*126, 174, 272*). In all cases the triatomic bridge M—O—As was *bent* at oxygen.

B. Phosphine Imines, $R_3P{=}NH$, and Related Compounds

1. *General Properties*

Phosphine imines are isoelectronic to silanols: R_3PNH/R_3SiOH. Though many derivatives of the former have been known for some time, it was not until the early sixties that the basic members of the series were obtained.

Various methods of preparation are now available (*16–18, 23, 45, 46, 290, 291, 310, 343, 345, 408*), the most useful of which are the deprotonation

$$(CH_3)_3P + 2\,HN_3 \rightarrow N_2 + [(CH_3)_3PNH_2]N_3$$

$$\downarrow Na[NH_3]$$

$$NaN_3 + \tfrac{1}{2}\,H_2 + (CH_3)_3\overset{+}{P}—\overset{-}{\underline{\overline{N}}}H$$

of aminophosphonium salts (*16–18, 290, 291*) and the desilylation of silyl phosphinimines (*45, 46, 343, 345*). The former has been used for the synthesis of the parent compound. The triorganophosphine imines are surprisingly stable, in marked contrast to the corresponding *amine imines* $R_3\overset{+}{N}—\overset{-}{N}H$, which are nonexistent in the absence of complexing agents (*20*).

Arsine and stibine imines, $R_3\overset{+}{As}—\underline{\overline{N}}H$ and $R_3\overset{+}{Sb}—\underline{\overline{N}}H$, are less stable than the phosphine imines, too, but some representatives bearing aryl substituents at arsenic and antimony have been isolated and characterized (*12, 13, 24, 308*).

Several groups of workers have been engaged in the studies of the nature of the P—N bond in phosphine imines and their derivatives. From *infrared* studies (*290, 345*) a rough estimate of the bond order was derived for a number of examples (Table XI). *NMR data* are also available for some of

TABLE XI

PHYSICAL PROPERTIES OF SOME PHOSPHINIMINES AND RELATED COMPOUNDS

	M.p. (°C)	B.p. (°C/torr)	References	
			IR/R	NMR
$(CH_3)_3NNH$	— (*20*)	— (*20*)	—	—
$(CH_3)_3PNH$	59°–60° (*343*)	216.5 (*345*)	— (*343, 345*)	— (*343, 345*)
$(C_2H_5)_3PNH$	—	94°/11 (*45*)	—	— (*344, 345*)
$(C_6H_5)_3PNH$	127.5° (*18, 46*)	—	— (*50, 452*)	—
$CH_3[(CH_3)_3C]_2AsNH$	— (*310*)	—	— (*310*)	— (*310*)
$(C_6H_5)_3AsNH$	130°–132° (*24*)	—	—	—
$(C_6H_5)_3SbNH$	— (*12, 13*)	—	—	—
$(C_6H_5)_3PNC_6H_5$	131°–133° (*172*)	—	— (*172, 452, 453*)	—

the phosphine imines (*291, 310, 345*). Investigations concerning organic derivatives, R_3PNR', will be summarized in Section 3 (*50, 78–81, 172, 248, 395, 452, 453*).

2. *Coordination Compounds*

The NH protons of phosphine imines may be replaced by metal atoms to form metal phosphine imides. Among these the alkali derivatives (*290, 291, 345*) are of high synthetic value, reminiscent of the important role of the isoelectronic silanolates in organolsilicon synthesis. Lithium trialkyl-

$$R_3PN^-Li^+ \qquad R_3SiO^-Li^+$$

phosphine imides are soluble and highly associated in nonpolar organic solvents (*290, 345*). Clearly the compounds are coordination oligomers similar to the silanolates. For the same reason some of the compounds are volatile in a good vacuum. The phosphinimido groups seem to function as polydentate ligands to the lithium atoms (Table V).

From other coordination compounds it is now well known that phosphinimide and silanolate anions are polyfunctional ligands, able to function as bridging units between as many as three metal atoms (*343–345*). Among these compounds the zinc, cadmium, and mercury derivatives are most illuminating and shall serve as initial examples. Ring-shaped species will be dealt with in later sections.

a. *Organo Zinc, Cadmium, Mercury, and Beryllium Derivatives of Silanols and Phosphine Imines.* Several years ago it was found that the zinc and cadmium dialkyls undergo a smooth reaction with trialkyl and triaryl silanols (*317*), leading to alkylmetal triorganosilanolates.

$$4(CH_3)_2Zn + 4(CH_3)_3SiOH \rightarrow 4CH_4 + [CH_3ZnOSi(CH_3)_3]_4$$

Mercury compounds of the same composition are obtained from the reaction of an alkali silanolate and an alkylmercury halide (*146*, *317*, *337*, *362*), e.g.,

$$4CH_3HgCl + 4NaOSi(CH_3)_3 \rightarrow 4NaCl + [CH_3HgOSi(CH_3)_3]_4$$

The products containing *zinc* or *cadmium* as a heteroatom form tetrameric molecules in the solid, in solution, and probably also in the vapor phase. The *mercuri*siloxanes, which are tetramers in the solid state as well (*113*), are degraded by solvation when dissolved in an organic solvent, showing molecular weights almost as low as the monomer (*337*).

Results of IR and NMR spectroscopic data (*317*, *337*, *362*) and from an X-ray structure investigation of single crystals of the mercury compound (*113*) show that the tetrameric alkylmetal silanolates form molecular units with a cubic structure. This is in agreement with findings for organozinc alkoxides, which are also known (*402*) to have cubic structures.

The metal atoms as well as the oxygen atoms form interpenetrating tetrahedra so that the siloxy oxygen atoms are *tetra*-coordinate. Thus all the lone pairs of electrons at the oxygen atoms are now engaged in direct bonding to metal atoms. In spite of this the bond distances d(SiO) are not markedly increased compared with those found in siloxy compounds with divalent oxygen atoms. This is confirmed by recent X-ray work on a beryllasiloxane (*250*), which was prepared by the same methods as the zinc and cadmium analogs. Here again this principle of structure is verified (Table XII) (Fig. 3B,C).

TABLE XII

ORGANOMETAL(II) SILANOLATES AND PHOSPHINIMIDES

	M.p. (°C)	Subl. (°C/torr)	References
$[CH_3BeOSi(CH_3)_3]_4$	—	—	*250*
$[CH_3ZnOSi(CH_3)_3]_4$	150°(dec)	125°/1	*317*
$[CH_3ZnOSi(C_2H_5)_3]_4$	155°–158°	—	*345*
$[CH_3CdOSi(CH_3)_3]_4$	145°(dec)	135°/1	*317*
$[CH_3ZnNP(CH_3)_3]_4$	350°(dec)	$240°/10^{-1}$	*345*
$[CH_3ZnNP(C_2H_5)_3]_4$	292°	—	*345*
$[CH_3CdNP(CH_3)_3]_4$	230°(dec)	$180°/10^{-2}$	*345*
$[CH_3CdNP(C_2H_5)_3]_4$	214°–218°	—	*345*
$[CH_3HgOSi(CH_3)_3]_4$	52°	50°/1	*113, 337*
$C_6H_5HgOSi(C_6H_5)_3$	—	—	*146*

The stability of the compounds described and some of their spectroscopic features point to the fact that an Si—O bond with "totally fixed" oxygen lone pairs is not entirely different from a group found in heterosiloxanes with no extra coordination at oxygen. This makes the significance of π-interactions in the latter somewhat doubtful. Similar conclusions had

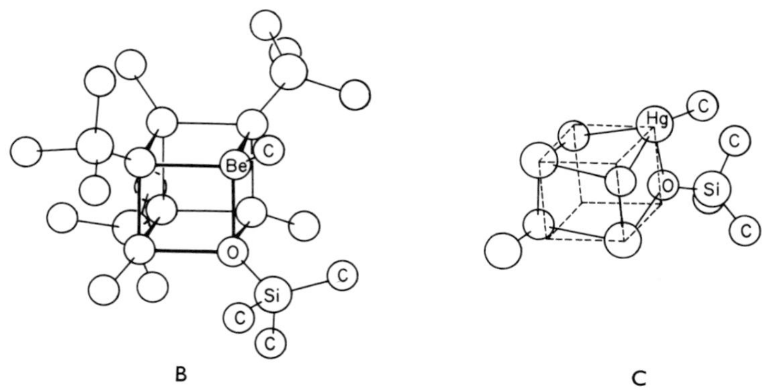

FIG. 3B,C. Molecular structures of tetramethylberylla- and tetramethylmercurasiloxane, as determined by X-ray diffraction (*113*, *250*). The mercury compound is distorted significantly from the regular cubic arrangement.

earlier been drawn from NMR spectra of aluminosiloxane compounds (*330*, *333*), though not unequivocally.

On the grounds of the isoelectric principle it was to be expected that *phosphinimide derivatives of Group II metals* should exhibit properties similar to those of the siloxane analogs. This expectation (*332*, *333*) has so far been verified by work on the alkyl*zinc* and alkyl*cadmium* trialkyl- and triarylphosphinimides, which could be synthesized (*343*, *345*) using exactly the same preparative procedures.

$$4(CH_3)_2Cd + 4(CH_3)_3PNH \rightarrow 4CH_4 + [CH_3CdNP(CH_3)_3]_4$$

$$4CH_3ZnCl + 4(CH_3)_3PNLi \rightarrow 4LiCl + [CH_3ZnNP(CH_3)_3]_4$$

These compounds again appear as tetrameric units in solution forming colorless crystals isomorphous with those of the heterosiloxane species. From these and some spectroscopic results it appears that the alkylmetal(II)-triorganophosphinimides also form cubic type molecules as represented by the following figure (Table XII):

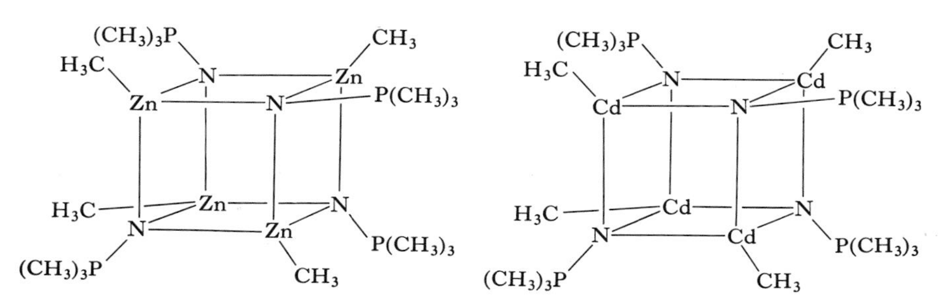

In these molecules the nitrogen atoms share their three lone pairs of electrons with three neighboring metal atoms. Such an interaction is, of course, only possible if the polar ylidic formula $R_3P—\overline{\underline{N}}|—$ is accepted for the R_3PN units. It is this form which is likely to contribute most to the ground state of the phosphine imines themselves as well.

$$R_3\overset{+}{P}—\overset{-}{\underline{\overline{N}}}H \leftrightarrow R_3P{=}\overline{N}H$$

b. *Phosphine Imine–Metal Alkyl Complexes.* A second type of phosphine imine complex is of interest: the adducts of Group IIIb metal alkyls (*23*, *343*). These addition compounds have the formula $R_3\overset{+}{P}—NH—\overset{-}{Al}R'_3$, which now clearly implies an isoelectronic relationship to the *disilazanes* $R_3Si—NH—SiR_3$. Compounds of this type have been obtained from carefully controlled reactions of metal alkyls with trialkylphosphine imines at low temperature (*345*). The temperature range of existence is limited

$$2\,(CH_3)_3PNH + [Al(CH_3)_3]_2 \rightarrow 2\,(CH_3)_3\overset{+}{P}—NH—\overset{-}{Al}(CH_3)_3$$

for these compounds; slightly above room temperature an irreversible decomposition reaction takes place. With evolution of alkane R′H (CH_4 in our particular example) dimerization products of the composition $[R_3PNAlR'_2]_2$ are formed (Section IX,C). At lower temperatures the substances are sufficiently stable to allow a study of their properties (Table XIII).

TABLE XIII

METAL ALKYL COMPLEXES OF PHOSPHINE IMINES

	M.p. (°C)	References
$(C_6H_5)_3PNHB(C_6H_5)_3$	—	*23*
$(CH_3)_3PNHAl(CH_3)_3$	44°–46°(dec)	*345*
$(C_2H_5)_3PNHAl(CH_3)_3$	28°–30°(dec)	*345*
$(C_2H_5)_3PNHAl(C_2H_5)_3$	—	*345*
$(C_2H_5)_3PNHGa(CH_3)_3$	15°–17°(dec)	*345*
$(C_2H_5)_3PNHIn(CH_3)_3$	12°–15°(dec)	*345*

Analogous addition compounds of metal alkyls with *silanols* have so far not been described. These species are decomposed at even lower temperatures, and their dimerization products are obtained from attempted synthesis under comparable conditions. (See Section IX,B). Undoubtedly it

$$2\ R_3SiOH + [AlR_3']_2 \rightarrow 2\ R_3Si{-}\overset{+}{\overline{\underset{\underset{H}{|}}{O}}}{-}\overset{-}{Al}R_3'$$

$$\xrightarrow{\text{Heat}}\ 2\ R'H + [R_3SiOAlR_2']_2$$

is the higher acidity of the silanol protons in the addition compounds, containing a positive charge at oxygen, which promotes the reaction with the (carbanionic) aluminum ligands to form the alkane. Thus the proton is expelled from the oxonium center of the molecules.

Similar observations have been made with the gallium and indium alkyl complexes of the phosphine imines and silanols (Table XIII).

3. *Structural Characteristics of Organic Derivatives*

It has been pointed out that little structural information is available on phosphine imines R_3PNH. Some organic derivatives have been studied in greater detail, however, and some of these results are briefly added here to give an idea of what is to be expected for the imines themselves (*78–82*).

Two phosphine imine derivatives were subjects of very recent X-ray structural investigations (*78–81*):

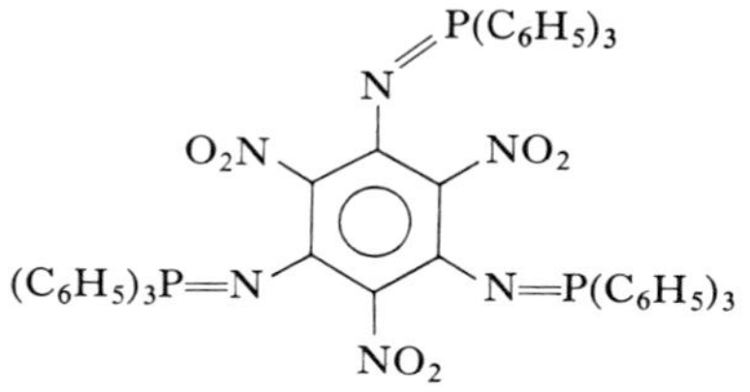

$P(C_6H_5)_3$ N O_2N NO_2 $(C_6H_5)_3P{=}N$ $N{=}P(C_6H_5)_3$ NO_2

(I)

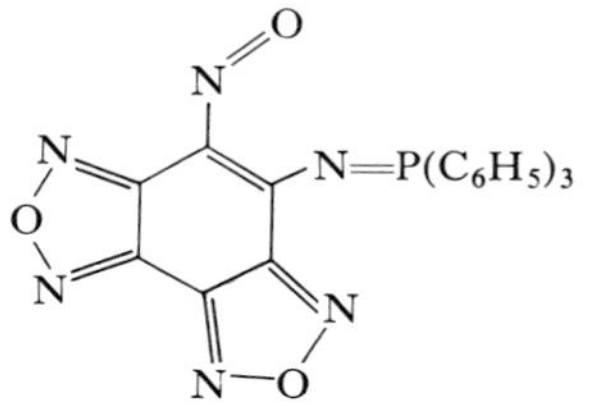

O N N O N $N{=}P(C_6H_5)_3$ N N—O

(II)

In both cases triphenylphosphinimino groups are bonded to an aromatic system. The P=C distances observed are 1.535, 1.585, and 1.553 Å for (I), and 1.63 Å for (II). The C–N=P bond angles were found to be 140°, 137°, and 134° for (I), and 130° for (II). Thus all the CNP systems are bent at nitrogen, as expected, with bond angles of 130°–140°. This is quite similar to what is found in the siloxane compounds, and even the bond distances are of comparable length. A most recent X-ray work on $(C_6H_5)_2FP{=}NCH_3$ gave d(PN) 1.64 Å and ∢ PNC 119° (*1a*).

In all cases the distances and angles are taken from open, noncyclic configurations and may thus be taken as characteristic for this class of compounds, as no ring size and configuration problems are included. The short distances P=C are supposed to originate from $(p{\rightarrow}d)\pi$ interactions, though this assumption is not entirely compulsory. Theoretical calculations by *Schuster* (*395*) seem to support the $(p{\rightarrow}d)\pi$ arguments, as quite reasonable figures have been obtained for the electronic system in triphenylphosphine phenylimide, $(C_6H_5)_3P{=}NC_6H_5$.

C. *Phosphine Methylenes, $R_3P{=}CH_2$, and Related Compounds*

Organophosphine alkylenes, "phosphorus ylids" in the classical sense, though chemically quite different, are yet closely related to phosphine imines and oxides as well as to silyl amines, hydroxides, and fluorides:

R_3SiF	R_3PO
R_3SiOH	R_3PNH
R_3SiNH_2	R_3PCH_2
R_3SiCH_3	R_3PBH_3

It is hardly necessary to mention that these species are of high preparative value to organic chemists and that their chemical reactions have been studied quite extensively (*185*). It was not until recently, however, that information became available on the state of structure and bonding in these molecules, particularly that of the functional group, usually referred to as the "ylidic" function.

A pair of resonance forms, originally proposed by Wittig, has long been in use (*185*) to describe the bonding in ylids. Therefore the "ylid problem"

$$R_3\overset{+}{P}—\overset{-}{\underline{C}}H_2 \leftrightarrow R_3P{=}CH_2$$

does not differ at all from that encountered with the molecules discussed earlier. For many years only very few of the simple ylid species were ever obtained pure and so structural studies were extremely difficult. New methods of preparation derived from organometallic chemistry of phosphorus ylids have now made available even the basic members of the series. The overwhelming amount of information from studies of chemical reactivity of ylids (*185*) can therefore now be related to physical data.

1. *Synthesis and Physical Properties*

The simple ylids necessary for structural work were first obtained from *desilylation* reactions of silylated phosphine alkylenes (*376, 377, 379*). This procedure yields the compounds free of by-products which could form undesired coordination compounds. [Eq. (1)]. The latter was not the case in the classical method of preparation from phosphonium salts, whereby highly stable salt adducts are produced; often it then was not possible to remove the ylids from the salt component [Eq. (2)]. The idea for conduct-

$$R_3P{=}CH—SiR'_3 + R'_3SiOH \rightarrow R_3P{=}CH_2 + R'_3SiOSiR'_3 \quad (1)$$

$$[R_3PCH_3]X + LiR' \rightarrow R_3PCH_2 \cdot LiX + R'H \quad (2)$$

ing the preparation according to Eq. (1) is basically the same as in the synthesis of phosphine *imines* from their silyl derivatives (*45, 46*). Both procedures make use of the high tendency of formation of the siloxane linkage to shift the equilibria completely to the right. The inert siloxane by-product causes no further trouble in the separation of the ylids from the reaction mixtures.

TABLE XIV

PHYSICAL PROPERTIES OF PHOSPHORUS AND ARSENIC YLIDS

	M.p. (°C)	B.p. °C/torr	References
$(CH_3)_3PCH_2$	13°–14°	118°–120°	*377*
$C_2H_5(CH_3)_2PCH_2$	(−16°)–(−14°)	143°–145°	*377*
$(C_2H_5)_2CH_3PCH_2$	(−45°)–(−43°)	60°–62°/12	*377*
$(C_2H_5)_3PCH_2$	(−17°)–(−15°)	80°–83°/12	*377*
$(C_2H_5)_3PCHCH_3$	(−38°)–(−36°)	86°–87°/12	*377*
$(C_4H_9)_3PCH_2$	—	$89°/10^{-2}$	*357*
$(C_6H_5)_3PCH_2$	—	—	*31, 375*
$(CH_3)_3AsCH_2$	33°–35°	30°–35°/1[a]	*381*

[a] Sublimes.

Only in cases where steric hindrance or resonance stabilization precludes strong interactions of the ylids with the metal salts can the desilylation procedure be circumvented (*185*). The ylids prepared by these methods are surprisingly stable being crystalline at lower temperatures and distillable without decomposition (*376*, *377*, *379*). There is evidence that the compounds are monomers in the solid, in solution, and in the gas phase.

The same synthetic procedures can be used for simple *arsenic ylids* (*381*), such as $(CH_3)_3AsCH_2$ (Table XIV). These ylids are of limited stability, but can nevertheless be isolated and characterized. No *trialkylantimony ylids* have been prepared.

Suitable experiments have shown that the ylidic function of phosphorus ylids is *de*stabilized by the inductive effect of alkyl groups at the carbanion (*354*, *355*, *376*, *377*, *379*). Therefore an ylid of the formula (III) cannot

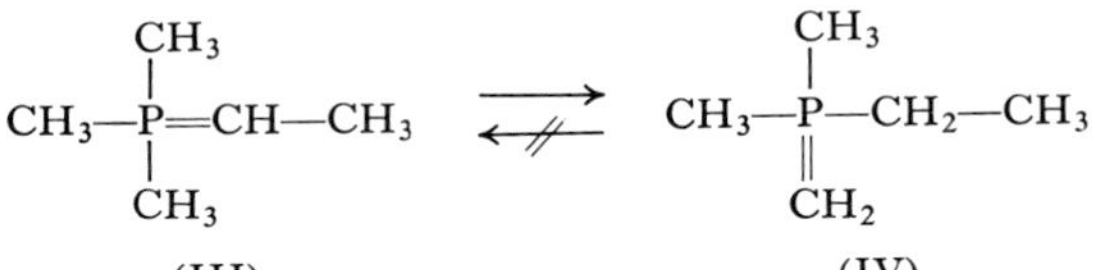

$$(CH_3)_3P{=}CH{-}CH_3 \;\; \underset{\not\leftarrow}{\rightarrow} \;\; (CH_3)_2(CH_2{=})P{-}CH_2{-}CH_3$$

(III) (IV)

$$(CH_3)_3P{=}C(CH_3)_2 \;\; \underset{\not\leftarrow}{\rightarrow} \;\; (CH_3)_2(CH_2{=})P{-}CH(CH_3)_2$$

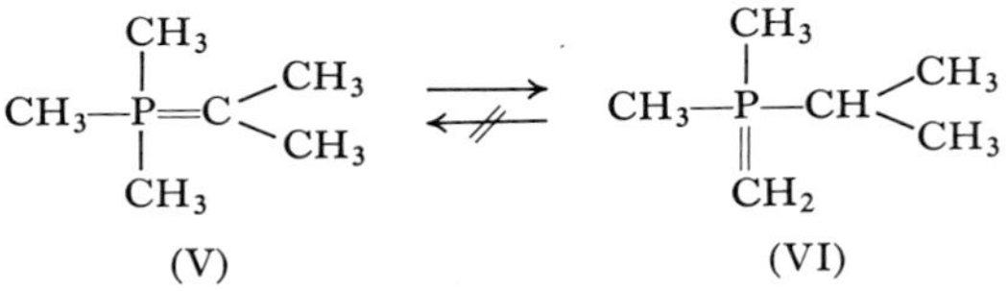

(V) (VI)

be prepared, as the isomer (IV) is highly favored energetically. As will be shown in the following section, the rearrangements (III) → (IV) are—if energetically feasible—so easily accomplished that the attempted preparation of (III) is immediately followed by isomerization. A 1,3-proton shift is sufficient to account for an isomerization of this type. Many experiments have demonstrated that proton exchange processes are quite common in ylid chemistry (*376, 378*) [e.g., (V) → (VI)].

2. *Proton Exchange Phenomena*

Mobility of protons in an α-position to the phosphorus atom in ylids (*376, 378*) was quickly recognized as soon as pure simple compounds were available. The PMR spectrum of trimethylphosphinemethylene shows, for instance, that proton exchange phenomena are involved (*378*) (Fig. 4).

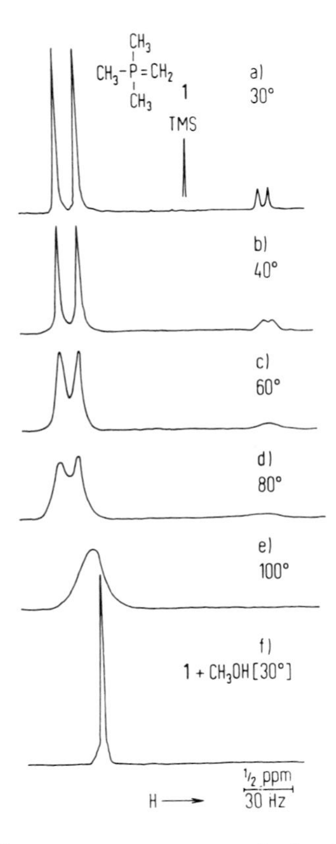

FIG. 4. Proton magnetic resonance spectrum of trimethylphosphinemethylene as a function of temperature, a–e, and catalyst, f. (*378*)

From the temperature dependence of the spectra of these and several other (*43, 44, 104*) molecules it was deduced that the carbanionic function of ylids often is not localized at only one site, but is subject to a relatively fast exchange process (*44, 104*). After initial discrepancies there is now general agreement on this. For $(CH_3)_3PCH_2$ this may be represented as follows:

$$\begin{array}{c} CH_3 \\ | \\ CH_3-P=CH_2 \\ | \\ CH_3 \end{array} \rightleftharpoons \begin{array}{c} CH_3 \\ | \\ CH_3-P-CH_3 \\ \| \\ CH_2 \end{array} \rightleftharpoons \begin{array}{c} CH_3 \\ | \\ CH_2=P-CH_3 \\ | \\ CH_3 \end{array} \rightleftharpoons \begin{array}{c} CH_2 \\ \| \\ CH_3-P-CH_3 \\ | \\ CH_3 \end{array}$$

The activation energy for this process amounts to about 18–20 kcal/mole in the absence of (detectable) impurities of a protic catalyst. It is lowered considerably, however, if traces of an acid are present. Under these conditions the exchange process is clearly *inter*molecular, whereas in the uncatalyzed version an *intra*molecular proton transfer is also possible.[4]

Though requiring higher activation energies, ylids with longer alkyl groups behave similarly (*378*). The same is true for the arsenic ylid (*381*) $(CH_3)_3AsCH_2$, the sulfur ylid (*382*) $(CH_3)_2SOCH_2$, and others. It appears that in ylid chemistry this phenomenon is a general one (*288, 289*).

It should be noted here that proton exchange processes had been detected in phosphonium salts such as $[(CH_3)_4P]X$ quite some time ago, and that the findings with the corresponding ylids are only a logical consequence of these older results (*114*). While the proton exchange of the phosphonium cations in the presence of a base B (sometimes the solvent, water, or methanol) takes place via the ylidic intermediate, the exchange between ylids in the presence of the protic catalyst HB occurs via the phosphonium cation intermediate.

$$\begin{array}{c} CH_3 \\ {}^{+}| \\ CH_3-P-CH_3 \\ | \\ CH_3 \end{array} \xrightarrow[-HB]{+B:} \begin{array}{c} CH_3 \\ {}^{+}| \quad {}^{-} \\ CH_3-P-\underline{C}H_2 \\ | \\ CH_3 \end{array} \xrightarrow[-B:]{+HB} \begin{array}{c} CH_3 \\ {}^{+}| \\ CH_3-P-CH_3 \\ | \\ CH_3 \end{array}$$

$$\begin{array}{c} CH_3 \\ {}^{+}| \quad {}^{-} \\ CH_3-P-\underline{C}H_2 \\ | \\ CH_3 \end{array} \xrightarrow[-B:]{+HB} \begin{array}{c} CH_3 \\ {}^{+}| \\ CH_3-P-CH_3 \\ | \\ CH_3 \end{array} \xrightarrow[-HB]{+B:} \begin{array}{c} CH_3 \\ {}^{+}| \quad {}^{-} \\ CH_3-P-\underline{C}H_2 \\ | \\ CH_3 \end{array}$$

[4] See a recent paper by Hoffmann, R., Boyd, D. B., and Goldberg, S. Z., for a theoretical treatment of this problem [*J. Am. Chem. Soc.* **92**, 3929 (1970)].

A similar process is typical also for compounds like perchloric acid or phosphoric acid, where the protons are not to be taken as localized at individual oxygen atoms. In these systems, however, the phenomenon is less easy to detect.

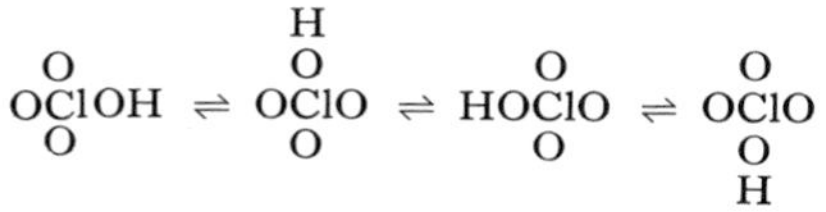

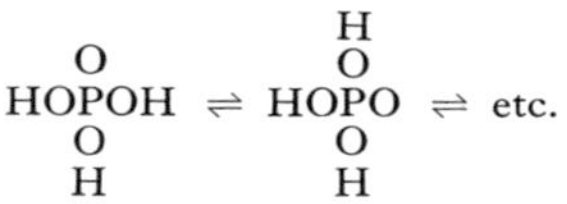

$$\begin{array}{ccccccc} & & \mathrm{H} & & & & \\ \mathrm{O} & & \mathrm{O} & & \mathrm{O} & & \mathrm{O} \\ \mathrm{OClOH} & \rightleftharpoons & \mathrm{OClO} & \rightleftharpoons & \mathrm{HOClO} & \rightleftharpoons & \mathrm{OClO} \\ \mathrm{O} & & \mathrm{O} & & \mathrm{O} & & \mathrm{O} \\ & & & & & & \mathrm{H} \end{array}$$

$$\begin{array}{ccccc} & & \mathrm{H} & & \\ \mathrm{O} & & \mathrm{O} & & \\ \mathrm{HOPOH} & \rightleftharpoons & \mathrm{HOPO} & \rightleftharpoons & \text{etc.} \\ \mathrm{O} & & \mathrm{O} & & \\ \mathrm{H} & & \mathrm{H} & & \end{array}$$

According to the broader definition these acids (and their amino and even methyl derivatives) are isoelectronic with trimethylphosphine methylene as $OH \sim NH_2 \sim CH_3$, and $O \sim NH \sim CH_2 \sim BH_3$ (*154–156*) (see above). The same is true for phosphine imines and oxides, for sulfoximines and -diimines, and a variety of related species. Recent work by Knoll *et al.* (*195*) left no doubt about this and provided more information on the energy characteristics of these exchange processes.

3. *Structure and Spectra*

a. *Single-crystal X-ray studies.* Only very few ylids have been the subject of crystal structure determinations. Among the first were triphenylphosphonium-benzoyliodomethylid (*419*) $(C_6H_5)_3P{=}CI(COC_6H_5)$, and its chloro analog (*420*), typical resonance-stabilized species with a carbonyl group adjacent to the carbanionic function. Results of X-ray work on an ylidic sulfone gave similar dimensions of the critical centers of the molecule (*448*). This work was later summarized and discussed by Speziale and Ratts (*416*) (*Table 15*), with an emphasis on the resonance interaction with multiple-bonded ligand systems. Daly *et al.* have studied the structure of an ylidic species containing a four-membered ring (a Wittig intermediate), where the carbanionic function is involved in bonding to a second phosphorus atom (*90*).

Finally, Bart has investigated *triphenylphosphinemethylene*, an ylid no longer containing stabilizing groups at the ylidic carbon (*31*, *32*). In this work the positions of the CH_2 hydrogen atoms could be determined! (See Table XV). For other ylids, see Cameron and Prout (*83*, *84*), Huisgen *et al.* (*173*), and Mark and Trotter (*234*).

TABLE XV

STRUCTURAL DATA FOR YLIDS

	d(P=C) (Å)	$P{=}C\langle^{X}_{Y}$ configuration	References
$(C_6H_5)_3P{=}CH_2$	1.661	Planar	*31, 32*
$(C_6H_5)_3P{=}CI(COC_6H_5)$	1.71	Planar	*419*
$(C_6H_5)_3P{=}CCl(COC_6H_5)$	1.736	Planar	*420*
$(C_6H_5)_3P{=}CHSO_2C_6H_4CH_3$	1.709	—	*448*
$(C_6H_5)_3P{=}C(CO_2CH_3)R$	1.70	Planar	*234*
	1.75	Planar	*173*
$(C_6H_5)_3P{=}C{-}P(C_6H_5)_3$, with C and P bridged by $O{-}C(CF_3)_2$	1.745	—	*90*
$[(C_6H_5)_3P{=}C_6N_4O_2]_2$	1.708	Planar	*83*
	1.767	Planar	
$(C_6H_5)_3P{=}C_6N_4O_5$	1.77	Planar	*84*

From X-ray data it now seems to be well established (*31*, *32*, *83*, *84*, *90*, *173*, *234*, *416*, *419*, *420*, *448*) that the phosphorus ylids are best described to be built up from sp^3-hybridized phosphorus atoms interacting with an sp^2-hybridized ylidic carbon atom. The tetrahedral geometry at P and the trigonal planar arrangements at C leave little doubt of this picture, as deviations from a possible trigonally bipyramidal phosphorus configuration sp^3d are too marked and as there is no indication for an sp^3 carbanion whatsoever.

The bond distance "P=C" is less easy to interpret. The values for stabilized ylids are less significant here and so interest has to focus on the distance of 1.661 Å in $(C_6H_5)_3PCH_2$. This is close to *Pauling's* double-bond length of 1.665 Å, including a correction according to the Shoemaker-Stevenson procedure for highly polar bonds. There are few means of control for this value proposed on theoretical or semiempirical grounds, because distances for true P=C double bonds are unknown. A bond distance for a true dipolar unit $>\overset{+}{P}{-}\overset{-}{\underline{C}}<$ is difficult to predict and hence a decision between the two resonance forms $R_3P{=}CH_2$ and $R_3\overset{+}{P}{-}\overset{-}{\underline{C}}H_2$ cannot be made on this basis alone. It should be stressed, however, that X-ray data would be well in agreement with what is expected from a $(p{\rightarrow}d)\pi$ interaction (C_{2p}—P_{3d}), following the theories of Craig, Cruickshank, Jaffe, and others, as both the geometries and distances provide all prerequisites for such an interaction (*101–103, 106, 107, 182*).

No arsenic ylids have been studied by X-ray diffraction.

b. *Vibrational Spectroscopic Studies.* Two attempts have been made to determine the force constants and bond orders of the R_3PCH_2 group in phosphorus ylids. Lüttke and Wilhelm (*230*) have investigated the IR spectra of $(C_6H_5)_3PCH_2$, while Sawodny (*304*) recently has turned to $(CH_3)_3PCH_2$ using IR and Raman spectroscopy. In the first study the PC frequencies have been assigned by making use of selective H/D and $^{12}C/^{13}C$ substitution. A force constant of 4.9 mdyne/Å and a bond order of 1.3 were obtained, which are much lower than those derived from the IR and Raman frequencies of the methyl homolog by Sawodny. In this treatment C_{3v} or pseudo-C_{3v} symmetries were assumed and combined with bond length and angles as found in earlier X-ray work. Siebert's formula, finally, gave a force constant of 5.59 mdyne/Å and a bond order of 1.65 for P═C, but only 3.08 mdyne/Å and a bond order of 1.02 for P—C. Thus a considerable strengthening of the PC bond of the ylidic group is found, which has to be interpreted in terms of covalent π-interactions or some other mechanism. The former is favored by both authors.

The arsenic ylids have so far only been studied by infrared spectroscopy, and some assignments of characteristic bands but no detailed studies have been made (*381*).

c. *NMR and ESR Spectroscopy.* Proton NMR spectroscopy provided interesting additional information (*153, 377*) on structure and bonding in phosphorus ylids. First of all it was shown that ylidic protons are highly shielded, their signals being shifted to exceedingly high fields (*378*). Ignoring the unlikely possibility of anisotropy contributions, this may be taken as evidence for a high negative charge load at the ylidic carbon, as expected from the dipolar formula $R_3\overset{+}{P}—\overset{-}{\underline{C}}H_2$. The shifts observed are close to those reported for alkali metal alkyls, where a distinct polarity R^-M^+ is beyond doubt. It should also be pointed out that proton resonances of a $=CH_2$ group involved in a true olefinic double bond appear at much lower fields than resonances of saturated alkyl systems!

The *coupling constants* observed in ylid spectra (*377, 378*) support the conclusions drawn from X-ray results as to what the hybridization of the phosphorus and carbon atoms is likely to be (*152, 153, 239*). A comparison with data obtained for phosphonium cations and related phosphorus compounds confirms the assumption of sp^3-hybridized phosphorus, sp^2-hybridized ylid carbon, and sp^3-hybridized alkyl carbon atoms.

The question of possible π-interactions in the ylidic bonds remains. Little can be contributed to this from the NMR results, but the high negative charge at the ylidic carbon rules out extensive electron transfer to phosphorus. This idea is supported from findings in *^{31}P spectroscopy.* The ^{31}P resonance of ylids is not drastically shifted to higher fields as compared to that of the corresponding phosphonium salts (*153*, *239*, *377*).

ESR Spectroscopy has also been used to investigate bonding in ylids (*228*, *229*). Spectra have been recorded for the crystal-matrix-trapped ylid radical cations $(C_6H_5)_3\overset{+}{P}—\dot{C}H(COOH)$ and $(C_6H_5)_3\overset{+}{P}—\dot{C}H_2$. Both from g factors and from hyperfine coupling constants it was concluded that there is little, if any electron delocalization to phosphorus d orbitals. The ^1H coupling constants and g tensors observed are too similar to those of non-ylidic radicals like $\dot{C}H(COOH)_2$ to make an implication of electron delocalization from carbon to phosphorus justified. ^{31}P coupling, of course, is more difficult to evaluate, but quite different coupling constants would be anticipated if such a delocalization amounted to a significant contribution to the overall P—C bonding. [Preliminary UV results (*152*).]

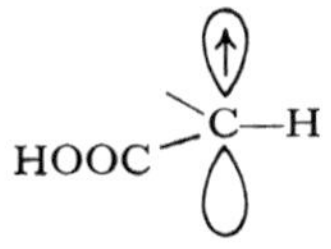

HOOC—C—H

The present state of affairs thus may be summarized as follows: From all methods for the determination of molecular structure it consistently follows that the ylidic groups contain a PC bond of high order, which is strongly polarized and allocates much of its excess electron density to the carbon atom. The latter is best described as being sp^2-hybridized, while the phosphorus atom is best referred to as being in an sp^3 configuration. No final conclusion can be reached, however, as to whether a true interaction of the p_C lone pair with a d_P orbital must be assumed to account for the bond distances and force constants observed. It has been pointed out that the overlap of the orbitals considered probably has its maximum very close to the carbon atom, so that NMR arguments concerning chemical shifts would not be touched. It is therefore not surprising that for arsenic ylids, which are unlikely to show a comparable stabilization, quite similar values of chemical shifts are recorded. Here the dipolar form $R_3\overset{+}{As}—\overset{-}{\underline{C}}H_2$ should contribute even more to the ground state of the molecules.

It is unfortunate that relatively little information is available on *nitrogen ylids* $R_3\overset{+}{N}—\overset{-}{\underline{C}}H_2$ (*185*, *252*). Though the chemistry of these species has been studied extensively, physical and spectroscopic data are almost non-existent. This is not unlike the chemistry of amine imines $R_3\overset{+}{N}—\overset{-\ -}{\underline{N}H}$ mentioned earlier. From qualitative observations it is clear, however, that lower bond energies are to be expected, which do not differ much from those found in compounds with true N—C single bonds. This may be understood in terms of the lone-pair versus bond-pair repulsions outlined above, or in terms of the nonavailability of nitrogen *d* orbitals.

4. *Coordination Compounds*

As expected from the above considerations, ylids are excellent donor molecules which form stable coordination compounds with many *Lewis* acids like borane, boron halides, metallic, and organometallic halides (*185*). All of these have been described as zwitterionic or ionic substances in which the ylidic carbon functions as a bridge between the positively charged phosphorus atom and a metalloid or metal atom, transferring its negative charge to the acceptor component.

A similar structure has been proposed for the compounds recently obtained from ylids and aluminum alkyls (*376*, *377*). These are of considerable interest, as they are true isoelectronics of disilylmethylene compounds:

$(CH_3)_3\overset{+}{P}—CH_2—\overset{-}{Al}(CH_3)_3$	$(CH_3)_3Si—CH_2—Si(CH_3)_3$
M.p. 62°C B.p. 130–134°C/1 torr	B.p. 134°C/760 torr

Nothing points to the fact that there is anything unusual in the structure and bonding in these species. With the lone pair at carbon being engaged in discrete bonding to the acceptor atom, the rehybridization of carbon ($sp^2 \rightarrow sp^3$) prevents any π-interactions with neighboring atoms. (See, however, Section III,D.)

Mention should be made here of the *lithium halide complexes* of ylids produced upon deprotonation of phosphonium salts using alkyllithium reagents (*379*). NMR studies of these compounds indicate that even there a direct interaction of the carbanionic center with the lithium cation has to be postulated. ^1H–^{13}C coupling constants, being as high as 150 cps in the free ylids, drop to 130 cps upon ylid coordination to Li^+, in agreement with an assumption of true $sp^2 \rightarrow sp^3$ rehybridization of the bridging atom.

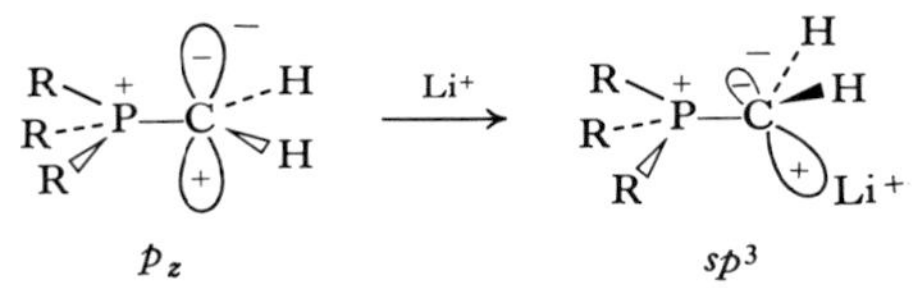

$$p_z \xrightarrow{Li^+} sp^3$$

The change in ^1H–^{31}P coupling constants is also consistent with this picture, although conclusions in this case are less straightforward.

D. Phosphine Boranes, $R_3\overset{+}{P}—\overset{-}{B}H_3$

Phosphine boranes are well known in the literature as compounds exhibiting anomalous properties (*266*). Triphenylphosphineborane is said not only to be stable towards air and water, but to withstand hot concentrated mineral acids equally well (*165*). It seems of interest here to summarize our knowledge on this unusual class of compounds and to relate the information available to what has been said about isoelectronic species, primarily about methylsilanes:

$$R_3\overset{+}{P}—\overset{-}{B}H_3 \qquad R_3Si—CH_3$$

Physical properties of some selected phosphine boranes are listed in Table XVI.

The *crystal structure* (*427*) of $(CH_3)_3\overset{+}{P}—\overset{-}{B}H_3$ has been determined; it consists of monomeric molecules having a P—B bond distance of 1.93 Å, just equal to that found in $H_3\overset{+}{P}—\overset{-}{B}H_3$ (*240*). A very similar P—B bond distance is reported (*259*) for $(NH_2)_3\overset{+}{P}—\overset{-}{B}H_3$, 1.89 Å. These values were taken as normal single-bond values, though the distinct polarity of the linkage should result in high polar contributions to the underlying σ-interaction.

A striking phenomenon is found when the relative *stabilities* of the borane complexes of trimethylamine, -phosphine, -arsine, and -stibine are considered (*151*). The basicities of the donor molecules seem to rank as follows: $(CH_3)_3P > (CH_3)_3N > (CH_3)_3As > (CH_3)_3Sb$. This phenomenon has been explained on the basis of a π-interaction between phosphorus d orbitals

TABLE XVI

SELECTED PHOSPHINE BORANES

	M.p. (°C)	References
$(CH_3)_3PBH_3$	103°–103.5°	*75, 170, 427*
$(C_2H_5)_3PBH_3$	46°	*29, 170*
$(n\text{-}C_3H_7)_3PBH_3$	22.5°–23°	*29, 170*
$(n\text{-}C_4H_9)_3PBH_3$	4°	*29, 257*
$(C_6H_5)_3PBH_3$	188°	*29, 40, 91, 136, 165*
$[(CH_3)_3Si]_3P \cdot BH_3$	100°–107°(dec)	*256, 267*
$(CH_3)_3AsBH_3$	73.5°–74.5°	*170, 422*
$(C_2H_5)_3AsBH_3$	40°(dec)	*170*
$(C_6H_5)_3AsBH_3$	78°(dec)	*40*
$(CH_3)_3SbBH_3$	−35°	*170*

and symmetry-adjusted combinations of the bond pairs of the BH_3 group (*151, 266*). Such an approach borrows from the picture of *hyperconjugation*, which has long been used in organic chemistry to explain the resonance effects of methyl groups. It has been pointed out by Graham and Stone, however, that in phosphine boranes the formal charge distribution should favor more strongly this type of "back-donation" as compared with the situation in methyl compounds (*151*). A possible description for this may be taken from the valence bond formalism:

$$R_3\overset{+}{P}—\overset{-}{B}H_3 \leftrightarrow R_3P{=}\overset{-}{B}H_2\,H^+$$

This formalism could account for the reduced "hydridic" character of the BH_3 hydrogens in phosphine boranes, which is observed in the chemical reactivity of these species. The phosphine boranes were also included in a discussion of coordination compounds using the concept of "Hard and Soft Acids and Bases" (HSAB) (*273, 274*). According to this classification [as in an earlier one (*2*)] phosphines and borane are supposed to be both of the *soft* type, thus giving rise to an interaction, which in this picture is highly favored. The reader may here be reminded of what has briefly been said on the isoelectronic methylsilane species. The "acidity" of the methylsilanes could equally well be considered from the point of view of hyperconjugation or π-bonding and HSAB. Thus the isoelectronic relation is not so artificial here as might be expected.

IV

ORGANOSILOXANES, $R_3Si—O—SiR_3$, AND RELATED COMPOUNDS

A. *Physical Characteristics*

Due to their practical importance organosiloxane compounds often have been studied and the results of these investigations have been reviewed many times (*36*, *119*, *258*). It is therefore certainly unnecessary to quote the conclusions drawn from the relations detected in organosiloxane chemistry. Some highlights, however, should be briefly mentioned, as they have been referred to frequently in earlier sections and will be mentioned in following sections.

Among these highlights are large *bond angles* of high flexibility at the oxygen atoms, mostly $140 \pm 10°$, short Si—O *bond distances* (*217*, *418*), mostly 1.60 ± 0.1 Å, large Si—O *bond energies* (~ 120 kcal/mole), and a very low basicity, the latter not only towards protonic acids but also towards Lewis acids (*121*). The reluctance to form a coordination compound is so pronounced that hitherto not one stable siloxane complex has been obtained. The significance of these characteristics for the theoretical treatment of the Si—O—Si bonding system has already been indicated in the Introduction.

B. *Neutral Heterosiloxanes*

One method for testing the state of bonding in a given system is to study its sensitivity to slight or more significant changes in its prerequisites. In siloxane chemistry this has been done by substituting heteroatoms for one or more of the silicon atoms (*7*, *7a*, *54*, *55*, *164*, *215*, *313*, *330*, *423*). On doing so disiloxanes are converted to germano-, stanno-, and plumbo-siloxanes, or to compounds containing the Si—O—C linkage (*330*). Some of the simple representatives are compiled in Table XVII. The investigations of chemical and physical properties of heterosiloxanes have invariably shown that the *disil*oxane structure is a relative optimum in thermal and chemical stability. All kinds of alterations lead to a reduction in these properties.

When *pairs* of silicon atoms are replaced by heteroatoms, again neutral molecules are obtained, even if the guest atoms have other valency characteristics than silicon, as, e.g., aluminum and phosphorus. Out of these

TABLE XVII

HETEROSILOXANE COMPOUNDS OF GROUP IVb ELEMENTS

	M.p. (°C)	B.p. (°C/torr)	References
$(CH_3)_3SiOGe(CH_3)_3$	−68°	117°/725	*339 365, 397*
$(CH_3)_3SiOSn(CH_3)_3$	−59°	141°/720	*340, 366, 397*
$(CH_3)_3SiOPb(CH_3)_3$	−1°	172°/720	*341, 366*
$[(CH_3)_3SiO]_2Ge(CH_3)_2$	−61°	165°/725	*339, 365*
$[(CH_3)_3SiO]_2Sn(CH_3)_2$	48°	75°/11	*340, 366*
$[(CH_3)_3SiO]_3GeCH_3$	—	77°/11	*339, 365*
$[(CH_3)_3SiO]_3SnCH_3$	34°	49°/1	*340, 366*
$[(CH_3)_3SiO]_4Ge$	−59°	198°/725	*339, 365*
$[(CH_3)_3SiO]_4Sn$	64°	60°/1	*340, 366*

TABLE XVIII

"DIPOLAR" HETEROSILOXANE COMPOUNDS AND IONIC ANALOGS

	M.p. (°C)	B.p. (°C/torr)	References
$[(CH_3)_3SiO]_3AlON(CH_3)_3$	87°	140°	*315*
$[(CH_3)_3SiO]_3AlOP(CH_3)_3$	76°	125°	*315*
$[(CH_3)_3SiO]_3GaON(CH_3)_3$	93°	132°	*315*
$[(CH_3)_3SiO]_3GaOP(CH_3)_3$	56°	105°	*315*
$[(CH_3)_3SiO]_3FeON(CH_3)_3$	90°	148°	*315*
$[(CH_3)_3SiO]_3FeOP(CH_3)_3$	65°	120°	*315*
$[(CH_3)_3SiOAl(CH_3)_2OSi(CH_3)_3]Na$	215°	—	*334*
$[(CH_3)_3SiOAl(CH_3)_2OSi(CH_3)_3]K$	125°	—	*334*
$[(CH_3)_3SiOGa(CH_3)_2OSi(CH_3)_3]Na$	130°	—	*334*
$[(CH_3)_3SiOGa(CH_3)_2OSi(CH_3)_3]K$	89°	—	*334*
$\{[(CH_3)_3SiO]_4Al\}Li$	190°(dec)	—	*326*
$\{[(CH_3)_3SiO]_4Al\}Na$	250°	—	*326*
$\{[(CH_3)_3SiO]_4Al\}K$	250°	—	*326*
$\{[(CH_3)_3SiO]_4Al\}(CH_3)_4Sb$	180.5°	180°/1[a]	*370*
$\{[(CH_3)_3SiO]_4Ga\}(CH_3)_4Sb$	190.5°	190°/1[a]	*329*
$\{[(CH_3)_3SiO]_4Fe\}(CH_3)_4Sb$	193°	190°/1[a]	*329*

[a] Sublimes.

series of compounds the addition products of phosphine oxides and aluminum alkyls have already been discussed in Section III,A,2.

$$R_2\overset{-}{Al}(R)\text{—}\overline{O}\text{—}\overset{+}{P}R_3 \qquad R_2Si(R)\text{—}\overline{O}\text{—}SiR_3$$

Similar species were obtained in the chemistry of *poly*siloxanes. Good examples to illustrate the broad scope of these systems may be selected from alumosiloxane chemistry (*7*, *215*, *330*, *423*). Tris(trimethylsiloxy)aluminum (Section II,B,2) readily forms 1:1 complexes with trimethylphosphine oxide, having the following composition and structure (*315*):

$$(R_3SiO)_2Al(\mu\text{-}OSiR_3)_2Al(OSiR_3)_2 + 2\,R_3PO \rightarrow 2\,R_3SiO\text{—}\overset{-}{Al}(OSiR_3)_2\text{—}O\overset{+}{P}R_3$$

$$R = CH_3$$

Similar heterosiloxanes are obtained with amine and arsine oxides, and with siloxygallium and iron(III) compounds. Table XVIII gives some additional examples. The close relation to branched siloxanes and heterosiloxanes is obvious:

$$R_3SiO\text{—}Si(OSiR_3)_2\text{—}OSiR_3 \qquad R_3SiO\text{—}\overset{-}{Ga}(OSiR_3)_2\text{—}O\overset{+}{P}R_3 \qquad R_3SiO\text{—}Ge(OSiR_3)_2\text{—}OSiR_3$$

All examples represent small structural moieties of the SiO_2 and $AlPO_4$ lattices, monomerized by alkyl groups (*7*, *215*, *330*, *423*). It is almost trivial to point out that silicon dioxide and aluminum phosphate are isostructural (*440*).

From tris(trimethylsilyl)phosphate and tris(trimethylsiloxy)aluminum a highly branched complex can be prepared, which is of a lower stability, however. Even upon storage at room temperature the product is rapidly decomposed with formation of hexamethyldisiloxane and aluminum phosphate (*333*). In this intermediate the formal charges at the hetero

$$\begin{matrix} [(CH_3)_3SiO]_3PO \\ \{[(CH_3)_3SiO]_3Al\}_2 \end{matrix} \rightarrow R_3SiO-\overset{\overset{SiR_3}{|}}{\underset{\underset{SiR_3}{|}}{\overset{O\,|\,+}{\underset{O}{P}}}}-O-\overset{\overset{SiR_3}{|}}{\underset{\underset{SiR_3}{|}}{\overset{O\,|\,-}{\underset{O}{Al}}}}-OSiR_3 \rightarrow \begin{matrix} AlPO_4 \\ + \\ 3\ (CH_3)_3SiOSi(CH_3)_3 \end{matrix}$$

atoms induce a polarization of opposite sign in the siloxy groups that favors the siloxane formation.

Another pair of such compounds are $(CH_3)_3SiOSiCl_3$ and $(CH_3)_3POAlCl_3$ wherein halogen has replaced the siloxy groups at the metal atom (*449*).

C. Ionic Heterosiloxane Species

If in some crystalline form of silicon dioxide, silicon nuclei are replaced by aluminum nuclei while maintaining the numbers of electrons, the lattice is transformed to a *silicate* structure, where now alkali or other cations can be accommodated to compensate the excess negative charge.

$$Si_4O_8 \rightarrow Na[AlSi_3O_8]$$

A similar "procedure" converts organosiloxanes to alkali *organoalumino-silicates* (*330*). This has been verified in many preparative experiments, which all lead to various types of heterosiliconate anions, the most simple of which (*319*) is $[R_3Si—O—AlR_3]^-$.

If instead of aluminum or its homologs phosphorus is used for the substitution of silicon, then *cationic* species are to be expected. These cations have also been obtained by appropriate methods of synthesis (*37*). Species

$$[R_3Si—O—AlR_3]^- \swarrow R_3Si—O—SiR_3 \searrow [R_3Si—O—PR_3]^+$$

of the *anionic type* are obtained from reactions of alkali silanolates and aluminum alkyls in an inert solvent and appear as colorless, air-sensitive crystalline materials (*319*). The corresponding *cationic species* were pre-

$$KOSi(CH_3)_3 + Al(CH_3)_3 \rightarrow K[(CH_3)_3SiOAl(CH_3)_3]$$

pared by Beattie and Parrett from trialkylphosphine oxides and trialkylhalosilanes (*37*). This procedure is successfully applied only with the iodide, bromide, or perchlorate as the counterion. Fluoro- or chlorosilanes do not undergo this reaction.

$$(CH_3)_3SiI + (CH_3)_3PO \rightarrow [(CH_3)_3SiOP(CH_3)_3]I$$

The products have in both cases been shown to be ionic in nature and the heterosiloxane ions were characterized by spectroscopic methods. The Si—O and P—O stretching frequencies of the starting materials are both shifted considerably towards lower values, as is to be expected if the Si—O—/P—O— groups become part of the triatomic units Si—O—Al or P—O—Si. No detailed structural work has been reported as yet. Compounds containing larger fragments of the silicate lattices have also been synthesized and studied in greater detail. Among them are the products of the reactions between the mono-, bis-, or tris(trialkylsiloxy)aluminum(alkyl) compounds with alkali or pseudo-alkali silanolates. In these cases ionic heterosiliconates with chainlike or branched-chain inorganic backbones are produced (*324*, *326*, *329*, *334*, *370*, *372*). The *bis*(*siloxy*)*aluminate* anions in the former

$(R_3SiOAlR_2)_2$ $\xrightarrow{MOSiR_2}$ $[R_2Al(OSiR_3)_2]^-$ M^+ (R, R, R_3SiO, $OSiR_3$ on Al)

$[(R_3SiO)_2AlR]_2$ $\xrightarrow{MOSiR_3}$ $[RAl(OSiR_3)_3]^-$ M^+ (R, R_3SiO, $OSiR_3$, $OSiR_3$ on Al)

$[(R_3SiO)_3Al]_2$ $\xrightarrow{MOSiR_3}$ $[Al(OSiR_3)_4]^-$ M^+ ($OSiR_3$ four times on Al)

M = Alkali, pseudo-alkali
R = Alkyl

are remarkable in that they are decomposed by water only quite slowly (*334*). The corresponding alkali salts are soluble in neutral water instantaneously and the clear solution evolves methane gas ($R{=}CH_3$) only if acidified with mineral acids. The same stability is found with the $[RAl(OSiR_3)_3]^-$ anions and their gallium analogs.

The structure of the symmetrical *tetrakis*(*trimethylsiloxy*)*metallate* anions has been determined by single-crystal X-ray diffraction (*447*). (See Fig. 5.) The anions were shown to contain tetracoordinate aluminum [gallium, iron(III)] atoms, with the oxygen atoms in a tetrahedral arrangement. Bond angles and distances were similar to those found in silicates and silica. This result supports earlier conclusions about the relations between isoelectronic species. The gallium and iron(III) analogs are also known, as indicated above (*328*, *372*), and are likely to be isostructural, as the tetramethylstibonium salts turned out to be isomorphous with the aluminum siliconate (*447*). The unit cell dimensions differ only slightly for the three compounds investigated.

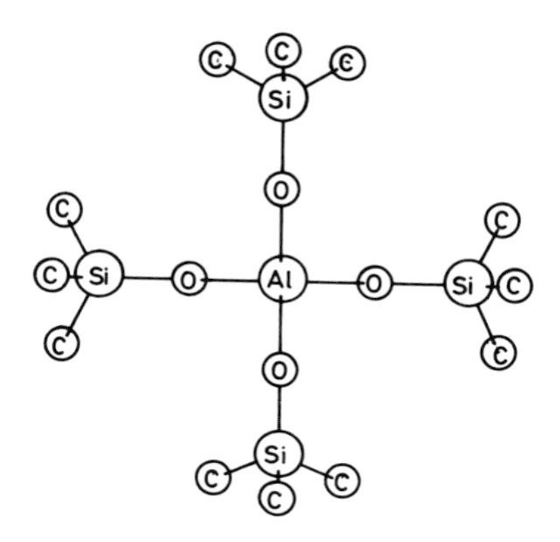

FIG. 5. Configuration of the tetrakis(trimethylsilyl)aluminate anion $Al[OSi(CH_3)_3]_4^-$ (*447*).

A tetrakis(trialkylsiloxy)phosphonium cation has not yet been reported. Such a species might be formed from reactions of tris(trimethylsilyl)-phosphate and trimethylsilyl iodide, i.e., where a low Si—X bond energy and a high lattice energy of the product should favor the right side of the equilibrium

$$(R_3SiO)_3PO + R_3SiX \rightleftharpoons \left[\begin{array}{c} SiR_3 \\ O \\ | \\ R_3SiO\text{—}P\text{—}OSiR_3 \\ | \\ O \\ SiR_3 \end{array} \right]^+ X^-$$

Alkoxy analogs $(RO)_4P^+$ are well known and therefore this expectation is not unrealistic. The same should be true with bis- and tris-(trialkylsiloxy)phosphonium cations $[(R_3SiO)_3PR]^+$ and $[(R_3SiO)_2PR_2]^+$, the synthesis of which so far seems not to have been attempted.

V

SILYL PHOSPHINE IMINES, $R_3Si—N=PR_3$, AND RELATED COMPOUNDS

Disiloxane compounds formally may be taken as the silyl derivatives of silanols. It follows then from the isoelectronic relation of silanols and phosphine imines that silyl derivatives of phosphine imines should also be closely related to the siloxanes. It is for this reason that this class of compounds is considered here in a section immediately following that for siloxanes and related compounds. Such a section finally is an important link to that on the chemistry of silazanes in Section VI, as silylated phosphine imines formally are the phosphoranylidene derivatives of silylamines.

$$R_3Si—\overline{\underline{O}}H \rightarrow R_3Si—\overline{\underline{O}}—SiR_3$$

$$R_3P=\underline{N}H \rightarrow R_3P=\underline{N}—SiR_3 \leftarrow H_2\underline{N}—SiR_3$$

A. Preparation and Properties

Two main routes to silylated phosphine imines are available and have been widely used for the synthesis of quite a number of homologs. The first of these is the classical *Staudinger* procedure, the reaction of silyl azides with a tertiary phosphine, which with evolution of nitrogen affords good yields of the products (*45–47*, *222*, *226*, *255*, *262*, *292*, *310*, *345*, *387*, *388*, *390*, *407*, *426*, *444*, *450*).

If the azides or phosphines are not available the more sophisticated second method may be employed. It makes use of the metallated phosphine imines, mostly lithiated, which are reacted with halosilanes or another organometallic halide (*290*, *291*, *344*). Via the first route analogous *german-*

$$R_3SiN_3 + R_3P \rightarrow R_3Si—\underline{N}=PR_3 + N_2$$

$$R_3SiX + R_3PNLi \rightarrow R_3Si—\underline{N}=PR_3 + LiX$$

ium compounds may also be obtained, if the corresponding azides are accessible (*222*, *226*, *292*, *387*, *388*, *390*). Related *tin* or *lead* species are best synthesized by the alkali phosphine imide method (*222*, *344*). Nonmetallated phosphine imines may be used as well along with an auxiliary base, such as triethylamine, but yields are often poor and work-up of the reaction mixtures is difficult (*319*).

A number of silylated phosphine imines and some of their germanium and tin analogs are listed in *Table XIX*, where the physical constants have

TABLE XIX

SILYL PHOSPHINE IMINES AND RELATED COMPOUNDS

	M.p. (°C)	B.p. (°C/torr)	References
$(CH_3)_3PNSi(CH_3)_3$	3°–4°	169°	*344, 387*
$(CH_3)_3PNGe(CH_3)_3$	—	69°–71°/72	*344, 388*
$(CH_3)_3PNSn(CH_3)_3$	—	85°–88°/11	*344, 388*
$(C_2H_5)_3PNSi(CH_3)_3$	—	88°–89°/11	*46, 344*
$(C_2H_5)_3PNGe(CH_3)_3$	—	55°–57°/0.5	*344, 388*
$(C_2H_5)_3PNSn(CH_3)_3$	—	73°–74°/0.5	*344*
$(C_6H_5)_3PNSi(CH_3)_3$	75°–76°	162°–164°/0.5	*46, 344*
$(C_6H_5)_3PNGe(CH_3)_3$	78–°80°	164°/0.1	*344*
$(C_6H_5)_3PNSn(CH_3)_3$	85°–86°	172°–176°/0.5	*344*
$[(CH_3)_3PN]_2Si(CH_3)_2$	24°–25°	77°–78°/0.3	*386*
$[(CH_3)_3PN]_2Ge(CH_3)_2$	9°–10°	72°–75°/10^{-2}	*388*

been tabulated. All of the silyl compounds are of remarkably high thermal stability, which allows distillation under ordinary pressure without venturing decomposition. All species are monomers in organic solvents and show a distinct basicity towards Lewis acids (*374, 386, 387, 390, 391, 456*). In this they differ markedly from their siloxane isosteres, which are unable to form any kind of stable addition compounds. Important examples for acid–base interactions with silyl phosphine imines are the hydrogen halide adducts, obtained with HBr and HI, etc. (*232, 254, 255, 455*), and the 1:1 complexes with metal(III) alkyls, like trimethylaluminum (*387*).

$$(CH_3)_3Si{-}\bar{\underline{N}}{-}\overset{+}{P}(CH_3)_3 \xrightarrow{HI} (CH_3)_3Si{-}\underline{N}{<}^{H}_{\overset{+}{P}(CH_3)_3}\ I^-$$

$$(CH_3)_3Si{-}\bar{\underline{N}}{-}\overset{+}{P}(CH_3)_3 \xrightarrow{Al(CH_3)_3} (CH_3)_3Si{-}\underline{N}{<}^{\overset{-}{Al}(CH_3)_3}_{\overset{+}{P}(CH_3)_3}$$

Silyl phosphine imines have been investigated in detail by means of IR and NMR spectroscopy (*344, 345, 386, 390*). The main skeletal frequencies $\nu(P{=}N)$ and $\nu(Si{-}N)$ have been located and chemical shifts as well as coupling constants have been compiled. These data indicate a high bond order for the PN unit and considerable electron density at the bridging nitrogen atom, but no decision can be made as to what extent a formalism

$$R_3Si{-}\overset{=}{\underline{N}}{-}\overset{+}{P}R_3 \leftrightarrow R_3Si{-}\underline{N}{=}PR_3 \leftrightarrow R_3\overset{-}{Si}{=}\underline{N}{-}\overset{+}{P}R_3$$

is justified. The ease with which coordination compounds are formed from silyl phosphine imides favors strongly the first of these formulas. This formula explains also why siloxanes, lacking a negative charge at the bridging atom, are much poorer donors.

B. *Coordination Compounds*

1. *Hydrogen Halide Adducts*

From equimolar amounts of silyl phosphine imines and hydrogen bromide or iodide stable 1:1 addition compounds are obtained, which are ionic in nature (*455*). Thus they may be classified as silylamino trialkylphosphonium salts containing the Si—NH—P linkage. It is this linkage that relates these species to the silazanes. And in fact spectroscopic data have revealed many parallels pointing to the similarity of Si—NH—P and Si—NH—Si.

The compounds are quite stable if a heavy halide ion is present as the counterion. With F^- ions, which exhibit a pronounced affinity for silicon, no stable compounds are detectable. Cleavage of the Si—N linkages leads to secondary products, which are to be identified as aminophosphonium salts. The same process takes place upon further addition of HX reagent of any kind (*455*), e.g.,

$$\left[R_3Si{-}\underline{N}\begin{smallmatrix}H \\ \overset{+}{P}R_3'\end{smallmatrix}\right]X^- \xrightarrow{HX} R_3SiX + [R_3'\overset{+}{P}{-}\underline{N}H_2]X^-$$

Some representative silylamino phosphonium salts are listed in Table XX.

TABLE XX

SILYLAMINOPHOSPHONIUM SALTS

	M.p. (°C)	References
$[(CH_3)_3PNHSi(CH_3)_3]Cl$	126°–128°	*455*
$[(CH_3)_3PNHSi(CH_3)_3]Br$	170°–172°	*455*
$[(CH_3)_3PNHSi(CH_3)_3]I$	171°–173°	*455*
$[(CH_3)_3PNHGe(CH_3)_3]Cl$	128°–130°	*455*
$[(CH_3)_3PNHGe(CH_3)_3]Br$	167°–169°	*455*
$[(CH_3)_3PNHGe(CH_3)_3]I$	194°–195°	*455*
$[(C_6H_5)_3PNHSi(CH_3)_3]Br$	—	*255*

2. *Metal Alkyl Coordination*

Among the metal alkyl coordination compounds of silyl phosphine imines those containing aluminum alkyls merit detailed consideration

TABLE XXI

METAL ALKYL ADDUCTS OF SILYL PHOSPHINE IMINES

	M.p. (°C)	B.p. (°C/1 torr)	References
$[(CH_3)_3Al, (CH_3)_3Si, (CH_3)_3P]N$	79°–81°	120°	*387*
$[(CH_3)_3Al, (CH_3)_3Si, (C_2H_5)_3P]N$	169°	135°	*387*
$[(C_2H_5)_3Al, (CH_3)_3Si, (CH_3)_3P]N$	28°–30°	130°	*387*
$[(C_2H_5)_3Al, (CH_3)_3Si, (C_2H_5)_3P]N$	57°–59°	135°	*387*
$[(CH_3)_3Al, (CH_3)_3Si, (C_6H_5)_3P]N$	126°–130°	—	*387*
$[(CH_3)_3Ga, (CH_3)_3Si, (CH_3)_3P]N$	32°–34°	59°	*387*
$[(CH_3)_3Ga, (CH_3)_3Si, (C_2H_5)_3P]N$	113°–114°	115°	*387*
$[(CH_3)_3Ga, (CH_3)_3Si, (C_6H_5)_3P]N$	87°–89°	—	*387*
$[(CH_3)_3In, (CH_3)_3Si, (CH_3)_3P]N$	43°–44°	67°	*387*
$[(CH_3)_3In, (CH_3)_3Si, (C_2H_5)_3P]N$	107°–110°	125°–128°	*387*

(*385, 387, 390, 456*). The preparation of this type of compound was attempted in order to obtain species which are truly isoelectronic with the intriguing trisilylamines (*385*). Many members of this series, having the three neighbors in the Periodic Table Al, Si, and P as a group of ligands around a central nitrogen atom, have finally been synthesized and investigated (Table XXI).

A representative example is trimethylaluminumtrimethylsilyltrimethylphosphine imide (*385*, *387*):

$$[(CH_3)_3Si]_3N \qquad (CH_3)_3\overset{-}{Al}-\underset{|}{\overset{Si(CH_3)_3}{N}}-\overset{+}{P}(CH_3)_3$$

A planar arrangement of the four-atom skeleton of this compound and its homologs has been predicted on the basis of its relation to that of the planar trisilylamine molecules. Though this expectation has not yet been fully confirmed, none of the pertinent data give reason to doubt it.

The assymmetrical substitution of a pair of silicon atoms in the trisilylamine skeleton by an Al/P pair of atoms has, of course, spoiled the original trigonal symmetry, but the overall electron density persists in a newly distributed pattern. This is evident from mean values of chemical shifts and coupling constants in NMR spectra, and even from some infrared characteristics (Table XXII).

TABLE XXII

NMR AND IR SPECTRA OF TRIMETHYLALUMINUMTRIMETHYLSILYLTRIMETHYLPHOSPHINE IMIDE AND TRIS(TRIMETHYLSILYL)AMINE

	NMR (Hz)			IR (cm^{-1})	
	δCH_3	$J(^1H^{13}C)$	$J(^1H^{29}Si)$	νNM	References
$[(CH_3)_3Si]_3N$	−11 (Si)	118	6.7	917 (Si) 438 (Si)	*150, 321*
$[(CH_3)_3Al, (CH_3)_3Si, (CH_3)_3P]N$	+61 (Al)	109	—	? (Al)	*387*
	−13 (Si)	119	6.6	520 (Si)	
	−104 (P)	130	—	1071 (P)	

Substances of the above type are of moderate stability, depending on the nature of the acceptor metal (Al, Ga, In) and of the ligands R attached to the metal, the silicon, and the phosphorus atoms. Four different routes of thermal decomposition have been detected which may be represented by the following equations (*387*, *389*, *390*, *456*):

$$(CH_3)_3Si{-}\underline{N}{<}\genfrac{}{}{0pt}{}{\overset{-}{Al}(CH_3)_3}{\overset{+}{P}(CH_3)_3} \underset{20°C}{\overset{200°C}{\rightleftharpoons}} (CH_3)_3SiNP(CH_3)_3 + (CH_3)_3Al$$

$$2\,(CH_3)_3Si{-}\underline{N}{<}\genfrac{}{}{0pt}{}{\overset{-}{Al}Br_3}{\overset{+}{P}(CH_3)_3} \xrightarrow{250°C} 2\,(CH_3)_3SiBr + [(CH_3)_3PNAlBr_2]_2$$

$$(CH_3)_3Sn{-}\underline{N}{<}\genfrac{}{}{0pt}{}{\overset{-}{Al}(CH_3)_3}{\overset{+}{P}(CH_3)_3} \xrightarrow{20°C} (CH_3)_4Sn + [(CH_3)_3PNAl(CH_3)_2]_2$$

$$(CH_3)_3Si{-}\underline{N}{<}\genfrac{}{}{0pt}{}{\overset{-}{Al}(C_6H_5)_3}{\overset{+}{P}(C_6H_5)_3} \xrightarrow{230°C} C_6H_6 + (CH_3)_3Si{-}N{<}\genfrac{}{}{0pt}{}{(C_6H_5)_2\overset{-}{Al}{-}}{(C_6H_5)_2\overset{+}{P}{-}}C_6H_4$$

The second and third mode of decomposition are of preparative value for the synthesis of aluminum phosphine imides, which are discussed later in Section IX,C.

Germanyl and stannyl phosphine imines are cleaved by metal alkyls much more readily than their silicon analogs (see above) (*456*). Some of the corresponding adducts are unstable even under very mild conditions ($-50°C$), the relative rates of cleavage being Sn—NP > Ge—NP > Si—NP. This is to be expected on grounds of bond energies and the ease with which higher coordination numbers may be achieved at the metal atoms in a possible transition state.

These findings are reminiscent of what has long been known in heterosiloxane chemistry. Selective cleavage experiments had shown that it is the Si—O bond which is most resistant towards heterolytic fission with metal alkyls or halides (*330*, *365*). However, it is important to note again

$$2(CH_3)_3Si{-}O{-}Ge(CH_3)_3 + [AlBr_3]_2 \rightarrow 2(CH_3)_3GeBr + [(CH_3)_3SiOAlBr_2]_2$$

that no stable metal alkyl adducts of heterosiloxanes are known. The likely primary products of the processes have not yet been detected in this class of compounds.

3. *Bis(silyl)aminophosphonium salts*, $[(R_3Si)_2N{-}PR_3]^+X^-$

An ionic species isoelectronic with trisilylamine is the bis(silyl)substituted aminophosphonium cation.

For this ion again the structure and bonding are anticipated to be similar to the neutral trisilylamine isosteres (*333*).

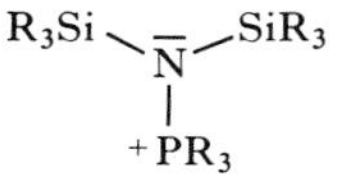

$$R_3Si\diagdown\overline{N}\diagup SiR_3 \quad (N\text{—}{}^{+}PR_3)$$

The synthesis of members of this series was achieved only recently by Wolfsberger (*333, 455*), who showed that highly reactive halosilanes, like trimethyliodosilane, are added smoothly to silyl phosphine imines even under mild conditions, whereas fluoro and chlorosilanes do not react at all.

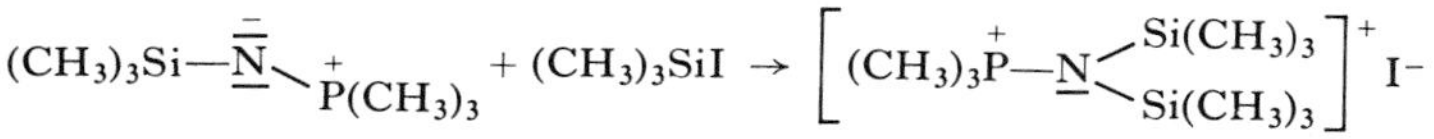

$$(CH_3)_3Si\text{—}\overline{\underline{N}}\diagdown\overset{+}{P}(CH_3)_3 + (CH_3)_3SiI \rightarrow \left[(CH_3)_3\overset{+}{P}\text{—}\underline{N}\begin{matrix}\diagup Si(CH_3)_3\\ \diagdown Si(CH_3)_3\end{matrix}\right]^+ I^-$$

The products obtained are typical saltlike compounds, and most of their IR and NMR absorptions are independent of the nature of the anion. Analogous compounds with germanium- and tin-containing ligands have also been studied (Table XXIII).

TABLE XXIII

BIS(SILYL)AMINOPHOSPHONIUM SALT[a]

Compound		
$\{(CH_3)_3P\text{—}N[Si(CH_3)_3]_2\}^+I^-$	M.p.	154°–155°C
$\{(C_2H_5)_3P\text{—}N[Si(CH_3)_3]_2\}^+I^-$	M.p.	124°–126°C

[a] Reference (*455*).

The high affinity of F^- and Cl^- towards silicon precludes the existence of salts with these anions, but ClO_4^- and SO_3R^- may function again as counterions.

C. Bis(phosphoranylidene)ammonium Salts, $[R_3P{=\!=}N{=\!=}PR_3]^+X^-$, and Related Compounds

The introduction of triorganophosphino groups at the iminofunction of phosphine imines leads to species of the formula $R_3P{=}N{—}PR_2$. Only few of these compounds have been described, but some of their arsenic and antimony analogs are also known (Table XXIV). This series of compounds is closely related to the heterosiloxanes containing phosphorus, arsenic, or antimony in the trivalent state as heteroatoms. Several members

TABLE XXIV

DIORGANOPHOSPHINO PHOSPHINE IMIDES AND SILOXIDES AND QUARTERNIZATION PRODUCTS

	M.p. (°C)	B.p. (°C/torr)	References
$(CH_3)_3SiOP(C_6H_5)_2$	—	103°–106°/0.5	*89, 181*
$(CH_3)_3SiOAs(CH_3)_2$	−70°	116°/725	*335, 367*
$(CH_3)_3SiOSb(CH_3)_2$	—	144°/720	*335, 367*
$(CH_3)_3SiOBi(CH_3)_2$	42°–44°	45°/0.1	*336*
$(CH_3)_3PNP(CH_3)_2$	8.5°–10°	85°–86°/12	*345*
$(CH_3)_3PNAs(CH_3)_2$	—	96°–99°/12	*345*
$(C_6H_5)_3PNSb(C_6H_5)_2$	123.5°–124°	—	*293*
$(CH_3)_3PNP(CH_3)_3I$	267°–269° (dec)	—	*345*
$(CH_3)_3PNAs(CH_3)_3I$	237° (dec)	—	*345*
$(C_6H_5)_3PNAs(C_6H_5)_3Br$	226°	—	*19*

of this series were synthesized some years ago and their properties are well known (Table XXIV) (*54, 181, 335, 336, 367*). Both types of compounds can be prepared via the route from metallated phosphine imines or silanols, and halophosphines, arsines, or stibines (*181, 335, 336, 345, 367*).

$$(CH_3)_3SiOLi + ClAs(CH_3)_2 \rightarrow (CH_3)_3Si\text{—}\overline{\underline{O}}\text{—}\underline{As}(CH_3)_2 + LiCl$$

$$(CH_3)_3PNLi + ClSb(CH_3)_2 \rightarrow (CH_3)_3P\text{=}\underline{N}\text{—}\underline{Sb}(CH_3)_2 + LiCl$$

The substances are sensitive to hydrolysis and oxidation and must be handled in an inert atmosphere.

The high reactivity is in part due to the lone pair of electrons at the metalloid atom. Very stable derivatives are therefore obtained, if this function is engaged in σ-bonding to an additional organic ligand. Attempts to quaternize the compounds with alkyl halides led to products wherein the new ligands in fact were introduced at the metalloid, and not at the bridging nitrogen atom (*345*). The cations of these salts are the bis(phosphoranylidene)-

$$R_3\overset{+}{P}\text{—}\overset{-}{\underline{\overline{N}}}\text{—}\underline{P}R_2' + R'X \rightarrow [R\ \overset{+}{P}\text{—}\overset{-}{\underline{\overline{N}}}\text{—}\overset{+}{P}R_3']X^-$$

ammonium species (*290, 345*), well known in organophosphorus-nitrogen chemistry. In many aminolysis reactions of triorganophosphorus(V) compounds these symmetrical ions are produced more or less unexpectedly (*14, 15, 19, 21, 38, 39, 134, 135, 263, 291, 392, 409, 410, 417*).

This high tendency to formation is evidence for the strongly favored type of structure and bonding in these and related systems. The phosphoranylidene groups are NMR equivalent and probably equally spaced from the nitrogen atom (*345*). The following formulas are therefore employed (*19*):

$$R_3\overset{+}{P}—\overset{-}{\underline{\overline{N}}}—\overset{+}{P}R_3 \leftrightarrow R_3P{=}\underline{N}—\overset{+}{P}R_3 \leftrightarrow R_3\overset{+}{P}—\underline{N}{=}PR_3$$

The geometry of the PNP unit is not known with certainty, but is it probably bent, as are those in the phosphonitrilic compounds of various types. The angle at nitrogen in SNS groups of $R_2SNSR_2^+$ cations (*221*) is 138°, similar to that in disiloxanes, and for that reason a similar value is likely for the bis(phosphoranylidene)ammonium ions. Infrared spectra are consistent with this assumption.

If one of the phosphorus atoms is replaced by an *arsenic* atom, the resulting cation is an unsymmetrical $R_3P{\equiv}N{\equiv}AsR_3^+$ species. Examples of this kind are also known and have been obtained via similar routes (*19*, *345*).

$$R_3PNLi + ClAsR_2' \rightarrow R_3P{=}N—\underline{As}R_2' + LiCl$$

$$\downarrow R'X$$

$$[R_3\overset{+}{P}—\overset{-}{\underline{\overline{N}}}—\overset{+}{As}R_3']X^-$$

The $R_3PNPR_3^+$ cations are quite stable towards hydrolysis and may be investigated in aqueous solution. Only under vigorous conditions does solvolytic cleavage occur gradually, leading to ammonium salts and phosphine oxides.

VI

DISILAZANES AND TRISILYLAMINES

A. General Characteristics

There have been enormous activities in the field of silicon-nitrogen chemistry in recent years, many of which were dedicated to research on silazanes and on trisilylamines in particular (*127*, *130*, *305*, *432*). This chemistry has been reviewed repeatedly, so here only some highlights will be mentioned, to facilitate the following discussion of isoelectronic species.

Questions of interest are the geometry of the Si_2N and Si_3N units, the nature of the SiN bond, and the acid–base behavior of nitrogen atoms or imino groups attached to silicon (and aluminum or phosphorus). All of these properties of SiN compounds are known to be more or less exceptional and *prima facie* unexpected. This is particularly true for the planarity of the Si_3N unit and the low basicity of this moiety (*121*). Though the $(p \to d)\pi$ concept offers an explanation for these findings, it is not always satisfying or unequivocal.

The situation is even worse in germanium– and tin–nitrogen chemistry, where arguments in favor of and against π-bonding are well balanced (*284–287*, *305*, *394*).

B. Heterosilazanes and Heterosilylamines

It is unfortunate that in *silazane chemistry* very little has been done on species where silicon is partly replaced by heteroatoms, $R_3Si—NH—XR_n$. In contrast to siloxane chemistry, here very few compounds have been prepared and characterized. Among them are some boron and aluminum silylamides (*54*), but nothing has been reported on *germano*- or *stanno*-silazanes (*305*). Therefore little information is contributed from this area to date.

The *aluminosilazane* compounds $[R_3Si—NH—AlR_2]_2$ are of some interest, as they appear as coordination *dimers*, in which the silazane nitrogen is *tetra*coordinate (*368*). This is quite exceptional for a nitrogen atom attached to silicon, and only few examples are known (*451*) in which this phenomenon occurs. Wiberg has observed aluminum halide complexes of hexamethyldisilazane as primary products in the silazane cleavage with AlX_3 reagents. The existence of such compounds is a proof for the availability of the nitrogen lone pair of electrons for further coordination, not necessarily to be expected if the $(p \to d)\pi$ bonding concept is accepted (*451*).

$$2\,(CH_3)_3Si—NH—Si(CH_3)_3 + [AlBr_3]_2 \longrightarrow 2\,\left[(CH_3)_3Si(H)N(\to AlBr_3)Si(CH_3)_3\right]$$

$$\xrightarrow{\text{Heat}} 2\,(CH_3)_3SiBr + \left[(CH_3)_3Si(H)N{\to}AlBr_2\right]_2$$

(cyclic dimer: N(H)(Si(CH_3)_3) and AlBr_2 units alternating in a four-membered Al_2N_2 ring, N→Al coordination)

Many more examples are known where one or two silicon atoms of a trisilylamine are replaced by heteroatoms (*54, 305*). A recent review article lists numerous methods of synthesis for compounds of this type and describes their physical and chemical properties (*305*). Substances with up to three different Group IVb metals at nitrogen have been prepared, but little is yet known about the exact arrangement of the ligands and the relative basicities of the nitrogen atoms. No stable coordination compounds have been reported (Table XXV).

TABLE XXV

TRISILYLAMINES AND RELATED COMPOUNDS

	M.p. (°C)	B.p. (°C/torr)	References
$[(CH_3)_3Si]_3N$	67°–69°	78°–80°/13	*150, 432*
$[(CH_3)_3Si]_2NGe(CH_3)_3$	29°–32°	54°–56°/1	*312*
$[(CH_3)_3Si]_2NSn(CH_3)_3$	20°–22°	58°–59°/1	*227, 312*
$[(CH_3)_3Si]_2NPb(CH_3)_3$	—	85°–87°/3	*312*
$(C_2H_5)_3SiN[Ge(CH_3)_3]_2$	—	—	*306, 307*
$(CH_3)_3SiN[Sn(CH_3)_3]_2$	—	—	*311*
$(C_2H_5)_3SiN, [Ge(CH_3)_3, Sn(CH_3)_3]$	—	138°–140°/10	*306, 307*

C. Bis(triorganosilyl) Amide Anions, $R_3SiNSiR_3^-$, and Related Species

Bis-silylated amide anions are isoelectronic with disiloxane molecules and the bis(phosphoranylidene)ammonium cations, other symmetrical and unsymmetrical isosteres being neglected (*311*). After 10 years of research compounds containing these anions have also gained high theoretical and practical importance. Numerous derivatives have been prepared and carefully investigated (*130*, *432*). The studies have provided valuable information on the structure and bonding in metal bis(silyl)amides (*434, 435*). Though the anion cannot be dealt with in complete isolation from the cation, the findings are of general significance.

Four *crystal structures* have been investigated in recent years, all of which gave new and reliable data for bond distances and angles along with other results on the geometry of bonding. Figures 6–9 depict the more important features of the new structures (*56*, *169*, *250*, *404*). In all four cases a planar arrangement of the ligands of nitrogen has been confirmed. The classical findings on trisilylamines are thus no longer exceptional and a generalization seems justified. The structure of $\{[(CH_3)_3Si]_2N\}_2Be$ has been deter-

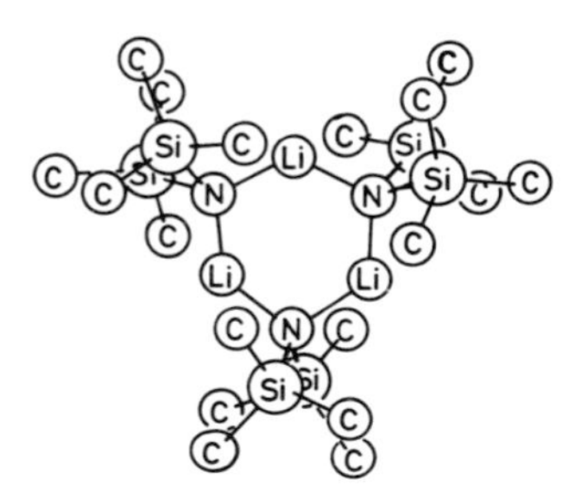

Fig. 6. Molecular structure of lithium bis(trimethylsilyl) amide, (*250*).

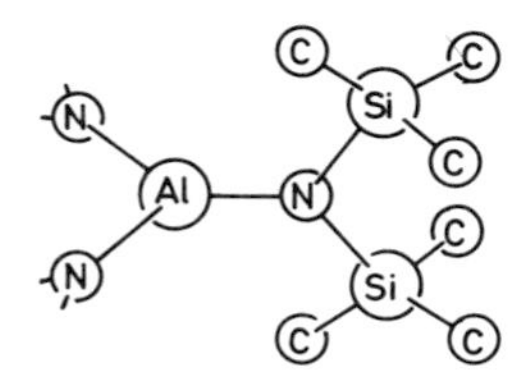

Fig. 7. Molecular structure of aluminum tris[bis(trimethylsilyl)amide], as determined by single-crystal X-ray analysis (*56*, *404*). Only one-third of the molecule is shown.

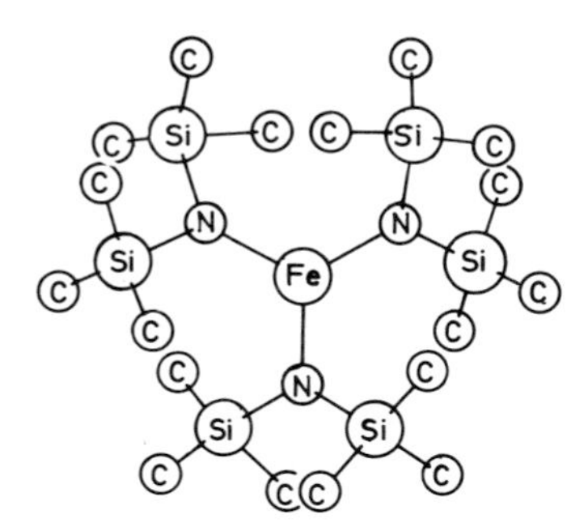

Fig. 8. Molecular structure of iron(III) tris[bis(trimethylsilyl)amide], as determined by single-crystal X-ray analysis (*56*, *404*).

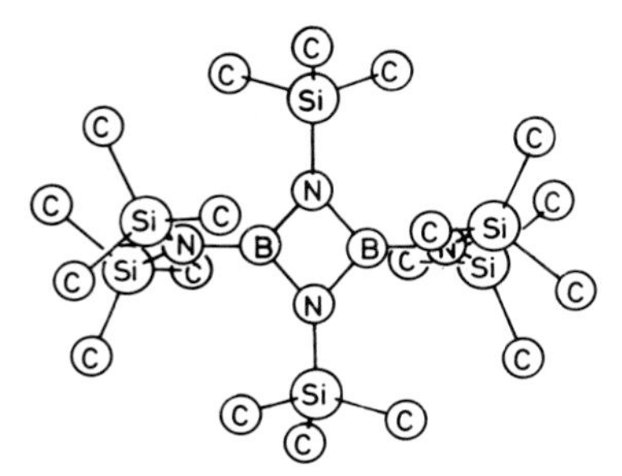

FIG. 9. Molecular structure of the borasilazane compound $B_2N_4[Si(CH_3)_3]_6$, as determined by single-crystal X-ray diffraction (*169*). The planes of the disilylamino groups are perpendicular to the plane of the four-membered ring.

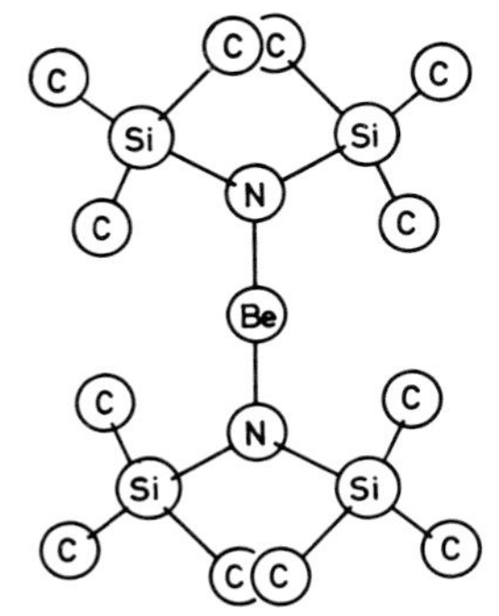

FIG. 10. Molecular structure of bis[bis(trimethylsilyl)amino]beryllium, as determined by electron diffraction (*93*).

TABLE XXVI

SOME METAL BIS-SILYL-AMIDES

	M.p. (°C)	B.p. (°C/torr)	References
$LiN[Si(CH_3)_3]_2$	70°–72°	115°/1	*436*
$NaN[Si(CH_3)_3]_2$	165°–167°	170°/2	*436*
$KN[Si(CH_3)_3]_2$	—	—	*436*
$RbN[Si(CH_3)_3]_2$	—	—	*70*
$CsN[Si(CH_3)_3]_2$	—	—	*70*
$Be\{N[Si(CH_3)_3]_2\}_2$	(−3°)–(−1°)	110°/3	*73, 93*
$Zn\{N[Si(CH_3)_3]_2\}_2$	12.5°	82°/0.5	*74*
$Cd\{N[Si(CH_3)_3]_2\}_2$	8°	93°/0.5	*74*
$Hg\{N[Si(CH_3)_3]_2\}_2$	11°	78°/0.15	*74*
$Al\{N[Si(CH_3)_3]_2\}_3$	—	subl.	*281, 404*

mined by electron diffraction (*93*) (Fig. 10). In the lithium "salt" $LiN[Si(CH_3)_3]_2$ the nitrogen atoms are four-coordinate and there are large SiNSi bond angles (*250*). This may be taken as a hint for what is to be expected from the "free" anion. Nothing points to a linear geometry in this and other cases where vibrational spectroscopy has been employed (*69, 71*). The agreement with the siloxane structures is thus satisfactory.

Further literature on bis(silyl) amides is available through Table XXVI, where representative compounds have been compiled.

VII

THE ORGANOSILICON CHEMISTRY OF PHOSPHORUS YLIDS

Phosphorus ylids are an outstanding class of compounds, both as versatile synthetic reagents and as exceedingly interesting chemical species (*185*). It is therefore surprising that it was not until recently that the *organosilicon* chemistry of such an important chemical family has attracted any scientific interest (*143, 235, 244, 245, 267, 354, 355, 376–381, 398–400*). During the last five years this situation has changed, however, and this branch of chemistry is now a rapidly growing field. It is of interest here, as the silyl ylids are easily recognized as genuine isosteres of silazanes, trisilylamines, and other isoelectronic systems. It is for this reason that their chemistry

$$R_3\overset{+}{P}—\underline{\overset{-}{C}}H—SiR_3 \qquad R_3Si—\underline{N}H—SiR_3$$

$$(R_3Si)_2\underline{C}^{-}—{}^{+}PR_3 \qquad (R_3Si)_2\underline{N}—SiR_3$$

will briefly be considered here, with special attention being paid to the specific influence of the silyl substituents on the ylidic function of the phosphorane.

A. *Synthesis and Physical Properties*

The basic method for the preparation of silylated phosphorus ylids is the deprotonation of the corresponding phosphonium salts. Various procedures then differ only in the choice of deprotonating agents employed for this purpose (*143, 235, 244, 245, 276, 354, 355, 376–381, 398–400*).

Among them are organolithium compounds, alkali hydrides, and non-silylated ylids. The latter function as transylidation components (*244*, *245*, *354*, *377*, *379*). It is the success of the transylidation procedure which shows that the silylated ylids are *weaker* bases than their nonsilylated analogs. In no case could an inverse reaction be detected. The low basicity

$$[R_3\overset{+}{P}—CH_2—SiR_3]X^- \xrightarrow{\text{LiR, MH}} R_3\overset{+}{P}—\overset{-}{\underline{C}}H—SiR_3$$

$$[R_3\overset{+}{P}—CH_2—SiR_3]X^- \xrightarrow{R_3'PCH_2} R_3\overset{+}{P}—\overset{-}{\underline{C}}H—SiR_3 + [R_3'PCH_3]X$$

of silylated ylids is also evident from the observation that these ylids do not form stable addition compounds with lithium halides, the by-products of the first synthetic method. Apart from methods in which silylated phosphonium salts are essential starting materials, *transsilylation* procedures have been developed (*353*, *354*, *356*). It has been found that silyl groups may be transferred from one ylid to another quite easily, and that such transilylations are entirely feasible with ylids and silylated phosphonium salts under suitable conditions as well. Finally, even a direct transsilylation

$$R_3\overset{+}{P}—\overset{-}{\underline{C}}H—SiR_3 + R_3'PCH_2 \rightarrow R_3PCH_2 + R_3'\overset{+}{P}—\overset{-}{\underline{C}}H—SiR_3$$

$$[R_3\overset{+}{P}—CH_2—SiR_3]X + R_3'PCH_2 \rightarrow [R_3PCH_3]X + R_3'\overset{+}{P}—\overset{-}{\underline{C}}H—SiR_3$$

not requiring a second ylidic species is possible (*356*). Organohalosilanes have been found to exchange silyl groups with silylated ylids, if the ylid produced is favored by inductive or electronic effects. Making use of this

$$R_3\overset{+}{P}—\overset{-}{\underline{C}}\begin{matrix}SiR_3\\SiR_3\end{matrix} + 2\,RSiX_3 \rightarrow R_3\overset{+}{P}—\overset{-}{\underline{C}}\begin{matrix}SiRX_2\\SiRX_2\end{matrix} + 2\,R_3SiX;$$

variety of synthetic methods a number of mono or bis silylated ylids have been prepared and characterized by analytical and spectroscopic procedures. Table XXVII gives a selection of compounds described in the literature in recent years.

An investigation of the properties of these compounds reveals interesting phenomena, which *per se* are significant for a deeper understanding of their chemistry:

(a) *The silyl groups exert a distinct stabilizing effect* on the carbanionic function of the ylid (*244*, *245*, *354*, *377*, *400*). This is *not* to be expected

TABLE XXVII

SILYLATED PHOSPHORUS YLIDS AND RELATED COMPOUNDS

	M.p. (°C)	B.p. (°C/torr)	References
$(CH_3)_3PCHSi(CH_3)_3$	−36°	66°/11	*244, 245, 377*
$(C_6H_5)_3PCHSi(CH_3)_3$	76°–77°	150°–153°/1	*143, 377, 398–400*
$(CH_3)_3PCHGe(CH_3)_3$	(−33°)–(−32°)	77°–80°/14	*379*
$(CH_3)_3PC[Si(CH_3)_3]_2$	14°–18°	60°–62°/1	*244, 245, 354, 377*
$(CH_3)_3PC[Si(CH_3)_3,Ge(CH_3)_3]$	14°–15°	60°–65°/1	*377*
$(CH_3)_3PC[Si(CH_3)_3,Sn(CH_3)_3]$	11°–13°	51°–53°/1	*377*
$(CH_3)_3PC[Ge(CH_3)_3]_2$	—	91°–95°/1	*379*
$(CH_3)_3PC[Sn(CH_3)_3]_2$	(−30°)–(−28°)	73°–76°/0.1	*379*
$(C_6H_5)_3PC[Ge(CH_3)_3]_2$	145°–147°	158°–161°/10^{-3}	*377*
$(C_6H_5)_3PC[Sn(CH_3)_3]_2$	129°–130°	183°/1	*377*
$(CH_3)_3PCHSiH_3$	−16°	—	*355*
$(C_2H_5)_3PCHSiH_3$	—	36°–38°/10^{-4}	*355*
$(CH_3)_3PC(SiH_3)_2$	11°–13°	24°–25°/10^{-2}	*355*

on the grounds of simple inductive effects, as the electropositive nature of the metal should induce additional charge density at the carbanion. Other ligands with a similar +I effect, such as alkyl groups, indeed give rise to a *de*stabilizing effect, in line with expectation (*355*, *377*). Steric effects are not likely to be responsible for the experimental results either, for the SiH_3 derivatives appear to be quite similar (*355*, *400*). The markedly reduced basicity of silylated ylids is therefore the consequence of a true *electronic* effect of a kind familiar in the chemistry of many isoelectronic species.

(b) *The silyl groups* attached to the ylidic carbanion *are highly mobile* (*354*, *380*). The transfer of the organosilicon moieties from one ylid to another (*354*, *356*), the exchange process with organosilicon halides (*356*), and the rearrangement phenomena observed on various occasions (*354*), illustrate this feature of silyl ylid chemistry. The transition state of the exchange reactions is probably lowered energetically by the easy access to higher coordination numbers at silicon, and the nucleophilic character of the ylidic centers.

It should be pointed out that equilibration processes in siloxane and silazane chemistry have exactly the same characteristics and are true parallels to the silyl exchange processes found with silylated ylids. It is of little surprise therefore that in silyl-phosphinimide chemistry similar reactivities have now been detected (*455*).

B. Structure and Spectra

The silylated ylids tabulated in Table XXVII have been investigated by IR and NMR spectroscopy (*355*, *377*, *379*, *381*). The vibrational spectra show great similarities to those registered for analogous siloxane, silazane, and silyl phosphine imine compounds. Characteristic frequencies have been assigned to the most prominent structural units and were used for a rough estimation of the P—C bond order, which is again found to be about 1.4–1.6 (*319*). The low symmetry of the molecules precludes more accurate evaluations. The coupling constants and chemical shifts in their NMR spectra are consistent with a high electron density at the ylidic sp^2 center (*355*, *377*).

No complete structure determination has been undertaken, but it is assumed that in mono- and bis-silylated ylids the ylidic carbon has its three ligands in a trigonally planar arrangement, as is the case with other ylids (*31*, *32*, *83*, *84*, *90*, *173*, *234*, *416*, *419*, *420*, *448*). Thus the situation at this carbon atom is almost identical to that at the nitrogen atom in trisilylamines and (probably) in silazane molecules (*69*, *71*, *120*, *121*).

A series of corresponding resonance formulas can therefore be written (*244*, *245*, *377*) to allow for a possible description of bonding, which is a counterpart to that in use for the isosteres, e.g.,

$$R_3Si{-}\overset{\overset{{}^{+}PR_3}{|}}{\bar{C}^{-}}{-}SiR_3 \leftrightarrow R_3Si{-}\overset{\overset{PR_3}{\|}}{C}{-}SiR_3 \leftrightarrow R_3\bar{Si}{=}\overset{\overset{{}^{+}PR_3}{|}}{C}{-}SiR_3 \leftrightarrow R_3Si{-}\overset{\overset{{}^{+}PR_3}{|}}{C}{=}\bar{Si}R_3$$

C. Rearrangement Reactions

From several kinds of rearrangement processes detected in the chemistry of silylated ylids it appears that the maximum in stability is reached when the ylidic carbon atom is "saturated" with two silicon ligands (*354*, *355*, *380*). A typical example is the thermally induced silyl migration in silyl-

$$(CH_3)_3Si{-}CH_2{-}\overset{+}{P}(CH_3)_2{-}\overset{-}{C}H{-}Si(CH_3)_3 \xrightarrow{\text{Heat}} (CH_3)_3\overset{+}{P}{-}\overset{-}{C}[Si(CH_3)_3]_2$$

methyl-substituted ylids. This process is completely irreversible and has numerous parallels in this area of chemistry. In some cases the nonrearranged ylid may not even be trapped, as silyl migration starts even under very mild conditions (*353*). The rearrangement often is a multistep process leading to products in which as many silyl groups as possible are gathered at the ylidic centers (*354*).

A theoretical evaluation of the "silicon effect" in ylid chemistry is difficult. Of course, there is always the $(p\rightarrow d)\pi$ bonding approach on hand, conferring the difficulties to a more sophisticated general problem. A simple electrostatic description of the situation is not impossible, however. In silylated ylids the high charge density of the carbanion is given more space between those regions where bonding electrons are located. Due to the larger atomic radii of silicon and phosphorus, as compared with carbon and nitrogen, the charge density accumulated at the ylidic carbon is less severe and thus is favored over that in ylids destabilized by *alkyl* substituents.

An optimum in space seems to be available for the lone pair in the *planar* arrangements of the ligands, but this is not to be overemphasized, because bond-angle deformations are energetically "cheap". This is particularly true for atoms between elements of higher periods, and is a well known fact in siloxane chemistry (*296*).

D. Coordination Compounds

Contrary to what is found in silylamine chemistry, the silylated ylids have been shown to form stable coordination compounds. Typical Lewis acids, such as BH_3 and others, add to the ylids under very mild conditions, and all evidence is in favor of an addition to the ylidic carbon (*235*, *244*, *245*). The products obtained are thus zwitterionic or ionic substances, the structure of which is nonproblematic. It is probably the negative charge at carbon that causes the donor properties of the ylids to be stronger than those of the trisilylamine isosteres.

VIII

BIS(PHOSPHORANYLIDENE)METHANES, $R_3P{=}C{=}PR_3$, AND RELATED COMPOUNDS

A. Phosphino-Substituted Phosphorus Ylids

In agreement with anticipation, the stabilizing influence of substituents is not limited to silicon and its homologs, but is also observed with phosphorus, arsenic, and antimony as ligands to ylids (*379*). A number of ylids of this nature have been synthesized following straightforward preparative procedures, or more elaborate pathways. The following equations give an idea of the synthetic methods involved:

$$2\,(CH_3)_3PCH_2 + (CH_3)_2PCl \rightarrow (CH_3)_3\overset{+}{P}{-}\overset{-}{\underline{C}}H{-}\underline{P}(CH_3)_2 + [(CH_3)_4P]Cl$$

$$(CH_3)_3\overset{+}{P}{-}\overset{-}{\underline{C}}H{-}Si(CH_3)_3 + (CH_3)_3SiO\underline{As}(CH_3)_2 \rightarrow (CH_3)_3\overset{+}{P}{-}\overset{-}{\underline{C}}H{-}\underline{As}(CH_3)_2 + (CH_3)_3SiOSi(CH_3)_3$$

$$(CH_3)_2P(CH_2)_2Li + (CH_3)_2\underline{Sb}Cl \rightarrow (CH_3)_3\overset{+}{P}{-}\overset{-}{\underline{C}}H{-}\underline{Sb}(CH_3)_2 + LiCl$$

The compounds available from these experiments are summarized in Table XXVIII. It should be pointed out that there is again an interesting

TABLE XXVIII

SOME DIORGANOMETALLOID-SUBSTITUTED YLIDS AND QUATERNIZATION PRODUCTS

	M.p. (°C)	B.p. (°C/torr)	References
$(CH_3)_3PCHP(CH_3)_2$	(−12°)–(−10°)	80°–82°/12	*379*
$(CH_3)_3PCHAs(CH_3)_2$	(−37°)–(−35°)	85°–87°/12	*379*
$(CH_3)_3PCHSb(CH_3)_2$	(−26°)–(−25°)	40°–42°/0.1	*379*
$(CH_3)_3PC[Si(CH_3)_3,P(CH_3)_2]$	(−8°)–(−6°)	122°–123°/12	*379*
	(−2°)–0	54°/0.1	*235*
$(C_6H_5)_3PCHP(C_6H_5)_2$	113°–115°	—	*177–179*
$(C_6H_5)_3PC(CH_3)P(C_6H_5)_2$	148°–150°	—	*177–179*
$(C_6H_5)_3PC(CH_3)P(C_2H_5)_2$	173°–176°	—	*177–179*
$(C_6H_{11})_3PCHP(C_6H_5)_2$	160°(dec)	—	*177–179*
$[(CH_3)_3PCHP(CH_3)_3]I$	84°–87°	—	*379*
$\{(CH_3)_3PC[Si(CH_3)_3]P(CH_3)_3\}I$	240°–243° (dec)	—	*379*

isoelectronic relation to other classes of compounds mentioned in earlier sections. Among those are the phosphino phosphine imines, and the phosphasiloxanes and silylaminophosphines:

$$R_3\overset{+}{P}—\overset{-}{\underline{C}}H—PR_2 \qquad R_3\overset{+}{P}—\overset{-}{\underline{\overline{N}}}—PR_2$$

$$R_3Si—\underline{N}H—PR_2 \qquad R_3Si—\underline{\overline{O}}—PR_2$$

The substances investigated to date are all exceedingly sensitive to oxidation, a result of the lone pair of electrons at phosphorus, arsenic, or antimony, and, of course, of the carbanionic function. These two functional sites would be expected to compete for possible electrophilic reactants.

B. *Phosphoranylidenemethylphosphonium ions, $R_3P{=}CH—PR_3^+$*

Among several reactions of the ylidic organometalloids the quaternization with alkyl halides is of general interest. It has been confirmed that these reactants exclusively prefer the *phosphorus* (or arsenic, antimony) *nucleophile*, thus leaving the ylidic function untouched and giving rise to the formation of novel quaternary ylid salts (*177–179, 235, 379*). The cations present in

$$(CH_3)_3\overset{+}{P}—\overset{-}{\underline{C}}H—\underline{P}(CH_3)_2 + CH_3I \rightarrow [(CH_3)_3P\overset{\cdots}{=}\overset{+}{C}H\overset{\cdots}{=}P(CH_3)_3]I^-$$

these salts are analogous to the bis(phosphoranylidene)ammonium ions, $R_3P{=}N{=}PR_3^+$, and resemble those in many of their properties (*379*). The R_3P groups again are equivalent in their bonding to the central nitrogen atom, as indicated in the formula. Corresponding resonance forms would be an alternative way of description (*48, 116, 180, 236, 237, 282, 283*).

$$R_3P{=}CH—\overset{+}{P}R_3 \leftrightarrow R_3\overset{+}{P}—\overset{-}{C}H—\overset{+}{P}R_3 \leftrightarrow R_3\overset{+}{P}—CH{=}PR_3$$

C. *Bis(phosphoranylidene)methanes, $R_3P{=}C{=}PR_3$*

A cation carrying only phenyl groups as ligands to phosphorus in $R_3P{=}CH—PR_3^+$ has been known for some time, as it is available via much more conventional routes (*236, 283*). It is this cation, which can be converted to the bis(triphenylphosphoranylidene)methane, the only example of such a type known at present. No compound from the alkyl series has been prepared, but only a few efforts to do so have been documented (*48, 116, 236, 237, 282, 283*). Little is known about the structure

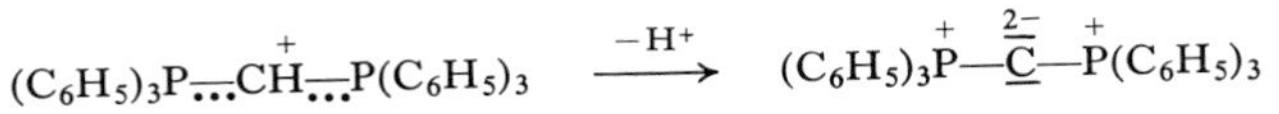

$$(C_6H_5)_3P \overset{+}{\cdots} CH \cdots P(C_6H_5)_3 \xrightarrow{-H^+} (C_6H_5)_3\overset{+}{P}—\overset{2-}{\underline{C}}—\overset{+}{P}(C_6H_5)_3$$

of $(C_6H_5)_3PCP(C_6H_5)_3$, but its chemistry has been studied in some detail, several derivatives being prepared and characterized (*236*).

D. *Cationic Trisilylamine Isosteres of the Ylid Series*

The chemistry of the phosphorus ylids has provided two additional types of cationic species that are important in this context. As nomenclature presents considerable difficulties only the formulas are used for. their representation. A salt containing the former cation with R = methyl

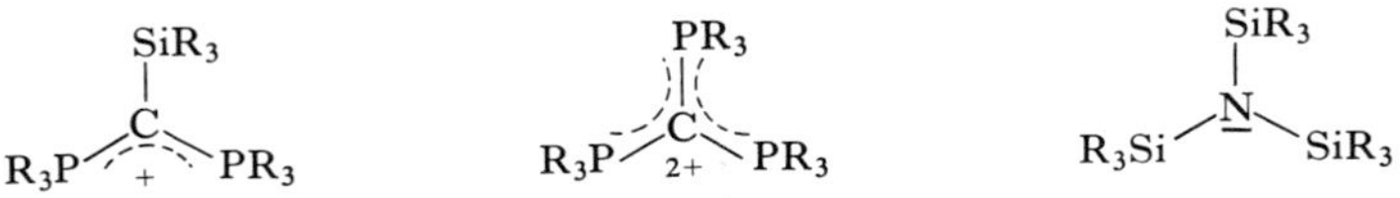

$$R_3P \overset{\overset{SiR_3}{|}}{\underset{+}{C}} PR_3 \qquad R_3P \overset{\overset{PR_3}{\|}}{\underset{2+}{C}} PR_3 \qquad R_3Si \overset{\overset{SiR_3}{|}}{N} SiR_3$$

throughout was prepared from a phosphino- and silyl-substituted ylid through addition of methyl iodide to the trivalent phosphorus center (*379*). This two-step synthesis affords high yields of a product which is soluble in methylene chloride. The NMR equivalence of the triorganophosphorus

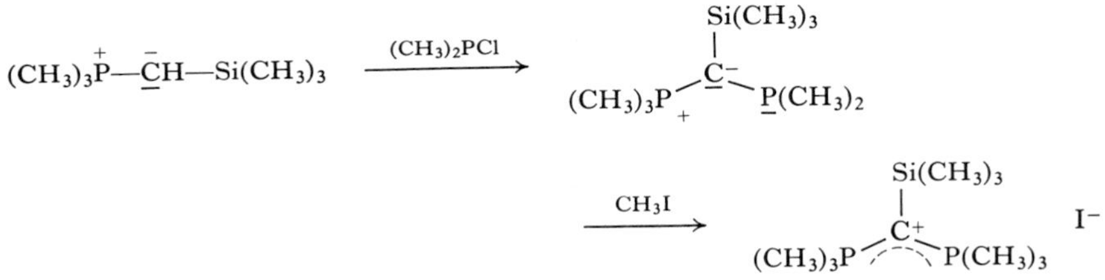

$$(CH_3)_3\overset{+}{P}—\overset{-}{\underline{C}}H—Si(CH_3)_3 \xrightarrow{(CH_3)_2PCl} (CH_3)_3\overset{+}{P}—\overset{\overset{Si(CH_3)_3}{|}}{\underline{C}^-}—\underline{P}(CH_3)_2$$

$$\xrightarrow{CH_3I} \left[(CH_3)_3P \overset{\overset{Si(CH_3)_3}{|}}{C^+} P(CH_3)_3\right] I^-$$

groups confirms the symmetrical structure depicted by the formula (*379*).

A di-cation $(R_3P)_3C^{2+}$ is the product of an addition of methyl iodide to a phosphino-substituted monocation similar to that used in our earlier example (*48*):

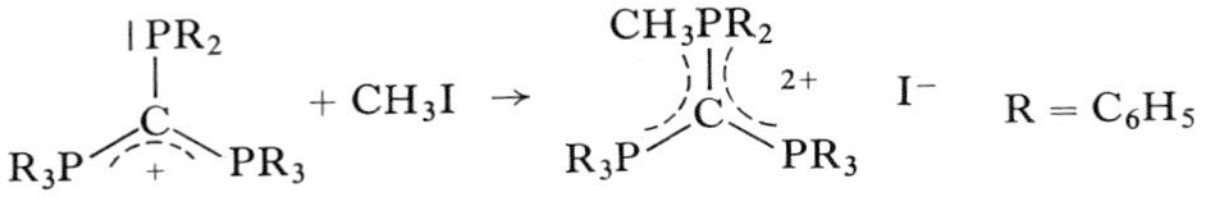

$$R_3P \overset{\overset{|PR_2}{|}}{\underset{+}{C}} PR_3 + CH_3I \rightarrow R_3P \overset{\overset{CH_3PR_2}{\|}}{\underset{2+}{C}} PR_3 \quad I^- \qquad R = C_6H_5$$

The final proof for this structure is not so straightforward, however, as the phenyl substituents cause the usual difficulties, in that the solubilities are poor, and IR as well as NMR spectra are exceedingly complicated. However, chemical evidence and ^{31}P NMR both favor the proposed structure (*236*).

Both cations are likely to have planar SiP_2C and P_3C skeletons, but no single-crystal X-ray investigations have hitherto been undertaken to confirm this most critical prediction.

IX

ISOELECTRONIC SMALL RING SYSTEMS

Small ring compounds are not very common in inorganic chemistry and organometallic chemistry. The recent preparation of a whole series of four-membered organosilicon and organophosphorus ring compounds is therefore somewhat surprising. This is probably not by chance, as most of these compounds belong to an isoelectronic series comprising eight different types of species. In this section these four-membered ring structures will be considered, thus excluding other ring sizes more or less arbitrarily.

Very little is yet known about three- or five-membered rings. This is unfortunate, because there are several indications that very interesting species are to be expected in this field. An almost classical example is a three-membered ring in silazane chemistry detected by Fink more than 10 years ago (*129*, *321*). This unique example has never been generalized or modified. A number of isoelectronic systems may be thought of, but none of them has been synthesized.

$$(CH_3)_3Si{-}N\Big\langle\begin{matrix}Si(CH_3)_2\\ |\\ Si(CH_3)_2\end{matrix}$$

A. Four-Membered Ring Cyclosilazanes

Synthetic studies in silazane chemistry have revealed a high tendency for formation of four-membered ring systems (*130*, *432*). In many careful studies numerous representatives of this class of compounds have been prepared and their composition and structure confirmed by analytical and spectroscopic procedures. A selection is listed in Table XXIX, excluding polymeric species for clarity. Methods of synthesis have been reviewed repeatedly and may therefore be excluded from this text (*128*, *130–133*, *432*).

Though a considerable ring strain is to be expected, the cyclosilazanes exhibit good chemical and, in particular, thermal stability. As in other areas

TABLE XXIX

FOUR-MEMBERED RING CYCLOSILAZANES

$$
\begin{array}{c}
\quad R' \quad\quad R' \\
\quad\quad \searrow M \swarrow \\
R'''R_2Si{-}N \quad\quad N{-}SiR_2R''' \\
\quad\quad \nearrow M \nwarrow \\
\quad R'' \quad\quad R''
\end{array}
$$

R	R′	R″	R‴	M	M′	(°C) M.p.	References
CH_3	CH_3	CH_3	CH_3	Si	Si	39°	*128, 131–133*
CH_3	CH_3	CH_3	Cl	Si	Si	70°	*128, 131–133, 433*
CH_3	CH_3	CH_3	Br	Si	Si	96°–97°	*72, 434*
CH_3	CH_3	CH_3	I	Si	Si	108°–109°	*72, 434*
CH_3	CH_3	Cl	CH_3	Si	Si	28°–29°	*72, 128, 129, 131–133*
CH_3	CH_3	C_2H_5	H_3	Si	Si	b.p. 120°/0.03	*128, 129, 131–133*
C_2H_5	CH_3	CH_3	C_2H_5	Si	Si	—	*305–307*
C_2H_5	CH_3	CH_3	C_2H_5	Si	Ge	—	*305–307*
C_2H_5	CH_3	CH_3	C_2H_5	Si	Sn	—	*305–307*
C_2H_5	CH_3	CH_3	C_2H_5	Ge	Ge	—	*305–307*
C_2H_5	CH_3	CH_3	C_2H_5	Ge	Sn	1°–3°	*305–307*

of organosilicon chemistry, it is observed here that long chains or macrocyclic silazanes are transformed into small ring systems in high yields upon heating (*62, 76, 128, 129, 131–133, 432*).

Spectroscopic data are in agreement with the structure initially proposed (*72, 321*). A full proof was provided by single-crystal X-ray studies (*445*) in 1962. Figure 11 displays the overall arrangements of the atoms, except for the hydrogens. The most interesting result of this study was the planarity of the heavy-atom skeleton, leading to a trigonally planar geo-

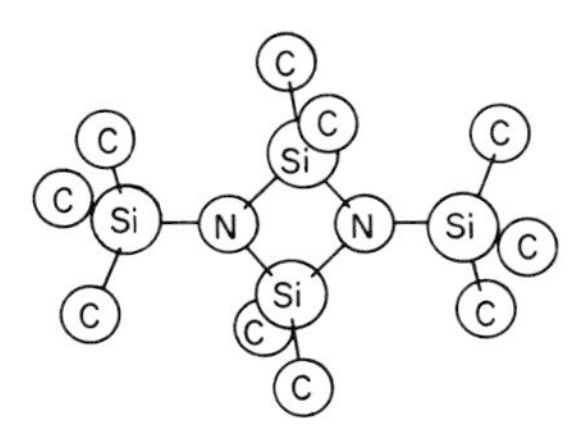

FIG. 11. The molecular structure of the molecule $Si_4N_2(CH_3)_{10}$, as determined by single-crystal X-ray analysis (*445*).

metry of ligands at the nitrogen atoms. This may be taken as an important parallel to the elusive geometry of the acyclic trisilylamines, discussed frequently in this chapter (*120*, *433*, *434*).

The ligands R attached to the silicon atoms have been modified quite extensively, but the four-membered ring structure is retained with surprising steadiness. It seems to be absolutely necessary, however, that the nitrogen atoms have three silicon ligands each, in order to preserve the structure; or at least a bulky alkyl or aryl group, such as *tert*-butyl or phenyl, in addition to one or two silyl ligands. Nothing therefore rules out the assumption that it is mainly for steric reasons that the small ring structure arises in this family of compounds. However, the $(p\rightarrow d)\pi$ argument cannot be rejected, as the arrangement of atoms nicely meets the requirements for this type of bonding.

In recent work by Scherer compounds have been described wherein germanium and tin atoms have replaced the silicon atoms of the ring system at least in part (*305*). Characteristic examples are listed in Table XXIX.

B. *Aluminosiloxane Heterocycles*

Aluminum derivatives of silanols, in which by coordination interaction a four-membered ring system occurs, are mentioned in Section II,B. This principle of structure has turned out to be a general one in aluminosiloxane chemistry and many members of this class of compounds have been assigned this constitution (*330*).

Table XXX gives some examples taken from recent literature. Preparative procedures for these compounds have been summarized in review articles and need not repeated here (*54*, *330*). Analytical and spectroscopic data along with three X-ray crystal investigations have afforded sufficient evidence to confirm the symmetrical structure:

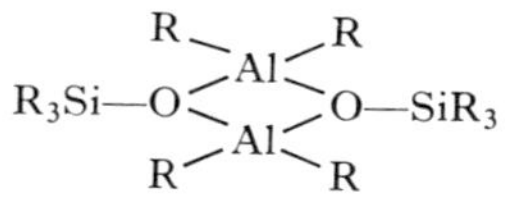

$$
\begin{array}{ccccc}
 & R & & R & \\
 & & Al & & \\
R_3Si{-}O & & & & O{-}SiR_3 \\
 & & Al & & \\
 & R & & R &
\end{array}
$$

It is the coplanarity of the oxygen valencies that is most interesting in this structure (*51*, *53*, *445*, *446*), initially taken as truly exceptional (*100*). As the compounds are isostructural with the cyclosilazanes similar arguments should be used to account for their structural characteristics (*445*, *446*) (see below).

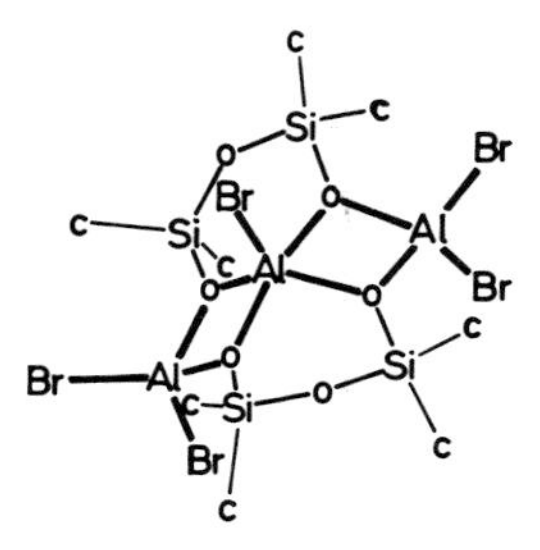

FIG. 12. The molecular structure of the compound $[(CH_3)_2Si]_4O_6Al_3Br_5$, as determined by single-crystal X-ray diffraction (*52*).

The four-membered ring structure appears even in complicated polycyclic arrangements like that of $R_8Si_4O_6Al_3X_5$ molecules (*52*). This is further evidence for the importance of this structural principle (Fig. 12).

TABLE XXX

ALUMINOSILOXANES AND RELATED COMPOUNDS

	M.p. (°C)	B.p. (°C/torr)	References
$[(CH_3)_3SiOAlH_2]_2$	76°(dec)	40°/1[a]	*361*
$[(CH_3)_3SiOAlCl_2]_2$	41°–42°	140°–142°/2	*342*
$[(CH_3)_3SiOAlBr_2]_2$	76°–78°	172°–175°/2	*342*
$[(CH_3)_3SiOAlJ_2]_2$	100°(dec)	dec	*342*
$[(CH_3)_3SiOAlHCl]_2$	19.5°–20.5°	63°–65°/1	*361*
$[(CH_3)_3SiOAlHBr]_2$	7°–8°	54°–57°/1	*361*
$[(CH_3)_3SiOAl(BH_4)_2]_2$	111°–112°	90°–100°/1[a]	*26*
$[(CH_3)_3SiOAlH(BH_4)]_2$	—	44°–46°/1	*26*
$[(CH_3)_3SiOAl(CH_3)_2]_2$	45.5°	81°–85°/1	*323*
$[(CH_3)_3SiOAl(C_2H_5)_2]_2$	105°–113°	115°/1	*323*
$[(CH_3)_3SiSAlCl_2]_2$	56°	50°/1[a]	*320*
$[(CH_3)_3SiOGa(CH_3)_2]_2$	16.5°	34°–35°/1	*363*
$[(CH_3)_3SiOIn(CH_3)_2]_2$	16°	57°/3	*363*
$[(CH_3)_3SiOTl(CH_3)_2]_2$	98°–100°	90°/1[a]	*337*
$[(CH_3)_3GeOAl(CH_3)_2]_2$	64°–66°	128°–130°/15	*25*
$[(CH_3)_3GeOGa(CH_3)_2]_2$	42°–44°	84°–85°/1	*25*
$[(C_6H_5)_3GeOGa(CH_3)_2]_2$	175°–178°	—	*25*
$[(CH_3)_3GeOGa(C_6H_5)_2]_2$	186°–188°	—	*25*
$[(C_6H_5)_3GeOGa(C_6H_5)_2]_2$	291°–293°	—	*25*
$[(CH_3)_3GeOIn(CH_3)_2]_2$	14°–16°	98°–100°/1	*25*

[a] Sublimes.

Whereas for cyclosilazanes only very few analogous systems containing heavier Group IVb elements are known, the aluminosiloxane structure has been shown to occur also in almost all derivatives of gallium, indium, and thallium (*25, 337, 363*). A gallogermoxane was subjected to a preliminary X-ray investigation and turned out to be again isomorphous with the aluminosiloxane species (*25*). It appears therefore, that tricoordinate oxygen

$$\begin{array}{ccccc} & CH_3 & & CH_3 & \\ & & Ga & & \\ (CH_3)_3Ge{-}O & & & & O{-}Ge(CH_3)_3 \\ & & Ga & & \\ & CH_3 & & CH_3 & \end{array}$$

atoms having a planar arrangement of ligands are a widespread phenomenon, which is much more common than anticipated earlier. This is particularly true for small ring coordination oligomers occurring frequently in metal complexes.

In this connection it is appropriate to point out that this is not true, however, with *sulfur* as a donor atom. A recent X-ray investigation of an aluminum mercaptide has shown that a pyramidal geometry is typical for this moiety, as it is in many transition metal sulfur derivatives (*34, 233*). A silylmercapto derivative of aluminum is known, but no information is available as to its structure: $[(CH_3)_3SiSAlCl_2]_2$. It shows a pronounced tendency for polymerization and differs at least in this property from the siloxane analog (*319*). Simple sulfonium salts $R_3S^+X^-$ are known to have a pyramidal arrangement at sulfur (*461*).

$$\begin{array}{ccccc} & Cl & & Cl & \\ & & Al & & \\ (CH_3)_3Si{-}S & & & & S{-}Si(CH_3)_3 \\ & & Al & & \\ & Cl & & Cl & \end{array}$$

C. Aluminophosphinimide Heterocycles

The isoelectronic relation of silanols and phosphines imines, R_3SiOH/R_3PNH, suggests the existence of aluminophosphinimides showing the same structural characteristics as the aluminosiloxanes, and in fact a whole family of aluminophosphinimide heterocycles is now known (*332, 333*). The methods of synthesis are summarized in the scheme below, which illustrates the four pathways used to date. From all procedures the aluminophosphinimide products are obtained in good yields and in the dimeric four-membered ring form only. No other oligomeric state has been detected. In molecular weight determinations the dimeric nature was established beyond doubt (*345*, *387*, *390*). The formulas drawn on this basis were confirmed by comparative Debye-Scherrer studies, from which a distinct similarity in the diffraction pattern was obvious (*345*).

$2\ R_3PNH + (AlR_3)_2$ ↘ $\qquad$ ↙ $2\ R_3PNLi + (R_2AlX)_2$

$$\begin{array}{c} PR_3 \\ \| \\ R_2Al\langle N, N\rangle AlR_2 \\ \| \\ PR_3 \end{array}$$

$[R_3PNAlX_2]_2 + 4\ LiR$ ↗ $\qquad$ ↖ $2\ R_3PNSnR_3 + (AlR_3)_2$

TABLE XXXI

ALUMINOPHOSPHINIMIDE HETEROCYCLES AND RELATED COMPOUNDS

	M.p. (°C)	B.p. (°C/torr)	References
$[(CH_3)_3PNAlBr_2]_2$	291°–294°	—	*390*
$[(CH_3)_3PNAl(CH_3)_2]_2$	129°–130°	110°–115°/0.2[a]	*345, 387, 389*
$[(C_2H_5)_3PNAl(CH_3)_2]_2$	138°–240°	160°–165°/0.02	*345, 389*
$[(C_2H_5)_3PNAl(C_2H_5)_2]_2$	104°–107°	195°–198°/0.02	*345, 389*
$[(CH_3)_3PNGa(CH_3)_2]_2$	107°–108°	100°–105°/0.2[a]	*389, 390*
$[(C_2H_5)_3PNGa(CH_3)_2]_2$	100°–103°	172°/0.02	*345, 389*
$[(CH_3)_3PNIn(CH_3)_2]_2$	110°–112°	118°–120°/0.2	*389, 390*
$[(C_2H_5)_3PNIn(CH_3)_2]_2$	83°–85°	192°/0.02	*345, 389*
$[(C_6H_5)_3PNAl(CH_3)_2]_2$	268°–272°	—	*352*
$[(C_6H_5)_3PNGa(CH_3)_2]_2$	238°–242°	—	*352*
$[(C_6H_5)_3PNIn(CH_3)_2]_2$	230°–232°	—	*352*

[a] Sublimes.

Table XXXI lists the members of the homologous series, synthesized by the methods mentioned above. The chemical and thermal stability of the aluminophosphinimides is quite remarkable. Melting points of 250°–300°C without decomposition are not exceptional, and in most cases volatilities are sufficient for a distillation or sublimation *in vacuo*. As with metal siloxanes, the existence and structural principles are not limited to the aluminum derivatives. Gallium as well as indium form similar phosphinimide complexes, almost exclusively as stable dimers containing Ga_2N_2 or In_2N_2 four-membered rings.

D. Cationic Isosteres of Aluminophosphinimides

1. *Mono-cations*

Substitution of a silicon atom for an aluminum atom in the four-membered ring systems of the aluminophosphinimides formally leads to a cationic species, which is a new type of an inorganic ring system. Compounds containing this skeleton are available from a quite peculiar chemical reaction discovered recently (*391*). Bis(trimethylphosphinimino)dialkylsilanes of the type $(R_3PN)_2SiR_2$ were found to add two equivalents of metal trialkyls to form an ionic coordination compound. The products are compounds of a tetraalkylmetallate anion R_4M^-, and novel cations, in which the nitrogen atoms of the starting material have been bridged by a cationic dialkylmetal moiety, e.g.:

$$R_3P{=}N{-}SiR_2{-}N{=}PR_3 + (AlR_3)_2 \rightarrow R_3P{=}N\langle{}^{SiR_2}_{AlR_2}{}^{+}\rangle N{=}PR_3 \quad AlR_4^-$$

Thus trimethyl aluminum may be said as to react in a polarized form R_2Al^+ AlR_4^-, in equilibrium with the neutral dimers $(R_3Al)_2$. Gallium and, in certain cases, indium alkyls were shown to behave similarly. Some of the compounds known to date are presented in Table XXXII.

For a proof of the structure only spectroscopic methods have been employed so far, but the results seem to be conclusive. The proton magnetic resonance spectra provide direct evidence for a $(CH_3)_4Al^-$ anion, and for a cation exhibiting the characteristic $A_9XX'A'_9$ spin system, known from other four-membered ring systems. The infrared absorptions are also consistent with the formula proposed in each case.

2. *Di-cations*

The substitution of both aluminum atoms in aluminophosphinimides by silicon atoms in principle leads to dications of analogous structure. Ionic compounds built from these cations and suitable anions have been recently reported. More than one synthetic method has been developed and a variety of substances are already known (*455*).

The most obvious method of synthesis consists of the addition of a dialkyldihalosilane to a bis(phosphinimido)dialkylsilane. An alternative procedure makes use of the transsilylation process, in which difunctional dialkylsilyl groups replace the monofunctional trialkylsilyl groups. The

TABLE XXXII

CATIONIC ISOSTERES OF THE ALUMINOPHOSPHINIMIDES ($R = CH_3$)

		M.p. (°C)	References
$R_3P{=}N\langle(SiR_2)(AlR_2)\rangle^{+}N{=}PR_3$	AlR_4^-	136°–142° (dec)	*391*
$R_3P{=}N\langle(SiR_2)(AlR_2)\rangle^{+}N{=}PR_3$	GaR_4^-	132°–137° (dec)	*391*
$R_3P{=}N\langle(SiR_2)(GaR_2)\rangle^{+}N{=}PR_3$	GaR_4^-	135°–138° (dec)	*391*
$R_3P{=}N\langle(SiR_2)(AlR_2)\rangle^{+}N{=}PR_3$	InR_4^-	105°–107° (dec)	*455*
$R_3P{=}N\langle(SiR_2)(SiR_2)\rangle^{2+}N{=}PR_3$	2 Cl^-	179°–181°	*455*
$R_3P{=}N\langle(SiR_2)(SiR_2)\rangle^{2+}N{=}PR_3$	2 Br^-	305°–312° (dec)	*455*
$R_3P{=}N\langle(SiR_2)(SiR_2)\rangle^{2+}N{=}PR_3$	2 I^-	225°–240° (dec)	*455*
$R_3P{=}N\langle(GeR_2)(GeR_2)\rangle^{2+}N{=}PR_3$	2 Cl^-	193°–194°	*455*

$$R_3P{=}N{-}SiR_2{-}N{=}PR_3 + R_2SiX_2 \longrightarrow \left[R_3P{=}N\langle(SiR_2)_2\rangle N{=}PR_3\right]^{2+}\ 2\,X^-$$

$$2\,R_3P{=}N{-}SiR_3 + 2\,R_2SiX_2 \longrightarrow \left[R_3P{=}N\langle(SiR_2)_2\rangle N{=}PR_3\right]^{2+}\ 2\,X^-$$

corresponding trialkylhalosilanes are obtained as by-products. This process resembles the transsilylation in the chemistry of phosphorus ylids (*356*, *455*) in Section VII,A.

Analytical and spectroscopic data support the formulas proposed for the compounds. Hydrolytic and alcoholytic degradation reactions also confirm composition and structure of the compounds, though no final proof has been achieved (Table XXXII).

E. Cationic and Dipolar Isosteres of the Cyclosilazanes

The substitution of a pair of silicon atoms in a molecule by a pair of Al/P atoms is a theoretical approach to design an isoelectronic molecule. This method is also successfully applied in the chemistry of the four-membered ring cyclosilazane. The experiments for the synthesis of such a dipolar

$$R_3Si{-}N\underset{Si(R_2)}{\overset{Si(R_2)}{\lessgtr}}N{-}SiR_3 \qquad R_3Si{-}N\underset{Al^{-}R_2}{\overset{P^{+}R_2}{\lessgtr}}N{-}SiR_3$$

compound are more or less straightforward, as suitable starting materials are known and easy to prepare (*262, 309, 374*). The reactions of silylamino-silylimino-phosphoranes with aluminum trialkyls lead directly to the desired ring system with evolution of alkane (*374*). The products are crystalline materials, soluble in organic solvents and exhibiting the expected molecular weight in the solvents. The structure has not been determined, but all other experimental evidence is in favor of the zwitterionic four-membered ring formula. Gallium and indium analogs have also been prepared and show the corresponding composition and molecular weight.

$$R_3Si{-}N(H){-}PR_2{=}N{-}SiR_3 + AlR_3 \rightarrow R_3Si{-}N\underset{Al^{-}R_2}{\overset{P^{+}R_2}{\lessgtr}}N{-}SiR_3 + RH$$

From spectroscopic analogies the suggestion of an analogous structure is convincing (*374*). When the silylamino-silylimino-phosphorane is not

$$R_3Si{-}N\underset{Ga^{-}R_2}{\overset{P^{+}R_2}{\lessgtr}}N{-}SiR_3 \qquad R_3Si{-}N\underset{In^{-}R_2}{\overset{P^{+}R_2}{\lessgtr}}N{-}SiR_3$$

reacted with an aluminum alkyl, but (after lithiation) with a dialkyldihalo-silane, then a cationic species is found (*373*). Instead of the dialkylaluminum cation, a dialkylsilicon dication now forms the bridging unit between the nitrogen atoms of the donor. Thus a monocation has been produced which

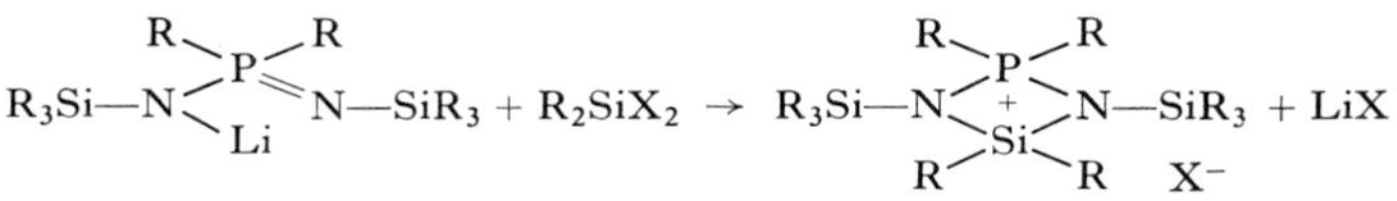

$$R_3Si{-}N\overset{\text{Li}}{\underset{}{<}}\overset{R_2}{P}{=}N{-}SiR_3 + R_2SiX_2 \rightarrow \left[R_3Si{-}N\!<\!\begin{matrix}PR_2\\ \overset{+}{} \\ SiR_2\end{matrix}\!>\!N{-}SiR_3\right] X^- + LiX$$

is closely related to the cyclosilazanes. Only one silicon atom has been replaced by a phosphorus atom to form the isoelectronic species.

The corresponding germanium compounds are formed using dialkyldihalogermanes. So far only very few members of this series have been described, and not all possible methods of synthesis have been tested (Table XXXIII).

TABLE XXXIII

CATIONIC AND DIPOLAR ISOSTERES OF CYCLOSILAZANES

($R = CH_3$; $R' = C_6H_5$)

	M.p. (°C)	References
$R_3Si{-}N\!<\!\begin{matrix}PR_2'\\ AlR_2\end{matrix}\!>\!N{-}SiR_3$	114°–116°	*374*
$R_3Si{-}N\!<\!\begin{matrix}PR_2'\\ GaR_2\end{matrix}\!>\!N{-}SiR_3$	78°–88°	*374*
$R_3Si{-}N\!<\!\begin{matrix}PR_2'\\ InR_2\end{matrix}\!>\!N{-}SiR_3$	62°–65°	*374*
$R_3Si{-}N\!<\!\begin{matrix}PR_2'\\ + \\ SiR_2\end{matrix}\!>\!N{-}SiR_3 \quad Cl^-$	—	*373*
$R_3Si{-}N\!<\!\begin{matrix}PR_2'\\ + \\ GeR_2\end{matrix}\!>\!N{-}SiR_3 \quad Cl^-$	—	*373*

F. Silylated Phosphorus Ylids Containing a Four-Membered Ring

Much emphasis has been given to the analogy between the silylamines and silylated phosphorus ylids throughout this chapter. In order to describe one of the most recently discovered four-membered ring systems we will return to this relation.

$$R_3Si{-}N\underset{Si R_2}{\overset{Si R_2}{\diamond}}N{-}SiR_3 \qquad R_3P{=}C\underset{Si R_2}{\overset{Si R_2}{\diamond}}C{=}PR_3$$

The preceding formulas make it immediately obvious that a cyclic bis-ylidic compound containing two silicon atoms should be a species highly favored energetically, if the stability of the cyclosilazanes is of significance. Experiments designed to test this prediction show that this is indeed the case (*356*, *357*). Three main preparative methods have been developed, two of which yielded the new ylids without significant difficulties. The reaction pathways are, in fact, quite complicated and it is surprising that multistep processes of this type can afford these products in good yields. From this experience it seems apparent that the cyclic bis-ylid structure has a high tendency to formation and is favored over all other possible types of oligomers. A single-crystal structure analysis is in progress (*204*)

$$6\ R_3PCH_2 + 2\ R_2SiX_2 \searrow$$

$$R_3P{=}C\underset{Si R_2}{\overset{Si R_2}{\diamond}}C{=}PR_3$$

$$R_3P{=}C(SiR_2X)_2 + 2\ R_2P(CH_2)_2Li \nearrow$$

$R = CH_3$; m.p. 70°–71°C

to confirm the findings of spectroscopic and analytical studies, though the data provided by the latter are fully consistent with the constitution proposed in the formulas (*357*).

G. Discussion

Eight different four-membered ring systems, most of them novel in type, have been presented in this section, all of which belong to the same isoelectronic series:

SiR_3	SiR_3	PR_3	SiR_3
|	|	‖	|
N	O	N	N
R_2Si SiR_2	R_2Al AlR_2	R_2Al AlR_2	R_2P AlR_2
N	O	N	N
|	|	‖	|
SiR_3	SiR_3	PR_3	SiR_3

SiR_3	PR_3	PR_3	PR_3
|	‖	‖	‖
N	N	N	C
R_2P + SiR_2	R_2Si + AlR_2	R_2Si 2+ SiR_2	R_2Si SiR_2
N	N	N	C
|	‖	‖	‖
SiR_3	PR_3	PR_3	PR_3

For most of them analogs containing heavier elements of the same groups of the Periodic Table are known to exist and to have the same structural characteristics. This family of compounds is probably one of the most remarkable groups of isoelectronic compounds, as most of them *per se* would be considered as highly strained systems of limited stability, whereas experiments tell us that all of them are highly favored by thermodynamics and/or kinetics.

The reason for this is not clear and possible explanations have been offered very briefly, where it occasionally seemed to be appropriate. It is probably more important, however, to know about the effect and its scope now displayed by the numerous classes of compounds, than to produce a theoretical explanation of any kind from these early results.

X

SIX- AND EIGHT-MEMBERED RING SYSTEMS

It has long been recognized that in the chemistry of six- and eight-membered ring molecules the isoelectronic principle is of high significance. Cyclic metaphosphates and silicates, together with the modifications of sulfur trioxide, are well-known examples of isoelectronic families of a cyclic structure. In *organo*phosphorus and *organo*silicon chemistry similar

$$SiO_3^{2-}, PO_3^-, SO_3$$

relations exist. Familiar representatives are the cyclic diorganosiloxanes and diorganophosphonitrilic compounds.

Other species have been described in recent literature, however, that have shown these relations in a much broader scope and these examples will briefly be considered here. No complete consideration of the cyclic siloxanes and phosphonitriles is justified, as these materials have often been reviewed in earlier and recent literature. However, some remarks about them are appropriate, to point out the most interesting features relevant for this discussion.

A. Cyclic Diorganophosphonitrilic Systems

Compounds of the composition $(R_2PN)_n$ have long been known and many methods of preparation have been developed (*264*). The size of the molecules depends largely on the nature of the residues R and, in cases where the system is not in thermodynamic equilibrium, on the experimental conditions of the synthetic procedure.

Only one member of the series will be considered here, as it is most closely related to the isosteres to be discussed later. Tetrameric dimethylphosphonitrile $[(CH_3)_2PN]_4$ is a basic member of the series and has been investigated in considerable detail. Its preparation, however, is difficult and poor yields have to be tolerated. Other molecular sizes are also known, but are less well characterized (*264*).

The structure of the tetramer, as revealed by X-ray crystallographic methods (*115*), is depicted in Fig. 13. It is clear from this picture that the

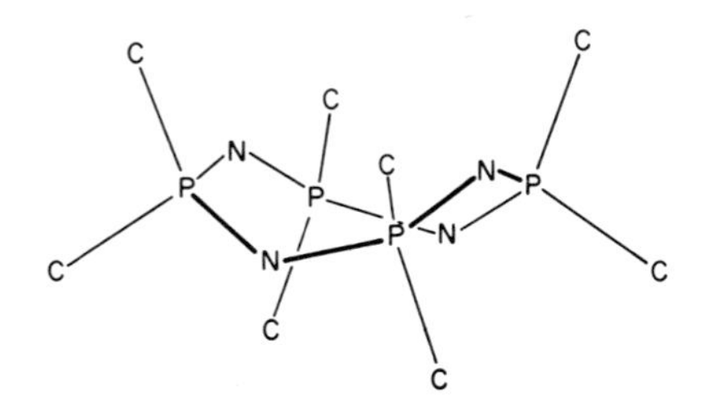

FIG. 13. The molecular structure of the dimethylphosphonitrile tetramer $[NP(CH_3)_2]_4$. After Dougill (*115*).

ring system is not planar, but has equidistant PN bonds and displays large bond angles at nitrogen (132°). These findings are again most significant for the description of bonding, which has often been discussed and attempted on various grounds. As anticipated, no final conclusion has been reached as yet (*265*).

Other phosphonitrilic systems exhibit a similar constitution, varying slightly with the nature of the substituents. More bulky groups, of course, will give rise to more serious distortions which can be attributed to sheer steric factors, other intermolecular interactions in the crystal being neglected. The corresponding dialkylarsenonitriles $(R_2AsN)_n$ have not been prepared to date.

B. *Cyclic Diorganosiloxane Systems*

Diorganosiloxane compounds, known for more than half a century, are existent in a variety of molecular sizes and structures, many of which have been explored quite carefully. Again the substituent R in $(R_2SiO)_n$ is responsible for the thermodynamic preference for a certain number n for a given compound under selected conditions (*7a*, *36*, *119*, *258*).

Di*methyl*siloxane oligomers are of eminent importance in the chemistry of silicones, most notably the *tetrameric* modification $[(CH_3)_2SiO]_4$. For this molecule the structure has been determined (*418*) as described in Fig. 14.

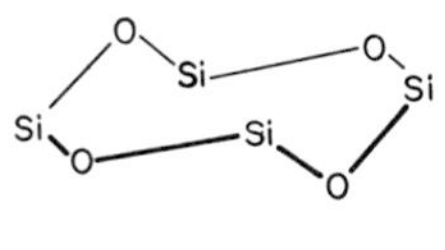

FIG. 14. Configuration of the eight-membered ring in octamethylcyclotetrasiloxane. After Steinfink *et al.* (*418*).

In its characteristics the structure is surprisingly similar to that of the phosphonitrilic isostere. It is therefore legitimate to consider both problems jointly, as has been done frequently in the literature (*101–103*, *106*, *107*, *111*, *182*, *246*, *401*, *421*, *424*). The trimeric species, which is not favored thermodynamically under similar conditions, has a six-membered ring structure with somewhat different dimensions, concerning mainly the bond angles at oxygen or nitrogen. It is probably this parameter which in fact dominates in the preference of one oligomer or the other (Table XXXIV).

Dialkyl*germoxanes* are also known to exist as trimers and tetramers, but these are much more easily transformed into each other (*68, 247, 297, 301*). The mobile equilibrium seems to be shifted towards the tetramer under standard conditions. No detailed structure analysis has been reported.

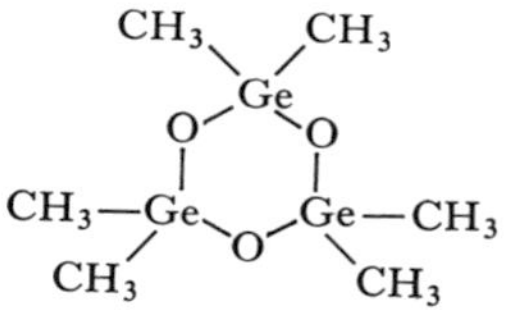

$[(CH_3)_2GeO]_3$ 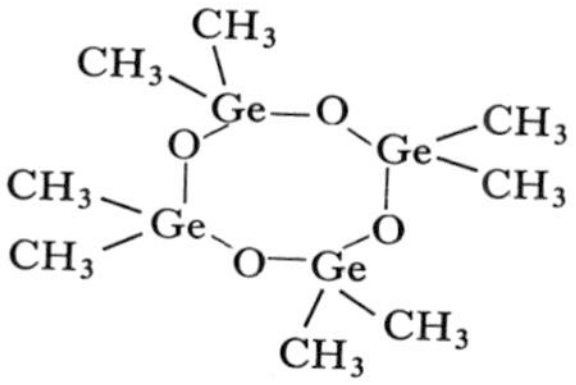 $[(CH_3)_2GeO]_4$

TABLE XXXIV

SOME DIALKYLPHOSPHONITRILES, -SILOXANES, -ALUMINUM FLUORIDES, -ALUMINUM PHOSPHINATES, -ALUMINUM SULFOXIMIDES, -SILICON SULFDIIMIDES, AND RELATED COMPOUNDS

	M.p. (°C)	B.p. (°C/torr)	References
$[(CH_3)_2PN]_3$	195°–196°	—	*264, 396*
$[(CH_3)_2PN]_4$	163°–164°	—	*264, 396*
$[(CH_3)_2SiO]_3$	64°–65°	135°/760	*36, 119, 258*
$[(CH_3)_2SiO]_4$	17.5°	175°/760	*36, 119, 258, 418*
$[(CH_3)_2GeO]_3$	—	—	*68*
$[(CH_3)_2GeO]_4$	91°–92°	211°/760	*68, 247, 297, 301*
$[(CH_3)_2AlF]_4$	—	98°–100°/80	*183, 197, 220, 349, 438, 459*
$[(CH_3)_2GaF]_3$	20°–22°	75°/20	*384*
$[(CH_3)_2GaF]_4$	27.5°	—	*350*
$[(CH_3)_2GaOH]_4$	87°–88.5°	—	*194, 412*
$[(CH_3)_2AlO_2P(CH_3)_2]_2$	42°	100°/0.01	*96, 97*
$[(CH_3)_2GaO_2As(CH_3)_2]_2$	144°–145°	110°/0.01[a]	*96, 347, 402*
$[(CH_3)_2AlONS(CH_3)_2]_2$	184°–185°	160°/0.01[a]	*347*
$[(CH_3)_2GaONS(CH_3)_2]_2$	151°–152°	100°/0.01[a]	*347*
$[(CH_3)_2InONS(CH_3)_2]_2$	219°	—	*347*
$[(CH_3)_2SiN_2S(CH_3)_2]_2$	154°	90°–100°/0.1[a]	*22*

[a] Sublimes.

C. Diorganoaluminum Fluoride Oligomers

Though it was evident from the physical properties of dialkylaluminum fluorides that the substances were oligomeric, it was not until recently that the molecular size has been determined. Work by Laubengayer and Lengnick (*220*) and by Schmidbaur and Klein (*349*, *351*) has then shown that diethyl-, dimethyl-, and diphenylaluminum fluoride exist as distinct *tetramers* in solution. From ^1H NMR studies it was derived that two fluorine atoms were in equivalent coordination interaction to each aluminum atom, giving rise to a symmetrical 1:2:1 triplet at the methyl resonances (*349*) for $[(CH_3)_2AlF]_4$.

A detailed study of the vibrational spectra provided evidence for planar or quasiplanar arrangements of the aluminum and fluorine atoms in an eight-membered ring, indicated by an idealized D_{4h} symmetry (*438*). This symmetry is probably not retained in the liquid and glassy form of the undiluted material, where intermolecular interactions gain importance.

Various methods of preparation are available for dialkylaluminum fluorides at present, but in all cases only the tetramers were produced, no hint for a trimer being detectable. It is therefore quite meaningful that

$$R_2AlCl + NaF \xrightarrow{-NaCl} \qquad (183, 197, 220, 459)$$

$$R_3Al + R_3SiF \xrightarrow{-R_4Si} \qquad (349)$$

$$R_3Al + R_3SnF \xrightarrow{-R_4Sn} (R_2AlF)_4 \qquad (351)$$

$$R_3Al + F_2 \xrightarrow{-RF} \qquad (438)$$

$$R_3Al + BF_3 \xrightarrow{-BR_3} \qquad (438)$$

the recently prepared dialkyl*gallium* fluorides were found to exist in trimeric *and* tetrameric forms (*350*, *384*). The latter seemed to be most stable under standard conditions again, it is true, but the trimers are easily obtained upon distillation and undergo rearrangement with ring expansion only quite slowly upon storage.

IR and Raman data are consistent with a planar or nearly planar structure of the trimer (D_{3h}), and, less certain, of the tetramer (D_{4h}). It then appears that dialkylgallium fluorides nicely resemble the dialkylgermoxanes, existing in trimers and tetramers, easily transformed into each other.

Dimethylgallium *hydroxides* were found to exist as trimers and tetramers more than 15 years ago (*194*, *412*), and the crystal structure of the tetramer

(*412*) fits satisfactorily the picture drawn for the family of the isosteres (Table XXXIV), (Fig. 15). Dialkyl*aluminum* hydroxides have not yet been prepared!

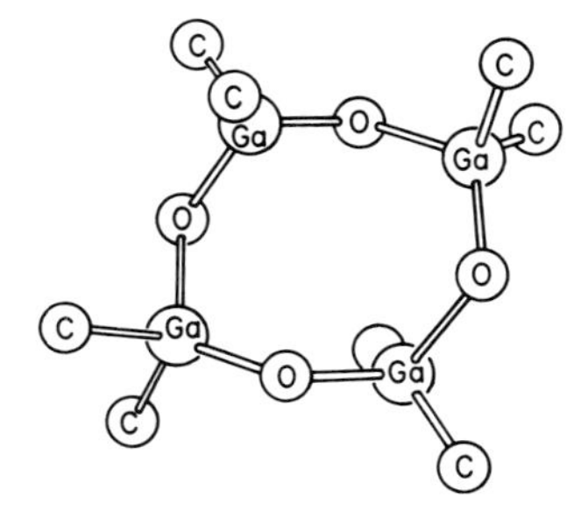

FIG. 15. Model of the tetrameric molecule $[(CH_3)_2GaOH]_4$. After Smith and Hoard (*412*).

D. Diorganoaluminum Diorganophosphinates

In early work by Coates *et al.* some dialkylaluminum dialkylphosphinates were prepared and assigned an eight-membered ring structure by the authors (*96*, *97*). It is easy to recognize this type of a cyclic system as a true isostere of the tetrameric dialkylsiloxanes. Pairwise substitution of silicon atoms by Al/P pairs of atoms transforms these species into one another.

In later experiments dimeric structures have also been confirmed for dialkylgallium and diorganoindium diorganophosphinates and arsonates (*97*, *347*), and an X-ray structure determination of a gallium phosphinate provided final proof for the cyclic constitution (*402*). Spectroscopic results had also left little doubt that this proposal was correct (Table XXXIV).

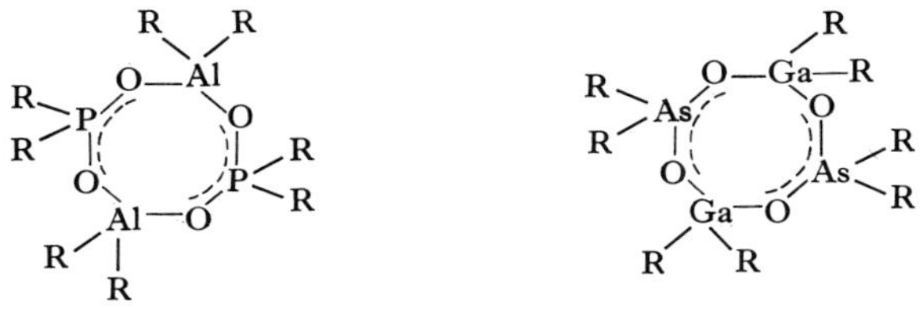

The structural analysis again disclosed an eight-membered ring system having large bond angles at the bridging oxygen atoms, similar to those detected in phosphonitrilic and siloxane compounds (Fig. 16). Deviations from planarity are small, as expected (*402*).

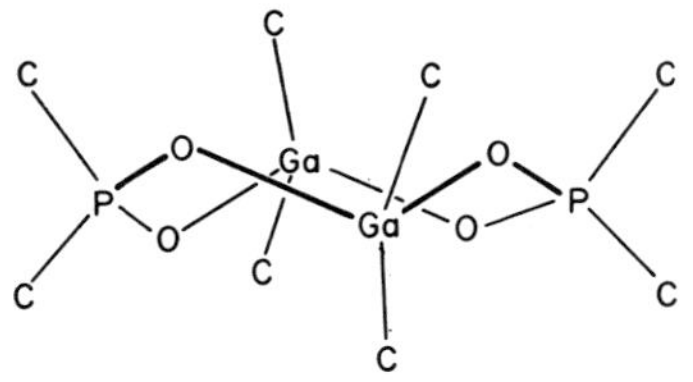

FIG. 16. Molecular structure of dimethylgalliumdimethylphosphinate $[(CH_3)_2GaOOP(CH_3)_2]_2$. After Shearer and Spencer (*402*).

The homologous mono- and dithiophosphinate compounds of aluminum and the heavier Group IIIb elements do not form dimeric species with an eight-membered ring, but appear as monomers with four-membered ring structures instead (*96*, *97*). This resembles the properties of silthiane compounds (*161*), known to be dimers with a similar atomic arrangement.

The above structural characteristics are thus clearly confined to the nitrogen, oxygen, and fluorine compounds of silicon and its neighbors in the Periodic Table. The preference of phosphorus, sulfur, and their heavier analogs for small valency angles causes new structural features.

E. Diorganoaluminum Diorganosulfoximides

Diorganosulfoximines, R_2SONH, are isosteres of diorganophosphinic acids, R_2POOH (*333, 346*). It is therefore not surprising that the recently discovered diorganoaluminum sulfoximides were found to have similar properties and structures as the corresponding phosphinates (*347*). Following various pathways of chemical synthesis these compounds are invariably obtained as coordination dimers, the structure being based on an eight-membered ring system. Analytical and spectroscopic data are in agreement

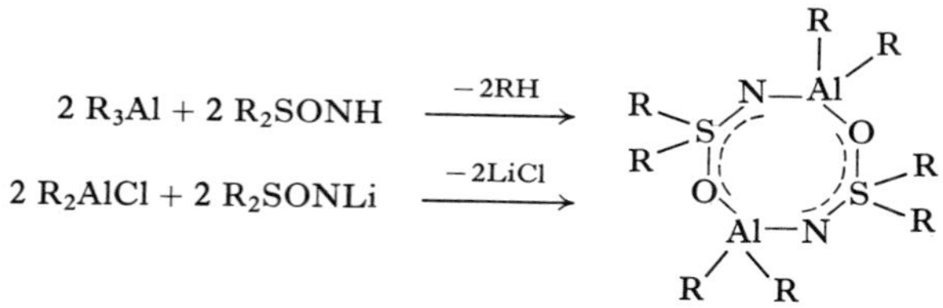

$$2\,R_3Al + 2\,R_2SONH \xrightarrow{-2RH}$$

$$2\,R_2AlCl + 2\,R_2SONLi \xrightarrow{-2LiCl}$$

$$\begin{array}{ccc} & N-AlR_2 & \\ R_2S & & O \\ O & & SR_2 \\ & R_2Al-N & \end{array}$$

with this formula and the physical properties are fully consistent with it (*347*). The same is true for a gallium and indium analog (Table XXXIV).

Principles of a polymeric structure are found for organozinc and organocadmium sulfoximides and other coordination polymers on the sulfoximide basis (*348*). For many of those there are obvious parallels in the chemistry of metal and organometal phosphinate polymers (*49*, 298), too, so that the isoelectronic relationship proves its validity for these polymeric systems as well: $\{[(CH_3)_2SON]_2Zn\}_n$ and $\{[(CH_3)_2PO_2]_2Zn\}_n$ [For example, see ref. (*348*)].

F. Diorganosilicon Diorganosulfdiimides

Appel and co-workers (*22*) have synthesized compounds closely related to the phosphonitrilic systems. The diorganosilicon diorganosulfdiimides are seen to appear, if phosphorus atoms of the phosphonitrilic tetramer are replaced pairwise by Si/S pairs of atoms. Such species are in fact obtained without experimental difficulties following straightforward preparative procedures. Analytical and molecular weight studies support a formula with an eight-membered ring system, as depicted in the equations. No indication for the existence of isomers with a lower or higher molecular weight was recorded and it therefore is again observed that it is the eight-membered heterocycle which presents an optimum in thermodynamic stability (Table

← $R_2S(NH)_2 + R_2SiX_2$

← $R_2S(NH)_2 + R_2Si(NR_2)_2$, etc.

XXXIV). The reason for this has often been discussed for the known isosteres. The synthesis of new species of this and other kinds may contribute to a final solution to this vital problem of organometallic chemistry.

References

1. Abel, E. W., and Singh, A., *J. Chem. Soc.* p. 690 (1959).
1a. Adamson, G. W., and Bart, J. C. J., *J. Chem. Soc., A* p. 1452 (1970).
2. Ahrland, S., Chatt, J., and Davies, N. R., *Quart. Rev. (London)* **12**, 265 (1958).
3. Aksnes, G., and Brudvik, L. J., *Acta Chem. Scand.* **17**, 1616 (1963).
4. Aksnes, G., and Gramstadt, T., *Acta Chem. Scand.* **14**, 1485 (1960).
5. Allegra, G., and Perego, G., *Acta Cryst.* **16**, 185 (1963).
6. Allred, A. L., Rochow, E. G., and Stone, F. G. A., *J. Inorg. & Nucl. Chem.* **2**, 416 (1956).
7. Andrianov, K. A., *Usp. Khim.* **26**, 895 (1957) and **27**, 1257 (1957).
7a. Andrianov, K. A., Haiduc, I., and Kananashvili, L. M., *Russ. Chem. Rev. (English Transl.)* **32**, 243 (1963).
8. Andrianov, K. A., and Zhdanov, A. A., *J. Polymer Sci.* **30**, 513 (1958).
9. Andrianov, K. A., Zhdanov, A. A., and Kazakova, K., *Izv. Akad. Nauk SSSR, Otd. Khim. Nauk* p. 466 (1959).
10. Andrianov, K. A., Zhdanov, A. A., Kurasheva, N. A., and Dulova, W. G., *Dokl. Akad. Nauk. SSSR* **112**, 1050 (1957).
11. Andrianov, K. A., Zhdanov, A. A., and Pavlov, S. A., *Dokl. Akad. Nauk SSSR* **102**, 85 (1955).
12. Appel, R., *Angew. Chem.* **73**, 533 (1961).
13. Appel, R., *Angew. Chem.* **75**, 220 (1963).
14. Appel, R., and Büchler, G., *Z. Anorg. Allgem. Chem.* **320**, 3 (1963).
15. Appel, R., and Büchler, G., *Z. Naturforsch.* **17b**, 422 (1962).
16. Appel, R., Büchner, W., and Guth, E., *Ann. Chem.* **618**, 53 (1958).
17. Appel, R., and Hauss, A., *Angew. Chem.* **71**, 626 (1959).
18. Appel, R., and Hauss, A., *Chem. Ber.* **93**, 405 (1960).

19. Appel, R., and Hauss, A., *Z. Anorg. Allgem. Chem.* **311**, 290 (1961).
20. Appel, R., Heinen, H., and Schöllhorn, R., *Chem. Ber.* **99**, 3118 (1966).
21. Appel, R., Köhlein, G., and Schöllhorn, R., *Chem. Ber.* **98**, 1355 (1965).
22. Appel, R., Siekman, L., and Hoppen, H. O., *Chem. Ber.* **101**, 2861 (1968).
23. Appel, R., and Voigt, E., *Chem. Ber.* **95**, 2225 (1962).
24. Appel, R., and Wagner, D., *Angew. Chem.* **72**, 209 (1960).
25. Armer, B., and Schmidbaur, H., *Chem. Ber.* **100**, 1521 (1967).
26. Armer, B., and Schmidbaur, H., *Chem. Ber.* **101**, 2256 (1968).
27. Armstrong, R. S., Aroney, M. J., LeFevre, R. J. W., Pierens, R. K., Saxby, J. D., and Wilkins, C. J., *J. Chem. Soc., A* p. 2735 (1969).
28. Atoji, M., and Lipscomb, W. N., *Acta Cryst.* **7**, 597 (1154).
29. Baldwin, R. A., and Washburn, R. M., *J. Org. Chem.* **26**, 3549 (1961).
30. Barraclough, C. G., Bradley, D. C., Lewis, J., and Thomas, J. M., *J. Chem. Soc.* p. 2601 (1961).
31. Bart, J. C. J., *Angew. Chem.* **80**, 697 (1968).
32. Bart, J. C. J., *J. Chem. Soc., B* p. 350 (1969).
33. Batujev, M. J., Shostakowskij, M. F., Belyaev, U. J., Matveyeva, A. D., and Dulova, E. V., *Dokl. Akad. Nauk SSSR* **95**, 531 (1954).
34. Bauer, D. J., and Stucky, G. D., *J. Am. Chem. Soc.* **91**, 5462 (1969).
35. Baumgärtner, R., Sawodny, W., and Goubeau, J., *Z. Anorg. Allgem. Chem.* **333**, 171 (1964).
36. Bažant, V., Chvalovsky, V., and Rathousky, J., "Organosilicon Compounds." Publ. House Czech. Acad. Sci., Prague, 1965.
37. Beattie, J. R., and Parrett, F. W., *J. Chem. Soc., A* p. 1784 (1966).
38. Becke-Goehring, M., and Lehr, W., *Chem. Ber.* **94**, 1591 (1961).
39. Becke-Goehring, M., and Lehr, W., *Z. Anorg. Allgem. Chem.* **325**, 287 (1963).
40. Becke-Goehring, M., and Thielmann, H., *Z. Anorg. Allgem. Chem.* **308**, 33 (1961).
41. Bent, H. A., *J. Chem. Educ.* **37**, 616 (1960); **43**, 170 (1966).
42. Bertrand, J. A., *Inorg. Chem.* **6**, 495 (1967).
43. Bestmann, H. J., Liberda, H. G., and Snyder, J. P., *J. Am. Chem. Soc.* **90**, 2963 (1968).
44. Bestmann, H. J., and Snyder, J. P., *J. Am. Chem. Soc.* **89**, 3936 (1967).
45. Birkhofer, L., and Kim, S. M., *Chem. Ber.* **97**, 2100 (1964).
46. Birkhofer, L., Ritter, A., and Kim, S. M., *Chem. Ber.* **96**, 3099 (1963).
47. Birkhofer, L., Ritter, A., and Richter, P., *Chem. Ber.* **96**, 2750 (1963).
48. Birum, G. H., and Matthews, C. N., *J. Am. Chem. Soc.* **88**, 4198 (1966).
49. Block, B. P., Simkin, J., and Ocone, L., *J. Am. Chem. Soc.* **84**, 1749 (1962).
50. Bock, H., and tom Dieck, H., *Z. Naturforsch.* **21b**, 739 (1966).
51. Bonamico, M., and Dessy, G., *J. Chem. Soc., A* p. 1786 (1967).
52. Bonamico, M., and Dessy, G., *J. Chem. Soc.* p. 291 (1968).
53. Bonamico, M., Dessy, G., and Ercolani, C., *Chem. Commun.* p. 24 (1966).
54. Borisov, S. N., Woronkow, M. G., and Lukevits, E. R., "Silico-elementorganic Compounds," p. 189. Khimia, Leningrad, 1966.
55. Bradley, D. C., *Advan. Chem. Ser.* **23**, 10 (1959).
56. Bradley, D. C., Hursthouse, M. B., and Rodesiler, P. F., *Chem. Commun.* p. 14 (1969).
57. Bradow, H. L., Van der Werf, C. A., and Kleinberg, J., *J. Chem. Educ.* **24**, 433 (1947).
58. Bränden, C. J., *Acta Chem. Scand.* **17**, 1363 (1963).
59. Bränden, C. J., *Arkiv Kemi* **22**, 485 (1964).
60. Bränden, C. J., and Lindqvist, I., *Acta Chem. Scand.* **15**, 167 (1961).
61. Braune, H., and Pinnow, P., *Z. Physik. Chem.* **B35**, 239 (1937).

62. Breed, L. W., Budde, W. L., and Elliott, R. L., *J. Organometal. Chem.* (*Amsterdam*) **6**, 676 (1966).
63. Brockway, L. O., and Wall, F. T., *J. Am. Chem. Soc.* **56**, 2373 (1934).
64. Brook, A. G., and Gilman, H., *J. Am. Chem. Soc.* **76**, 77 (1954).
65. Brown, D. A., Mohammed, A., and Sharp, D. W. A., *Spectrochim. Acta* **21**, 1013 (1965).
66. Brown, H. C., *J. Chem. Educ.* **36**, 424 (1959).
67. Brown, M. G., *Trans. Faraday Soc.* **55**, 9 (1959).
68. Brown, M. P., and Rochow, E. G., *J. Am. Chem. Soc.* **82**, 4166 (1960).
69. Bürger, H., *Fortschr. Chem. Forsch.* **9**, 1 (1967–1968).
70. Bürger, H., *Organometal. Chem. Rev.* **A3**, 451 (1968), Ref. 40.
71. Bürger, H., *Organometal. Chem. Rev.* **A3**, 425 (1968).
72. Bürger, H., Bogusch, E., and Geymayer, P., *Z. Anorg. Allgem. Chem.* **349**, 124 (1967).
73. Bürger, H., Forker, C., and Goubeau, J., *Monatsh. Chem.* **96**, 597 (1965).
74. Bürger, H., and Wannagat, U., *J. Organometal. Chem.* (*Amsterdam*) **3**, 113 (1965).
75. Burg, A. B., and Wagner, R. J., *J. Am. Chem. Soc.* **75**, 3872 (1953).
76. Bush, R. P., Lloyd, N. C., and Pearce, C. A., *J. Chem. Soc., A* p. 253 and 808 (1969).
77. Caldow, C. L., and Coulson, C. A., *Trans. Faraday Soc.* **58**, 633 (1962).
78. Cameron, T. S., and Prout, C. K., *Chem. Commun.* p. 455 (1967).
79. Cameron, T. S., and Prout, C. K., *Chem. Commun.* p. 684 (1968).
80. Cameron, T. S., and Prout, C. K., *J. Chem. Soc., C* p. 2281 (1969).
81. Cameron, T. S., and Prout, C. K., *J. Chem. Soc., C* p. 2285 (1969).
82. Cameron, T. S., and Prout, C. K., *J. Chem. Soc., C* p. 2289 (1969).
83. Cameron, T. S., and Prout, C. K., *J. Chem. Soc., C* p. 2292 (1969).
84. Cameron, T. S., and Prout, C. K., *J. Chem. Soc., C* p. 2295 (1969).
85. Caron, A., and Donohue, J., *Acta Cryst.* **15**, 1052 (1962).
86. Caron, A., Palenik, G. J., Goldish, E., and Donohue, J., *Acta Cryst.* **17**, 102 (1964).
87. Caunt, A. D., Mackle, H., and Sutton, L. E., *Trans. Faraday Soc.* **47**, 943 (1951).
88. Caunt, A. D., Short, L. N., and Woodward, L. A., *Trans. Faraday Soc.* **48**, 873 (1952).
89. Chernyshev, E. A., and Bugarenko, E. F., *Organometal. Chem. Rev.* **A3**, 469 (1969).
90. Chioccola, G., and Daly, J. J., *J. Chem. Soc., A* p. 568 (1968).
91. Chopard, P. A., and Hudson, R. F., *J. Inorg. & Nucl. Chem.* **25**, 801 (1963).
92. Chremos, G. N., and Zingaro, R. A., *J. Organometal. Chem.* (*Amsterdam*) **22**, 637 and 647 (1970).
93. Clark, A. H., and Haaland, H., *Chem. Commun.* p. 912 (1969).
94. Clark, H. C., O'Brien, R. J., and Trotter, J., *Proc. Chem. Soc.* p. 85 (1963); *J. Chem. Soc.* p. 2332 (1964).
95. Clark, J. P., Langford, V. M., and Wilkins, C. J., *J. Chem. Soc.* p. 792 (1967), and literature quoted therein.
96. Coates, G. E., and Mukherjee, D., *J. Chem. Soc.* p. 1295 (1964).
97. Coates, G. E., and Ridley, D., *J. Chem. Soc.* p. 1870 (1965).
98. Cotton, F. A., Barnes, R. D., and Bannister, E., *J. Chem. Soc.* p. 5267 (1960).
99. Cotton, F. A., and Soderberg, R. H., *J. Am. Chem. Soc.* **85**, 2402 (1963).
100. Cotton, F. A., and Wilkinson, G., "Advanced Inorganic Chemistry," 2nd ed., p. 363. Wiley (Interscience), New York, 1966.
101. Craig, D. P., Maccoll, A., Nyholm, R. S., Orgel, L. E., and Sutton, L. E., *J. Chem. Soc.* p. 332 (1954).
102. Craig, D. P., and Mitchell, K. A. R., *J. Chem. Soc.* p. 4682 (1965); p. 2683 (1968).
103. Craig, D. P., and Paddock, N. L., *Nature* **181**, 1052 (1958); *Chem. & Ind.* (*London*) p. 3 (1958).

104. Crews, P., *J. Am. Chem. Soc.* **90**, 2961 (1968).
105. Cross, P., Hartmann, C., and Bingham, J. T., *Trans. Faraday Soc.* **62**, 2388 (1966).
106. Cruickshank, D. W. J., *J. Chem. Soc.* p. 5486 (1961).
107. Cruickshank, D. W. J., Webster, B. C., and Mayers, D. F., *J. Chem. Phys.* **40**, 3733 (1964).
108. Daasch, L. W., and Smith, D. C., *J. Chem. Phys.* **19**, 22 (1951).
109. Daasch, L. W., and Smith, D. C., *Anal. Chem.* **23**, 857 (1951).
110. Damm, K., and Noll, W., *Kolloid-Z.* **158**, 97 (1958).
111. Dewar, M. J. S., Lucken, E. A. C., and Whitehead, M. A., *J. Chem. Soc.* p. 2423 (1960).
112. Dilthey, W., and Eduardoff, F., *Ber. Deut. Chem. Ges.* **37**, 1139 (1904).
113. Dittmar, A., and Hellner, E., *Angew. Chem.* **81**, 701 (1969).
114. Doering, W. E., and Hoffmann, A. K., *J. Am. Chem. Soc.* **77**, 521 (1955).
115. Dougill, M. W., *J. Chem. Soc.* p. 5471 (1961).
116. Driscoll, J. S., Grisley, D. W., Pustinger, J. V., Harris, J. E., and Matthews, C. N., *J. Org. Chem.* **29**, 2427 (1964).
117. Duncan, J. L., and Mills, I. M., *Spectrochim. Acta* **20**, 1089 (1964).
118. Eaborn, C., *J. Chem. Soc.* p. 2846 (1952).
119. Eaborn, C., "Organosilicon Compounds." Butterworth, London and Washington, D.C., 1960.
120. Ebsworth, E. A. V., "Volatile Silicon Compounds." Pergamon Press, Oxford, 1963.
121. Ebsworth, E. A. V., *in* "Organometallic Compounds of the Group IV Elements" (A. G. MacDiarmid, ed.), Vol. I, Part 1, pp. 1–104. Marcel Dekker, New York, 1968.
122. Egorov, Yu. P., Leites, L. A., Kravtsova, I. D., and Mironov, V. F., *Izv. Akad. Nauk SSSR, Otd. Khim. Nauk* p. 1114 (1963).
123. Epstein, E. F., Bernal, I., and Balch, A. L., *Chem. Commun.* p. 136 (1970).
124. Eto, M., Kinoshita, Y., and Kato, T., *Agr. Biol. Chem.* (*Tokyo*) **27**, 789 (1963).
125. Fenton, D. E., Massey, A. G., and Urch, D. S., *J. Organometal. Chem.* (*Amsterdam*) **6**, 352 (1966).
126. Ferguson, G., and Macauly, E. W., *J. Chem. Soc., A* p. 1 (1969).
127. Fessenden, R., and Fessenden, J. S., *Chem. Rev.* **61**, 361 (1961).
128. Fink, W., *Angew. Chem.* **73**, 736 (1961).
129. Fink, W., *Helv. Chim. Acta* **46**, 720 (1963).
130. Fink, W., *Angew. Chem.* **78**, 803 (1966).
131. Fink, W., *Helv. Chim. Acta* **51**, 111 (1968).
132. Fink, W., *Angew. Chem.* **81**, 499 (1969).
133. Fink, W., *Helv. Chim. Acta* **52**, 2261 (1969).
134. Fluck, E., *Z. Naturforsch.* **18b**, 664 (1963); *Chemiker Ztg.* **88**, 956 (1964).
135. Fluck, E., and Goldman, F. L., *Chem. Ber.* **96**, 3091 (1963).
136. Frisch, M. A., Heal, H. G., Mackle, H., and Madden, I. O., *J. Chem. Soc.* p. 899 (1965).
137. Fukukawa, S., and Kohama, S., *Sci. Ind.* **29**, 70 (1955); *Chem. Abstr.* **49**, 13888 (1955).
138. Gans, P., and Smith, B. C., *J. Chem. Soc.* p. 4172 (1964).
139. Giguère, P. A., and Chin, D., *Can. J. Chem.* **39**, 1214 (1961).
140. Gillis, R. G., *J. Chem. Educ.* **35**, 66 (1958).
141. Gilman, H., and Gerow, C. W., *J. Am. Chem. Soc.* **78**, 5435 (1956).
142. Gilman, H., and Marrs, O. L., *J. Org. Chem.* **25**, 1194 (1960).
143. Gilman, H., and Thomasi, R. A., *J. Org. Chem.* **27**, 3647 (1962).
144. Götz, H., Nerdel, F., and Wiechel, K. H., *Ann. Chem.* **665**, 1 (1963).
145. Gol'danskii, V. I., Rochev, V. Ya., and Khrapov, V. V., *Dokl. Akad. Nauk SSSR* **156**, 909 (1964).

146. See also Gosh, A. K., Hansing, C. E., Stutz, A. L., and MacDiarmid, A. G., *J. Chem. Soc.* p. 404 (1962).
147. Goubeau, J., *Naturwissenschaften* **35**, 246 (1948).
148. Goubeau, J., and Baumgärtner, R., *Z. Elektrochem.* **64**, 598 (1960).
149. Goubeau, J., and Berger, W., *Z. Anorg. Allgem. Chem.* **304**, 147 (1960).
150. Goubeau, J., and Jimenez-Barbera, J., *Z. Anorg. Allgem. Chem.* **303**, 217 (1960).
151. Graham, W. A. G., and Stone, F. G. A., *J. Inorg. & Nucl. Chem.* **3**, 164 (1956).
152. Grim, S. O., and Ambrus, J. H., *J. Org. Chem.* **33**, 2993 (1968).
153. Grim, S. O., McFarlane, W., and Marks, T. J., *Chem. Commun.* p. 1191 (1967).
154. Grimm, H. G., *Z. Elektrochem.* **31**, 474 (1925).
155. Grimm, H. G., *Naturwissenschaften* **17**, 535 and 557 (1929).
156. Grimm, H. G., *Z. Angew. Chem.* **42**, 367 (1929).
157. Grubb, W. T., and Osthoff, R. C., *J. Am. Chem. Soc.* **75**, 2330 (1953).
158. Gunton, R. C., Ollom, F. J., and Rexroad, H. N., *J. Chem. Phys.* **22**, 1942 (1954).
159. Gutowsky, H. S., and Hoffmann, C. J., *J. Chem. Phys.* **19**, 1259 (1961).
160. Haake, P., Miller, W. B., and Tyssee, D. A., *J. Am. Chem. Soc.* **86**, 3577 (1964).
161. Haas, A., *Angew. Chem.* **77**, 1066 (1965).
162. Halmann, M., and Pinchas, S., *J. Chem. Soc.* p. 3264 (1958).
163. Harris, G. S., and Inglis, F., *J. Chem. Soc., A* p. 497 (1967).
164. Harrison, P. G., *Organometal. Chem. Rev.* **4**, 379 (1969).
165. Heal, H. G., and Madden, I. O., *Nature* **195**, 280 (1962).
166. Hendrickson, J. B., Maddox, M. L., Sims, J. J., and Kaesz, H. D., *Tetrahedron* **20**, 449 (1964).
167. Herber, R. H., Stöckler, H. A., and Reichle, W. T., *J. Chem. Phys.* **42**, 2447 (1965).
168. Hess, G. G., Lampe, F. W., and Sommer, L. H., *J. Am. Chem. Soc.* **87**, 5327 (1965).
169. Hess, H., *Angew. Chem.* **79**, 995 (1967).
170. Hewitt, F., and Holliday, A. K., *J. Chem. Soc.* p. 530 (1953).
171. Hoppe, R., and Dähne, W., *Naturwissenschaften* **49**, 254 (1962).
172. Horner, L., and Oediger, H., *Ann. Chem.* **627**, 142 (1959).
173. Huisgen, R., Brunn, E., Gilardi, R., and Carle, I., *J. Am. Chem. Soc.* **91**, 7766 (1969).
174. Hunter, S. H., Emerson, K., and Rodley, G. A., *Chem. Commun.* p. 1398 (1969).
175. Hunter, S. H., Langford, V. M., Rodley, G. A., and Wilkins, C. J., *J. Chem. Soc., A* p. 305 (1968), and literature quoted therein.
176. Hyde, J. F., Johannson, O. K., Daudt, W. H., Fleming, R. F., Laudenslager, H. B., and Roche, M., *J. Am. Chem. Soc.* **75**, 5615 (1953).
177. Issleib, K., and Lindner, R., *Ann. Chem.* **699**, 40 (1966).
178. Issleib, K., and Lindner, R., *Ann. Chem.* **707**, 120 (1967).
179. Issleib, K., and Lindner, R., *Ann. Chem.* **713**, 12 (1968).
180. Issleib, K., and Lischewski, M., *J. Prakt. Chem.* **311**, 857 (1969).
181. Issleib, K., and Walther, B., *Angew. Chem.* **79**, 59 (1967).
182. Jaffé, H. H., *J. Chem. Phys.* **58**, 185 (1954).
183. Jenkner, H., *Chemiker Ztg.* pp. 527 and 563 (1962).
184. Jensen, K. A., *Z. Anorg. Allgem. Chem.* **250**, 268 (1943).
185. Johnson, A. W., "Ylid Chemistry." Academic Press, New York, 1966.
186. Jones, E. A., Kirby-Smith, J. S., Woltz, P. J. H., and Nielsen, A. H., *J. Chem. Phys.* **19**, 242 (1951).
187. Kakudo, M., Kasai, P. N., and Watase, T., *J. Chem. Phys.* **21**, 1894 (1953).
188. Kakudo, M., and Watase, T., *J. Chem. Phys.* **21**, 167 (1953).
189. Kartsev, G. N., Syrkin, Ya. K., Kravchenko, A. L., and Mironov, V. F., *Zh. Strukt. Khim.* **5**, 639 (1964).

190. Kasai, P. N., and Watase, T., *J. Chem. Phys.* **21**, 167 (1953).
191. Kasai, P. N., and Watase, T., *J. Chem. Phys.* **21**, 1894 (1953).
192. Kasai, N., Yasuda, K., and Okawara, R., *J. Organometal. Chem.* (*Amsterdam*) **3**, 172 (1965).
193. Kasatochkin, V. J., Shostakowskij, M. F., Zil'berbrand, O. J., and Kochkin, D. A., *Izv. Akad. Nauk SSSR, Ser. Fiz.* **18**, 726 (1954).
194. Kenney, M. E., and Laubengayer, A. W., *J. Am. Chem. Soc.* **76**, 4839 (1954).
195. Knoll, F., Gronebaum, J., and Appel, R., *Chem. Ber.* **102**, 848 (1969).
196. Kochkin, D. A., Luk'yanova, L. U., and Resnikova, E. B., *Izv. Akad. Nauk SSSR* p. 2255 (1961).
197. Köster, R., *Ann. Chem.* **618**, 13 (1958).
198. Köster, R., and Morita, Y., *Angew. Chem.* **77**, 589 (1965); *Angew. Chem. Intern. Ed. Engl.* **4**, 593 (1965).
199. Köster, R., and Morita, Y., *Ann. Chem.* **704**, 70 (1967).
200. Kraus, C. A., and Bullard, R. H., *J. Am. Chem. Soc.* **51**, 3605 (1929).
201. Kraus, C. A., and Foster, L. S., *J. Am. Chem. Soc.* **49**, 457 (1927).
202. Kraus, C. A., and Rosen, R., *J. Am. Chem. Soc.* **47**, 2739 (1925).
203. Krause, E., *Ber. Deut. Chem. Ges.* **51**, 1447 (1918).
204. Krebs, B., unpublished report, University of Göttingen.
205. Kreshkov, A. P., Myshlyaeva, L. V., and Soboleva, D. A., *Dokl. Akad. Nauk SSSR* **148**, 843 (1963).
206. Kriegsmann, H., private communication (1968).
207. Kriegsmann, H., *Z. Anorg. Allgem. Chem.* **294**, 113 (1958).
208. Kriegsmann, H., *Z. Anorg. Allgem. Chem.* **299**, 138 (1959).
209. Kriegsmann, H., Hoffmann, H., and Pischtschan, S., *Z. Anorg. Allgem. Chem.* **315**, 283 (1962).
210. Krusic, P. J., and Kochi, J. K., *J. Am. Chem. Soc.* **91**, 6161 (1969).
211. Langmuir, I., *J. Am. Chem. Soc.* **41**, 868 (1919).
212. Langmuir, I., *J. Am. Chem. Soc.* **41**, 1543 (1919).
213. Langmuir, I., *J. Am. Chem. Soc.* **42**, 274 (1920).
214. Langmuir, I., *Science* **54**, 65 (1921).
215. Lappert, M. F., and Leigh, G. J., "Development in Inorganic Polymer Chemistry." Elsevier, Amsterdam, 1962.
216. Larsson, E., *Kgl. Fysiograf. Sallskap. Lund, Forh.* **28**, 1 (1958); *Chem. Abstr.* **53**, 21622 (1959).
217. Larsson, E., *Arkiv. Kemi* **16**, 203 and 209 (1960).
218. Larsson, E., and Marin, R., *Acta Chim. Scand.* **5**, 1173 (1951).
219. Larsson, E., and Smith, B., *Acta Chim. Scand.* **3**, 487 (1949).
220. Laubengayer, A. W., and Lengnick, G. F., *Inorg. Chem.* **5**, 503 (1966).
221. Laughlin, R. G., private communication (1968).
222. Lehn, W. L., *Inorg. Chem.* **6**, 1061 (1967).
223. Licht, K., *Z. Chem.* **7**, No. 6, 242 (1967).
224. Lindqvist, I., "Inorganic Adduct Molecules of Oxo-compounds." Springer, Berlin, 1963.
225. Lister, M. W., and Sutton, L. E., *Trans. Faraday Soc.* **35**, 495 (1939).
226. Lorberth, J., Krapf, H., and Nöth, H., *Chem. Ber.* **100**, 3511 (1967).
227. Lorberth, J., and Kula, M. R., *Chem. Ber.* **98**, 520 (1965).
228. Lucken, E. A. C., and Mazeline, C., *J. Chem. Soc., A* p. 1074 (1966).
229. Lucken, E. A. C., and Mazeline, C., *J. Chem. Soc., A* p. 439 (1967).
230. Lüttke, W., and Wilhelm, K., *Angew. Chem.* **77**, 867 (1965).

231. Luijten, J. G. A., *Rec. Trav. Chim.* **82**, 1179 (1963).
232. Mardersteig, H. G., Meinel, L., and Nöth, H., *Z. Anorg. Allgem. Chem.* **368**, 254 (1969), and earlier publications.
233. Magnuson, V. R., and Stucky, G. D., *J. Am. Chem. Soc.* **90**, 3269 (1968).
234. Mark, T. C. W., and Trotter, J., *Acta Cryst.* **18**, 81 (1965).
235. Mathiason, D. R., and Miller, N. E., *Inorg. Chem.* **7**, 709 (1968).
236. Matthews, C. N., and Birum, G. H., *Accounts Chem. Res.* **2**, 373 (1969).
237. Matthews, C. N., Driscoll, J. S., Harris, J. E., and Wineman, J. R., *J. Am. Chem. Soc.* **84**, 4349 (1962).
238. Matwiyoff, N. A., and Drago, R. S., *J. Organometal. Chem.* (*Amsterdam*) **3**, 393 (1965).
239. McFarlane, W., Davidoff, E. F., Grim, S. O., and Marks, T. J., *J. Phys. Chem.* **70**, 581 (1966).
240. McGandy, E. L., *Dissertation Abstr.* **22**, 754 (1961).
241. McKean, D. C., *Spectrochim. Acta* **22**, 269 (1960).
242. Mehrota, R. C., and Pant, B. C., *Indian J. Appl. Chem.* **26**, 109 (1963); *Chem. Abstr.* **60**, 13265 (1964).
243. Merijanian, A., and Zingaro, R. A., *Inorg. Chem.* **5**, 187 (1966).
244. Miller, N. E., *Inorg. Chem.* **4**, 1458 (1965).
245. Miller, N. E., *J. Am. Chem. Soc.* **87**, 390 (1965).
246. Mitchell, K. A. R., *Chem. Rev.* **69** No. 2, 157 (1969).
247. Moedritzer, K., *J. Organometal. Chem.* (*Amsterdam*) **5**, 254 (1966).
248. Moeller, T., and Vandi, A., *J. Org. Chem.* **27**, 3511 (1962).
249. Monagle, J. J., *J. Org. Chem.* **27**, 3851 (1962).
250. Mootz, D., Zinnius, A., and Böttcher, B., *Angew. Chem.* **81**, 398 (1969).
251. Mulliken, R. S., *J. Am. Chem. Soc.* **77**, 884 (1955).
252. Musker, W. K., and Stevens, R. R., *Inorg. Chem.* **8**, 255 (1969), and literature quoted therein.
253. Natta, G., Allegra, G., Perego, G., and Zambelli, A., *J. Am. Chem. Soc.* **83**, 5033 (1961).
254. Nöth, H., and Meinel, L., *Z. Anorg. Allgem. Chem.* **349**, 225 (1967).
255. Nöth, H., Meinel, L., and Madersteig, H., *Angew. Chem.* **77**, 734 (1965).
256. Nöth, H., and Schrägle, W., *Z. Naturforsch.* **16b**, 473 (1961).
257. Nöth, H., and Vetter, H. J., *Chem. Ber.* **96**, 1298 (1963).
258. Noll, W., "Chemie und Technologie der Silicone," 2nd ed. Verlag Chemie, Weinheim, 1968.
259. Nordman, C. E., *Acta Cryst.* **13**, 535 (1960).
260. Nykerk, K. M., and Eyman, D. P., *Inorg. Nucl. Chem. Letters* **4**, 253 (1968).
261. Okawara, R., and Yasuda, K., *J. Organometal. Chem.* (*Amsterdam*) **1**, 356 (1964).
262. Paciorek, K. L., and Kratzer, R. H., *J. Org. Chem.* **31**, 2426 (1966).
263. Paddock, N. L., *Quart. Rev., Chem. Soc.* **18**, 168 (1964).
264. Pantel, S., and Becke-Goehring, M., "Sechs- und achtgliedrige Ringsysteme in der Phosphor-Stickstoff-Chemie," p. 232. Springer, Berlin, 1969 (earlier literature is covered therein).
265. Pantel, S., and Becke-Goehring, M., "Sechs- und achtlgiedrige Ringsysteme in der Phosphor-Stickstoff-Chemie," p. 32. Springer, Berlin, 1969.
266. Parshall, G. W., *in* "The Chemistry of Boron and its Compounds" (E. L. Muetterties, ed.), p. 260. Wiley, New York, 1967.
267. Parshall, G. W., and Lindsey, R. V., *J. Am. Chem. Soc.* **81**, 6273 (1959).
268. Pasarev, A. N., Telisheva, T. F., and Dawliova, W. P., *Dokl. Akad. Nauk SSSR* **158**, 648 (1964).

269. Pauling, L., "The Nature of the Chemical Bond," 3rd ed. Cornell Univ. Press, Ithaca, New York, 1960.
270. Pauling, L., "The Nature of the Chemical Bond," 3rd ed. Cornell Univ. Press, Ithaca, New York, 1960, p. 260.
271. Pauling, L., and Brockway, L. O., *J. Am. Chem. Soc.* **57**, 2684 (1935).
272. Pauling, P., Robertson, G. B., and Rodley, G. A., *Nature* **207**, 73 (1965).
273. Pearson, R. G., *J. Am. Chem. Soc.* **85**, 3533 (1963).
274. Pearson, R. G., *Science* **151**, 172 (1966).
275. Peterson, D. J., *J. Organometal. Chem. (Amsterdam)* **9**, 373 (1967).
276. Peterson, D. J., *J. Org. Chem.* **33**, 780 (1968).
277. Pitzer, K. S., *J. Chem. Phys.* **23**, 1735 (1955).
278. Pitzer, K. S., *Advan. Chem. Phys.* **2**, 59 (1959).
279. Politzer, P., *J. Am. Chem. Soc.* **91**, 6235 (1969).
280. Ponomarenko, V. A., and Vzenkova, G. Ya., *Izv. Akad. Nauk SSSR, Otd. Khim. Nauk* p. 994 (1957).
281. Pump, J., Rochow, E. G., and Wannagat, U., *Angew. Chem.* **75**, 374 (1963).
282. Ramirez, F., Desai, N. B., Hansen, B., and McKelvie, N., *J. Am. Chem. Soc.* **83**, 3539 (1961).
283. Ramirez, F., Pilot, J. F., Desai, N. B., Smith, C. P., Hansen, B., and McKelvie, N., *J. Am. Chem. Soc.* **89**, 6273 (1967).
284. Randall, E. W., Ellner, J. J., and Zuckerman, J. J., *J. Am. Chem. Soc.* **88**, 622 (1966).
285. Randall, E. W., Ellner, J. J., and Zuckerman, J. J., *Inorg. Nucl. Chem. Letters* **1**, 109 (1966).
286. Randall, E. W., and Zuckerman, J. J., *Chem. Commun.* p. 732 (1966).
287. Randall, E. W., and Zuckerman, J. J., *J. Am. Chem. Soc.* **90**, 3167 (1968).
288. Randall, F. J., and Johnson, A. W., *Can. J. Chem.* **46**, 461 (1968).
289. Randall, F. J., and Johnson, A. W., *Tetrahedron Letters* p. 2841 (1968).
290. Rave, T. W., *J. Org. Chem.* **32**, 3461 (1967).
291. Rave, T. W., and Hays, H. R., *J. Org. Chem.* **31**, 2894 (1966).
292. Reichle, W. T., *Inorg. Chem.* **3**, 402 (1964).
293. Reichle, W. T., *J. Organometal. Chem. (Amsterdam)* **13**, 529 (1968).
294. Rerat, C., *Acta Cryst.* **13**, 63 (1960).
295. Richards, R. E., and Thompson, H. W., *J. Chem. Soc.* p. 124 (1949).
296. Robinson, D. W., Lafferty, W. J., Aronson, J. R., Durig, J. R., and Lord, R. C., *J. Chem. Phys.* **35**, 2245 (1961).
297. Rochow, E. G., *J. Am. Chem. Soc.* **70**, 1801 (1948).
298. Rose, S. H., and Block, B. P., *J. Am. Chem. Soc.* **87**, 2076 (1965).
299. Ruidisch, I., Schmidbaur, H., and Schumann, H., *in* "Halogen Chemistry" (V. Gutmann, ed.), Vol. 2, pp. 233–711. Academic Press, New York, 1967.
300. Ruidisch, I., and Schmidt, M., *Angew. Chem.* **75**, 575 (1963); *Chem. Ber.* **96**, 821 (1963).
301. Ruidisch, I., and Schmidt, M., *Chem. Ber.* **96**, 821 (1963).
302. Sanderson, R. T., *J. Inorg. & Nucl. Chem.* **28**, 1553 (1966).
303. Sanderson, R. T., *J. Inorg. & Nucl. Chem.* **30**, 375 (1968).
304. Sawodny, W., *Z. Anorg. Allgem. Chem.* **368**, 284 (1969).
305. Scherer, O. J., *Angew. Chem.* **81**, 871 (1969).
306. Scherer, O. J., and Biller, D., *Angew. Chem.* **79**, 410 (1967).
307. Scherer, O. J., and Biller, D., *Z. Naturforsch.* **22b**, 1079 (1967).
308. Scherer, O. J., and Janssen, W. M., personal communication (1970).
309. Scherer, O. J., and Klusmann, P., *Angew. Chem.* **80**, 560 (1968).

310. Scherer, O. J., and Schieder, G., *Chem. Ber.* **101**, 4184 (1968).
311. Scherer, O. J., Schmidt, J. F., and Schmidt, M., *Z. Naturforsch.* **19b**, 447 (1964); also unpublished results (305).
312. Scherer, O. J., and Schmidt, M., *J. Organometal. Chem.* **1**, 490 (1964).
313. Schindler, F., and Schmidbaur, H., *Angew. Chem.* **79**, 67 (1967).
314. Schindler, F., and Schmidbaur, H., *Chem. Ber.* **100**, 3655 (1967).
315. Schindler, F., and Schmidbaur, H., *Chem. Ber.* **101**, 1656 (1968).
316. Schindler, F., Schmidbaur, H., and Jonas, G., *Angew. Chem.* **77**, 170 (1965).
317. Schindler, F., Schmidbaur, H., and Krüger, U., *Angew. Chem.* **77**, 865 (1965).
318. Schlemper, E. O., and Hamilton, W. C., *Inorg. Chem.* **5**, 995 (1966).
319. Schmidbaur, H., unpublished results, University of Munich (1962 and 1968).
320. Schmidbaur, H., unpublished work, University of Marburg (1963).
321. Schmidbaur, H., *J. Am. Chem. Soc.* **85**, 2336 (1963).
322. Schmidbaur, H., Habilitationsarbeit, University of Marburg (1963–1964).
323. Schmidbaur, H., *J. Organometal. Chem.* (*Amsterdam*) **1**, 28 (1963).
324. Schmidbaur, H., *Angew. Chem.* **75**, 137 (1963).
325. Schmidbaur, H., *Chem. Ber.* **96**, 2692 (1963).
326. Schmidbaur, H., *Chem. Ber.* **97**, 459 (1964).
327. Schmidbaur, H., *Chem. Ber.* **97**, 830 (1964).
328. Schmidbaur, H., *Chem. Ber.* **97**, 836 (1964).
329. Schmidbaur, H., *Chem. Ber.* **97**, 842 (1964).
330. Schmidbaur, H., *Angew. Chem.* **77**, 206 (1965).
331. Schmidbaur, H., *Chem. Unserer Zeit* **1**, 184 (1967).
332. Schmidbaur, H., *Allgem. Prakt. Chem.* **18**, 138 (1967).
333. Schmidbaur, H., *Fortschr. Chem. Forsch.* **13**, No. 1, 167 (1969).
334. Schmidbaur, H., Armer, B., and Bergfeld, M., *Z. Chem.* **8**, 254 (1968).
335. Schmidbaur, H., Arnold, H. S., and Beinhofer, E., *Chem. Ber.* **97**, 449 (1964).
336. Schmidbaur, H., and Bergfeld, M., *Z. Anorg. Allgem. Chem.* **363**, 84 (1968).
337. Schmidbaur, H., Bergfeld, M., and Schindler, F., *Z. Anorg. Allgem. Chem.* **363**, 73 (1968).
338. Schmidbaur, H., and Hussek, H., *Angew. Chem.* **75**, 575 (1963).
339. Schmidbaur, H., and Hussek, H., *J. Organometal. Chem.* (*Amsterdam*) **1**, 235 (1964).
340. Schmidbaur, H., and Hussek, H., *J. Organometal. Chem.* (*Amsterdam*) **1**, 244 (1964).
341. Schmidbaur, H., and Hussek, H., *J. Organometal. Chem.* (*Amsterdam*) **1**, 257 (1964).
342. Schmidbaur, H., Hussek, H., and Schindler, F., *Chem. Ber.* **97**, 255 (1964).
343. Schmidbaur, H., and Jonas, G., *Angew. Chem.* **79**, 413 (1967).
344. Schmidbaur, H., and Jonas, G., *Chem. Ber.* **100**, 1120 (1967).
345. Schmidbaur, H., and Jonas, G., *Chem. Ber.* **101**, 1271 (1968).
346. Schmidbaur, H., and Kammel, G., *Chem. Ber.* **102**, 4128 (1969).
347. Schmidbaur, H., and Kammel, G., *J. Organometal Chem.* (*Amsterdam*) **14**, P28 (1968).
348. Schmidbaur, H., and Kammel, G., *J. Organometal. Chem.* (*Amsterdam*) **15**, P10 (1968).
349. Schmidbaur, H., and Klein, H. F., *Angew. Chem.* **78**, 750 (1966).
350. Schmidbaur, H., and Klein, H. F., *Chem. Ber.* **101**, 2278 (1968).
351. Schmidbaur, H., and Klein, H. F., unpublished Dissertation, H. F. Klein, University of Würzburg (1968).
352. Schmidbaur, H., Kuhr, G., and Krüger, U., *Angew. Chem.* **77**, 866 (1965).
353. Schmidbaur, H., and Malisch, W., *Chem. Ber.* (1970) in press.
354. Schmidbaur, H., and Malisch, W., *Chem. Ber.* **102**, 83 (1969).
355. Schmidbaur, H., and Malisch, W., *Angew. Chem.* **81**, 329 (1969).

356. Schmidbaur, H., and Malisch, W., *Angew. Chem.* **82**, 84 (1970).
357. Schmidbaur, H., and Malisch, W., *Chem. Ber.* **103**, 97 (1970).
358. Schmidbaur, H., and Mitschke, K. H., unpublished. Diplomarbeit, K. H. Mitschke, University of Würzburg (1969).
359. Schmidbaur, H., Perez-Garcia, J. A., and Arnold, H. S., *Z. Anorg. Allgem. Chem.* **328**, 105 (1964).
360. Schmidbaur, H., and Ruidisch, I., *Inorg. Chem.* **3**, 599 (1964).
361. Schmidbaur, H., and Schindler, F., *Chem. Ber.* **97**, 952 (1964).
362. Schmidbaur, H., and Schindler, F., *Angew. Chem.* **77**, 865 (1965).
363. Schmidbaur, H., and Schindler, F., *Chem. Ber.* **99**, 2178 (1966).
364. Schmidbaur, H., Schindler, F., and Jonas, G., *Chem. Ber.* **98**, 3345 (1965).
365. Schmidbaur, H., and Schmidt, M., *Chem. Ber.* **94**, 1138, 1349, and 2137 (1961).
366. Schmidbaur, H., and Schmidt, M., *J. Am. Chem. Soc.* **83**, 2963 (1961).
367. Schmidbaur, H., and Schmidt, M., *Angew. Chem.* **73**, 655 (1961).
368. Schmidbaur, H., and Schmidt, M., *Angew. Chem.* **74**, 327 (1962).
369. Schmidbaur, H., and Schmidt, M., *Angew. Chem.* **74**, 328 (1962).
370. Schmidbaur, H., and Schmidt, M., *Angew. Chem.* **74**, 589 (1962).
371. Schmidbaur, H., and Schmidt, M., *J. Am. Chem. Soc.* **84**, 1069 (1962).
372. Schmidbaur, H., and Schmidt, M., *J. Am. Chem. Soc.* **84**, 3600 (1962).
373. Schmidbaur, H., and Schwirten, K., unpublished results, University of Würzburg (1969).
374. Schmidbaur, H., Schwirten, K., and Pickel, H. H., *Chem. Ber.* **102**, 564 (1969).
375. Schmidbaur, H., and Tronich, W., unpublished, University of Würzburg (1967).
376. Schmidbaur, H., and Tronich, W., *Angew. Chem.* **79**, 412 (1967).
377. Schmidbaur, H., and Tronich, W., *Chem. Ber.* **100**, 1032 (1967); **101**, 595 (1968).
378. Schmidbaur, H., and Tronich, W., *Chem. Ber.* **101**, 604 (1968).
379. Schmidbaur, H., and Tronich, W., *Chem. Ber.* **101**, 3556 and 3545 (1968).
380. Schmidbaur, H., and Tronich, W., *Angew. Chem.* **80**, 239 (1968).
381. Schmidbaur, H., and Tronich, W., *Inorg. Chem.* **7**, 168 (1968).
382. Schmidbaur, H., and Tronich, W., *Tetrahedron Letters* p. 5335 (1968).
383. Schmidbaur, H., and Waldmann, S., *Angew. Chem.* **76**, 753 (1964).
384. Schmidbaur, H., Weidlein, J., Klein, H. F., and Eiglmeier, K., *Chem. Ber.* **101**, 2268 (1968).
385. Schmidbaur, H., and Wolfsberger, W., *Angew. Chem.* **78**, 306 (1966).
386. Schmidbaur, H., and Wolfsberger, W., *Angew. Chem.* **79**, 411 (1967).
387. Schmidbaur, H., and Wolfsberger, W., *Chem. Ber.* **100**, 1000 (1967).
388. Schmidbaur, H., and Wolfsberger, W., *Chem. Ber.* **101**, 1664 (1968).
389. Schmidbaur, H., and Wolfsberger, W., *J. Organometal. Chem.* (*Amsterdam*) **16**, 188 (1966).
390. Schmidbaur, H., Wolfsberger, W., and Kröner, H., *Chem. Ber.* **100**, 1023 (1967).
391. Schmidbaur, H., Wolfsberger, W., and Schwirten, K., *Chem. Ber.* **102**, 556 (1969).
392. Schmidpeter, A., and Düll, K., *Chem. Ber.* **100**, 1116 (1967).
393. Schmitz-Dumont, O., *Z. Anorg. Allgem. Chem.* **248**, 289 (1941).
394. Schumann, H., *Angew. Chem.* **81**, 871 (1969).
395. Schuster, P., *Monatsh. Chem.* **98**, 1310 (1967).
396. Searle, H. T., *Proc. Chem. Soc.* p. 7 (1959).
397. Seyferth, D., and Alleston, D. S., *Inorg. Chem.* **2**, 418 (1963).
398. Seyferth, D., and Grim, S. O., *J. Am. Chem. Soc.* **83**, 1610 (1961).
399. Seyferth, D., and Singh, G., *J. Am. Chem. Soc.* **87**, 1457 (1965).

400. Seyferth, D., Singh, G., and Suzuki, R., *Pure Appl. Chem.* **13**, 1596 (1966).
401. Shaw, R. A., *Endeavour* **27**, 74 (1968).
402. Shearer, H. M. M., and Spencer, C. B., *Chem. Commun.* p. 194 (1966).
403. Shearer, H. M. M., and Willis, J., cited in Magnuson and Stucky (*233*).
404. Sheldrick, G. M., and Sheldrick, W. S., *J. Chem. Soc., A* p. 2279 (1969).
405. Shimanouchi, T., Nakagawa, I., Hiraishi, J., and Ishii, M. *J. Mol. Spectry.* **19**, 78 (1966).
406. Siebert, H., *Z. Anorg. Allgem. Chem.* **274**, 34 (1953).
407. Singh, G., and Zimmer, H., *Organometal. Chem. Rev.* **2**, 282 (1967).
408. Sisler, H. H., Ahuja, H. S., and Smith, N. L., *J. Org. Chem.* **26**, 1819 (1961).
409. Sisler, H. H., Ahuja, H. S., and Smith, N. L., *Inorg. Chem.* **1**, 84 (1962).
410. Sisler, H. H., and Stratton, C., *Inorg. Chem.* **5**, 2003 (1966).
411. Skinner, H. A., and Pilcher, G., *Quart. Rev.* (*London*) **17**, 264 (1963).
412. Smith, G. S., and Hoard, J. L., *J. Am. Chem. Soc.* **81**, 3907 (1959).
413. Sommer, L. H., Green, L. Q., and Whitmore, F. C., *J. Am. Chem. Soc.* **71**, 3253 (1949).
414. Sommer, L. H., Pietrusza, E. W., and Whitmore, F. C., *J. Am. Chem. Soc.* **68**, 2282 (1946).
415. Sommer, L. H., and Whitmore, F. C., *J. Am. Chem. Soc.* **70**, 453 (1948).
416. Speziale, A. J., and Ratts, K. W., *J. Am. Chem. Soc.* **87**, 5603 (1965).
417. Staudinger, H., and Meyer, J., *Helv. Chim. Acta* **2**, 635 (1919).
418. Steinfink, H., Post, B., and Fankuchen, I., *Acta Cryst.* **8**, 420 (1955).
419. Stephens, F. S., *J. Chem. Soc.* p. 5640 (1965).
420. Stephens, F. S., *J. Chem. Soc.* p. 5658 (1965).
421. Stone, F. G. A., *Quart. Rev.* (*London*) **9**, 174 (1955).
422. Stone, F. G. A., and Burg, A. B., *J. Am. Chem. Soc.* **76**, 386 (1954).
423. Stone, F. G. A., and Graham, W. A. G., eds., "Inorganic Polymers." Academic Press, New York, 1962.
424. Stone, F. G. A., and Seyferth, D., *J. Inorg. & Nucl. Chem.* **1**, 112 (1955).
425. Tatlock, W. S., and Rochow, E. G., *J. Org. Chem.* **17**, 1555 (1952).
426. Thayer, J. S., *Organometal. Chem. Rev.* **1**, 157 (1966).
427. Thomas, T., and Eriks, K., *Am. Cryst. Soc. Meeting, Cornell Univ., 1959* as quoted in Parshall (*266*).
428. Timms, P. L., Kent, R. A., Elhert, T. C., and Margrave, J. C., *J. Am. Chem. Soc.* **87**, 2824 (1965).
429. Venezky, D. L., *Abstr. 156th Meeting Am. Chem. Soc., Atlantic City, 1968* Nr. 73.
430. Voelz, F. L., Meister, A. G., and Cleveland, F. F., *J. Chem. Phys.* **19**, 1084 (1951).
431. Voorhoeve, R. J. H., "Organohalosilanes—Precursors to Silicones." Elsevier, Amsterdam, 1967.
432. Wannagat, U., *Advan. Inorg. Chem. Radiochem.* **6**, 265 (1964); *Fortschr. Chem. Forsch.* **9**, 102 (1967–1968).
433. Wannagat, U., *Angew. Chem.* **77**, 626 (1965).
434. Wannagat, U., *Pure Appl. Chem.* **13**, 263 (1966).
435. Wannagat, U., *Proc. 3rd Intern. Conf. Organosilicon Chem., Bordeaux, 1968.*
436. Wannagat, U., and Niederprüm, N., *Chem. Ber.* **94**, 1540 (1961).
437. Ward, R., *J. Chem. Educ.* **40**, 277 (1963).
438. Weidlein, J., and Krieg, V., *J. Organometal. Chem.* (*Amsterdam*) **11**, 9 (1968).
439. Weiss, E., Alsdorf, H., and Kuhr, H., *Angew. Chem.* **79**, 816 (1967).
439a. Weiss, E., Hoffmann, K., and Grützmacher, H. F., *Chem. Ber.* **103**, 1190 (1970).

440. Wells, A. F., "Structural Inorganic Chemistry," 3rd ed. Oxford Univ. Press (Clarendon), London and New York, 1962.
441. West, R., and Baney, R. H., *J. Inorg. Nucl. Chem.* **7**, 297 (1958).
442. West, R., and Baney, R. H., *J. Am. Chem. Soc.* **81**, 6145 (1959).
443. West, R., Baney, R. H., and Powell, D. L., *J. Am. Chem. Soc.* **82**, 6269 (1960).
444. West, R., and Thayer, J. S., *J. Am. Chem. Soc.* **84**, 1763 (1962).
445. Wheatley, P. J., *J. Chem. Soc.* p. 1721 (1962).
446. Wheatley, P. J., *J. Chem. Soc.* p. 2562 (1963).
447. Wheatley, P. J., *J. Chem. Soc.* p. 3200 (1963).
448. Wheatley, P. J., *J. Chem. Soc.* p. 5785 (1965).
449. Wiberg, E., and Hastreiter, A., Dissertation, A. Hastreiter, University of München (1959).
450. Wiberg, N., and Neruda, B., *Chem. Ber.* **99**, 740 (1966).
451. Wiberg, N., and Schmid, K. H., *Z. Anorg. Allgem. Chem.* **345**, 93 (1966).
452. Wiegräbe, W., and Bock, H., *Chem. Ber.*, **101**, 1414 (1968).
453. Wiegräbe, W., Bock, H., and Lüttke, W., *Chem. Ber.* **99**, 3737 (1966).
454. Williams, Q., Sheridan, J., and Gordy, W., *J. Chem. Phys.* **20**, 164 (1952).
455. Wolfsberger, W., unpublished results (1969).
456. Wolfsberger, W., and Schmidbaur, H., *J. Organometal. Chem.* (*Amsterdam*) **17**, 41 (1969).
457. Woronkow, M. G., and Orlov, N. F., *Izv. Akad. Nauk Latv. SSR, Ser. Khim.* p. 93 (1961).
458. Woronkow, M. G., and Sgonnik, W. N., *Zh. Obsch. Khim.* **27**, 1476 (1957).
459. Ziegler, K., and Köster, R., *Ann. Chem.* **608**, 1 (1956).
460. Ziegler, K., Köster, R. Lehmkuhl, H., and Reinert, K., *Ann. Chem.* **629**, 33 (1960).
461. Zuccaro, D. E., and McCullough, J. D., *Z. Krist.* **112**, 401 (1959).

Organolanthanides and Organoactinides

HENRY GYSLING*

Department of Inorganic Chemistry
University of Newcastle upon Tyne
Newcastle, England

MINORU TSUTSUI

Department of Chemistry
Texas A & M University
College Station, Texas

I

INTRODUCTION

Although the lanthanide and actinide elements have been the subject of considerable research by metallurgists and coordination chemists during the past 20 years, relatively little work has been reported dealing with the organic derivatives of these two groups of elements. Several general texts are available for the lanthanides (*1–8*) and actinides (*7, 9*) as well as review articles on unusual oxidation states and the coordination chemistry of the lanthanides (*10–12*) and actinides (*12–14*). Most of the reported research in the area of the coordination chemistry of these elements has been directed at improved methods for their separation by solvent extraction (*4, 10, 15–19*), ion-exchange chromatography (*20–23*), and more recently by

* Present address: Research Laboratories, Eastman Kodak Company, Rochester, New York.

vapor-phase chromatography of β-diketone chelates and their fluorinated derivatives (*24*). The replacement of the tedious fractional crystallization method of separation by the ion-exchange techniques used commercially today has made most of the lanthanide elements available in large-scale quantities of high purity. The increased availability of these metals and their compounds in the past few years has in turn promoted research which has resulted in new commercial applications (*25*). It is to be expected, therefore, that increased attention will be directed toward the syntheses of new types of compounds of these two unique groups of elements as well as toward the theoretically interesting area of the elucidation of the role of *f* orbitals (*26–34*) in the bonding in these compounds. The recent report by Streitwieser and Müller-Westerhoff of bis(cyclooctatetraenyl)uranium(IV) ("uranocene") (*35*), a uranium-based, ferrocene-like organometallic is indicative of this increased interest in expanding the scope of the chemistry of these elements.

II

THE RARE EARTHS

The rare earth series consists of the elements 57, lanthanum, through 71, lutetium. Yttrium, element 39, is also found to occur with these elements in nature and to display similar chemical behavior and is therefore generally classified with them. Scandium has sufficiently different chemical properties, by virtue of its smaller ionic radius, to make its inclusion somewhat arbitrary. Table I lists the rare earths along with some of their pertinent data. Promethium, whose existence was predicted by Moseley in 1913, was first isolated in 1947 by ion-exchange chromatography on uranium fission products (*36*). It occurs in nature only in small traces as a spontaneous fission fragment of uranium in its ores. However, the recent report of an improved ion-exchange method of separation and purification of promethium from rare earth fission products (*37*) should result in increased research into the chemistry of this element.

Although the 3+ state is the most characteristic for these elements, 2+ and 4+ species are also known, the most stable di- and tetrapositive ions being formed by the elements which can thus attain the f^0, f^7, and f^{14} configurations. Cerium and terbium reach the f^0 and f^7 configurations, respectively, in the 4+ oxidation state, while Eu and Yb have f^7 and f^{14} configurations in the 2+ state (*38*). The limitation, however, of this concept of special stability of empty, half-filled, or filled f shells is seen from a consideration of Table I. Clearly other thermodynamic and kinetic factors, in addition to the possible special stability of the f^0, f^7, and f^{14} configurations are of equal or greater importance in determining the stability of oxidation states. Also these oxidation states are those found in aqueous solution

TABLE I

THE RARE EARTHS

Element	Symbol	Atomic No.	Oxidation states	Electronic atom	Configuration M^{3+}	Radii of Ln^{3+} (Å)
Yttrium	Y	39	3	$[Kr]4d5s^2$	[Kr]	0.98
Lanthanum	La	57	3	$[Xe]5d6s^2$	[Xe]	1.061
Cerium	Ce	58	3, 4	$4f^2 6s^2$	$4f$	1.034
Praseodymium	Pr	59	3, 4	$4f^3 6s^2$	$4f^2$	1.013
Neodymium	Nd	60	2, 3, 4	$4f^4 6s^2$	$4f^3$	0.995
Promethium	Pm	61	3	$4f^5 6s^2$	$4f^4$	0.979
Samarium	Sm	62	2, 3	$4f^6 6s^2$	$4f^5$	0.964(Sm^{II}, 1.11)
Europium	Eu	63	2, 3	$4f^7 6s^2$	$4f^6$	0.950(Eu^{II}, 1.10)
Gadolinium	Gd	64	3	$4f^7 5d6s^2$	$4f^7$	0.938
Terbium	Tb	65	3,4	$4f^9 6s^2$	$4f^8$	0.923
Dysprosium	Dy	66	3, 4	$4f^{10} 6s^2$	$4f^9$	0.908
Holmium	Ho	67	3	$4f^{11} 6s^2$	$4f^{10}$	0.894
Erbium	Er	68	3	$4f^{12} 6s^2$	$4f^{11}$	0.881
Thulium	Tm	69	2, 3	$4f^{13} 6s^2$	$4f^{12}$	0.869
Ytterbium	Yb	70	2, 3	$4f^{14} 6s^2$	$4f^{13}$	0.858(Yb^{II}, 0.93)
Lutetium	Lu	71	3	$4f^{14} 5d6s^2$	$4f^{14}$	0.848

while in the nonaqueous media employed in organometallic syntheses, considerable deviation from this behavior may well be observed. The II–III oxidation potentials for Sm (1.55 V), Eu (0.43 V), Tm (2.2 V), and Yb (1.15 V) have been measured (*12*) and correlated with the lowest energy electron-transfer absorption of the respective trivalent halides, measured in anhydrous ethanol solutions (*39*).

The two most widely applicable physical techniques employed in the study of the rare earths are magnetic susceptibility measurements and electronic spectroscopy. The magnetic behavior of these elements (*40, 41*) is idealized by both the shielded nature of the $4f$ electrons and the large multiplet separation between the ground state and first excited state relative to kT (at ordinary temperatures equal to approx. 200 cm^{-1}). The magnetic moment in such cases is given by

$$\mu = g[J(J+1)]^{1/2} \tag{1}$$

$$g = 1+\frac{J(J+1)+S(S+1)-L(L+1)}{2J(J+1)} \tag{2}$$

where g is the Landé splitting factor and J is the value of the total angular momentum derived from the Russell-Saunders coupling scheme. Only in the cases of Sm^{3+} and Eu^{3+} does this formula fail to give good agreement with experimental data. In the case of Sm^{3+} the first excited state is significantly populated, while for Eu^{3+} the first three excited states must all be taken into account in calculating the magnetic moment (*42*). The magnetic moments of the trivalent ions are listed in Table II (*43*, *44*).

The shielding of the f orbitals from any surrounding ligand field is manifested in the electronic spectra of these elements by the sharp, almost linelike character of the f–f transitions (*45*, *46*) occurring in the visible and near-ultraviolet region in contrast to the rather broad bands observed for d–d electronic transitions. A considerable amount of research has been

TABLE II

MAGNETIC DATA FOR THE TRIVALENT LANTHANIDES

Ln	Unpaired electrons	Theoretical μ_{eff} (B.M.) (Van Vleck)	Observed μ_{eff} (B.M.), $Ln_2(SO_4)_3 \cdot 8\ H_2O$
Y^{3+}	0	0	—
La^{3+}	0	0	—
Ce^{3+}	1	2.56	2.46
Pr^{3+}	2	3.62	3.47
Nd^{3+}	3	3.68	3.52
Pm^{3+}	4	2.83	—
Sm^{3+}	5	1.55–1.65	1.58
Eu^{3+}	6	3.40–3.51	3.54
Gd^{3+}	7	7.94	7.9
Tb^{3+}	6	9.7	9.6
Dy^{3+}	5	10.6	10.3
Ho^{3+}	4	10.6	10.4
Er^{3+}	3	9.6	9.4
Yb^{3+}	2	7.6	7.0
Tm^{3+}	1	4.5	4.3
Lu^{3+}	0	0	—
Eu^{2+}	7	7.9	—

directed at studying changes in positions and intensities of such absorptions in the presence of various complexing agents (*47*). Such data (*48, 49*) have been interpreted in terms of partly covalent interactions, much of the theory having been developed by Jørgensen in terms of the nephelauxetic effect (*32, 46, 50–53*).

III

ORGANOLANTHANIDES

In contrast to the large number of organic derivatives of the transition metals, the only reported organolanthanides contain the cyclopentadienyl (*54–66*), indenyl (*67, 68*), cyclooctatetraenyl (*68a*), and phenyl (*71b*) groups. Promethium is the only member of the series for which no organic derivatives have been reported and it will not be included in the following discussion.[1] Aside from the divalent compounds $Eu(C_5H_5)_2$ (*57, 63*), $Yb(C_5H_5)_2$ (*57, 65*), $Sm(C_5H_5)_2 \cdot OC_4H_8$ (*66*), and $M(C_8H_8)$ (M = Eu, Yb) (*68a*), all of these compounds involve the 3 + oxidation state of the lanthanides. Although some attempts have been made to prepare alkyl and aryl derivatives (*69–71*), no well-characterized compounds of these types have been prepared until recently (*71a–c*). Biphenyl was the only product isolated from both the sealed tube reaction of diphenylmercury with metallic lanthanum at 135°C for 100 days followed by treatment with carbon dioxide, and of lanthanum trichloride with phenyllithium in ether (*69*). The stoichiometric coupling reaction of phenylmagnesium bromide has been studied in the presence of samarium trichloride (*71*). The formation of biphenyl in all these systems suggests the possibility of a transitory bond formation between the phenyl groups and the metal. The reaction of $SmCl_3$ with 3 equivalents of sodium phenylacetylide in THF (*71*) gives an immediate color change to yellow brown. A product of the approximate formula $(C_6H_5C{\equiv}C)_3Sm \cdot THF$ was crystallized from the filtered reaction solution but could not be recrystallized to give an analytically pure compound. Evidence has also been found (*71*) for catalysis by the lanthanide tricyclopentadienides in the cyclization of diphenylacetylene and methyl- or phenylacetylene to form a benzene ring. The polymerization of butadiene in the presence of $Sm(C_5H_5)_3$ (*71*) produces a solid product whose infrared spectrum indicates a 1,4-trans configuration.

[1] The tricyclopentadienyl derivative of Pm has recently been reported. See the last paragraph of this chapter.

The first well-characterized aryl derivatives of this series have been prepared by the reaction of the anhydrous trichlorides and phenyllithium in tetrahydrofuran-ethyl ether media (*71a*, *b*). The compounds $M(C_6H_5)_3$ ($M = Sc$, Y) and $Li[M(C_6H_5)_4]$($M = La$, Pr) have been isolated. The insolubility of these compounds has precluded extensive structural investigations, their formulation being based on elemental analyses and infrared spectra. All four compounds are pyrophoric, rather thermally stable, and give positive tests with Michler's ketone. Reactions with mercuric chloride, carbon dioxide, and benzophenone give, respectively, phenyl mercuric chloride, benzoic acid, and triphenylcarbinol in good yields. A polymeric formulation has been suggested to explain the involatility and insolubility of the dried products, the initially isolated solids being benzene soluble, possibly as the result of monomer stabilization by tetrahydrofuran coordination.

Tris(phenylacetylide)scandium has also been isolated by an analogous preparative route (*71b*). The dark brown pyrophoric product is stable to 250° C *in vacuo* and gives phenylpropiolic acid upon carbonation. Similarly, the reactions of methyllithium with the trichlorides of Sc, Y, and La have given products postulated as $M(CH_3)_3 \cdot (C_4H_8O)_n$ derivatives (*71b*). These involatile, pyrophoric derivatives have not yet been isolated in analytically pure forms due to the similarity of their solubility characteristics with the lithium chloride contaminate. They are stable indefinitely at room temperature and give positive tests with Michler's ketone.

Ytterbium analogs of the Grignard reagents have recently been prepared by the reaction of metallic ytterbium with alkyl and aryl iodides in tetrahydrofuran below −15° C (*71c*). The resulting brown solutions have a Yb:I ratio of approximately one and give a positive test with Michler's ketone, and Grignard type reactions with water, aldehydes, ketones, and isocyanatobenzene. In a typical reaction, a 72% yield of triphenylcarbinol was obtained from the reaction of C_6H_5YbI and benzophenone.

With the exception of the recently reported tris(indenyl)samarium (*67*, *68*), all of the organolanthanides are considered to be essentially ionic on the basis of their magnetic moments and infrared spectra as well as their physical properties and chemical reactivities. Detailed studies of the electronic spectra of the tris(cyclopentadienyl) derivatives of Yb (*72*) and Tm (*73*) show an unusually large ligand field splitting of their $4f^n$ multiplet terms. Estimates of the Racah parameters indicate a rather large nephelauxetic effect (*50*) for the $4f$ electrons. However, although there is spectral evidence for a degree of covalence in a few cases, as yet no organolanthanide is known in which spin pairing of 4*f* electrons occurs.

A. *Tris(cyclopentadienyl)lanthanides, $M(C_5H_5)_3$*

All of the trivalent derivatives of the type $M(C_5H_5)_3$ (*45–59*, *65*) have been reported with the exception of radioactive promethium (Table III).

TABLE III

$M(C_5H_5)_3$ LANTHANIDES

M	Color	M.p. (°C)	$\chi_{Mol} \times 10^6$ (°K)	Δ (°C)	μ_{eff} (B.M.)	References
Sc	Straw	240°	Diamag	—	—	*54, 55, 58*
Y	Pale yellow	295°	Diamag	—	—	*54, 55*
La	Colorless	395°	Diamag	—	—	*54, 55, 90*
Ce	Orange-yellow	435°	2,230 (295°)	15	2.46	*54, 55, 58*
Pr	Pale green	420°	4,700 (295°)	37	3.61	*54, 55, 93*
Nd	Pale blue	380°	4,260 (295°)	72	3.63	*54, 55, 58, 91, 93*
Sm	Orange	365°	1,080 (295°)	0	—	—
			1,160 (194°)	60	1.54	*54, 55, 58*
			1,550 (77°)	113	—	—
Eu	Brown		51,562 (295°)	—	3.74	*56, 59*
Gd	Yellow	350°	26,800 (295°)	0	7.98	*54, 55, 90*
Tb	Colorless	316°	33,500 (300°)	—	8.9	*57*
			114,000 (85°)	—	—	—
Dy	Yellow	302°	40,000 (295°)	15	10.0	*55*
Ho	Yellow	295°	44,700 (300°)	—	10.2	*57, 93*
Er	Pink	285°	35,600 (295°)	17	9.45	*55*
Tm	Yellow-green	278°	21,800 (300°)	—	7.1	*57, 73, 93*
			69,000 (85°)	—	—	—
Yb	Dark green	273°	6,160 (295°)	21	4.00	*55, 65, 72, 92, 93*
Lu	Colorless	264°	Diamag	—	—	*57*

The tricyclopentadienyl compounds of the formula $(C_5H_5)_3M$ [M = Sc, Y, La, Ce, Pr, Nd, Sm, and Gd], reported in a 1954 communication by Wilkinson and Birmingham (*54*) represent the first examples of organic derivatives of the rare earths. They were synthesized by the reaction of the corresponding anhydrous metal trichloride (*74*) with sodium cyclopentadienide in tetrahydrofuran (THF) media and isolated by vacuum sublimation at 200°–250° C of the residue obtained after removal of the solvent.

The resulting crystalline solids are thermally stable to at least 400° C and sublime above 220° C at 10^{-4} mm. They are insoluble in hydrocarbon solvents but moderately soluble in THF, pyridine, dioxane, and glycol dimethyl ether, while rapidly decomposing in aqueous solution to give cyclopentadiene and the corresponding hydroxide, together with some polymeric organic material. Rapid decomposition occurs with CS_2, CCl_4, and $CHCl_3$. While all the members of the series are air-sensitive, the Ce derivative displays the lowest oxidative stability, being blackened instantaneously by even traces of oxygen. The subsequent full paper (*55*) details some physical and chemical properties of these compounds and reports also the isolation of the analogous derivatives of Dy, Er, and Yb by a similar preparative technique.

The chemical and physical properties of these compounds support an electrostatic formulation of the metal–ring interaction. The formation of ferrocene upon the addition of THF solutions of $FeCl_2$ (*75*, *76*) and their nonreactivity toward maleic anhydride (*77*) are typical of the cyclopentadienide ion. An ionic bonding mode is further supported by the electronic spectral and magnetochemical properties of these compounds, both of which are remarkably similar to those of the "free ions" in aqueous solution (*78*, *79*). It has recently been shown (*65*) that the tricyclopentadienide of ytterbium reported by Birmingham and Wilkinson (*55*) was probably the ammine adduct, $(C_5H_5)_3Yb \cdot NH_3$ or at least contaminated to a considerable degree by this compound. This has been attributed to the method of preparation of the $YbCl_3$ used in the subsequent synthesis, namely, the high-temperature reaction of Yb_2O_3 and NH_4Cl (*74*).

It has also been shown (*65*) that the compound $Yb(C_5H_5)_3$ can be prepared by the reaction of anhydrous $YbCl_3$ [obtained from the reaction of thionyl chloride with the hydrated trichloride (*80*)] and KC_5H_5 in toluene, a procedure described by Fisher *et al.* for the preparation of the tetracyclopentadienyls of uranium (*81*) and thorium (*82*). The infrared spectrum of this product (*65*) supports its assigned formulation, while that of the compound prepared by the method of Birmingham and Wilkinson shows the presence of coordinated ammonia (3325, 2350, 1600, and 1240 cm^{-1}). The compound (*65*) prepared by the reaction of $YbCl_3$ (prepared by the thionyl chloride method (*80*)) with NaC_5H_5 in THF and isolated by the crystallization from the filtered reaction solution shows the presence of coordinated THF (*83*) (bands assigned to THF at 2970, 2880, 1160, and 960 cm^{-1} in the infrared spectrum). Sublimation of this adduct at 120° C/

10^{-3} mm Hg failed to remove all of the coordinated solvent as evidenced by the infrared spectrum of the green sublimate. Heating the ammine adduct under nitrogen above 200° C gives the reaction:

$$(C_5H_5)_3Yb \cdot NH_3 \xrightarrow{200°-250°C} (C_5H_5)_2YbNH_2 + C_5H_6 \quad (3)$$

The amide (*64*) was obtained by repeated high-vacuum sublimation as yellow crystals (m.p. 345° C). The ammonia adducts of the lighter lanthanides (*55*), however, are not so sublimable without decomposition. The ammonia adduct can also be prepared by the treatment of a THF solution of $(C_5H_5)_3Yb \cdot OC_4H_8$ with a stoichiometric amount of NH_3, followed by sublimation of the dry reaction residue at 120°–150° C/10^{-2} mm Hg. The absorption spectra of these various Yb(III) cyclopentadienides in the 10,000 cm^{-1} region, arising from the $^2F_{7/2}$ to $^2F_{5/2}$ transition (*84*, *85*) in the $4f^{13}$ configuration of Yb(III), have been shown to be diagnostic of the trivalent oxidation state of ytterbium (*65*).

The thermal instability of the Eu analog of this series prevented its preparation by the method of Birmingham and Wilkinson (*55*). It was, however, isolated as the monotetrahydrofuranate (*59*) by concentration of the filtrate from a similar reaction mixture and displays properties analogous to the other tricyclopentadienides. Although the THF cannot be removed under vacuum at room temperature and decomposition occurs on heating at 100° C (*56*), it was found that removal of the THF to give $Eu(C_5H_5)_3$ could be effected by heating at 70° C under vacuum (*59*).

The final members of this series [$M(C_5H_5)_3$; M = Tb, Tm, Ho, and Lu] were prepared (*57*) by a modification of the procedure of Birmingham and Wilkinson (*55*) employing the systems ethyl ether–KC_5H_5 or benzene–NaC_5H_5 in place of THF–NaC_5H_5. In their chemical and physical properties they follow the general trend observed for the other members of the series. The ^1H NMR (*57*) of the diamagnetic $Lu(C_5H_5)_3$ exhibits only one signal in THF at τ 4.17. The infrared spectra (*57*) of these four derivatives indicate the presence of three identical five-membered rings in a trigonal pyramidal arrangement for which the metal–ring bonding is of a very polar character. For a C_5H_5 ring of local C_{5v} symmetry five infrared-active normal vibrational modes are expected. The γ_{CH} vibrations in the 800–770 cm^{-1} region indicate, however, partial central σ-bonding.[1A] The observed shift to higher wavenumbers implies a reduction of negative charge in the ring

[1A] In ionic KC_5H_5 the corresponding vibrations are found in the 731–702 cm^{-1} region.

and with this a decrease in the metal–ring bond polarity (*86*). The trigonal pyramidal geometry (C_{3v} molecular symmetry) suggested by the infrared data is further supported by dipole moment measurements (*57, 64*) in benzene for $Lu(C_5H_5)_3$ ($\mu = 0.85 \pm 0.09$ D) and $Y(C_5H_5)_3$ (1.46 ± 0.06 D).

The tricyclopentadienides of Ce, Nd, Sc, and Sm have also been prepared by the reaction of molten $Mg(C_5H_5)_2$ with the corresponding anhydrous trifluorides in sealed tubes at 200°–260° C (*58*). Although $Mg(C_5H_5)_2$ is thermodynamically more stable than even ferrocene, the high free energies of formation of the magnesium halides render this a general method of preparing cyclopentadienyls from any halides other than those of the alkali metals and some of the alkaline earths. After removal of any excess

TABLE IV

ADDUCTS OF $M(C_5H_5)_3$ LANTHANIDES

Compound	Color	M.p. (°C)	$\chi_{Mol} \times 10^6$ (300° K)	μ_{eff} (BM)	References
$(C_5H_5)_3YCNC_6H_{11}$	Colorless	165°	Diamag	—	*64*
$(C_5H_5)_3NdCNC_6H_{11}$	Violet	147°	4,740	3.4	*64, 93*
$(C_5H_5)_3TbCNC_6H_{11}$	Colorless	162°	42,100	10.1	*62, 64*
$(C_5H_5)_3HoCNC_6H_{11}$	Yellow	165°	47,300	10.6	*62, 64, 93*
$(C_5H_5)_3YbCNC_6H_{11}$	Dark green	167°	8,120	4.4	*62, 64, 72, 93*
$(C_5H_5)_3YbP(C_6H_5)_3$	Dark green	—	—	—	*64, 72*
$(C_5H_5)_3Yb \cdot OC_4H_8$	Green	—	—	—	*64, 65, 72*
$(C_5H_5)_3Eu \cdot OC_4H_8$	Mahogany brown	—	5,589	—	*56*
$(C_5H_5)_3Yb \cdot NH_3$	Green	—	—	—	*64, 65, 72*
$(C_5H_5)_3Pr \cdot NH_3$	Pale green	—	—	—	*55*
$(C_5H_5)_3Sm \cdot NH_3$	Yellow	—	—	—	*55*

$Mg(C_5H_5)_2$ by heating at 80°–120° C under vacuum, the desired products were isolated from the residue by sublimation at 180°–200° C. This method offers the convenience of using the fluorides, which do not react in the previously described solution preparations but which are more readily prepared in the anhydrous state than the chlorides (*87*).

In addition to the monotetrahydrofuranate of $Eu(C_5H_5)_3$ (*56*) and the derivatives $(C_5H_5)_3Yb \cdot L$ (*65*) ($L = NH_3$, OC_4H_8) discussed above, several other examples of adducts of the tricyclopentadienides with Lewis bases have been reported (*55, 62, 64*) (Table IV). The ammoniates, $(C_5H_5)_3M \cdot$

NH_3, have been isolated for Pr and Sm by dissolution of the corresponding tricyclopentadienides in liquid ammonia followed by removal of the solvent at room temperature under vacuum (*55*). On heating the ammoniates at 100°–150° C ammonia is lost and the tricyclopentadienides are recovered.

The reaction of $M(C_5H_5)_3$, (M = Y, Yb, Ho, Tb, Nd) with cyclohexyl isonitrile in benzene results in the formation of compounds of the formula, $(C_5H_5)_3M \cdot CNC_6H_{11}$ (*62*, *64*). These adducts, isolated by extraction with pentane or sublimation of the crude reaction residue, have been claimed to represent the first examples of a stable metal–carbon σ-bond involving a lanthanide. They are all quite unstable with respect to oxidation and hydrolysis but relatively thermally stable, melting without decomposition under nitrogen in the range 147°–167° C. The infrared spectra of these adducts are all quite similar and the bands assigned to the C_5H_5 rings closely approximate those observed in the corresponding tricyclopentadienides, the notable feature again being the shift of the γ_{CH} bands to higher wavenumbers than observed in "ionic" compounds (i.e., NaC_5H_5, KC_5H_5). Further support for a degree of covalance in the bonding in these systems is found in the appearance of vibrations assigned to ring–metal modes in the 600–60 cm^{-1} region (*64*). The infrared data suggest a C_{3v} symmetry for the $M(C_5H_5)_3$ moiety in these adducts, as has been suggested for the parent compounds (*57*). The shift of the ν_{CN} observed in these adducts by 73–78 cm^{-1} to higher wavenumbers relative to the "free" ligand (2130 cm^{-1}), supports the formation of a metal–carbon σ donor bond with the isonitrile, this type of ligand having been shown to function as both a pure donor (*88*) as well as a donor–acceptor (*89*) ligand.

The ability of the $M(C_5H_5)_3$ derivatives to function as acceptors for sufficiently strong Lewis bases has been shown further by the preparation of the complexes $(C_5H_5)_3Yb \cdot X$ [X = $P(C_6H_5)_3$ (*64*, *72*) (C_5H_5N) (*72*)].

The question of the bonding in these compounds has been the subject of several papers (*65*, *72*, *73*, *90–93*) but more detailed studies are required before the definitive answer is available. The original assignments of ionic bonding in these compounds were based primarily on their physical properties and magnetochemical data. However, more recent studies of infrared (*57*, *64*) and electronic (*72*, *73*, *90–92*) spectra of these derivatives suggest that while *f*-orbital involvement in bonding is not sufficient to result in spin pairing of electrons in these shielded orbitals, there is in some cases a degree of *f*-orbital interaction in the bonding. Calderazzo *et al.* (*65*) have proposed, on the basis of electronic spectral data, that the bonding in the $(C_5H_5)_3M$ and $(C_5H_5)_3M \cdot B$ species is essentially electrostatic and have suggested that the physical properties of these compounds (i.e., volatility, low melting points, solubilities) can be explained by a consideration of the steric effects of the ligands. They propose that the rather bulky anions effectively screen the positive charge of the central metal so that little or no residual attraction is exerted intermolecularly. On the other hand, the electronic spectral measurements (*72*, *73*, *90–92*), admittedly subject to ambiguity in interpretation, suggest a degree of covalence. In the case of europium, Mössbauer spectroscopy (*94*) would be useful in obtaining information on the degree of covalence in these compounds, as well as giving an indication of which metal orbitals are involved in the bonding.

Recently the ^1H NMR spectra of a series of compounds of the type $M(C_5H_5)_3$ (M = Pr, Nd, Ho, Tm, Yb) and $(C_5H_5)_3M \cdot B$ (M = Pr, Nd, Ho, Tm, Yb; B = neutral Lewis base) have been reported (*93*). Within a particular series, $(C_5H_5)_3M \cdot B$, similar chemical shifts and linewidths were observed for a variety of ligands B (B = nicotine, *N*-methylpyrolidine, pyridine, THF, α-methyltetrahydrofuran, and cyclohexyl isonitrile) with the same central metal. However, for the three $M(C_5H_5)_3$ derivatives, which could be studied by virtue of their adequate solubility in noncoordinating benzene, a dependence of these NMR parameters on the central metal ion was found for the transition $(C_5H_5)_3M \rightarrow (C_5H_5)_3M \cdot B$. For the Ho(III) and Tm(III) derivatives this transition is accompanied by significant changes in these two NMR parameters, while in the case of Yb(III) the corresponding transition produces only minor changes. The factors determining the NMR parameters in such paramagnetic complexes have been the subject of a recent review (*93a*).

Only one crystal structure has been reported for an organolanthanide, that of $(C_5H_5)_3Sm$ (*95*).

B. *Bis(cyclopentadienyl)lanthanide Chlorides, $[(C_5H_5)_2MCl]$*

The bis(cyclopentadienyl)lanthanide chlorides (*60*) for the heavier lanthanides from samarium to lutetium have been prepared by the stoichiometric reaction of the corresponding anhydrous chloride with NaC_5H_5 in THF, followed by sublimation of the reaction residues at 150°–250° C (10^{-5} mm). They can also be prepared (*60*) by the reaction of the trichloride with its corresponding tricyclopentadienide derivative.

$$2(C_5H_5)_3M + MCl_3 \rightarrow 3(C_5H_5)_2MCl \qquad (M = Sm, Gd, Dy, Ho, Eu, Yb) \tag{4}$$

As for the parent tricyclopentadienides, the chemical and physical properties of these compounds suggest that the metal–ring bonding is essentially electrostatic. Attempts to prepare the analogs of the lighter lanthanides by several different methods failed, traces of the $M(C_5H_5)_3$ derivatives being the only products detected. This change in reactivity as one transverses the series has been ascribed to the lanthanide contraction (*96*). The bis(methylcyclopentadienyl)lanthanide chlorides of Gd, Eu, and Yb have been synthesized by the same methods and, as a result of their enhanced solubilities over the unsubstituted analogs, molecular weight determinations (*60*) have been made in benzene and THF solutions. These measurements indicate a dimeric formulation of the complexes in benzene while monomers are present in THF. The species present in benzene solution have been formulated as involving relatively weak chloride bridges which in THF solution are cleaved, solvation by this hard Lewis base (*97, 98*) being significant in the overall thermodynamics of the process. Although the decreased solubilities of the unsubstituted compounds precluded molecular weight determinations, similar behavior in these cases would seem reasonable.

The only examples of air-stable organolanthanides have been prepared (*60*) by the displacement reactions of the bis(cyclopentadienyl)lanthanide chlorides with a variety of other anions.

$$NaY + (C_5H_5)MCl \xrightarrow{THF} (C_5H_5)_2MY + NaCl \tag{5}$$

Y = phenoxide, formate, acetate, and benzoate

Although these compounds show a marked increase in oxidative stability over the analogous chlorides, they remain quite hydrolytically unstable. A molecular weight measurement (*60*) of bis(methylcyclopentadienyl)erbium acetate in benzene indicates that this compound exists as a dimer in that solvent, a structure involving acetate bridges having been proposed.

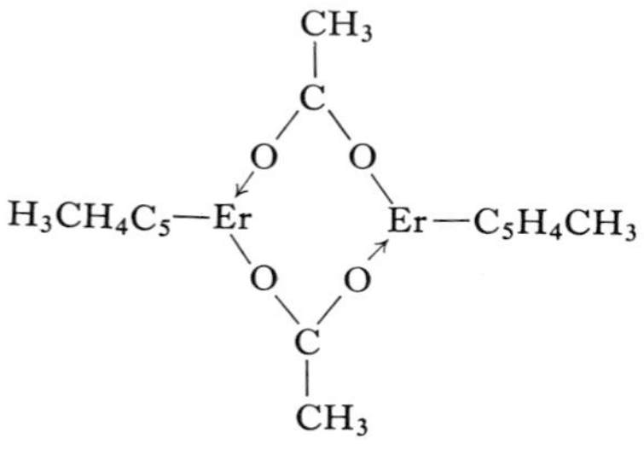

```
                      CH3
                       |
                       C
                      / \
                     O   O
                    ↙     \
H3CH4C5—Er               Er—C5H4CH3
          \              ↗
           O            O
            \          /
                  C
                  |
                 CH3
```

TABLE V: DICYCLOPENTADIENYL LANTHANIDES[a]

Compound	Color	M.p. (°C)	M_{obs}	M_{calc}	$\chi_{Mol}^{corr} \times 10^{6}$ [b] (°K)	Δ (°C)	μ_{eff} (B.M.)
$Sm(C_5H_5)_2Cl$ [b]	Yellow	dec > 200°	—	—	1,068 (300°)	0 [c]	1.62
						50	1.74
					1,145 (195°)	100	1.94
$Gd(C_5H_5)_2Cl$	Colorless	dec > 140°	375 [d]	323	24,610 (301°)	98	8.86
$Dy(C_5H_5)_2Cl$	Yellow	343°–346°dec	—	—	45,000 (300°)	11	10.6
					52,891 (195°)		
$Ho(C_5H_5)_2Cl$	Yellow-orange	340°–343°(dec)	—	—	43,110 (300°)	10	10.3
$Er(C_5H_5)_2Cl$	Pink	dec > 200°	340 [d]	333	36,480 (300°)	29	9.79
$Yb(C_5H_5)_2Cl$	Orange-red	dec > 240°	353 [d]	339	7,141 (301°)	108	4.81
$Lu(C_5H_5)_2Cl$	Pale green	318°–320°	—	—	−13 (300°)	0	
$Gd(C_6H_7)_2Cl$	Colorless	188°–197°	394 [d]	—	—	—	—
			746 [e]	351	—	—	—
$Er(C_6H_7)_2Cl$	Pink	119°–122°	759 [e]	361	—	—	—
$Yb(C_6H_7)_2Cl$	Red	115°–120°	395 [d]	—	—	—	—
			757 [e]	368	—	—	—
$Er(C_5H_5)_2O_2CCH_3$	Pink	331°–335°	—	—	—	—	—
$Yb(C_5H_5)_2O_2CCH_3$	Orange	325°–329°(dec)	—	—	—	—	—
$Gd(C_6H_7)_2O_2CCH_3$	White	207°–209°	—	—	—	—	—
$Er(C_6H_7)_2O_2CCH_3$	Pink	199°–201°	811 [e]	385	—	—	—
$Yb(C_5H_5)_2O_2CC_6H_5$	Orange	350°–375° (dec)	—	—	—	—	—
$Er(C_5H_5)_2O_2CH$	Pink	dec > 270°	—	—	—	—	—
$Dy(C_5H_5)_2OCH_3$	Yellow	dec > 235°	—	—	—	—	—
$Er(C_5H_5)_2OCH_3$	Pink	256°–240°	—	—	—	—	—
$Yb(C_5H_5)_2OCH_3$	Orange	290°–305°	—	—	—	—	—
$Er(C_5H_5)_2NH_2$	Pink	330°–334°	—	—	—	—	—
$Yb(C_5H_5)_2NH_2$	Yellow	345°	—	—	—	—	—
$Yb(C_5H_5)_2OC_6H_5$	Red	392°–386°	—	—	—	—	—

[a] Reference (*60*). [b] Includes correction of -116×10^{-6} for 2 $C_5H_5^-$ rings and 1 Cl^-.
[c] These Δ values assumed for Sm compound, the true value being uncertain because Δ varies for Sm with T.
[d] THF solution. [e] Benzene solution.

When Y is methoxide or amide the derivatives closely resemble the parent chlorides, being quite reactive both hydrolytically and oxidatively and being sublimable at 160°–200° C/10^{-5} mm. The 90 Mc/sec ^1H NMR spectra of $[(C_5H_5)_2YbL]_2$ (L = NH_2, Cl) in THF and deuterobenzene have been measured and display significant variations with L as well as solvent (*93*). The known dicyclopentadienyl derivatives are listed in Table V, along with some of their properties.

C. Cyclopentadienyllanthanide Dichlorides, $(C_5H_5)MCl_2$

The cyclopentadienyllanthanide dichlorides, isolated as the tris tetrahydrofuranates, have been reported for Sm, Gd, Dy, Ho, Er, Yb, and Lu (*61*). They were prepared by the reaction of the respective trichloride with 1 equivalent of $Na(C_5H_5)$. Unlike the $M(C_5H_5)_3$ (*55, 57, 59*) and $(C_5H_5)_2MCl$ (*60*) derivatives, they cannot be sublimed but must be isolated by crystallization from the filtered reaction solution. They have also been prepared by the reaction of the tricyclopentadienide and 2 equivalents of

TABLE VI

$(C_5H_5)MCl_2 \cdot 3$ THF LANTHANIDES

M	Color	M.p. (under N_2) (°C)	$\chi_{Mol}^{corr} \times 10^6$ [a,b]	Δ (°C)	μ_{eff} (B.M.)
Sm	Beige	dec > 50°	—	—	—
Eu	Purple	dec > 50°	4,870 6,336	157	4.24
Gd	Lavender	82°–86° (dec)	—	—	—
Dy	Colorless	85°–90° (dec)	44,254 60,744	90.9	11.81
Ho[c]	Yellow	84°–92°	—	—	—
Er	Pink	91°–94°	35,904 53,344	24.2	9.68
Yb	Orange	78°–81°	7,589	7.52	4.33
Lu	Colorless	76°–78°	—	—	—

[a] Susceptibilities corrected for contributions of $C_5H_5^-$, 2 Cl^-, and 3 C_4H_8O.
[b] Susceptibilities measured at 300° and 194° K.
[c] Molecular weight determination by differential ebulliometric method in THF gave 579 (calc 517).

the respective trichloride (*6*), or by treatment of the bis(cyclopentadienyl) chloride with an equivalent of HCl (*7*).

$$(C_5H_5)_3M + 2\ MCl_3 + 9\ C_4H_8O \xrightarrow{C_4H_8O} 3\ (C_5H_5)MCl_2 \cdot 3\ OC_4H_8 \tag{6}$$

$$(C_5H_5)_2MCl + HCl + 3\ C_4H_8O \xrightarrow{C_4H_8O} (C_5H_5)MCl_2 \cdot 3\ OC_4H_8 \tag{7}$$

The known compounds of this series are listed in Table VI along with some of their properties. Their extreme oxidative and hydrolytic instabilities, insolubilities in nonpolar solvents, and magnetic moments all support an ionic formulation of the metal–ring interaction. As was observed in the $(C_5H_5)_2MCl$ series (*60*), the compounds below samarium cannot be prepared. The THF in these compounds is rather lightly bound to the metal. Prolonged heating of the ytterbium derivative at 40° C under high vacuum causes a color change from light orange to purple, suggesting a degree of orbital interaction between the coordinated THF and the Yb(III) ion.

D. *Tris(indenyl)lanthanides*

A series of organolanthanides containing the indenyl group and having the general formula $M(C_9H_7)_3 \cdot OC_4H_8$ (M = La, Sm, Gd, Tb, Dy, and Yb) (*67, 68*) has recently been prepared by the reaction of the corresponding anhydrous trichloride with sodium indenide in THF solution. The samarium analog (*67*) is of special interest in that a covalent bonding mode between the samarium and indenyl moiety has been proposed. The magnetic moment of this derivative, $Sm(C_9H_7)_3 \cdot OC_4H_8$, of 1.75 BM is close to that observed for the free ion (*99*), as is found for the corresponding cyclopentadienide (*55*) derivative. This is not unexpected in view of the shielding of these $4f$ electrons by the outer $5s^2\,5p^6$ electrons. Indeed, with the exception of the recently reported antiferromagnetism in the case of $Eu(bipy)_4$ (*100*), no example of spin pairing of $4f$ electrons is known. Evidence for the assignment of a covalent bonding mode between the samarium and indenyl moieties, however, is found in the proton NMR spectrum of the compound in THF-d_8. In addition to a complex band, centered at τ 3.02 of relative intensity 4 and assigned to the four protons of the aromatic six-membered ring, three other bands, each of relative intensity 1, are observed: τ 3.33 (doublet), 3.75 (double doublet), and 6.82 (doublet). Such an ABX pattern for the five-membered ring is similar to that reported by Cotton *et al.* (*101*), for the nonfluxional species[2] (π-C_5H_5)Fe$(CO)_2$(1-ind) and supports a structure as in (**I**).

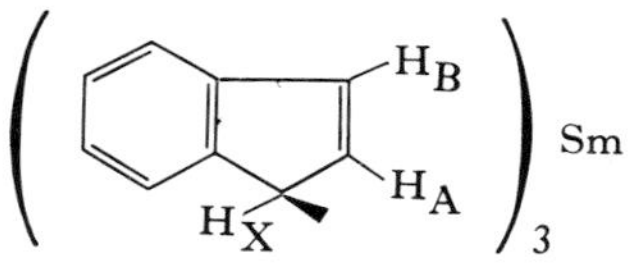

(I)

The proton NMR spectra of $(CH_3)_3M(C_9H_7)$ (M = Si, Ge, Sn) have recently been reported to display a similar pattern at low temperature, the "dynamic" spectrum (AX_2 system for the protons of the five-membered ring) resulting from intramolecular rearrangement being actually attained for the Sn analog above 140° C but only approached at high temperature by the other two derivatives (*102*). Diindenylmercury also exhibits such fluxional behavior (*102a*, *102b*). The indenyl group, in which there is an enhanced electron density at the C-1 position would be expected to promote covalent bonding to the hard (*97*, *98*) trivalent rare earth ions relative to the soft cyclopentadienyl group in which there is complete charge delocalization. The proton NMR spectrum of $NaC_9H_7 \cdot 2\ OC_4H_8$ (*103*), a pale yellow solid isolated from a THF solution, displays an A_2X pattern. Such a pattern has been observed for π-bonded indenyl compounds of Fe (*104*, *105*) and Ru (*104*) and would also be expected for the ionic bonding mode of the indenide group.[3] The formulation of the sodium salt as the bis(tetrahydrofuranate) was based on the relative intensities of 1:8 for the H_X resonance (τ 7.35) compared to each of the two THF signals (τ 7.01, τ 9.02) observed in pyridine solution (*68*). By a similar technique the initial product isolated in the reaction of anhydrous samarium trichloride with sodium indenide was formulated as the monotetrahydrofuranate. The removal of the coordinated THF was readily effected by heating at 70° C/0.1 mm for 1 hour, as evidenced by the absence of the two THF signals in the NMR spectrum of a pyridine solution of the resulting deep red product. This is in marked contrast to $(C_5H_5)_3Yb \cdot OC_4H_8$, which can be sublimed unchanged (*65*). The lability of the THF in $Sm(C_9H_7)_3 \cdot OC_4H_8$ is further shown by its replacement by

[2] H_A, τ 3.28 (double doublet); H_B, 3.47 (doublet); H_X, τ 6.03 (doublet) in $CDCl_3$ at 25° C.

[3] The proton NMR spectrum of Co(π-$C_9H_7)_2$ has recently been reported (*106*). The paramagnetism here causes the appearance of only one rather broad signal arising from the three protons of the five-membered ring.

1,4-dioxane at room temperature on dissolution in that solvent and subsequent removal of the solvent. The NMR spectrum of this product in pyridine solution shows only a broadened signal at τ 6.42 due to 1,4-dioxane.

Further support for structure (I) is found in the electronic spectrum of this compound. Although the relatively weak *f–f* bands in the visible region (363, 375, and 402 mμ for a THF solution of $SmCl_3$) are masked by an intense charge-transfer band at 248 mμ, the shift of this latter absorption from its position of 350 mμ for ionic NaC_9H_7 supports a styrenelike chromophore. The analogs of La, Gd, Tb, Dy, and Yb have also been prepared by the same method (*68*). These derivatives have been characterized by elemental analysis and magnetic susceptibility measurements, and in the case of the diamagnetic La derivative by proton NMR spectroscopy. Structural elucidation of the others by NMR spectroscopy was precluded by the large paramagnetism of the tripositive lanthanide ions. All the analogs of this series closely resemble the corresponding cyclopentadienides in their magnetochemistry. The proton NMR spectrum of $La(C_9H_7)_3 \cdot OC_4H_8$ in THF-d_8 solution closely resembles the ionic sodium species. Two low-field double doublets at τ 2.64 and τ 3.24, both of relative intensity 2, are assigned to the protons of the six-membered ring. The singlet at τ 4.50 has a relative intensity of 2. The reason for its failure to split into the expected doublet as observed in NaC_9H_7 is unknown. The triplet of relative intensity 1 at τ 6.81 is assigned to H_x.

IV

ORGANIC DERIVATIVES OF DIVALENT LANTHANIDES

Dicyclopentadienides of Eu^{2+}, (*57*, *63*) Yb^{2+} (*57*), and Sm^{2+} (*66*) have been reported. The europium and ytterbium analogs, $M(C_5H_5)_2$, have both been prepared by the reaction of the metal with cyclopentadiene in liquid ammonia (*57*).

$$M + 3\ C_5H_6 \xrightarrow{NH_3} M(C_5H_5)_2 + C_5H_8 \tag{8}$$

This reaction is possible because these two metals dissolve in liquid ammonia to give M^{2+} and solvated electrons (*78*). The products are isolated by removal of the solvent and the solvated ammonia is readily removed by heating at 120° C under high vacuum. The magnetic moments of these two compounds are those expected for the free divalent ions, and the infrared spectra indicate the presence of ionically bonded symmetrical five-membered rings in both compounds. The Debye–Scherrer patterns of $Eu(C_5H_5)_2$ and $Sr(C_5H_5)_2$ show that these compounds are isostructural (*57*). It has recently been shown (*65*) that $Yb(C_5H_5)_2$ prepared by this method is contaminated by a Yb^{3+} species. The presence of such a trivalent impurity is based on the electronic spectrum of the product in the 10,000 cm^{-1} region where Yb^{3+} displays characteristic absorptions. The presence of even small amounts of $Yb(C_5H_3)_3$ would seem to be excluded from the brick red sublimate obtained at 360° C from the reaction in liquid ammonia because of the large difference in volatility of the two species. It has, therefore, been suggested (*65*) that $Yb(C_5H_5)_2H$ is the possible impurity, this resulting from the retention of hydrogen on the metal rather than its elimination as H_2 or its consumption by the excess cyclopentadiene as originally proposed (*57*). However, since a good analysis was obtained for this compound in the original paper (*57*) and its magnetic moment does not suggest any considerable amount of Yb^{3+}, it would seem that little of this impurity is present. Ytterbium dicyclopentadienide which is both analytically and spectrally pure can be prepared by three different routes, namely, (i) reduction of $Yb(C_5H_5)_2Cl$ by sodium in THF; (ii) reduction of $Yb(C_5H_5)_2Cl$ by ytterbium metal; (iii) reduction of $Yb(C_5H_5)_3 \cdot C_4H_8O$ by sodium metal (*65*). The best results were obtained with method (i) starting from $Yb(C_5H_5)_2Cl$ prepared *in situ* from $Yb(C_5H_5)_3 \cdot C_4H_8O$ and the stoichiometric amount of hydrogen chloride (*60*). The proton NMR spectrum (*65*) of the violet-red solution of this diamagnetic (f^{14}) compound shows a sharp singlet for the ring resonance at 4.36 τ, a value similar to that for the ionic sodium cyclopentadienide (4.44 τ) (*108*), and $Mg(C_5H_5)_2$ (4.17 τ)[4] (*108*). Precipitation of $Yb(C_5H_5)_2$ by hexane from the THF reaction solution gives a yellow solid which becomes green on pumping under high vacuum at room temperature. The green residue can be sublimed with considerable decomposition at 360° C/10^{-3} mm to give the analytically pure compound whose infrared spectrum shows no THF bands (*65*). The greater ease of removal of coordinated THF for $Yb(C_5H_5)_2$ compared to $Yb(C_5H_5)_3$ has been attributed to the lower charge and larger ionic radius of Yb^{2+} compared to Yb^{3+} (1.10 Å vs. 0.858 Å).

The dicyclopentadienide of Sm^{2+}, isolated as the monotetrahydro-

[4] Ferrocene has a value of 5.92 τ (*108*).

furanate (*66*), represents the first example of such a derivative for a lanthanide metal which is insoluble in liquid ammonia. The synthesis of this pyrophoric purple compound employed a previously described technique (*109*) using the naphthalide anion as the reducting agent for Sm^{3+}.

$$Sm(C_5H_5)_3 + K + C_{10}H_8 \xrightarrow[(KC_{10}H_8)]{THF} Sm(C_5H_5)_2 \cdot THF + KC_5H_5 + C_{10}H_8 \tag{9}$$

The infrared spectrum of this compound closely resembles that of $Sm(C_5H_5)_3$ (*66*).

The europium Mössbauer of the divalent compound $Eu(C_5H_5)_2$ has been reported (*110*). Its isomer shift for the 21.7 keV γ line of ^{151}Eu relative to the source of EuF_3 is -1.32 cm/sec. The similarity of this parameter to that of the corresponding chloride (-1.34 cm/sec) supports an ionic bonding mode for the cyclopentadienide.

The cyclooctatetraene derivatives of divalent ytterbium and europium, $M(C_8H_8)$, have been synthesized by the reaction of the hydrocarbon with the corresponding metals dissolved in anhydrous ammonia (*68a*). The pink ytterbium derivative, obtained by heating (200° C/10^{-3} mm) the orange solvate, is diamagnetic, while the corresponding orange europium species has an epr spectrum which is consistent only with Eu^{2+}. At 77° K, the solid state epr spectrum consists of a strong resonance 4 kG wide, peak-to-peak, centered on $g = 2.00$. Both compounds are extremely air and moisture sensitive but thermally stable to 500° under vacuum. Although the two derivatives are insoluble in hydrocarbons and ethers, dissolution in more basic solvents (ammonia, pyridine, and dimethylformamide) is accompanied by the formation of brightly colored solutions, complete removal of coordinated solvent being effected by heating the solutions' residues under vacuum.

V

ORGANOACTINIDES

A. *Chemistry of Actinides*

The actinide elements (Table VII), comprising elements actinium, $Z = 89$ to, at present, lawrencium, $Z = 103$ derive their unique properties, like the lanthanides, from the filling of an inner electronic level, in this case

TABLE VII

THE ACTINIDE ELEMENTS

Element	Symbol	Atomic No.	Oxidation states[a]	Ionic radius (Å) M^{3+}	Ionic radius (Å) M^{4+}	Electronic configuration
Actinium	Ac	89	**3**	1.11	0.99	$6d7s^2$
Thorium	Th	90	3, **4**	—	0.96	$6d^2 7s^2$
Protactinium	Pa	91	3, 4, **5**	—	0.93	$5f^2 6d7s^2$ or $5f6d^2 7s^2$
Uranium	U	92	3, 4, 5, **6**	1.03	0.93	$5f^3 6d7s^2$
Neptunium	Np	93	3, 4, **5**, 6, 7	1.01	0.92	$5f^5 7s^2$
Plutonium	Pu	94	3, **4**, 5, 6, 7	1.00	0.90	$5f^6 7s^2$
Americium	Am	95	**3**, 4, 5, 6	0.99	0.89	$5f^7 6d7s^2$
Curium	Cm	96	**3**, 4	—	0.88	$5f^7 6d7s^2$
Berkelium	Bk	97	**3**, 4	—	—	$5f^8 6d7s^2$ or $5f^9 7s^2$
Californium	Cf	98	**3**	—	—	$5f^{10} 7s^2$
Einsteinium	Es	99	**3**	—	—	$5f^{11} 7s^2$
Fermium	Fm	100	**3**	—	—	$5f^{12} 7s^2$
Mendelevium	Md	101	2, **3**	—	—	$5f^{13} 7s^2$
Nobelium	No	102	**2**, 3	—	—	$5f^{14} 7s^2$
Lawrencium	Lw	103	—	—	—	$5f^{14} 6d7s^2$

[a] Most stable state, boldface.

the $5f$ shell. The chemistry of these elements has been extensively described elsewhere (*7, 9, 12–14*) and will not be discussed at any length here. While these elements show general trends analogous to those observed in the lanthanide series, their chemistry is somewhat more complicated as the result of the lower binding energies and less effective shielding by the outer electrons of the $5f$ electrons compared to the $4f$ electrons. As a result the energies of the $5f$, $6d$, $7s$, and $7p$ orbitals are comparable over a range of atomic numbers (especially U–Am). The results of this complication relative to the $4f$ elements are as follows:

(1) More variable oxidation states of the $5f$ elements compared to the $4f$ elements for which the 3+ state is the only oxidation state of great importance (*111, 112*). The 7+ state has recently been obtained for Np and Pu by ozone oxidation in strongly alkaline solutions (*113*) while Md(II) is less reducing than Eu(II) (*114, 115*) and No(II) is rather difficult to oxidize to the 3+ state in aqueous solution (*116*). As a generalization higher oxidation states are favored in the beginning of the $5f$ group while at the end the lower oxidation states are considerably more stable (*113*).

(2) Enhanced tendency for covalent bonding as the result of less effective shielding by the outer electrons of the $5f$ electrons compared to $4f$ electrons.

(3) Rather complex magnetochemistry.

(4) Electronic absorption spectra, which while still characterized by relatively sharp bands, display broadening and increased intensity relative to the lanthanides.

B. *Organoactinides*

The amount of work reported in the literature dealing with organic derivatives of the actinide series is considerably less than for the lanthanide elements. At present organoactinides have been reported for the first nine (excluding actinium) members of this series (*35, 35a, b, 58, 81, 82, 117–128d*). With the exception of the recently reported bis(cyclooctatetraenyl) derivatives of uranium (*35, 35b*), thorium (*121a*), and neptunium (*126a*) and tetra(π-allyl) uranium (*35a*), all of these organoactinides contain the cyclopentadienyl group.

Reynolds and Wilkinson (*117*) reported the first such compound (Table VIII) in 1954, $(\pi\text{-}C_5H_5)_3UCl$. The reaction of anhydrous UCl_4 with NaC_5H_5 in the molar ratio 1:3.8 followed by sublimation of the reaction residue at 240° C/10^{-4} to 10^{-5} mm gave the dark red air-sensitive compound. It is thermally stable to at least 360° C, melting in an evacuated sealed tube to a red liquid at 260°–265°C. The failure of the compound to react with a THF solution of ferrous chloride (*75, 76*) or maleic anhydride (*77*) suggests that the C_5H_5 groups are bound to the metal by a sandwich-type bond. Although a THF solution of the compound is only weakly conducting, the immediate formation of a precipitate on the addition of $AgClO_4$ supports an ionic bonding mode of the chloride. The drastic change in the visible spectrum of a THF or pyridine solution of this red compound from that of U(IV) in aqueous solution is in contrast to the behavior observed in the "ionic" rare earth cyclopentadienides. For $(\pi\text{-}C_5H_5)_3UCl$ there is an increase in the number of bands in the visible region and also the magnitudes of the molar extinction coefficients increase, e.g., 715 mμ, (ϵ =75); 502 mμ (ϵ =216); 458 mμ (ϵ = 219), relative to the aquo U(IV) ion for which there are only four groups of bands in the visible region, all having ϵ values of 15–60. The green solution which results from dissolution of the compound in water is stable only for a short time and gives a visible spectrum similar to that of the THF solution. The compound

TABLE VIII

ORGANOURANIUM COMPOUNDS

Compound	Color	μ (B.M.)	Sublimation temp. (°C; mm)	M.p. (°C)	References
$(C_5H_5)_3U$					*117a*
$(\pi\text{-}C_5H_5)_3UCl$	Dark green	3.16 ($\Delta = 138°$)	210°; 10^{-4}	260°–265° (dec)	*93, 117,* 118, *119, 129*
$(\pi\text{-}C_5H_5)_3U \cdot OC_4H_9$	Green	2.68 ($\Delta = 82°$)	120°; 10^{-4}	148°–150°	*123*
$(\pi\text{-}C_5H_5)_3U \cdot OCH_3$	Green	—	120°; 10^{-4}	dec	*123*
$(\pi\text{-}C_5H_5)_3UBH_4$	Dark red	—	170°; 10^{-4}	—	*118–120, 132, 133a*
$(\pi\text{-}C_5H_5)_4U$	Bright red	2.78	195°; 10^{-4}	dec > 250°	*81, 118, 119, 133, 133a*
$(\pi\text{-}C_8H_8)_2U$	Green	—	180°; 0.03	—	*35, 35b*
$(\pi\text{-}C_3H_5)_4U$	Dark green	2.6 ($\Delta \sim = 100$)		dec > −30°	*35a*

follows the Curie-Weiss law with $\Delta = 138°$ and $\mu = 3.16$ BM in the solid state, indicating two unpaired electrons. The ^1H NMR spectra of $(C_5H_5)_3UX$ (X = F, Cl, Br, I) have been measured in deuterobenzene at 90 Mc/sec and give one sharp ring proton signal, the chemical shifts in ppm relative to the diamagnetic thorium(IV) homologs being, respectively, +12.6 (line-width, 3.2 Hz), +9.56 (1.5 Hz), +9.79 (1.1 cps), and +10.4 (1.3 cps) (*93*).

Attempts to prepare $U(C_5H_5)_3$ (*117*) by the reaction in THF gave only a small yield of a very unstable red compound on sublimation of the dried reaction mixture. Analysis showed the compound to be free from chloride and approximately fit for $U(C_5H_5)_3$ but reproducible analyses were not obtained. This derivative has been referred to in a recent paper (*128b*) but details of its preparation and properties have not yet been published (*117a*).

It was subsequently shown (*123*) that $(C_5H_5)_3U \cdot OC_4H_9$ can be prepared by a similar reaction. Here an oxidation–reduction process is involved in which the ether is cleaved and reduced to the butoxide anion and the U(III) is oxidized to the 4+ state. This compound can be better prepared (*123*) from UCl_4 in dimethoxyethane solvent by the scheme.

$$UCl_4 + NaOC_4H_9 \rightarrow NaCl + UCl_3OC_4H_9 \quad (10)$$

$$UCl_3OC_4H_9 + 3\ NaC_5H_5 \rightarrow U(C_5H_5)_3\ OC_4H_9 + 3\ NaCl \quad (11)$$

The formulation of both these products is supported by the liberation of 1 equivalent of *n*-butanol on decomposition with methanolic HCl. The magnetic susceptibility of the solid shows the presence of two unpaired electrons ($\Delta = 82°$, $\mu = 2.68$ BM). The analogous methoxide compound (*123*) was also prepared by the latter method using $NaOCH_3$. Both compounds are green and of similar volatility and stability.

The structure of $(\pi\text{-}C_5H_5)_3UCl$ suggested by Reynolds and Wilkinson (*117*) has been verified by an X-ray study (*129*). The results indicate the U—Cl bond is essentially ionic (U—Cl distance, 2.559 ± 0.016 Å) and that the C_5H_5—U bonds are of the sandwich type (U—C distance, 2.74 Å). The C_5H_5 rings and the chloride atom form a distorted tetrahedron about the U atoms.

An increased yield of $(C_5H_5)_3UCl$ over the method of Reynolds and Wilkinson (*117*) has been effected by the replacement of NaC_5H_5 by TlC_5H_5 (*118, 119*). In addition to improving the yield, the use of TlC_5H_5 (*130*) offers the experimental advantages of being an air- and water-stable solid, allowing careful control of stoichiometry.

The synthesis of $(C_5H_5)_3UBH_4$ (*118–120*) has been achieved by the reaction of a two-fold excess of $NaBH_4$ with $(C_5H_5)_3UCl$ in THF at room temperature. After removal of the solvent the dark red product was isolated by sublimation. Interestingly, no reaction occurs on carrying out the reaction at reflux temperature. The X-ray diffraction powder pattern (*118*) of this compound shows it not to be isostructural with $(C_5H_5)_3UCl$. The presence of a terminal BH_2 stretching vibration (2463 cm^{-1}) as well as bridging BH_2 absorptions (2140, 1442–1284 cm^{-1}) suggest a bridged structure for the borohydride ion with the bond to the uranium more ionic than that in $(C_5H_5)_2TiBH_4$ but less so than in $(C_5H_5)_2Zr(BH_4)_2$ (*131*). The mass spectrum of $(C_5H_5)_3UBH_4$, along with that of the analogous chloride, have been reported (*118, 119*). The proton NMR (*132, 133a*)[5] of the borohydride has been interpreted in terms of a nonrigid structure in which there is rapid ring rotation around the 3 fivefold axes defining the C_5H_5—U bonds as well as very rapid intramolecular opening and reformation of new U—H—B bonds.

Tetracyclopentadienyluranium has been prepared by the reaction of anhydrous UCl_4 with a large excess of KC_5H_5 in refluxing benzene for

[5] The ^1H NMR spectrum measured in C_6D_6 with water as the reference shows: $C_5H_5^-$, 13.77 ppm (linewidth = 2.4 cps); BH_4^-, 67.2 ppm (linewidth = 20 cps); J_{H-B} (cps) = 86.5 ± 1.5).

24 hours (*81*). The bright red product which is moderately air stable in the solid state, was obtained in 6% yield by extraction of the reaction residue for 10 days with *n*-heptane. This compound has subsequently been prepared in 10% yield by the reaction of UCl_4 with a 2.5-fold excess of NaC_5H_5 in refluxing THF and characterized by mass spectroscopy (*118*, 119).[6] It has also been prepared (*58*) by the reaction of UF_4 with molten $Mg(C_5H_5)_2$, a method previously described for several lanthanide tricyclopentadienides (*58*). The infrared (*81*, *118*, *119*) spectrum of $U(C_5H_5)_4$ indicates the presence of symmetrical cyclopentadienyl ligands and excludes the possibility of σ-bonded rings with diene structures by the absence of the typical absorptions of C=C associated with such a structure. The dipole moment of 0.0 D (*81*), measured in benzene, indicates a highly symmetrical molecular structure. The ^{1}H NMR spectrum (*133*, *133a*) has recently been reported to consist of a rather narrow singlet at 20.42 ppm upfield from benzene as the internal reference. The interpretation of the NMR spectrum in terms of possible mechanisms of spin delocalization onto the rings has been considered (*133*, *133a*, *133b*).

An especially interesting and novel type of organic derivative of uranium is bis(cyclooctatetraenyl)uranium ("uranocene") reported recently by Streitwieser and Müller-Westerhoff (*35*). This green pyrophoric compound was prepared by the reaction of the dianion of cyclooctatetraene in dry oxygen-free THF at $-30°$C with UCl_4. After stirring overnight green crystals were isolated in 80% yield by the addition of degassed water followed by extraction of the resulting precipitate with benzene or toluene. The compound is stable to water, acetic acid, and aqueous sodium hydroxide and is considerably more volatile than the other organouranium derivatives, subliming at 180°C/0.03 mm. The mass spectrum[7] supports a sandwich structure of the ferrocene type with planar eight-membered rings above and below the central uranium atom in a D_{8d} or D_{8h} arrangement. The unique structure of this compound results from the symmetry properties of the ligands, each with 10 π-electrons, which permit overlap of the rings' highest occupied π-molecular orbitals with the *f* atomic orbitals of uranium.

[6] Fischer and Treiber (*81*) report $U(C_5H_5)_4$ to be nonvolatile and to decompose under nitrogen above 250°C while Anderson and Crisler (*118*) report its isolation by sublimation at 195°C/10^{-4} mm.

[7] The mass spectrum shows the high-intensity peaks at m/e=446 [molecular ion, $(C_8H_8)_2U^+ \equiv M$]; 342 (M-COT) and 104 (COT) and a series of lower intensity peaks attributable to the cations of M—C_6H_6(368), U+C_6H_6(316), U(238), M/2(223) and C_9H_7(91).

A single crystal X-ray diffraction analysis of this compound has confirmed that it is an authentic sandwich complex of the 5*f* series; the two eclipsed planar C_8H_8 rings have average distances for alternating sets of four bonds of 1.391 and 1.398 Å and an average U—C bond length of 2.648 Å (*35b*).

The reaction of UCl_4 with allyl magnesium bromide in ethyl ether at −30° C has been reported to give $U(C_3H_5)_4$ (*35a*). Low temperature filtration of the MgClBr formed, followed by pentane extraction of the residue

TABLE IX

ORGANOACTINIDES

Compound	Color	M.p. (°C)	Sublimation temp. (°C)	References
$Th(C_5H_5)_4$	Colorless	dec > 170°	170°–190°	*82, 133*
$Th(C_5H_5)_3BH_4$[a]	—	—	—	*121, 132*
$Th(C_8H_8)_2$	Yellow	dec > 190°	160° (0.01 ton)	*121a*
$Pa(C_5H_5)_4$	Yellow-orange	dec > 210°	[b]	*93, 122*
$Np(C_5H_5)_4$	Red-brown	dec > 220°	[b]	*126*
$Np(C_5H_5)_3Cl$	Dark brown	dec > 300°	100°	*93, 124, 125*
$Np(C_8H_8)_2$	—	—	—	*126a*
$Pu(C_5H_5)_3$	Green	dec > 195°	170°–165°	*93, 127*
$Am(C_5H_5)_3$	Flesh colored	—	160°–205°	*128*
$^{248}Cm(C_5H_5)_3$	Colorless	—	—	*128a*
$^{244}Cm(C_5H_5)_3$	Colorless	—	180°	*128a, b*
$^{249}Bk(C_5H_5)_3$	—	—	—	*128c, d*
$^{249}Cf(C_5H_5)_3$	—	—	—	*128c, d*

[a] Preparative details not yet published.
[b] Compound too thermally unstable to sublime and was isolated by benzene extraction.

obtained by evaporation of the filtrate gave deep red pyrophoric crystals which are thermally stable up to −20° C and are soluble in organic solvents. Recrystallization can be effected at low temperatures from pentane or hexane solution. The infrared spectrum supports a π-allylic bonding mode, while the magnetic moment of 2.6 B.M. ($\Theta = \sim 100°$ K in the temperature range 213°–253°K) is quite similar to the values observed for other π-bonded organouranium compounds. Thermal decomposition gave a C_3 product: uranium ratio of 2.46 (81.5% propylene and 18.5% propane). Hydrolysis produced a gas mixture identified as propylene (97.3%) and 1,5-hexadiene and cyclohexene (2.7%). The only other reported organoactinides include a few derivatives of thorium (*58, 82, 121, 121a, 123, 132, 133*) as well as $(C_5H_5)_3NpCl$ (*93, 124, 125*), $(C_5H_5)_4Np$ (*126*), $Np(C_8H_8)_2$ (*126a*), $Pa(C_5H_5)_4$ (*122*), and the tricyclopentadienyls of Pu (*93, 127*), Am (*128*), ^{244}Cm (*128a–b*), ^{248}Cm (*128a*), ^{249}Bk (*128c–d*) and ^{249}Cf (*128c–d*).

Reynolds and Wilkinson (*117*) sublimed a white product in 1% yield from the dried reaction mixture of anhydrous $ThCl_4$ and excess NaC_5H_5. Analysis of this very air sensitive compound indicated an approximate composition, $Th(C_5H_5)_4$. However the thermal instability of the compound prevented its further purification and characterization. If the THF reaction solution of $ThCl_4$ and NaC_5H_5 in a 1:2 molar ratio is evaporated and extracted with 6*N* HCl, an unstable colorless solution is obtained which gives precipitation reactions characteristic of di(π-cyclopentadienyl) metal cations (e.g., with silicotungstic acid, Reinecke's salt, and bromine water). While no pure compounds were obtained, the infrared spectra of these dried precipitates were similar to the di(π-cyclopentadienyl)zirconium compounds (*134*). This is not surprising in view of the usual similarity between Zr and Th.[8]

Fischer and co-workers prepared the air-stable $(C_5H_5)_4Th$ (*82*) by the reaction of $ThCl_4$ with excess KC_5H_5 in refluxing benzene. By sublimation of the dried reaction residue under high vacuum at 250°–290°C colorless crystals were obtained and freed of an oily organic impurity by washing with *n*-pentane. Resublimation and subsequent washing with pentane gave an approx. 10% yield of the reasonably air stable colorless crystals. The infrared spectrum (*82*) is quite similar to that of $(C_5H_5)_4U$ (*81*) and similar bonding is proposed for the two compounds. The presence of two bands in the CsBr region at 603 and 393 cm^{-1} suggests covalent bonding, although its solubilities and decomposition in water to form cyclopentadiene are indicative of an ionic species. The ^1H NMR of a saturated $CDCl_3$ solution shows one sharp signal at τ 3.6 (*82*). The ^1H NMR of this diamagnetic derivative has also been recently reported in several other solvents (*133*). The reaction of molten $Mg(C_5H_5)_2$ with ThF_4 at 200°C gives a 61% yield of $Th(C_5H_5)_4$, (*58*), this general method being applicable to a wide variety of metal halides. The product sublimed with 1–2% of a hydrocarbon decomposition product and was finally purified by washing with petroleum ether. The use of ThI_4 in this reaction gave a product which appeared to be $(C_5H_5)_2ThI_2$ (*58*). The derivatives $(C_5H_5)_3ThOR$

[8] ZrI_4 like ThI_4 gives only $(C_5H_5)_2ZrI_2$ on reaction with molten $Mg(C_5H_5)_2$ (*58*).

($R = C_4H_9$, CH_3) (*123*) were prepared by the method previously described for the uranium analogs (*123*) and have properties similar to the latter. The butoxides of U and Th have been shown by X-ray powder patterns to be isostructural (*123*).

Tricyclopentadienylthorium chloride was prepared by the reaction of KC_5H_5 and anhydrous $ThCl_4$ in ethyl ether in a molar ratio of 13:1 and was characterized by elemental analysis, molecular weight determination in methylene chloride, infrared, and ^1H NMR spectroscopy (*123*). The solid is moderately air stable but solutions are quite labile. Chemical and spectroscopic evidence indicates that the bonding in $(C_5H_5)_3ThX$ ($X = OC_4H_9$, OCH_3, Cl) involves metal–ring interactions which are somewhat more polar in character than is the case in ferrocene. Some ferrocene is produced when these derivatives are treated with ferrous chloride. The rather low field ring proton signals (τ 3.70–3.90) in the NMR spectra of these compounds are consistent with such a polar interaction in which there is less reduction of electron density from the rings than is the case with strongly covalent bonding [i.e., τ 5.96 for $(\pi\text{-}C_5H_5)_2Fe$] (*135*). This has been attributed to deshielding of the C_5H_5 protons by induced ring currents in the relatively electron-rich rings.

The borohydride analog, $(C_5H_5)_3ThBH_4$, has been prepared and, although the experimental details and its properties have not yet been published, the ^1H NMR (*132*) of this diamagnetic compound has been measured in C_6D_6 ($C_5H_5^-$, 1.12 ppm; BH_4^-, 3.76 ppm ($J_{H-B} = 85.8 \pm 1.5$ cps).

Bis(π-cyclooctatetraenyl)thorium ("thoracene") has been synthesized from thorium tetrachloride and 2 equivalents of $K_2C_8H_8$ in tetrahydrofuran (*121a*). The bright yellow crystals obtained by sublimation of the reaction residue are characterized by a mass spectrum with a parent peak at m/e 440 [Th(COT)$_2$] with major fragment peaks at m/e 336 (ThCOT), 111 and 109 (unassigned), and 104 (COT). Unlike uranocene (*35*), thoracene is readily decomposed by water. While also air sensitive, it does not enflame in air as does the former. Although X-ray analysis shows the compound to be isostructural with the D_{8h} sandwich configuration of the uranium analog (*35b*), its NMR spectrum in DMSO solution shows a complex multiplet at 6.2 ppm rather than the sharp singlet expected for such a structure. Complexation by DMSO, accompanied by lowering of the rings' symmetry corresponding to that of diene ligands, has been suggested to explain this observation. Such Lewis acidity can be rationalized in terms of the molecular orbital scheme proposed for these bis(π-cyclooctatetraenyl) actinide derivatives and the $5f^{\circ}$ electron configuration of thorium (IV).

The synthesis of the first transuranic cyclopentadienyl derivative, $(C_5H_5)_3Pu$ (*127*), was achieved by the reaction of $PuCl_3$ with a melt of $Be(C_5H_5)_2$ at 70° C. The pyrophoric green product was isolated in 60% yield by sublimation in high vacuum at 140°–165°C after subliming out excess $Be(C_5H_5)_2$. It is readily attacked by oxygen-free water with the evolution of a gas and by deaerated 1*N* HCl or 18% HNO_3 with the formation of a blue Pu(III) solution. The infrared spectrum shows the presence of symmetrical five-membered rings [characteristic bands at 779/793 (γ_{CH}); 841, 1007 (δ_{CH}); 1447 (ω_{CC}); 3100 (ν_{CH})]. On the basis of these band positions as well as the absence of any appreciable absorption at 1000 cm^{-1} it was concluded that the metal–ring linkages had strong ionic character. The flesh-colored tricyclopentadienyl of americium (*128*) was prepared by a method similar to that employed for the Pu analog but it is less volatile and more thermally stable. It is not pyrophoric like $Pu(C_5H_5)_3$ and in fact decomposes only slowly in air at room temperature in the solid state although benzene and THF solutions are quite hydrolytically and oxidatively unstable. The higher sublimation temperature, greater thermal stability (m.p. > 330° C under argon), behavior in solution, and the lowered position of the γ_{CH} bands at 768/788 cm^{-1} indicate that this compound more closely resembles the lanthanide tricyclopentadienides than does $Pu(C_5H_5)_3$.

A radiochemical synthesis involving the neutron bombardment of the ^{238}U analog for 4 hours was employed to prepare $(C_5H_5)_3NpCl$ (*124*):

$$^{238}U(C_5H_5)_3X \xrightarrow{(n)} {}^{239}U(C_5H_5)_3X \xrightarrow[23\ min]{\beta^-} {}^{239}Np(C_5H_5)_3X \qquad (12)$$

$$(X = Cl, F)$$

The moderately air sensitive radioactive product, which decays, itself, by β^- emission, has a half-life of 2.3 days and was isolated by sublimation at 230° C. Its formulation was based on its volatility, solubilities in organic solvents, high thermal stability, and moderate stability toward oxygen, all of which are similar to the other known $(C_5H_5)_3AcX$ species. The ^{237}Np derivative (*125*) has been prepared by a chemical method.

$$2\ NpCl_4 + 3\ Be(C_5H_5)_2 \xrightarrow[70°C]{\text{Molten } Be(C_5H_5)_2} 2\ (C_5H_5)_3NpCl + 3\ BeCl_2$$

The infrared spectrum [789, 808, 825 cm^{-1} (γ_{CH}); 866, 907, 1012 cm^{-1} (δ_{CH}); 1060, 1100 cm^{-1} (γ_{CH}); 1393 cm^{-1} (ω_{CH}); 3094 cm^{-1} (ν_{CH})] of the product, isolated by sublimation at 100° C, further supports its structural similarity to $(C_5H_5)_3UCl$. Neptunium, like uranium, but unlike plutonium and americium favors the 4+ oxidation state over the 3+ state. Thus

NpX_3 (X = Cl, F) both give $(C_5H_5)_3NpX$ upon reaction with $Be(C_5H_5)_2$. This preference for higher oxidation states has been recently discussed by Jørgensen (*113*).

The synthesis of $Np(C_5H_5)_4$ (*126*) has been achieved by the method employed for the Th and U derivatives (*81*, *82*).

$$NpCl_4 + 4\ KC_5H_5 \xrightarrow[\text{Reflux 160 hrs}]{C_6H_6} Np(C_5H_5)_4 + 4\ KCl \qquad (13)$$

Extraction of the dried reaction residue with benzene for 50 hours gave a 72% yield of this reddish brown product, which is considerably less sensitive to oxidation and hydrolysis than $Pu(C_5H_5)_3$ (*127*) and $Am(C_5H_5)_3$ (*128*). The infrared spectrum [780, 810 cm^{-1} (γ_{CH}); 1008 cm^{-1} (δ_{CH}); 1447 (ω_{CC}); 3077 (ν_{CH})] shows bands of similar intensities and positions to those of $U(C_5H_5)_4$ (*81*), suggesting a similar molecular structure. It dissolves in benzene as a monomer to give a green solution. Dissolution in THF results in a yellow-brown solution.

Bis(cyclooctatetraenyl) neptunium(IV) (*126a*) has been prepared by an analogous preparative route to that used for the uranium (*35*) and thorium (*121a*) homologs. It resembles the uranium derivative in its hydrolytic and oxidative stability and solubility properties. The visible spectrum has major absorptions at 5170, 5605, 5805, and 5957 Å. Its infrared spectrum shows absorptions at 1470, 890, 740, and 688 cm^{-1}. An interesting feature of the infrared spectra of both the uranium and neptunium compounds is the absence of any C—H stretching frequency (2900–3000 cm^{-1}). This phenomenon has been suggested to possibly indicate metal–hydrogen bonding. The Mössbauer spectrum (*126b*) at 4.2° K is magnetically split and exhibits an isomer shift of +2.50 cm/sec, a value considerably out of range of ionic Np(IV) compounds. This observation along with the significant change of the visible absorption spectrum, suggests 5*f* orbital participation in the bonding of the compound.

The only reported organic derivative of protactinium, $Pa(C_5H_5)_4$ (*122*), has been prepared by the reaction of the chlorination product of Pa_2O_5 with molten $Be(C_5H_5)_2$ at 65° C. It was isolated in 54% yield as orange-yellow crystals by benzene extraction of the reaction residue and characterized by infrared and mass spectroscopy. Its mass spectrum displays a molecular ion peak (491) and a fragmentation pattern similar to that of $Th(C_5H_5)_4$ (*82*). In thermal stability, however, it resembles the tetracyclopentadienyl of uranium rather than thorium, not being sublimable and decomposing above 210° C. The infrared spectrum is quite similar to the other reported tetracyclopentadienyls of the 5*f* elements [788, 811 cm^{-1} (γ_{CH}); 1008 cm^{-1} (δ_{CH}); 1445 (ω_{CC}); 3078 (ν_{CH})].

As the result of the availability of weighable amounts of the relatively long-lived isotopes of the transamericium elements and the development of the techniques required for organometallic syntheses on the microgram scale, four tricyclopentadienyls of such isotopes have recently been isolated (*128a–d*). The ^{248}Cm ($T_{1/2} = 4 \times 10^5$ yr, (α-decay) derivative was prepared by the reaction of the trichloride with molten $Be(C_5H_5)_2$ in a fine capillary (*128a*). After the excess $Be(C_5H_5)_2$ was distilled away, pure $Cm(C_5H_5)_3$, which is thermally stable above 300° C, was isolated by fractional sublimation and shown to be isomorphous with $Pr(C_5H_5)_3$ by X-ray diffraction analysis of a single crystal. The electronic spectrum of $^{248}Cm(C_5H_5)_3$ is characterized by several sharp absorption lines near 6400 Å as well as a bright red fluorescence which can be excited by 3600 Å irradiation.

The corresponding derivative of ^{244}Cm ($T_{1/2} = 18$ yr, α-decay) (*128b*) was subsequently prepared by a similar technique using $Mg(C_5H_5)_2$ and was identified by its mass spectrum which has a parent ion peak at m/e = 439 and a fragmentation pattern similar to the corresponding Pu (*127*) and U (*117a*) species. Attempts to isolate $^{244}Cm(C_5H_5)_3$ on the milligram scale were precluded by radiolytic decomposition reactions arising from the high α-activity of such reaction mixtures.

The microchemical preparative techniques employed for the above transamericium elements as well as the isolation of the ^{147}Pm, ^{249}Bk and ^{249}Cf tricyclopentadienyls have been reported in detail (*128d*). The X-ray powder diagrams of the latter three derivatives are in good agreement with those of $M(C_5H_5)_3$ (M = Pr, Sm, Gd).

References

1. O. M. Yost, H. Russell, and C. S. Garner, "The Rare Earth Elements and Their Compounds." Wiley, New York, 1947.
2. R. C. Vickery, "Chemistry of the Lanthanons." Academic Press, New York, 1953.
3. F. H. Spedding and A. M. Daane, eds., "The Rare Earths." Wiley, New York, 1961.
4. T. Moeller, "The Chemistry of the Lanthanides." Reinhold, New York, 1963.
5. N. E. Topp "The Chemistry of the Rare Earth Elements." Elsevier, Amsterdam, 1965.
6. S. P. Sinha, "Complexes of the Rare Earths." Pergamon Press, Oxford, 1966.
7. D. Brown, "Halides of the Lanthanides and Actinides." Wiley (Interscience), New York, 1968.
8. S. P. Sinha, "Europium." Springer, Berlin, 1967.
9. J. J. Katz and G. T. Seaborg, "The Chemistry of the Actinide Elements." Methuen, London, 1957.

10. T. Moeller, D. F. Martin, L. C. Thompson, R. Ferrus, G. R. Feistel, and W. J. Randall, *Chem. Rev.* **65**, 1 (1965).
11. A. J. Downs, *in* "New Pathways in Inorganic Chemistry" (E. A. V. Ebsworth, A. G. Maddock, and A. G. Sharpe, eds.), p. 15. Cambridge Univ. Press, London and New York, 1968.
12. L. B. Asprey and B. B. Cunningham, *Progr. Inorg. Chem.* **2**, 267 (1960).
13. A. E. Comyns, *Chem. Rev.* **60**, 115 (1960).
14. K. W. Bagnall, *Coord. Chem. Rev.* **2**, 145 (1967).
15. J. Stary, "The Solvent Extraction of Metal Chelates." Pergamon Press, Oxford, 1964.
16. T. R. Sweet and H. W. Parlett, *Anal. Chem.* **40**, 1885 (1968).
17. W. Fischer, W. Diety, and O. Jübermann, *Naturwissenschaften* **25**, 348 (1937).
18. F. V. Robinson and N. E. Topp, *J. Inorg. & Nucl. Chem.* **26**, 473 (1964).
19. S. P. Sinha, "Europium," p. 12. Springer, Berlin, 1967.
20. S. W. Mayer and E. R. Tompkins, *J. Am. Chem. Soc.* **69**, 2866 (1947).
21. E. R. Tompkins and S. W. Mayer, *J. Am. Chem. Soc.* **69**, 2859 (1947).
22. D. B. James, J. E. Powell, and F. H. Spedding, *J. Inorg. & Nucl. Chem.* **19**, 133 (1961).
23. S. P. Sinha, "Europium," p. 14. Springer, Berlin, 1967.
24. K. J. Eisentraut and R. E. Sievers, *J. Am. Chem. Soc.* **87**, 5254 (1965).
25. *Chem. Eng. News* **43**, 78 (May 10, 1965).
26. H. G. Friedman, G. R. Choppin, and D. G. Feuerbacher, *J. Chem. Educ.* **41**, 354 (1964).
27. C. Becker, *J. Chem. Educ.* **41**, 358 (1964).
28. K. Street and G. T. Seaborg, *J. Am. Chem. Soc.* **72**, 2790 (1950).
29. R. E. Connick and Z. Z. Hugus, *J. Am. Chem. Soc.* **74**, 6012 (1952).
30. J. C. Eisenstein, *J. Chem. Phys.* **25**, 142 (1956).
31. C. A. Coulson and G. R. Lester, *J. Chem. Soc.* p. 3650 (1956).
32. C. K. Jørgensen, R. Pappalardo, and H. H. Schmidtke, *J. Chem. Phys.* **39**, 1422 (1963).
33. Z. Maksić and M. Randić, *Theoret. Chim. Acta* **7**, 253 (1967).
34. S. F. A. Kettle and A. J. P. Pioli, *J. Chem. Soc., A* p. 122 (1968).
35. A. Streitwieser and U. Müller-Westerhoff, *J. Am. Chem. Soc.* **90**, 7364 (1968).
35a. G. Lugli, W. Marconi, A. Mazzei, N. Paladino, and U. Pedretti, *Inorg. Chim. Acta* **3**, 253 (1969).
35b. A. Zalkin and K. N. Raymond, *J. Am. Chem. Soc.* **91**, 5667 (1969).
36. E. R. Tompkins, J. X. Khym, and W. E. Cohn, *J. Am. Chem. Soc.* **69**, 2769 (1947).
37. *Chem. Eng. News* **46**, 11 (April 15, 1968).
38. F. A. Cotton and G. Wilkinson, "Advanced Inorganic Chemistry," 2nd ed., p. 1052. Wiley (Interscience), New York, 1966.
39. L. J. Nugent, R. D. Baybarz, and J. L. Burnett, *J. Phys. Chem.* **73**, 1177 (1969).
40. R. Nyholm, *J. Inorg. & Nucl. Chem.* **8**, 401 (1958).
41. B. N. Figgis and J. Lewis, *Progr. Inorg. Chem.* **6**, 37 (1964).
42. J. H. Van Vleck, "The Theory of Electric and Magnetic Susceptibilities," p. 226. Oxford Univ. Press, London and New York, 1932.
43. T. Moeller, "The Chemistry of the Lanthanides," p. 27. Reinhold, New York, 1963.
44. P. W. Selwood, "Magnetochemistry," p. 142. Wiley (Interscience), New York, 1956.
45. J. H. Van Vleck, *J. Phys. Chem.* **41**, 67 (1937).
46. C. K. Jørgensen, "Orbitals in Atoms and Molecules," p. 146. Academic Press, New York, 1962.

47. S. P. Sinha, "Europium," p. 120. Springer, Berlin, 1967.
48. L. I. Katzin and M. L. Barnett, *J. Phys. Chem.* **68**, 3779 (1964).
49. G. R. Choppin, D. E. Henrie, and K. Buijs, *Inorg. Chem.* **5**, 1743 (1966).
50. C. K. Jørgensen, *Progr. Inorg. Chem.* **4**, 73 (1962).
51. C. K. Jørgensen, R. Pappalardo, and E. Rittershaus, *Z. Naturforsch.* **19a**, 424 (1964).
52. C. K. Jørgensen and B. R. Judd, *Mol. Phys.* **8**, 281 (1964).
53. C. K. Jørgensen, "Absorption Spectra and Chemical Bonding in Complexes." Pergamon Press, Oxford, 1962.
54. G. Wilkinson and J. M. Birmingham, *J. Am. Chem. Soc.* **76**, 6210 (1954).
55. J. M. Birmingham and G. Wilkinson, *J. Am. Chem. Soc.* **78**, 42 (1956).
56. S. Manastyrskyj and M. Dubeck, *Inorg. Chem.* **3**, 1647 (1964).
57. E. O. Fischer and H. Fischer, *J. Organometal. Chem. (Amsterdam)* **3**, 181 (1965).
58. A. F. Reid and P. C. Wailes, *Inorg. Chem.* **5**, 1213 (1966).
59. M. Tsutsui, T. Takino, and D. Lorenz, *Z. Naturforsch.* **21b**, 1 (1966).
60. R. E. Maginn, S. Manastyrskyj, and M. Dubeck, *J. Am. Chem. Soc.* **85**, 672 (1963).
61. S. Manastyrskyj, R. E. Maginn, and M. Dubeck, *Inorg. Chem.* **2**, 904 (1963).
62. E. O. Fischer and H. Fischer, *Angew. Chem.* **77**, 261 (1965).
63. E. O. Fischer and H. Fischer, *Angew. Chem.* **76**, 52 (1964).
64. E. O. Fischer and H. Fischer, *J. Organometal. Chem. (Amsterdam)* **6**, 141 (1966).
65. F. Calderazzo, R. Pappalardo, and S. Losi, *J. Inorg. & Nucl. Chem.* **28**, 987 (1966).
66. G. W. Watt and E. W. Gillow, *J. Am. Chem. Soc.* **91**, 775 (1969).
67. M. Tsutsui and H. J. Gysling, *J. Am. Chem. Soc.* **90**, 6880 (1968).
68. M. Tsutsui and H. J. Gysling, *J. Am. Chem. Soc.* **91**, 3175 (1969).
68a. R. G. Hayes and J. L. Thomas, *J. Am. Chem. Soc.* **91**, 6876 (1969).
69. H. Gilman and R. G. Jones, *J. Org. Chem.* **10**, 505 (1945).
70. F. A. Cotton, *Chem. Rev.* **55**, 554 (1955).
71. M. Tsutsui, unpublished work (1965).
71a. F. A. Hart and M. S. Saran, *Chem. Commun.* 1614 (1968).
71b. F. A. Hart, A. G. Massey, and M. S. Saran, *J. Organometal. Chem.* (in press).
71c. D. F. Evans, G. V. Fazakerly, and R. F. Phillips, *Chem. Commun.* 244 (1970).
72. R. D. Fischer and H. Fischer, *J. Organometal. Chem. (Amsterdam)* **4**, 412 (1965).
73. R. D. Fischer and H. Fischer, *J. Organometal. Chem. (Amsterdam)* **8**, 155 (1967).
74. J. B. Reed, B. S. Hopkins, and L. F. Audrieth, *Inorg. Syn.* **1**, 28 (1931).
75. T. S. Piper and G. Wilkinson, *J. Inorg. & Nucl. Chem.* **3**, 104 (1956).
76. G. Wilkinson, F. A. Cotton, and J. M. Birmingham, *J. Inorg. & Nucl. Chem.* **2**, 95 (1956).
77. T. S. Piper and G. Wilkinson, *J. Inorg. & Nucl. Chem.* **2**, 32 (1956).
78. T. Moeller, "The Chemistry of the Lanthanides," p. 4. Reinhold, New York, 1963.
79. O. M. Yost, H. Russell, and C. S. Garner, "The Rare Earth Elements and Their Compounds," p. 14. Wiley, New York, 1947.
80. A. R. Pray, *Inorg. Syn.* **5**, 153 (1957).
81. E. O. Fischer and Y. Hristidu, *Z. Naturforsch.* **17b**, 275 (1962).
82. E. O. Fischer and A. Treiber, *Z. Naturforsch.* **17b**, 276 (1962).
83. G. M. Barrow and S. Searles, *J. Am. Chem. Soc.* **75**, 1175 (1953).
84. R. Pappalardo and D. L. Wood, *J. Chem. Phys.* **33**, 1734 (1960).
85. J. C. Eisenstein, *J. Chem. Phys.* **35**, 2097 (1961).
86. L. B. Jassie, *Spectrochim. Acta* **20**, 169 (1964).
87. A. I. Popov and G. Glockler, *J. Am. Chem. Soc.* **74**, 1357 (1952).

88. F. A. Cotton and G. Wilkinson, "Advanced Inorganic Chemistry," 2nd ed., p. 744. Wiley (Interscience), New York, 1966.
89. F. A. Cotton and F. Zingales, *J. Am. Chem. Soc.* **83**, 351 (1961).
90. R. Pappalardo and S. Losi, *J. Inorg. & Nucl. Chem.* **27**, 733 (1965).
91. R. Pappalardo, *Helv. Phys. Acta* **38**, 178 (1965).
92. R. Pappalardo and C. K. Jørgensen, *J. Chem. Phys.* **46**, 632 (1966).
93. R. V. Ammon, B. Kanellakopulos, R. D. Fischer, and P. Laubereau, *Inorg. Nucl. Chem. Letters* **5**, 315 (1969).
93a. H. J. Keller and K. E. Schivarzhans, *Angew. Chem. Intern. Ed. Engl.* **9**, 196 (1970).
94. A. F. Clifford, *Advan. Chem. Ser.* **68**, 113 (1967).
95. C.-H. Wong, T.-Y. Lee, and Y.-T. Lee, *Abstr. 10th Intern. Conf. Coord. Chem., Tokyo*, 1967 p. 95.
96. N. N. Sidgwick, "The Chemical Elements and Their Compounds," Vol. 1, p. 445. Oxford Univ. Press, London and New York, 1950.
97. R. G. Pearson, *J. Chem. Educ.* **45**, 643 (1968).
98. J. L. Burmeister, S. D. Patterson, and H. J. Gysling, *Proc. 10th Intern. Conf. Coord. Chem., Tokyo, 1967* p. 356.
99. T. Moeller, "The Chemistry of the Lanthanides," p. 27. Reinhold, New York, 1963.
100. G. R. Feistel and T. P. Mathai, *J. Am. Chem. Soc.* **90**, 2988 (1968).
101. F. A. Cotton, A. Musco, and G. Yagupsky, *J. Am. Chem. Soc.* **89**, 6136 (1967).
102. P. E. Rakita and A. Davison, *Inorg. Chem.* **8**, 1164 (1969).
102a. F. A. Cotton and T. J. Marks, *J. Am. Chem. Soc.* **91**, 3178 (1969).
102b. E. Samule and M. Bigorgne, *J. Organometal. Chem. (Amsterdam)* **19**, 9 (1969).
103. R. B. King, "Organometallic Synthesis," Vol. 1, p. 74. Academic Press, New York, 1965.
104. J. H. Osiecki, C. J. Hoffman, and D. P. Hollis, *J. Organometal. Chem. (Amsterdam)* **3**, 107 (1965).
105. R. B. King and M. B. Bisnette, *Inorg. Chem.* **3**, 796 (1964).
106. H. P. Fritz, F. H. Köhler, and K. E. Schwarzhans, *J. Organometal. Chem. (Amsterdam)* **16**, p. 14 (1969).
107. W. J. Jolly, *Progr. Inorg. Chem.* **1**, 235 (1959).
108. G. Fraenkel, R. E. Carter, A. McLachlan, and J. H. Richards, *J. Am. Chem. Soc.* **82**, 5846 (1960).
109. G. W. Watt and F. O. Drummond, *J. Am. Chem. Soc.* **88**, 5926 (1966).
110. P. Brix, S. Hüfner, P. Kienle, and D. Quitman, *Phys. Letters* **13**, 140 (1964).
111. M. Haissinsky and C. K. Jørgensen, *J. Chim. Phys.* **63**, 1135 (1966).
112. C. K. Jørgensen, "Oxidation Numbers and Oxidation States." Springer, Berlin, 1968.
113. C. K. Jørgensen, *Chem. Phys. Letters* **2**, 549 (1968).
114. J. Maly and B. B. Cunningham, *Inorg. Nucl. Chem. Letters* **3**, 445 (1967).
115. E. K. Hulet, R. W. Lougheed, J. D. Brady, R. E. Stone, and M. S. Coops, *Science* **158**, 486 (1967).
116. J. Maly, T. Sikkeland, R. Silva, and A. Ghiorso, *Science* **160**, 1114 (1968).
117. T. L. Reynolds and G. Wilkinson, *J. Inorg. & Nucl. Chem.* **2**, 246 (1956).
117a. B. Kanellakopulos, E. O. Fischer, E. Dornberger, and F. Baumgärtner (to be published.
118. M. L. Anderson and L. R. Crisler, *154th Natl. Meeting Am. Chem. Soc., Chicago* Abstr. 0-30 (1967).
119. M. L. Anderson and L. R. Crisler, *J. Organometal. Chem. (Amsterdam)* **17**, 345 (1969)

120. Y. Hristidu, Ph.D. Dissertation, University of Munich (1962).
121. P. Laubereau *et al.*, to be published.
121a. A. Streitwieser and N. Yoshida, *J. Am. Chem. Soc.* **91**, 7528 (1969).
122. F. Baumgärtner, E. O. Fischer, B. Kanellakopulos, and P. Laubereau, *Angew. Chem. Intern. Ed. Engl.* **8**, 202 (1969).
123. G. L. Ter Haar and M. Dubeck, *Inorg. Chem.* **3**, 1648 (1964).
124. F. Baumgärtner, E. O. Fischer, and P. Laubereau, *Naturwissenschaften* **52**, 560 (1965).
125. E. O. Fischer, P. Laubereau, F. Baumgärtner, and B. Kanellakopulos, *J. Organometal. Chem. (Amsterdam)* **5**, 583 (1966).
126. F. Baumgärtner, E. O. Fischer, B. Kanellakopulos, and P. Laubereau, *Angew. Chem Intern. Ed. Engl.* **7**, 634 (1968).
126a. D. G. Karraker and J. A. Stone, *158th Natl. Meeting Am. Chem. Soc., New York* Abstr. Inorganic -80.
126b. W. L. Pillinger and J. A. Store, *in* "Mössbauer Effect Methodology" (I. J. Gruverman, ed.), Vol. 4, p. 217. Plenum Press, New York, 1968.
127. F. Baumgärtner, E. O. Fischer, B. Kanellakopulos, and P. Laubereau, *Angew. Chem. Intern. Ed. Engl.* **4**, 878 (1965).
128. F. Baumgärtner, E. O. Fischer, B. Kanellakopulos, and P. Laubereau, *Angew. Chem. Intern. Ed. Engl.* **5**, 134 (1966).
128a. P. G. Laubereau and J. H. Burns, *Inorg. Nucl. Chem. Letters* **6**, 59 (1970).
128b. F. Baumgärtner, E. O. Fischer, H. Billich, E. Dornberger, B. Kanellakopulos, W. Roth, and L. Stieglitz, *J. Organometal. Chem. (Amsterdam)* **22**, C17 (1970).
128c. P. G. Laubereau and J. H. Burns, paper to be presented at Eighth Rare-Earth Conference, Reno, Nevada (1970).
128d. P. G. Laubereau and J. H. Burns, *Inorg. Chem.* **9**, 1091 (1970).
129. C. Wong, T. Yen, and T. Lee, *Acta Cryst.* **18**, 340 (1965).
130. C. C. Hunt and J. R. Doyle, *Inorg. Nucl. Chem. Letters* **2**, 283 (1966).
131. B. D. James, R. K. Nanda, and M. G. H. Wallbridge, *J. Chem. Soc., A* p. 182 (1966).
132. R. Von Ammon, B. Kanellakopulos, R. D. Fischer, and P. Laubereau, *Inorg. Nucl. Chem. Letters* **5**, 219 (1969).
133. R. Von Ammon, B. Kanellakopulos, and R. D. Fischer, *Chem. Phys. Letters* **2**, 513 (1968).
133a. R. Von Ammon and B. Kanellakopulos, *Chem. Phys. Letters* **4**, 553 (1970).
133b. T. H. Siddall, W. E. Stewart, and D. G. Karraker, *Chem. Phys. Letters* **3**, 498 (1969).
134. G. Wilkinson and J. M. Birmingham, *J. Am. Chem. Soc.* **76**, 4281 (1954).
135. M. Rosenblum, "Chemistry of the Iron Group Metallocenes," Part I, p. 43. Wiley (Interscience), New York, 1965.

α-Heterodiazoalkanes and the Reactions of Diazoalkanes with Derivatives of Metals and Metalloids

M. F. LAPPERT and J. S. POLAND

School of Molecular Sciences
University of Sussex
Brighton, England

I

INTRODUCTION

Metal, metalloid, or nonmetal (M) diazo compounds, collectively termed α-heterodiazoalkanes, are defined as those which have the group CN_2^{2-} as a ligand. They are the subject of Section II of this review. These have one or another of the general formulas (I)–(III), in which the symbol L represents the sum of all other ligands attached to the element M and R is an organic group. Individual compounds are listed in Table I of Section IV. They are clearly organometallic, in the sense that they possess an element-to-carbon bond; for the sake of completeness, the cases where the element is a nonmetal (notably N, P, S, or halogen) are included.

$$LM{-}CHN_2 \qquad (LM)_2CN_2 \qquad \begin{matrix} LM \\ R \end{matrix}\!\!>\!CN_2$$

(I) (II) (III)

Mercury(II) derivatives of diazoacetic esters $Hg(CN_2COOR)_2$ (R = Me or Et) were described by Buchner in 1895 (*22*). The next contribution came in the early 1930s from Müller and co-workers (*117*, *122*) on sodiodiazomethane. After a further pause, the subject has only recently gathered momentum. Table I includes references to about 40 publications. Some of the chemistry of α-hetero derivatives is clearly related to that of organodiazomethanes (*74*, *178*, *211*).

It seems to us that a good deal of the chemistry of diazoalkanes is related to their 1,3-dipolar character. This seems to emerge more clearly by the possibility of isolating appropriate derivatives (*94*, *95*) with α-heterodiazoalkanes, where they may not be isolable with organo analogs. Even in their precursive chemistry, this type of behavior may usefully be kept in mind. As an illustration, reference is made to Section II,A.

A second aspect of diazoalkane chemistry, which is of interest to the organometallicist, forms the subject of Section III of this review. Diazoalkanes have proved to be extremely useful synthetic reagents in many branches of chemistry. They have been the subject of several reviews (e.g., see *74*, *211*) but these have been devoted to organic aspects. Some of the reactions of diazoalkanes with metal and metalloid compounds have, however, been surveyed (*13*, *133*, *169*, *199*).

The objective of Section III is threefold: to bring earlier reviews up to date, to consider the reactions of diazoalkanes with inorganic compounds as a whole, and to discuss some interesting and recent developments.

The structure of diazoalkanes may be considered in relation to the canonical forms (IV)–(VI). Although this is purely a formalism, the

$$RR'\overset{(-)}{C}{-}\overset{(+)}{N}{\equiv}\ddot{N} \qquad RR'C{=}\overset{(+)}{N}{=}\overset{(-)}{N}{:} \qquad RR'\overset{(-)}{C}{-}\ddot{N}{=}\overset{(+)}{N}$$

(IV) (V) (VI)

reactions of diazoalkanes may usefully be classified on this basis (*74*). Thus, diazoalkanes may react as nucleophiles through carbon [see (IV) and (VI)], or the ω-nitrogen, or as 1,3-dipoles (VI). Reactions in which the diazoalkane is essentially a carbene source generally proceed by the first of these mechanisms. In Section IV, a summary of reactions is provided in Table II.

There are a large number of papers in which catalysts and diazo compounds have been used in reactions which are not included in Section III,B; we are concerned solely with those systems wherein the nature of the catalyst-diazo compound interaction has been explored.

The literature coverage is as complete as possible up to September 1969. The following papers cover the intervening period up to April 1970, but are not discussed further in the text: an important review on developments in the chemistry of diazoalkanes (*30*); aspects of the chemistry of ethyl lithiodiazoacetate (*157b*), ethyl trialkylsilyl (*157b*, *158a*) and trialkylstannyl- (*157b*) diazoacetate, some phosphorus(V) diazoalkanes (*77a*, *77b*, *149*, *152*, *152a*); reactions of ethyl diazoacetate with π-allylbromonickel(II) (*206a*), and chlorides (*154c*) of copper(I), copper(II), cobalt(II), and mercury(II); and reactions of trialkylboranes with diazoacetaldehyde (*70a*) and diazoacetophenone (*137a*).

II

α-HETEROSUBSTITUTED DIAZOALKANES

A. *Tosyl Azide as a Preparative Reagent*

The protons of an active methylene group may be replaced by a diazo group using tosyl azide in the presence of base [Eq. (1)] (*148*). α-Phosphorus, sulfur, silicon, and germanium diazoalkanes have been synthesized by this route [Eqs. (2)–(6); TMEDA = tetramethylethylenediamine]. The preparations are carried out in the presence of a base, the strength of which is appropriate to the acidity of the methylene protons, and the tosyl amide is generally separated as a salt. Although disulfonyl diazomethanes may be prepared by this method [Eq. (3)] (*85*), attempts to prepare a mono derivative failed, presumably because the protons are not sufficiently acidic (*104*). If, however, a carbonyl group is adjacent to the methylene protons, the reaction does proceed [Eq. (4)] (*104*). Reactions (2)–(6) may be rationalized in terms of the 1,3-dipolar character of the azide $p\text{-Tos}\overset{-}{N}\text{—}N\text{=}\overset{+}{N}$; an acidic hydride will then react the more readily, with subsequent fragmentation of the product.

$$RR'CH_2 + p\text{-}MeC_6H_4SO_2N_3 \xrightarrow{\text{Base}} RR'CN_2 + p\text{-}MeC_6H_4SO_2NH_2 \quad (1)$$

$$Ph_2P(O)CH_2COOEt + p\text{-}MeC_6H_4SO_2N_3 \xrightarrow{tert\text{-}BuOK} Ph_2P(O)C(N_2)COOEt + p\text{-}MeC_6H_4SO_2NHK \quad (2)$$

$$(PhSO_2)_2CH_2 + p\text{-}MeC_6H_4SO_2N_3 \xrightarrow{NaOH/EtOH} (PhSO_2)_2CN_2 + p\text{-}MeC_6H_4SO_2NHNa \quad (3)$$

$$p\text{-}MeC_6H_4SO_2CH_2COCH_3 + p\text{-}MeC_6H_4SO_2N_3 \xrightarrow{NEt_3} p\text{-}MeC_6H_4SO_2C(N_2)COCH_3 + p\text{-}MeC_6H_4SO_2NH_2 \quad (4)$$

$$Me_3SiCH_2Ph + p\text{-}MeC_6H_4SO_2N_3 \xrightarrow{n\text{-}BuLi/TMEDA} Me_3SiC(N_2)Ph + p\text{-}MeC_6H_4SO_2NHLi \quad (5)$$

$$Ph_3GeCH_2Ph + p\text{-}MeC_6H_4SO_2N_3 \xrightarrow{n\text{-}BuLi/TMEDA} Ph_3GeC(N_2)Ph + p\text{-}MeC_6H_4SO_2NHLi \quad (6)$$

B. *Diazoalkanes as Preparative Reagents*

Bases may react with the acidic proton(s) of organo diazoalkanes affording α-heterodiazoalkanes [Eqs. (8)–(14)].

Methyllithium reacts with diazomethane in ether to give lithiodiazomethane [Eq. (8)] (*123*, *125*), but with diazoethane, a triazole is formed [Eq. (7)] (*126*). Tritylsodium did not provide a stable sodio derivative (*117*, *122*).

In light petroleum, yellow mercuric oxide reacts with the more acidic diazoalkanes to form the appropriate diazomercury compound [e.g., Eq. (10)]; related to this, it will be recalled that the oxidation of a monohydrazone with mercuric oxide in the presence of base is a well-known method for the preparation of organic diazoalkanes. The reaction of ethereal diazomethane and mercuric acetate [Eq. (11)] has been reported to afford bis(diazomethyl)mercury (*197*); but this has been refuted (*35*).

Mechanistically, reaction (12) (*92–94*) may be of the type (HA has protic H) $LM—NMe_2 + HA \rightarrow LMA + Me_2NH$. Since diazomethane reacts in the sense of (8), it certainly has protic character. Moreover, an electron-releasing (e.g., in $MeCHN_2$) substituent at carbon decreases the reactivity of the diazoalkane, whereas an electron-withdrawing (e.g., in $EtOOCCHN_2$) (*108*) substituent has the converse effect. A limitation on the amine elimination is that while germanium, tin, and lead amides react with CH_2N_2, amides of boron and silicon generally do not even with $EtOOCCHN_2$ (*93*). An alternative model for reaction (12) is that of a double two-step process, with initial 1,3-insertion to afford $Me_3SnCH_2—N{=}N—NMe_2$ and subsequent Me_2NH elimination. Some support for this view comes from the inability (*93*) to isolate Me_3SnCHN_2, even with a deficiency of tin amide. In terms of the protic hydrogen mechanism, the electron-releasing Me_3Sn group would have been expected to deactivate the monostannyldiazomethane. On the basis of the 1,3-dipolar hypothesis, the enhanced activity of Me_3SnCHN_2 compared with CH_2N_2 is explicable in terms of the stabilization of the 1,3-dipolar character of a diazoalkane by the organotin substituent (see also Section II,G,4). The compound $(\pi\text{-}C_5H_5)_2Zr(NMe_2)_2$ reacted with Me_3SiCHN_2 to evolve dimethylamine. The metal product was not well characterized, but may have been $(\pi\text{-}C_5H_5)_2Zr[C(N_2)SiMe_3]_2$ (*95*).

Chlorodiazomethane and bromodiazomethane are prepared [Eq. (14)] by the addition of slightly less than molar amounts of *tert*-butyl hypohalite to diazomethane at −100°C (*26*). Attempts to prepare the dihalogenodiazomethane by the addition of 2 moles of hypohalite were unsuccessful and nitrogen was evolved.

$$MeLi + CH_3CHN_2 \longrightarrow CH_3—C{=}N—NH—N{=}C—CH_3 \text{ (ring: } CH_3C\text{—}CCH_3 \text{ linked, 1,2,3-triazole)} \quad (7)$$

$$MeLi + CH_2N_2 \rightarrow Li(CHN_2) + CH_4 \quad (8)$$

$$Ag_2O + 2\,HC(N_2)COOEt \rightarrow 2\,Ag[C(N_2)COOEt] + H_2O \quad (9)$$
(not isolated)

$$HgO + 2\,HC(N_2)COOEt \rightarrow Hg[C(N_2)COOEt]_2 + H_2O \quad (10)$$

$$Hg(OOCCH_3)_2 + 4\,CH_2N_2 \rightarrow Hg(CHN_2)_2 + 2\,CH_3COOCH_3 + 2N_2 \quad (11)$$

$$2\,Me_3SnNMe_2 + CH_2N_2 \rightarrow (Me_3Sn)_2CN_2 + 2\,HNMe_2 \quad (12)$$

$$N_2O_5 + HC(N_2)COOBu\text{-}tert \rightarrow O_2NC(N_2)COOBu\text{-}tert \quad (13)$$

$$tert\text{-}BuOCl + CH_2N_2 \rightarrow CHClN_2 \quad (14)$$

C. Metal Diazoalkanes as Preparative Reagents

Interaction of (i) mercury, silver, or lithium diazo compounds and (ii) halides or sulfides, results in salt elimination to yield the appropriate α-heterodiazoalkane [Eqs. (15)–(21)]. The reactions are usually performed in ether, and, in the case of silver or lithium, the metal salts are prepared *in situ*.

The reaction of lithiodiazomethane with mercury(II) chloride in tetrahydrofuran failed to produce bis(diazomethyl)mercury; however, with cadmium chloride, infrared spectral evidence suggested the formation of a cadmium diazoalkane (*35*).

Reaction (21) is somewhat curious in affording not Me_3SnCHN_2 but $(Me_3Sn)_2CN_2$ (*92–94*), irrespective of reaction stoichiometry. This suggests that Me_3SnCHN_2 competes effectively with $LiCHN_2$ for Me_3SnCl, possibly because of the enhanced 1,3-dipolar character of the former compound. Silicon appears to be unique within Group IVB in forming a stable monosubstituted compound Me_3MCHN_2 (M = Si) (*92, 93*). Conversely, it is the only member of the group not to form a simple bis compound $(Me_3Si)_2CN_2$. Interaction of Me_3SiCl and $LiCHN_2$, irrespective of stoichiometry, affords as principal product a compound of that *empirical* formula (*157a*); this has not the spectral characteristics of a diazoalkane and may be a dimer (VII) (*93*).

$$\begin{array}{ccc} (Me_3Si)_2C & \overset{N}{\diagup \ \diagdown\!\!\diagdown} & N \\ | & & | \\ N & \underset{N}{\diagdown\!\!\diagdown \ \diagup} & C(SiMe_3)_2 \end{array}$$

(VII)

The use of $Li[Me_3SiCN_2]$ and the appropriate halide has furnished routes to $Me_3Si(X)CN_2$ [X = Me_3Sn (*93*), n-Bu_2B (*96*), and $\frac{1}{2}[(\pi\text{-}C_5H_5)_2Zr]$; however, $Li(CHN_2)$ and various transition metal halides did not afford characterized derivatives (*93*).

Attempts to prepare sulfonyl diazomethanes from sulfonyl chlorides and diazomethane were unsuccessful (*185*); this is in contrast with the formation of carbonyl diazomethanes from acyl chlorides and diazomethane [e.g., Eq. (22)].

$$Ag[C(N_2)COOEt] + ICN \rightarrow IC(N_2)COOEt + AgCN \tag{15}$$

$$Hg[C(N_2)COOEt]_2 + (Ph_3Sn)_2S \rightarrow 2\,Ph_3SnC(N_2)COOEt + HgS \tag{16}$$

$$Hg[C(N_2)COOEt]_2 + 2\,Et_3SiI \rightarrow 2\,Et_3SiC(N_2)COOEt + HgI_2 \tag{17}$$

$$Hg[C(N_2)COOEt]_2 + 2\,N_2O_5 \rightarrow 2\,O_2NC(N_2)COOEt + Hg(NO_3)_2 \tag{18}$$

$$Hg[C(N_2)COOEt]_2 + 2\,SO_2Cl_2 \rightarrow 2\,ClC(N_2)COOEt + HgCl_2 + 2\,SO_2 \tag{19}$$

$$Hg[C(N_2)COOEt]_2 + 2\,Br_2 \rightarrow 2\,BrC(N_2)COOEt + HgBr_2 \tag{20}$$

$$Li(CHN_2) + Me_3SnCl \rightarrow (Me_3Sn)_2CN_2 \quad (21)$$

$$CH_3COCl + 2\,CH_2N_2 \rightarrow CH_3COCHN_2 + CH_3Cl + N_2 \quad (22)$$

D. α-Hetero Amino, Amido, Hydrazino, and Nitroso Compounds as Preparative Reagents

This method is widely used for organodiazoalkanes (e.g., Ref. *45*, *188*), but has not been generally applied to the synthesis of α-hetero analogs. This is presumably because of the lengthy procedures involved and often the hydrolytic instability of appropriate intermediates.

The action of aqueous base on nitroso amides gives diazo compounds [Eq. (23)], where $R'' = -CONH_2$, $-COOEt$, $-COR'''$, $-SO_2R'''$, etc.

$$RR'CHN(NO)R'' + \text{Base} \rightarrow RR'CN_2 \quad (23)$$

Sulfonyl urethane intermediates have been synthesized in three ways [Eqs. (24)–(26)] (*40*, *105*, *106*, *185*). The urethanes are then treated with nitrosyl chloride in pyridine, and finally base or water [Eq. (27)]. Trimethylsilyldiazomethane was similarly prepared via the urea derivative [Eqs. (28) and (29)] (*171*), and this procedure is probably the best available for the silicon compounds, because it lends itself to large-scale operation.

$$Me_2NH + CH_2O + H_2NCOOEt \longrightarrow Me_2NCH_2NHCOOEt \xrightarrow{p\text{-}MeOC_6H_4SO_2H} p\text{-}MeOC_6H_4SO_2CH_2NHCOOEt \quad (24)$$

$$PhSO_2CH_2COOEt \xrightarrow{N_2H_4} PhSO_2CH_2CONHNH_2 \xrightarrow{HNO_2} PhSO_2CHCON_3 \xrightarrow{Heat/EtOH} PhSO_2CH_2NHCOOEt \quad (25)$$

$$PhSO_2H + Me_2NCH_2NHCOOEt \longrightarrow PhSO_2CH_2NHCOOEt \quad (26)$$

$$PhSO_2CH_2NHCOOEt \xrightarrow{NOCl} PhSO_2CH_2N(NO)COOEt \xrightarrow{OH^-} PhSO_2CHN_2 \quad (27)$$

$$Me_3SiCH_2Cl \xrightarrow{NH_3} Me_3SiCH_2NH_2 \xrightarrow{Urea/HCl} Me_3SiCH_2NHCONH_2 \quad (28)$$

$$Me_3SiCH_2NHCONH_2 \xrightarrow{HNO_2} Me_3SiCH_2N(NO)CONH_2 \xrightarrow{OH^-} Me_3SiCHN_2 \quad (29)$$

The action of nitrous acid on α-heteroamino compounds provides a synthetic route, but this procedure is limited to compounds having an amino function adjacent to an electron-withdrawing group. It has been used to prepare several phosphorus derivatives [e.g., Eq. (30)] (*72*), but the preparation of aminomethyl derivatives is frequently difficult.

$$Ph_2P(O)CH_2Cl \xrightarrow{NH_3} Ph_2P(O)CH_2NH_2 \xrightarrow{HNO_2} Ph_2P(O)CHN_2 \quad (30)$$

Diazoalkanes are often obtained by the oxidation of hydrazones, using mercury(II), manganese(IV) oxide, or $Pb(OOCCH_3)_4$ [e.g., for $(CF_3)_2CN_2$]; but sulfonyl hydrazones are internally oxidized as a result of base-catalyzed decomposition (*10*). α-Hetero-diazoalkanes have been prepared via hydrazone intermediates, from α-keto compounds and hydrazine [e.g., Eq. (31)] (*80*), or tosyl hydrazine [e.g., Eqs. (32) and (33)] (*20*, *173*). Bis(phenylsulfonyl)diazomethane is similarly prepared by oxidation of the hydrazone obtained from the reaction of sodium phenylsulfinate and tetrabromoazine [Eq. (34)] (*32*). Bis(methylthio)diazomethane has also been reported [Eq. (35)], but was not characterized (*166*).

$$Ph_3SiCOPh + N_2H_4 \longrightarrow Ph_3SiC({=}NNH_2)Ph \xrightarrow{MnO_2} Ph_3SiC(N_2)Ph \quad (31)$$

$$Me_3SiCOPh + p\text{-}MeC_6H_4SO_2NHNH_2 \longrightarrow Me_3SiC({=}NNHSO_2C_6H_4Me\text{-}p)Ph \xrightarrow{BuLi} Me_3SiC(N_2)Ph \quad (32)$$

$$(MeO)_2P(O)COMe + p\text{-}MeC_6H_4SO_2NHNH_2 \longrightarrow (MeO)_2P(O)C({=}NNHSO_2C_6H_4Me\text{-}p)Me \xrightarrow{Na_2CO_3} (MeO)_2P(O)C(N_2)Me \quad (33)$$

$$Br_2C{=}N{-}N{=}CBr_2 + PhSO_2Na \longrightarrow (PhSO_2)_2C{=}N{-}NH_2 \xrightarrow{MnO_2} (PhSO_2)_2CN_2 \quad (34)$$

$$CS_2 + MeCl + p\text{-}MeC_6H_4SO_2NHNH_2 \longrightarrow (MeS)_2C{=}NNHSO_2C_6H_4Me\text{-}p \xrightarrow{100°C} (MeS)_2CN_2 \quad (35)$$

E. Miscellaneous Preparative Methods

α-Heterodiazoalkanes containing an α-keto group may be converted into the corresponding diazomethane by treatment with acid or base, but the yields are low [Eqs. (36) and (37)]. The sulfur compound (Eq. (36)] was only isolated as the triphenylphosphine complex, the phosphazine (*64*).

$$p\text{-MeC}_6\text{H}_4\text{SO}_2\text{C(N}_2\text{)COPh} + \text{Et}_3\text{N} \longrightarrow$$

$$[p\text{-MeC}_6\text{H}_4\text{SO}_2\text{CHN}_2] \xrightarrow{\text{PPh}_3} p\text{-MeC}_6\text{H}_4\text{SO}_2\text{CH{=}NNPPh}_3 \qquad (36)$$

$$\text{O}_2\text{NC(N}_2\text{)COOBu-}tert + \text{CF}_3\text{COOH} \longrightarrow \text{O}_2\text{NCHN}_2 \qquad (37)$$

Lithiodiazomethane may be prepared by the reaction of methyllithium and nitrous oxide [Eq. (38)] (*127*), or from lithium methylamide and nitrosyl chloride [Eq. (39)] (*128*). A similar reaction to produce the CHN_2^- anion probably occurs with triphenylphosphinemethylene [Eq. (40)] (*154*).

$$2\,\text{MeLi} + \text{N}_2\text{O} \rightarrow \text{Li(CHN}_2) + \text{LiOH} + \text{CH}_4 \qquad (38)$$

$$3\,\text{CH}_3\text{NHLi} + \text{NOCl} \rightarrow \text{Li(CHN}_2) + 2\,\text{CH}_3\text{NH}_2 + \text{LiOH} + \text{LiCl} \qquad (39)$$

$$2\,\text{Ph}_3\text{PCH}_2 + \text{N}_2\text{O} \rightarrow \underset{\text{(not isolated)}}{(\text{Ph}_3\text{PCH}_3)(\text{CHN}_2)} + \text{Ph}_3\text{PO} \qquad (40)$$

F. Physical Properties

All the compounds are intensely colored, and range from yellow to red. Their stability is dependent on the size and nature of the substituent groups; the α-heterodiazomethanes with only one hydrogen atom replaced are the least stable. Thus, $Na(CHN_2)$, O_2NCHN_2, and $Hg(CHN_2)_2$ are dangerously explosive, $Li(CHN_2)$ explodes on contact with air when dry, and $CHClN_2$ and $CHBrN_2$ decompose in solution above –10°C. However, compounds with larger substituents are more stable; e.g., Me_3SiCHN_2 and $(Me_3Sn)_2CN_2$ may be distilled. They are all decomposed by light, and are best stored at low temperatures.

Diazoalkanes show an absorption in the range 2150–2000 cm^{-1}, mainly associated with vibrations of the group C—N—N [often referred to as $\nu(N{\equiv}N)$]. The position of $\nu(N{\equiv}N)$ may be related to R and R′ in $RR'CN_2$; electron-withdrawing groups shift $\nu(N{\equiv}N)$ to higher wave numbers, and electron-donating groups to lower wave numbers. The problem has been discussed in terms of resonance theory symbolism (*44, 209*). The infrared

TABLE I

α-HETERODIAZOALKANES

Compounds	Method of preparation[a]	Yield	M.p. (°C) (B.p., °/mm)	$\nu(N\equiv N)$ (cm^{-1})	References
$Li(CHN_2)$	B, H	—	—	—	*123, 127, 128*
$Na(CHN_2)$[b]	B	—	—	—	*117*
$Ag[C(N_2)COOEt]$[b]	B	—	—	2040	*161*
$Ag[C(N_2)COR]$[b] R = Alkyl or aryl	B	—	—	—	*163*
$Cd(CHN_2)_2$[b]	C	—	—	2090	*35*
$Hg[C(N_2)COOMe]_2$	B	—	123°	2080	*22, 35*
$Hg[C(N_2)COOEt]_2$	B	—	104°	2070	*22, 35*
			95°–98°		*197*
$Hg[C(N_2)CO—2,4,6—Me_3C_6H_2]_2$	B	80	138°–139.5°	2096	*208*
$Hg[C(N_2)COCMe_3]_2$	B	81	130.5°–131°	—	*208*
$Hg[C(N_2)COPh]_2$	B	97	148°–149.5°	—	*208*
$Hg[C(N_2)COCH_2Ph]_2$	B	55	118°–118.5°	—	*208*
$Hg[C(N_2)CF_3]_2$	B	95	~35°	2070	*35*
$Hg[C(N_2)CN]_2$	B	80	150°	2080	*35*
$Hg[C(N_2)COMe]_2$	B	83	120°–121°	2080, 2050	*35*
$Hg[C(N_2)COEt]_2$	B	65	69°–70°	2050	*35*
$Hg[C(N_2)CO\text{-i-}Pr]_2$	B	75	38°–40°	2045, 2100	*35*
$Hg[C(N_2)COO\text{-i-}Pr]_2$	B	50	83°–84°	2070	*35*
$Hg[C(N_2)COOAll]_2$	B	98	—	2080, 2085	*35*
$Hg[C(N_2)COO\text{-}tert\text{-}Bu]_2$	B	64	143°–144°	2070	*35*
$Hg[C(N_2)COOPh]_2$	B	79	116°–117°	2075	*35*
$Hg(CHN_2)_2$	B	5	—	2105	*197*
Me_3SiCHN_2[c]	D	56	(b.p. 96°)	2070	*171*
	C	5	(b.p. 42°–45°/128)		*92–94*
$Me_3SiC(N_2)Me$	C	72	(b.p. 70°–71°/170)	2041	*96*
$Me_3SiC(N_2)Et$	D	72	(b.p. 51°/75)	2039	*96*

$Me_3SiC(N_2)Ph$	A, F	—	—	—	*20*
$Me_3SiC(N_2)COOEt$	C	95	—	2090	*81, 162*
$Me_3SiC(N_2)B$-*n*-Bu_2	C	96	—	2048	*96*
$Me_3SiC(N_2)SnMe_3$	B, C	50–80	(b.p. 44°–46°/0.5)	2022	*93, 95*
$Et_3SiC(N_2)COOEt$	C	—	—	—	*81*
$Ph_3SiC(N_2)Me$	F	82	82°–84°	2045	*20*
$Ph_3SiC(N_2)Et$	F	72	72°–73°	2045	*20*
$Ph_3SiC(N_2)CH_2Ph$	F	48	65°–67°	2045	*20*
$Ph_3SiC(N_2)Ph$	F	95	150°–151°	2050	*80*
	A, F	73		2045	*20*
$Ph_3SiC(N_2)$-*p*-F—C_6H_4	F	63	143°–144°	2048	*20*
$Ph_3SiC(N_2)$-*p*-Cl—C_6H_4	F	71	143°–145°	2048	*20*
$Ph_3SiC(N_2)$-*p*-Br—C_6H_4	F	56	146°–147°	2048	*20*
$Ph_3SiC(N_2)COOEt$	C	—	—	—	*81*
$(Me_3Ge_2)CN_2$	B	58	(b.p. 45°–47°/100)	2050	*93*
$Me_3GeC(N_2)COOEt$	B	100	(b.p. 85°/10)	2078	*93*
$Ph_3GeC(N_2)Ph$	A	65	153°–154°	2041	*20*
$(Ph_3Ge)_2CN_2$	C	44	155°–156°	2032	*93*
$(Me_3Sn)_2CN_2$	B, C	95	(b.p. 64°–67°/0.1)	2000	*92–94*
$Me_3SnC(N_2)COOEt$	B	100	—	2060	*108*
$Me_2Sn[C(N_2)COOEt]_2$	B	60–70	—	2070	*108*
$(Et_3Sn)_2CN_2$	B	82	(b.p. 110°–112°/0.01)	1995	*93*
$Et_3SnC(N_2)COOEt$	B	85	—	2045	*108*
$Et_2Sn[C(N_2)COOEt]_2$	B	60	—	2059	*108*
(*n*-$Bu_3Sn)_2CN_2$	B	46	(b.p. 145°–148°/0.01)	1995	*93*
n-$Bu_3SnC(N_2)COOEt$	B	80	—	2070	*108*
n-$Bu_2Sn[C(N_2)COOEt]_2$	B	30–35	—	2065	*108*
$(Ph_3Sn)_2CN_2$	B, C	90	127°–130°	2002	*93*
$Ph_3SnC(N_2)COOEt$	C	80	—	2080	*162*
	B	100		2068	*108*
$(Me_3Pb)_2CN_2$	B	100	—	1950	*93*
O_2NCHN_2[c]	F	—	55°	2105	*159*
$(O_2N)_2CN_2$	B	42	65°	2120	*160*
$O_2NC(N_2)COOEt$	B, C	35	—	2140	*164, 165*
$O_2NC(N_2)COO$-*tert*-Bu	B, C	—	34°–35°	2140	*159, 165*

(Continued)

TABLE I (*Continued*)

Compounds	Method of preparation[a]	Yield	M.p. (°C) (B.p., °/mm)	$\nu(N{\equiv}N)$ (cm^{-1})	References
$O_2NC(N_2)CN$	B, C	—	—	2120, 2140	*165*
$O_2NC(N_2)CF_3$	B, C	—	—	2135	*165*
$(Ph_3PCH_3)(CHN_2)$[b]	B, C	—	—	—	*154*
$Ph_2P(O)CHN_2$	E	70	56°	—	*91*
$(PhCH_2)_2P(O)CHN_2$	E	90	99°	—	*91*
$Ph_2P(O)C(N_2)Ph$	A, E	30	156° 160°	2070	*72, 150* *140*
$Ph_2P(O)C(N_2)COMe$	A	45	83°–85°	2101	*149, 150*
$Ph_2P(O)C(N_2)COPh$	A	83 65	155° 138°	2092	*149, 150* *140*
$Ph_2P(O)C(N_2)COOEt$	A	60	104°	—	*140, 149*
$Ph_2P(O)C(N_2)P(O)Ph$	A	14	154°	—	*140, 149*
$(MeO)_2P(O)C(N_2)Me$	F	—	(b.p. 37°–38°/0.13)	2075	*149, 173*
$(MeO)_2P(O)C(N_2)Ph$	F	—	44°–45.5°	2080	*173*
$(EtO)_2P(O)C(N_2)Ph$	A	25	(b.p. 112°–115°/0.4)	2079	*150, 151*
$(EtO)_2P(O)C(N_2)$—*p*CN—C_6H_4	A	60	—	2088	*150, 151*
$(EtO)_2P(O)C(N_2)$—*p*NO_2—C_6H_4	A	35	—	2088	*150, 151*
$(EtO)_2P(O)C(N_2)COOEt$	A	37	(b.p. 103°–104°/0.4)	2132	*140, 151*
$(EtO)_2P)(O)C(N_2)COMe$	A	78	(b.p. 92°–93°/0.6)	2105	*151*
$(EtO)_2P(O)C(N_2)COPh$	A	25	—	2114	*150, 151*
$(EtO)_2P(O)C(N_2)PO(OEt)_2$	A	35	(b.p. 131°–133°/0.4)	2114	*150, 151*
$EtSO_2CHN_2$	D	35	—	—	*106*
n-$BuSO_2CHN_2$	D	30	—	—	*106*
tert-$BuSO_2CHN_2$	D	77	64°–65°	2106.7	*106*
n-$C_8H_{17}SO_2CHN_2$	D	68	30°–32°	2107.7	*106*
$PhSO_2CHN_2$[c]	D	81	—	2104.1	*106*
p-$MeC_6H_4SO_2CHN_2$[c]	D	80	34°–37°	2102.8	*106*
p-$MeOC_6H_4SO_2CHN_2$[c]	D	86	46°–47°	2101.3	*106, 185*
p-$ClC_6H_4SO_2CHN_2$[c]	D	55	40°–44°	2105.0	*106*

p-NO_2—$C_6H_4SO_2CHN_2$[c]	D	72	105°–106°	2108.2	*106*
m-$MeC_6H_4SO_2CHN_2$[c]	D	54	27.8°–29°	2108	*41*
m-$MeOC_6H_4SO_2CHN_2$[c]	D	48	64°–65.4°	2109	*41*
m-$ClC_6H_4SO_2CHN_2$[c]	D	46	41.5°–43.5°	2111	*41*
m-CF_3—$C_6H_4SO_2CHN_2$[c]	D	51	—	2112	*41*
m-NO_2—$C_6H_4SO_2CHN_2$[c]	D	53	99.7°–101.7°	2114	*41*
$PhCH_2SO_2CHN_2$	D	69	98°–99°	2109.7	*106*
p-$MeC_6H_4SO_2C(N_2)COMe$	A	70	109°–110°	2110	*104*
p-$MeC_6H_4SO_2C(N_2)COPh$	A	60	101°–102°	2100	*104*
p-NO_2—$C_6H_4SO_2C(N_2)COMe$	A	45	147°–149°	2115	*64*
p-NO_2—$C_6H_4SO_2C(N_2)COPh$	A	47	129.5°–131°	2098	*64*
2,4,6-$Me_3C_6H_2SO_2C(N_2)COMe$	A	76	114°–114.5°	2102	*64*
$(PhSO_2)_2CN_2$	A, F	55, 70	99°–100°	2130	*32, 85*
(p-$MeC_6H_4SO_2)_2CN_2$	A	75	121°–122°	2117	*85*
(2,4-$Me_2C_6H_3SO_2)_2CN_2$	A	85	135°–136°	2109	*85*
(2,4-$F_2C_6H_3SO_2)_2CN_2$	A	84	164°	2145	*85*
$(EtSO_2)_2CN_2$	A	46	88°–90°	2135	*85*
$[(PhEtN)SO_2]_2CN_2$	A	50	97°	2118	*85*
(benzo-fused ring: CO, CN_2, SO_2)	A	60–78	192°–193°	—	*147*
$PhSO_2C(N_2)COC(N_2)COMe_2$		41–45	115°–116°	2151, 2123	*152*
$PhSO_2C(N_2)COC(N_2)COPh$		—	110°–112°	2137, 2119	*152*
$(MeS)_2CN_2$[b]	F	—	—	—	*166*
$(PhCH_2S)_2CN_2$[b]	F	—	—	—	*166*
$ClCHN_2$	B	—	—	2066	*26*
$ClC(N_2)COOEt$	C	—	—	2100	*158*
$BrCHN_2$	B	—	—	2069	*26*
$BrC(N_2)COOEt$	C	80–90	—	—	*158*
$IC(N_2)COOEt$	C	70–90	—	2080	*50, 158, 161*

[a] Symbols A–H indicate the following starting materials: A, a tosyl azide; B, a diazoalkane; C, a metal diazoalkane; D, an *N*-nitroso compound; E, an amino compound; F, a hydrazino compound; G, a carbonyl derivative; H, nitric oxide or nitrosyl chloride.

[b] Not isolated.

[c] The ^1H NMR chemical shifts (τ) for $XCHN_2$: CH_2N_2, 6.92 (*98*); Me_3SiCHN_2, 7.77 (*93, 171*); $ArylSO_2CHN_2$, 4.98–4.57 (*106*); O_2NCHN_2, 4 (*159*).

spectra of α-heterodiazoalkanes [for $\nu(N{\equiv}N)$, see Table I] may similarly be rationalized (e.g., for S compounds, see Ref. *84*). From Table I, it will be seen that the position of $\nu(N{\equiv}N)$ in $XCHN_2$ and X_2CN_2 progressively decreases in the series $X = H > Me_3Si > Me_3Ge > Me_3Sn > Me_3Pb$, as is consistent with progressive electron release from X (*93*).

The ^1H nuclear magnetic resonance chemical shifts of the α-carbon proton in organic diazoalkanes have been discussed in terms of the relative significance of the canonical form (IV; $R' = H$) (*98*). For α-hetero compounds data are more sparse (see Table I), but may be interpreted in a similar sense. The pattern is clear: electron-releasing groups at carbon give rise to high-field absorption and conversely for electron-withdrawing groups.

α-Heterodiazoalkanes absorb in the visible region of the spectrum. The compound $(Me_3Sn)_2CN_2$ has λ_{max} at 280(vs) and 396(m) mμ (*92*). For compounds R_3MCN_2R' λ_{max} (mμ) decrease as follows (*20*): R_3M, $R' = Ph_3Ge$, Ph (451); Ph_3Si, Ph (440); and Ph_3Si, Me (426); this compares with 501 mμ for Me_3CCN_2Ph and 490 mμ for Me_3CCN_2Me.

G. Chemical Properties

The reactions of these compounds may conveniently be subdivided into five main types: (1) diazoalkanes as sources of carbenes, (2) diazoalkanes as nucleophiles, (3) diazoalkanes as electrophiles, (4) diazoalkanes as 1,3-dipoles, and (5) reactions involving metal–carbon bond cleavage. Reactions (1)–(3) are mainly characteristic of diazoalkanes bearing an α-hetero Group IVb–VIIb substituent, and have analogy with reactions of organic compounds. Reaction type (4) has been established principally for Me_3SiCHN_2 and $(Me_3Sn)_2CN_2$. Reactions (5) only occur for the more electropositive derivatives.

1. *α-Heterodiazoalkanes as Sources of Carbenes*

Irradiation with ultraviolet light leads to the loss of nitrogen and the production of substituted carbenes [Eq. (41)]. In some cases, the latter may

$$XYCN_2 \rightarrow XYC{:} + N_2 \qquad (41)$$

also be generated thermally. The carbenes may be trapped by olefins [Eq. (42)] [X, Y = Cl, H (*26*); Br, H (*26*); I, COOEt (*50*); RSO_2, H (*102*); RS, RS (*166*); $R_2P(O)$, R (*173*); Me_3Si, H (*171*); R_3Si, COOEt (*162*); R_3Sn, COOEt (*162*)].

$$XYCN_2 + A{=}B \xrightarrow{h\nu} XYC\text{—}A \text{ (three-membered ring with B)} \quad (42)$$

In some cases, an internal rearrangement, similar to the Wolff rearrangement, takes place (*20, 103*).

$$p\text{-}MeOC_6H_4SO_2CHN_2 \xrightarrow{h\nu} p\text{-}MeOC_6H_4SO_2\ddot{C}H \xrightarrow{MeOH}$$

$$p\text{-}MeOC_6H_4SO_2CH_2OMe\ (75\text{–}80\%) + p\text{-}MeOC_6H_4CH_2SO_2OMe\ (8\text{–}12\%) \quad (43)$$

$$Ph_3SiC(N_2)Me \longrightarrow Ph_3Si\ddot{C}Me \longrightarrow Ph_3SiCH{=}CH_2\ (55\%) \quad (44)$$

Photolysis of mercury derivatives leads, not only to the intermediate mercury substituted carbenes, but also to a carbyne (*33, 34*).

$$Hg[C(N_2)COOEt]_2 \xrightarrow{h\nu} Hg\ddot{C}COOEt\,(\text{—}C(N_2)COOEt) \longrightarrow \dddot{C}COOEt \quad (45)$$

2. *α-Heterodiazoalkanes as Nucleophiles*

The metallation of Me_3SiCHN_2 with methyllithium affords $[Me_3SiCN_2]Li$ (*96*); its identity was demonstrated by reactions with alkyl iodides (MeI and EtI) to afford $Me_3Si(R)CN_2$, and organometallic halides [Me_3SnCl (*93*) and n-Bu_2BCl (*96*)] to give α-heterodiazoalkanes (see Section II,C).

Reactions of phosphorus and sulfur compounds with hydrochloric acid leads to loss of nitrogen [e.g., Eq. (46)]. Presumably, the acid protonates the α-carbon, and the resulting α-heterodiazonium ion is then readily attacked by chloride ion; deuterium exchange has been shown to take place in acid or base (*43*). However, acetic acid reacts with trimethylsilyldiazomethane to give equimolar amounts of trimethylsilyl acetate and trimethylsilylmethyl acetate [Eq. (47)] (*171*); cleavage of the silyl group, as well as loss of nitrogen, takes place. The reactions of silylaryldiazoalkanes, Ph_3SiCN_2Ar, with a number of acids HA (A = F, Cl, Br, OAc, OTs) afford α-substituted benzylsilanes $Ph_3SiCHAAr$, in a manner analogous to reaction (46) (*21*). In none of the above cases did the intermediate α-silylcarbonium ion rearrange or give Friedel–Crafts substitution with an aromatic solvent; however, such processes did occur when the reagent was $BF_3 \cdot OEt_2$. The mechanism of hydrolysis of α-diazosulfones has been

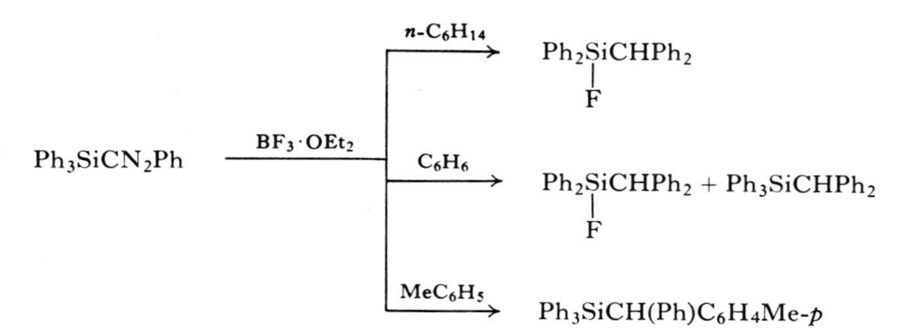

studied (*42*, *43*, *212*, *213*).

$$(MeO)_2P(O)C(N_2)Ph + HCl \longrightarrow [(MeO)_2P(O)CHPhN_2]^{(+)}Cl^{(-)} \longrightarrow (MeO)_2P(O)CHClPh \quad (46)$$

$$Me_3SiCHN_2 + AcOH \longrightarrow [Me_3SiCH_2N_2]^{(+)}OAc^{(-)} \xrightarrow{AcOH} Me_3SiCH_2OAc + Me_3SiOAc \quad (47)$$

A similar reaction with bromine results in displacement of nitrogen [Eq. (48)] (*80*). The reaction between thiohypohalites and sulfonyl diazomethanes has also been studied (*186*).

$$Ph_3SiC(N_2)COOEt + Br_2 \rightarrow Ph_3SiCBr_2COOEt + N_2 \quad (48)$$

3. *α-Heterodiazoalkanes as Electrophiles*

Phosphorus-, sulfur-, and halogen-containing diazoalkanes behave as electrophiles in their reactions with tertiary phosphines [e.g., Eq. (49)], to form phosphazines; organic diazo compounds behave similarly. The compounds RSO_2CHN_2 show protonic hydrogen in H-bonding to donor solvents (*39*).

$$PhSO_2CHN_2 + Ph_3P \longrightarrow PhSO_2CH{=}N{-}\overset{(-)}{N}{-}\overset{(+)}{P}Ph_3 \quad (49)$$

4. *α-Heterodiazoalkanes as 1,3-Dipoles*

1,3-Cycloadditions are well known in organic chemistry (*75*). Diazomethane rarely displays such reactivity, since much of its chemistry is dominated by the facility with which nitrogen is eliminated. However, it does behave as a 1,3-dipole with respect to formation of a pyrazole with disubstituted acetylenes. Clearly, the 1,3-dipolar character of an organodiazoalkane is enhanced by the presence of an electron-withdrawing substituent, as in $EtOOCCHN_2$ or $(CF_3)_2CN_2$. Surprisingly, the Group IVB diazoalkanes $(Me_3Sn)_2CN_2$ (*92, 94*), Me_3SiCHN_2 (*94, 171*), $Me_3SiC(N_2)CO_2Et$ (*81*), and $Me_3Si(Me_3Sn)CN_2$ (*96*), and some phosphorus derivatives (*81, 173*) have been shown to undergo 1,3-cycloadditions [Eq. (50), although LM migration is possible; X = LM, H, or an organic group]. It is clear (*94*) that the reactivity of the CN_2^{2-} ligand with respect to its 1,3-dipolar addition reactions is significantly governed by the nature of the groups attached to carbon: with $(Me_3Sn)_2CN_2$, for example, the dipolar structure $(Me_3Sn)_2\overset{-}{C}—N═\overset{+}{N}$ is probably particularly important as it may be stabilized by delocalization of the negative charge on carbon. The 1,3-dipolar character decreases in the series $(Me_3Sn)_2CN_2 > Me_3SiCHN_2 > CH_2N_2$ (*94*). This may be illustrated by noting that whereas diazomethane and phenyl isocyanate give nitrogen and the β-lactam of *N*-phenyl-β-alanine, the stannyldiazomethane gives the 1,3-cycloadduct, the triazolone (*92*).[1]

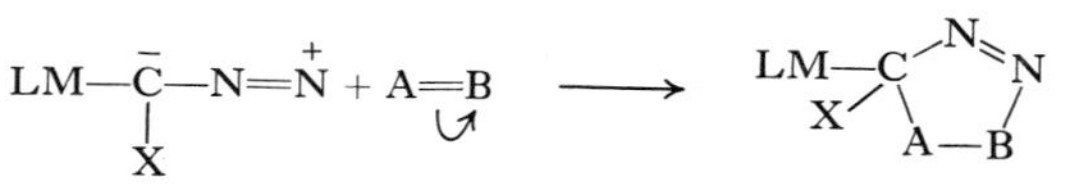

$$LM—\overset{-}{C}(X)—N═\overset{+}{N} + A═B \longrightarrow \underset{\text{(VIII)}}{\text{LM(X)C—N═N—B—A (five-membered ring)}} \quad (50)$$

In Eq. (50), the molecule AB is an unsaturated compound and has included (*94*) *p*-TolN═CNTol-*p*, PhNC═S, S═CS, PhN═CO, PhC≡N, $MeO_2CC≡CCO_2Me$, $CH_2═CHCN$, and $CH_2═C(Me)CN$. Reactions of type (50) have been incorporated in a general heterocyclic synthesis (*94*), comprising the use of the following consecutive operations: conversion of CH_2N_2 into $(Me_3Sn)_2CN_2$, reaction of the latter in the sense of Eq. (50), and protodestannylation of (VIII; LM = X = Me_3Sn) to give the parent heterocycle (VIII; LM = X = H) by treatment with 5*M* HCl. A complication is that migration of LM or X may take place during the course of reaction (50). This is illustrated by (IX) (*81*), obtained from $Me_3SiC(N_2)COOEt$ and MeOOCC≡CCOOMe. Migratory aptitudes appear to decrease in the series $Me_3Sn > Me_3Si > H > COOEt$ (*96*).

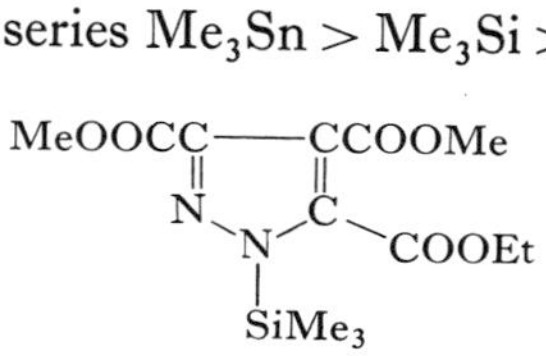

MeOOCC═N—N($SiMe_3$)—C(COOEt)═CCOOMe (ring)

(IX)

[1] An alternative argument is that particular substituents on carbon repress the nitrogen elimination pathway, whence the 1,3-dipolar behavior of such diazoalkanes becomes more prominent.

1,3-Dipolar activity of a different sort, an insertion reaction, is demonstrated by Eq. (51) (*95*); this is discussed in Section III,A,2.

$$\pi\text{-}C_5H_5(OC)_3M{-}H + Me_3SiCHN_2 \xrightarrow[\text{or W}]{M = Mo} \pi\text{-}C_5H_5(OC)_2M{-}N{=}N{-}CH_2SiMe_3 \quad (51)$$

5. *Reactions Involving M—C Cleavage*

Derivatives of the more electropositive elements undergo reactions in which the metal–carbon bond is broken. Reactions with halides and sulfides to yield appropriate α-heterodiazoalkanes have already been discussed in Section C.

Lithio- and sodio-diazomethane react with an aqueous solution of potassium dihydrogen phosphate or ammonium chloride at –80°C to form a tautomer of diazomethane, the so-called "isodiazomethane" [Eq. (52)] (*2*, *143*, *145*). The unstable compound (decomposes at 15°C and explodes at 35°–45°C) was originally formulated as (X) (*123*, *125*), but more recent evidence points to (XI) (*116*, *121*).

$$Li(CHN_2) + KH_2PO_4 \longrightarrow \underset{(X)}{H{-}\overset{(-)}{C}{=}\overset{(+)}{N}{=}\ddot{N}{-}H} \text{ or } \underset{(XI)}{\overset{(-)}{C}{\equiv}\overset{(+)}{N}{-}\ddot{N}H_2} \quad (52)$$

Carboxylic and sulfuric acids react with bis(carboxymethyl)mercury to give a mercury-containing polymer (*57*).

$$(Me_3Sn)_2CN_2 \xrightarrow{Br_2} Me_3SnBr + N_2 + C + HBr$$

$$(Me_3Sn)_2CN_2 \xrightarrow{360^\circ C} Me_4Sn + Me_3SnCN + N_2$$

$$(Me_3Sn)_2CN_2 \xrightarrow{PhC{\equiv}CH} Me_3Sn{-}C{\equiv}CPh$$

$$(Me_3Sn)_2CN_2 \xrightarrow{HCl} Me_3SnCl + N_2$$

$$(Me_3Sn)_2CN_2 \xrightarrow{C_5H_6} Me_3Sn{-}C_5H_5 \text{ (cyclopentadienyl)}$$

$$(Me_3Sn)_2CN_2 \xrightarrow{MeOH} Me_3SnOMe + N_2$$

$$(Me_3Sn)_2CN_2 \xrightarrow[(0^\circ C)\ OH^-]{H_2O} (Me_3SnOH)_2 + CH_2N_2$$

$$(Me_3Sn)_2CN_2 \xrightarrow{1M\ HCl} (Me_3SnOH)_2 + N_2 + CH_4 + C_2H_6 + C_3H_8$$

Lithiodiazomethane also reacts with benzoyl bromide, ethyl benzoate, benzophenone, and benzonitrile, affording organic nitrogen compounds and lithium salts [e.g., Eq. (53)] (*18*, *118*, *124*).

$$PhCOBr + Li(CHN_2) \longrightarrow LiBr + Ph\text{—}\overset{\displaystyle N\text{—}N}{C\diagdown_{O}\diagup CH} \qquad (53)$$

The tin–carbon bonds in $(Me_3Sn)_2CN_2$ are very readily cleaved (*92*, *93*). This is illustrated by the scheme at the bottom of p. 414. The reactions with C_5H_6 and $PhC{\equiv}CH$ (*93*) are noteworthy. SiC bonds are somewhat less labile (*20*, *81*, *171*).

III

REACTIONS OF DIAZOALKANES WITH DERIVATIVES OF METALS AND METALLOIDS

A. Formation of Carbon–Metal and Carbon–Metalloid Bonds

The formation of these bonds is a consequence of a formal carbene insertion reaction [Eq. (54); L′ is the sum of all the ligands except X attached to the metal or metalloid, M′].

$$L'M'\text{—}X + RR'CN_2 \rightarrow L'M'\text{—}CRR'X + N_2 \qquad (54)$$

The substrates have been mostly halides (see *169*) but reactions have been observed with hydrides, alkyls, or carboxylates (see Table II).

Carbene insertion into a multiple bond of a coordinated ligand has been demonstrated for reaction of (a) *all-trans*-cyclododecatriene-(1.5.9)-nickel(O) (CDTNi) and CH_2N_2 (*18a*), and (b) Cu(II) octaethylporphin and $CH(N_2)CO_2Et$ (*25a*). In (a), it is likely that a nickel–CH_2N_2 complex is formed initially, since CH_2N_2 does not react with CDTNi(CO) (*18a*). CDTNi forms a 1:1 complex with Ph_2CN_2, from which the diazoalkane is displaced by treatment with CO. CDTNi(Ph_2CN_2) decomposes at $-30°$ with evolution of nitrogen and formation of $Ph_2C{=}N\text{—}N{=}CPh_2$. It was postulated that the azine forms through initial formation of CDTNi-($Ph_2C \cdot N_2CPh_2$) (*18a*). A stable complex of this type $(Ph_3P)_2Pt[(CF_3)_2\text{-}C \cdot N_2C(CF_3)_2]$ has been isolated from the reaction between $(Ph_3P)_3Pt$ and $(CF_3)_2CN_2$ (*25c*); it is believed to have Pt in a 5-membered PtC_2N_2 ring.

TABLE II

REACTIONS OF DIAZOALKANES WITH DERIVATIVES OF METALS AND METALLOIDS[a]

Reactants	Products	References
LiCl	$LiCH_2Cl$	*65*
LiMe	$LiCHN_2$	*123, 125*
$BeCl_2$	Polymethylene and C_2H_4	*194*
$MgCl_2$	$Mg(CH_2Cl)_2$	*65*
$MgCl_2$	Polymethylene	*194*
RMgX	Hydrazones or hydrazines (on hydrolysis)	*27, 210*
$CaCl_2$	$Ca(CH_2Cl)_2$	*65*
$SrCl_2$	$Sr(CH_2Cl)_2$	*65*
Boron halides, alkyls, hydrides, and alkoxides	Polymethylene	*15, 25, 36, 46, 79, 112, 194, 198*
Boron hydrides or alkyls + N_2CHCO_2Et or N_2CHCOR	$:CHCO_2Et$ or :CHCOR insertion	*66–70*
BF_3	$F_2B(CH_2F)$	*53*
H ClB–N–BCl HN–B–NH Cl	H $ClCH_2B$–N–BCH_2Cl HN–B–NH CH_2Cl	*189*
$AlCl_3$	$Al(CH_2Cl)_3$	*1*
$AlBr_3$	$Al(CH_2Br)_3$	*1*
Aluminum alkyls, hydrides, and alkoxides	Some CH_2 insertion and polymethylene	*60–63*
$Al(OR)_3$; R electron-withdrawing	CH_3OR (on hydrolysis)	*155*
GaI_3	C_2H_4	*194*
InI_3	$In(CH_2I)_3$	*194*
$TlCl_3$	$ClTl(CH_2Cl)_2$	*198*
$TlCl_3 + CH_3CHN_2$	$[(CH_3CHCl)TlCl]_2O$ and $3\ TlCl \cdot TlCl_3$	*198*
$SiCl_4$	$Cl_nSi(CH_2Cl)_{4-n}$; $n = 1, 2, 3$	*174, 176, 201, 205*
$SiBr_4$	$Br_nSi(CH_2Br)_{4-n}$; $n = 0, 1, 2, 3$	*174, 201, 205*
$HSiCl_3$	$Cl_2Si(CH_2Cl)H$	*174*
$MeSiCl_3$	$Cl_2Si(CH_2Cl)Me$	*201, 205*
Ph_2SiH_2	Ph_2SiMeH	*88, 89*

$PhSiH_3$	$PhSiMeH_2$ and $PhSiMe_2H$	*88, 89*
$PhSiH_3 + Ph_2CN_2$	$Ph_2C{=}N{-}N{=}CPh_2$	*88, 89*
$MeSiH_3$	Me_2SiH_2	*111, 177*
$MeSiD_3$	$Me(CH_2D)SiD_2$	*111*
Me_3SiCl + 9-diazofluorene	Di-9-fluorenylidene and fluorenone azine	*176*
$GeCl_4$	$Cl_nGe(CH_2Cl)_{4-n}$; $n = 2, 3$	*174*
$MeGeCl_3$	$Cl_nGeMe(CH_2Cl)_{3-n}$; $n = 1, 2$	*174*
$(Aryl)GeCl_3$	$(Aryl)Ge(CH_2Cl)Cl_2$	*172*
R_3GeH; R = Et, n-Pr, n-Bu	R_3GeMe	*89*
$SnCl_4$	$SnCl_2 + CH_2Cl_2$	*134*
$SnCl_4$	$Cl_nSn(CH_2Cl)_{4-n}$; $n = 0, 1, 2, 3$	*204, 205*
$SnBr_4$	$BrSn(CH_2Br)_{4-n}$; $n = 0, 1, 2, 3$	*204, 205*
$(ClCH_2)_2SnCl_2 + CH_3CHN_2$	$(ClCH_2)_2Sn(CHClCH_3)_2$	*204, 205*
$SnCl_4 + N_2CHCOOEt$	$[N_2C = C(OEt)O]_2SnCl_2$	*134*
Me_2SnX_2; X = Cl, Br, I	$Me_2Sn(CH_2X)_2$	*175*
$PhSnCl_3$	$Cl_2Sn(CH_2Cl)Ph$	*90*
Ph_2SnCl_2	$ClSn(CH_2Cl)Ph_2$	*90*
$SnCl_2$	Ring: Cl_2Sn(–CH_2–$SnCl_2$–)(OEt_2O)(–CH_2–$SnCl_2$–) (in ether)	*204, 205*
$SnCl_2$	$(Cl_2SnCH_2)_n$ (in benzene)	*204, 205*
R_3SnH; R = Me, Et, n-Pr, n-Bu	R_3SnMe	*89, 101*
n-Bu_3SnH+ $RCHN_2$; R = EtOC(=O)—, MeC(=O)—, PhC(=O)—, –CN	n-Bu_3SnCH_2R	*101*
R_3SnNMe_2; R = Me, Et, n-Bu, Ph	$(R_3Sn)_2CN_2$	*92–94*
$R_3SnNMe_2 + N_2CHCOOEt$; R = Me, Et, n-Bu, Ph	$R_3SnC(N_2)COOEt$	*108*
$Me_3SnNMe_2 + Me_3SiCHN_2$	$Me_3Si(Me_3Sn)CN_2$	*93*
$R_2Sn(NMe)_2 + N_2CHCOOEt$; R = Me, Et, n-Bu	$R_2Sn[C(N_2)COOEt]_2$	*108*
$PbCl_4$	$PbCl_2$	*205, 206*
$Pb(OOCMe)_4$	$Pb(OOCMe)_2 + (MeCOO)_2CH_2$	*206*
$Me_3PbN(SiMe_3)_2$	$(Me_3Pb)_2CN_2$	*93*
Et_3PbCl	$Et_3Pb(CH_2Cl)$ and Et_4Pb	*205, 206*
Et_2PbCl_2	$Et_2Pb(CH_2Cl)_2$	*206*

(Continued)

TABLE II (*Continued*)

Reactants	Products	References
PCl_3	$Cl_2P(CH_2Cl)$	*200*
PBr_3	$Cl_nP(CH_2Cl)_{3-n}$; $n = 1, 2$	*200*
PCl_5	$(ClCH_2)_3P{=}O$	*200, 202*
$PCl_5 + CH_3CHN_2$	$(CH_3CHCl)_2P(O)OH$ (on hydrolysis)	*200, 202*
$(sec\text{-}BuO)_2PF$	$(sec\text{-}BuO)_2PCH_2F$	*157*
R_3P; R = Aryl, alkyl, or alkoxy	Phozphazines, tetrazines, azines, or ylids	*16, 17, 71, 78, 146, 182, 183, 192*
$AsCl_3$	$Cl_nAs(CH_2Cl)_{3-n}$; $n = 1, 2$	*25b, 65*
$AsCl_3 + CH_3CHN_2$	$Cl_nAs(CHClCH_3)_{3-n}$; $n = 0, 1$	*19, 202*
Ph_2AsCl	$PhAs(O)CH_2AsPh_2$	*29*
$SbCl_3$	$Cl_nSb(CH_2Cl)_{3-n}$; $n = 0, 1, 2$	*19, 202, 203*
$SbCl_5$	$SbCl_3 + CH_2Cl_2$	*202, 203*
$BiCl_3$	$(ClCH_2)BiO$	*202, 203*
EtSCl	$EtS(CH_2Cl)$	*139*
SCl_2	$S(CH_2Cl)_2$	*139*
S_2Cl_2	$(SCH_2Cl)_2$	*139*
$(Aryl)SH + Pr_2CN_2$	$Pr_2CHS(Aryl)$	*167, 168*
$(Aryl\ S)_2 + Ph_2CN_2$	$Ph_2C(SAryl)_2$	*167, 168*
$(Aryl)SCl + Ph_2CN_2$	$Ph_2C(Cl)(SAryl)$	*167, 168*
$SOCl_2$	$(ClCH_2)_2SO$	*157*
$SOCl_2 + Ph_2CN_2$	Ph_2CCl_2	*179*
$p\text{-}MeC_6H_4SOCl$	$p\text{-}MeC_6H_4S(O)CH_2Cl$	*5*
$MeSO_2Cl$	Polymethylene	*6*
SO_2Cl_2	$(ClCH_2)_2SO_2$	*139*
$SO_2Cl_2 + Ph_2CN_2$	Ph_2CCl_2	*179*
SO_2	$(MeO)_2SO$	*139*
$SO_2 + Ph_2CN_2$	$\overline{CPh_2CPh_2SO_2}$ and $Ph_2C{=}O$ (cyclic)	*184*
Nearly all the metals of the transition series catalyze the decomposition of diazoalkanes		*11, 130*
Cu, Cu_2Cl_2, $CuCl_2$, Cu_2Br_2, Cu_2I_2, $CuSO_4$, Cu^{II} stearate, Cu chelates	Polymethylene	*15, 24, 37, 46, 87, 100, 118, 137, 194*

Ag, $AgNO_3$	Polymethylene	*118*
$AgO + N_2CHCOOEt$	$Ag(CN_2COOEt)$	*162*
Ag, $AgO + (CH_3)_2CN_2$	$(CH_3)_2C{=}N{-}N{=}C(CH_3)_2$	*3*
Au, $AuCl_3$	Polymethylene	*97, 129a, 156*
$ZnCl_2$	$Zn(CH_2Cl)_2$	*65*
$ZnCl_2$	$ZnO + ClCH_2CH_2Cl$	*25b*
ZnI_2	$IZnCH_2I$ and $(ICH_2)_2Zn$	*193, 194*
ZnI_2	Polymethylene	*118, 194*
$ZnI_2 + (CH_3)_2CN_2$	$CH_3C{=}N{-}N{=}C(CH_3)_2$ and $(CH_3)_2C{=}C(CH_3)_2$	*3*
$ZnI_2 + Ph_2CN_2$	$Ph_2C{=}N{-}N{=}CPh_2$	*3*
$CdCl_2$	$Cd(CH_2Cl)_2$	*65*
CdI_2	$Cd(CH_2I)_2$	*194*
HgX_2; X = Cl, Br, I	$XHg(CH_2X)$ and $Hg(CH_2X)_2$	*49, 58*
$HgCl_2 + Ph_2CN_2$	$ClHgCClPh_2$	*58, 99*
$HgCl_2 + Ph_2CN_2$ (excess)	$ClHgCPh_2CPh_2Cl$	*99*
RHgCl; R = Ph or *p*-MeC_6H_4	$R_2Hg + Hg(CH_2Cl)_2$	*58*
$PhCH_2HgCl$	$Ph_2CH_2HgCH_2Cl$	*58*
$HgCl_2 + N_2CHCOOEt$	$Hg[CCl(HgCl)COOEt]_2 + ClCH_2COOEt$	*132*
PhHgOOCPh	$PhHgCH_2OOCPh$	*141, 142*
$HgO + N_2CHR$; R electron-withdrawing	$Hg(N_2CHR)_2$	*23, 35, 208*
$(\pi\text{-}C_5H_5)_2Zr(NMe_2)_2 + 2\ Me_3SiCHN_2$	$(\pi\text{-}C_5H_5)_2Zr[C(SiMe_3)N_2]_2$?	*95, 96*
$\pi\text{-}C_5H_5(OC)_3MNa$ (M = Mo or W) + $N_2CHCOOEt$	$\pi\text{-}C_5H_5(OC)_2M$ bonded by C= to a pyrazole ring: C(OH)–C(COOEt)=N–NH– (structure)	*55, 86*
$\pi\text{-}C_5H_5(OC)_3MH$ (M = Mo or W) + Me_3SiCHN_2	$\pi\text{-}C_5H_5(OC)_2MN{=}NCH_2SiMe_3$	*95*
$\pi\text{-}C_5H_5(OC)_3MoH$	$\pi\text{-}C_5H_5(OC)_3MoCH_3$	*144*
$\pi\text{-}C_5H_5(OC)_3WH$	$\pi\text{-}C_5H_5(OC)_3WCH_3$	*47, 48*
$(OC)_5MnH$	$(OC)_5MnCH_3$	*59*
$FeCl_3$, $FeCl_2$, $Fe(DPM)_3$	Polymethylene	*5, 15, 194*
$Fe_3(CO)_{12}$, $Fe(CO)_5 + Ph_2CN_2$	Complex adducts	*8, 9*
$IrCl_3$	Polymethylene	*11*
trans-$(Ph_2Me)_2Ir(CO)Cl$	$(Ph_2Me)_2Ir(CO)CH_2Cl$ and polymethylene	*109*
$Ni(CO)_4$, Cp_2Ni	Polymethylene	*118, 153*

(Continued)

TABLE II (*Continued*)

Reactants	Products	References
Ni	CH_2 +	*18a*
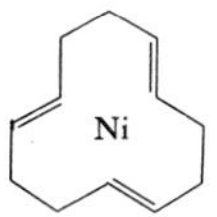 Ni + Ph_2CN_2	$Ph_2C{=}N{-}N{=}CPh_2$	*18a*
$PtCl_4$	Polymethylene	*190*
trans-$(Et_3P)_2PtHBr$	$(Et_3P)_2PtMeBr$	*170*
$[\pi C_3H_5PdCl]_2 + N_2CHCOOEt$	:CHCOOEt trapped by solvent	*4*
Transition metal hydride [e.g., $HMn(CO)_5$] or compound with metal–metal bond [e.g., $Co_2(CO)_8$] + $(CF_3)_2CN_2$	$(CF_3)_2C$: insertion	*7, 28*
trans-$(Ph_2MeP)_2Ir(CO)Cl + (CF_3)_2CN_2$	$(Ph_2MeP)_2Ir[C(CF_3)_2]Cl(CO)$?	*28*
Transition metal acetylacetonates	Reaction catalysts	*136*
$[Ph_3PPdCl_2]_2 + NCCHN_2$	:CHCN insertion	*110*
$[PPtCl_2]_2(P{=}Et_3P$ or $Me_2PhP) + (CF_3)_2CN_2$	$:C(CF_3)_2$ insertion	*25c*
$(Ph_3P)_3Pt + (CF_3)_2CN_2$	$(Ph_3P)_2Pt[(CF_3)_2CN_2C(CF_3)_2] + Ph_3P\cdot N_2C(CF_3)_2$	*25c*
Cu(II)octaethylporphin + N_2CHCO_2Et	$:CHCO_2Et$ addition to C=C of ligand	*25a*
Co(II)octaethylporphin + N_2CHCO_2Et	Compound with Co to $CHCO_2Et$ bond	*75a*

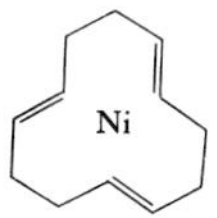

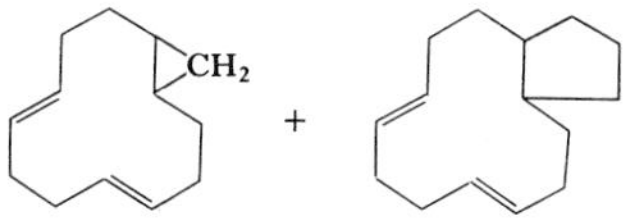

[a] Examples for diazomethane are given, though in many cases substituted diazomethanes also react. Where these give different products both are shown.

1. *Insertion into Metal–Halogen Bonds*

The reaction of diazoalkanes with metal or metalloid halides is a useful preparative route to α-halogenoalkyl derivatives. In some cases, this appears to be the only available method of synthesis [e.g., Eq. (55)]. For example, whereas chloromethyl derivatives of silicon may be prepared by reaction of chlorine with the methyl derivatives, the reaction with tin analogs affords the tin chlorides.

$$SnCl_4 + CH_2N_2 \rightarrow Cl_{4-n}Sn(CH_2Cl)_n + N_2 \tag{55}$$

The reactions are usually carried out in diethyl ether, which is frequently the solvent of choice for the diazoalkane synthesis. Additionally, the polarity of ether is a helpful feature; good yields are usually obtained. The rate of reaction is dependent on the solvent; benzene may be used if the reaction is too vigorous in ether; also the chloromethyl compounds may react with the solvent [e.g., Eq. (56) (*25b*)]. For this reason, protic and chlorinated solvents are not used.

$$ZnCl_2 + CH_2N_2 + Et_2O \rightarrow ZnO + ClCH_2CH_2Cl + C_4H_{10} + N_2 \tag{56}$$

The reactivity of the halides varies considerably, as demonstrated by the range of yield attainable for different chloromethyl derivatives (*65*). The ease of reaction is dependent on the particular halide used and on the other groups attached to the metal. Thus, tetrachlorosilane reacts with diazomethane in ether at –50°C, but dichlorodimethylsilane does not react even under more vigorous conditions (*201*, *205*). Also dichlorodimethylstannane and chlorotrimethylplumbane react, but dichlorodimethylgermane and chlorotrimethylstannane do not. Silicon tetrafluoride does not react; only a few fluorides react, and generally afford polyalkanes (see Table II). These factors may reflect the requirement of a relatively polar M—Hal bond.

In general, the ease of reaction depends upon the nucleophilicity of the diazoalkane (i.e., decreases with decreasing basicity of the α-carbon) and also upon steric effects. A large number of substrates have been subjected only to diazomethane; where substituted diazoalkanes have also been used, the reactions generally follow the same course, and differences are those in reaction rates.

Reactions are usually carried out at low temperatures; silicon tetrachloride may explode with diazomethane at room temperature (*205*). Phosphorus trichloride gives a tarry product at room temperature (*145*), but dichloro(chloromethyl)phosphine is formed at –60°C (*200*). Boron trifluoride reacts at room temperature to give polymethylene, but, using limited diazomethane diluted with nitrogen at low temperatures, difluoro(fluoromethyl)borane is obtained (*53*).

The use of variable molar ratios of diazomethane in some cases leads to good yields of different products. For example, mercury(II) chloride gives chloro(chloromethyl)mercury or di(chloromethyl)mercury, each in quantitative yield (*58*), while $SiCl_4$ gives a mixture of compounds $Cl_nSi(CH_2Cl)_{4-n}$ (*201*, *205*).

Some products are unstable and decomposition or polymerization of the diazoalkane may occur (see Section III,B,1). Disproportionation is also found [e.g., Eq. (57) (*58*)].

$$PhHgCl + CH_2N_2 \rightarrow PhHgCH_2Cl \rightarrow Ph_2Hg + Hg(CH_2Cl)_2 + N_2 \quad (57)$$

For halides in high oxidation states, reduction may take place [e.g., Eq. (58) (*202*, *203*)], while others may act as halogenating agents [e.g., Eq. (59) (*179*), cf. Eq. 60)].

$$SbCl_5 + CH_2N_2 \rightarrow SbCl_3 + CH_2Cl_2 + N_2 \quad (58)$$

$$SO_2Cl_2 + Ph_2CN_2 \rightarrow SO_2 + Ph_2CCl_2 + N_2 \quad (59)$$

$$Br_2 + RCHN_2 \rightarrow RCHBr_2 + N_2 \quad (60)$$

Few reactions (see Table II) of diazoalkanes with transition metal halogeno complexes have been reported. Only in one case, with Vaska's compound (XII), has the formation of a chloromethyl derivative [Eq. (61)] been reported (*109*); compound (XIII) decomposes upon further addition of diazomethane to give ethylene.

$$\underset{\textbf{(XII)}}{(Ph_3P)(OC)Ir(Cl)(PPh_3)} + CH_2N_2 \longrightarrow \underset{\text{(XIII)}}{(Ph_3P)(OC)Ir(CH_2Cl)(PPh_3)} \quad (61)$$

It was proposed that compound (XIII) arises from an intermediate five-coordinate Ir^I carbene complex $(Ph_3P)_2Ir(CO)(CH_2)Cl$. With $(CF_3)_2CN_2$ and *trans*-$(Ph_2Me)_2IrCOCl$, the balance of the evidence supported structure (XIV) rather than the bis(trifluoromethyl) analog of (XIII) (*28*). Evidence for the trapping of a carbene as a transition metal complex has been provided in another system: the reaction of

[1,3-diphenylimidazolidine with 2-H and 2-CCl_3] or [bis(1,3-diphenylimidazolidin-2-ylidene), C=C] with $[Et_3PPtCl_2]_2$ afforded $Et_3P(Cl_2)PtC$[1,3-diphenylimidazolidin-2-ylidene] (*25c*).

$$\begin{array}{c} C(CF_3)_2 \\ | \\ Ph_2MeP \diagdown \quad \diagup Cl \\ Ir \\ OC \diagup \quad \diagdown PMePh_2 \end{array}$$

(XIV)

Other transition metal chloride complexes which undergo carbene insertion into the M—Cl bond are $[Ph_3PPdCl_2]_2$ (with $NCCHN_2$) (*110*), $[PPtCl_2]_2$ [$P = Et_3P$ or Me_2PhP with $(CF_3)_2CN_2$] (*25c*), and *trans*-$(Et_3P)_2$-PtHX [$X = Br$ with CH_2N_2 (*170*) or $X = Cl$ with $(CF_3)_2CN_2$ (*28*)].

A polar mechanism has been proposed for the reaction of a mercury(II) halide with diazomethane (*58*). It was suggested that the reaction proceeds by nucleophilic attack of diazomethane on the metal, followed by loss of nitrogen [Eq. (62)].

$$RHgCl + CH_2N_2 \rightarrow [RHgCH_2N{\equiv}N]^+Cl^- \rightarrow [RHgCH_2]^+Cl^- \rightarrow RHgCH_2Cl \qquad (62)$$

A similar mechanism [Eq. (63)], but showing the initial complex as a zwitterion, has also been proposed (*74*). In either of these mechanisms, the

$$HgCl_2 + CH_2N_2 \longrightarrow Cl_2\overset{-}{Hg}CH_2\overset{+}{N}{\equiv}N \longrightarrow Cl_2\overset{-}{Hg}\overset{+}{C}H_2 \longrightarrow ClHgCH_2Cl \qquad (63)$$

timing of the covalency changes may be stepwise or concerted.

A free-radical mechanism was proposed (*201*) for the addition of diazomethane to silicon halides, but it is now generally accepted that a polar mechanism is required.

2. *Insertion into Metal –Hydrogen, –Carbon, –Oxygen, and –Metal′ Bonds*

The reaction of diazomethane with hydrides of the Group IVb elements, to form methyl derivatives, requires the use of ultraviolet irradiation or a copper catalyst. In both cases, loss of nitrogen is the first step, followed by insertion of the methylene into the Group IVb element–hydrogen bond. Where a catalyst is used, evidence does not support a free methylene intermediate (Section III,B). With aluminium alkyls and hydrides, methylene insertion takes place, and treatment with an alcohol leads to the production of hydrocarbons (*60–63*).

The only metal–oxygen bond which is known to be cleaved by diazomethane is the Hg—O bond in phenylmercuric benzoate [Eq. (64)] (*141, 142*), although some oxides react to give metal diazo compounds (Section III,B,2).

$$PhHgOOCPh + CH_2N_2 \rightarrow PhHgCH_2OOCPh + N_2 \quad (64)$$

The reactions of transition metal hydride complexes have been extensively explored (*28, 47, 59, 95, 144*). It appears that only acidic hydrides react: $(\pi\text{-}C_5H_5)_2ReH$ was unreactive (*54*). For the Mo (*144*) and W (*47, 48*) cyclopentadienylcarbonyl hydrides, yields are remarkably low [e.g., Eq. (65)]; carbene insertions into the Mn—H bond of $(OC)_5MnH$ with CH_2N_2 (*59*) and $(CF_3)_2CN_2$ (*28*) have been recorded. Likewise $(CF_3)_2C$ insertion into the metal–metal bond of $[\pi\text{-}C_5H_5(OC)_2Fe]_2$ and $Co_2(CO)_8$ has been achieved (*28*); hydrogen-abstracted products were obtained [e.g., Eq. (66)].

$$\pi\text{-}C_5H_5(OC)_3WH + CH_2N_2 \rightarrow \pi\text{-}C_5H_5(OC)_3W\text{—}Me\ (4\%) + N_2 \quad (65)$$

$$[\pi\text{-}C_5H_5(OC)_2Fe]_2 + (CF_3)_2CN_2 \rightarrow \pi\text{-}C_5H_5(OC)_2FeCH(CF_3)_2 + N_2 \quad (66)$$

The reactions of some hydrides with trimethylsilyldiazomethane [Eq. (67)] are particularly interesting (*95*), because they demonstrate initial 1,3-dipolar (see Section II,G,4) rather than carbene insertion. Significant also are the following points: (i) the 1,3-dipolar character of the CN_2^{2-} ligand is clearly enhanced by the attachment to C of an organometallic group; and (ii) the isolation of stable alkylazo transition metal complexes (XV) is unprecedented and the electron count at Mo or W suggests either an unusual 16-electron metal configuration, or NN π-electron delocalization into vacant transition metal *d*-orbitals. It is interesting that $\pi\text{-}C_5H_5(OC)_3W^-Na^+$ and $EtOOCCHN_2$ undergo a different reaction, providing compound (XVI) (*55, 86*).

$$\pi\text{-}C_5H_5(OC)_3M\text{—}H + Me_3SiCHN_2 \xrightarrow[\text{or W}]{M = Mo} \underset{(XV)}{\pi\text{-}C_5H_5(OC)_2M\text{—}N{=}N\text{—}CH_2SiMe_3} \quad (67)$$

$$\pi\text{-}C_5H_5(OC)_2W{=}C(OH)\text{—}CCO_2Et{=}N\text{—}N(H)\text{—}W \ \text{(ring)}$$

(XVI)

B. *Catalytic Reactions*

1. *Diazoalkane Polymerization*

Decomposition of diazoalkanes by a variety of compounds such as boron halides and alkyls, copper salts, and many transition metals and their salts, leads to the production of high molecular weight polymers.

For strong Lewis acids, such as the boron halides (see ref. *13*), the mechanism for polymerization is thought to be polar (*14*, *79*) and to proceed as shown in Eqs. (68) and (69). Other mechanisms have been postulated but they appear to conflict with experimental data (*13*).

$$BF_3 + RCHN_2 \longrightarrow F_3\overset{(-)}{=}B-\underset{\displaystyle R}{\underset{|}{C}}H\overset{+}{N_2} \longrightarrow F_3\overset{(-)}{=}B-\underset{\displaystyle R}{\underset{|}{\overset{(+)}{C}}}H \longrightarrow F_2B\underset{\displaystyle R}{\underset{|}{C}}HF \qquad (68)$$

$$F_2B\underset{\displaystyle R}{\underset{|}{C}}HF + RCHN_2 \longrightarrow F_2\overset{(-)}{=}\underset{\displaystyle CH(R)F}{\underset{|}{B}}-CH(R)\overset{+}{N_2} \longrightarrow F_2\overset{(-)}{=}\underset{\displaystyle CH(R)F}{\underset{|}{B}}-\overset{(+)}{C}-HR \longrightarrow F_2B\underset{\displaystyle R}{\underset{|}{C}}H\underset{\displaystyle R}{\underset{|}{C}}HF \qquad (69)$$

Transition metal-catalyzed decomposition of diazoalkanes is thought to proceed through a carbene–metal complex (*207*). This formulation assumes that the carbene is bound to the metal surface and that the valence electrons of the metal complete the octet around the carbon.

In several methylene insertion reactions described in Section III,A, polymer was also obtained. For a series of halides it has been noted [Eq. (70)] (*194*) that the reaction of diazomethane with more electropositive metal halides gives methylene insertion, while the stronger Lewis acids give polymers; ethylene and other lower hydrocarbons are also obtained.

$$\underbrace{\underbrace{MgX_2 \quad BeX_2 \quad AlX_3}_{\text{Polymethylene}} \quad GaX_3 \quad ZnX_2 \quad CdX_2}_{\text{Ethylene}} \quad InX_3 \quad TlX_3 \quad HgX_2 \qquad (70)$$

(Brace spanning ZnX_2 through HgX_2: $M(CH_2X)_n$)

2. *Miscellaneous Organic Reactions*

Many of the compounds used to polymerize diazoalkanes may also be used as catalysts in reactions involving diazoalkanes. In particular, boron trifluoride and copper are widely used.

Diazoalkanes react with acids to form esters [e.g., Eq. (71)]; the diazoalkane is protonated by the acid to form a diazonium salt, which is then readily attacked by the acid anion (*74, 211*).

$$CH_2N_2 + PhCOOH \rightarrow PhCOOCH_3 + N_2 \qquad (71)$$

Alcohols and amines, which are not sufficiently acidic to protonate diazoalkanes, do not react. However, the addition of a catalyst results in the immediate evolution of nitrogen and the formation of ethers or higher amines [e.g., Eqs. (72) and (73)] (*31, 113, 119, 120, 129, 129a, 131, 135, 154a, 154b, 187*).

$$CH_3CH_2OH + CH_2N_2 \xrightarrow{BF_3} CH_3CH_2OCH_3 + N_2 \qquad (72)$$

$$NH_3 + CH_2N_2 \xrightarrow{BF_3} CH_3NH_2 + (CH_3)_2NH + (CH_3)_3N + N_2 \qquad (73)$$

The catalyst may act in two ways. Firstly, it may activate the diazoalkane (as in the first step of the polymerization), which would then be rapidly solvolyzed by the alcohol or amine [Eq. (74)]. Secondly, the hydroxyl or amino group may be activated by complex formation with the catalyst [Eq. (75)]. The first mechanism seems more likely, since polymer is often

$$Cat + CH_2N_2 \longrightarrow \overset{(-)}{Cat}\text{—}\overset{(+)}{CH_2N_2} \longrightarrow \overset{(-)}{Cat}\text{—}\overset{(+)}{CH_2} \xrightarrow{ROH} ROCH_3 + Cat \qquad (74)$$

$$Cat + ROH \longrightarrow \overset{(-)}{Cat}\text{—}\overset{(+)}{O}(R)H \xrightarrow{CH_2N_2} \overset{(-)}{Cat}\text{—}\overset{(+)}{O}(R)CH_3 \longrightarrow ROCH_3 + Cat \qquad (75)$$

formed and higher ethers may be detected (*12*), but it is possible that both are operative.

Several other organic reactions involving diazoalkanes are affected by catalysts. For example, diazomethane reacts very slowly with ketones to give homologous carbonyl compounds and some olefin oxide; but in the presence of catalyst the reaction proceeds rapidly and no olefin oxide is formed (*73, 76, 77, 115*). Also, with olefins, cyclopropanes may be formed (*37, 38, 51, 52, 56, 82, 83, 107, 114, 143, 191, 195*). A further development is the reaction of an organoborane with a diazoketone which, on alkaline hydrolysis gives a homologated ketone [Eq. (76)] (*69*). Since the organoborane may be readily formed from an alkene and diborane, this reaction offers a new synthesis for the preparation of ketones from alkenes. Homologous series of nitriles, esters, and diketones may similarly be prepared by using diazoacetonitrile (*70*), ethyl diazoacetate, or bis(diazo)ketones (*66*). Using D_2O in the hydrolysis step of these various reactions offers routes to α-D- and α,α-D_2-esters and ketones (*68*). From an olefin and 9-BBN (XVII; R = H), the appropriate 9-alkyl-BBN (XVII; R = alkyl) is obtained, which upon treatment with an acetylene such an *n*-BuC≡CH provides a synthesis [Eq. (77)] for cyclooctyl derivatives (XVIII) (*67*).

$$R_3B + CH_3COCHN_2 \xrightarrow[\text{2. Hydrolysis}]{\text{1. } -N_2} RCH_2COCH_3 \tag{76}$$

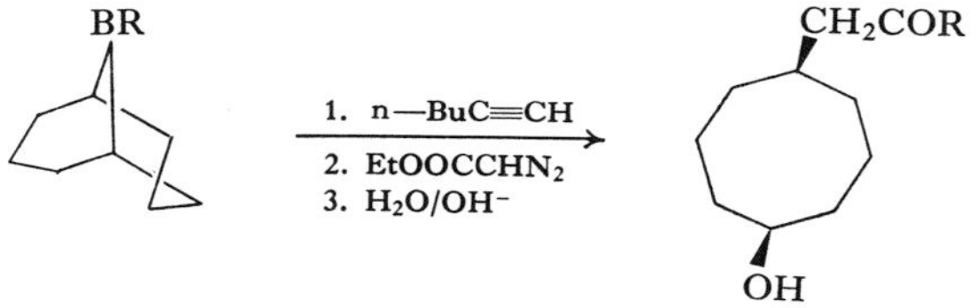

$$\text{(XVII), R = alkyl} \xrightarrow[\text{2. EtOOCCHN}_2 \text{ 3. } H_2O/OH^-]{\text{1. n—BuC}\equiv\text{CH}} \text{(XVIII)} \tag{77}$$

BR

(XVII)
R = alkyl

CH_2COR

OH

(XVIII)

C. Reactions in Which Nitrogen Is Retained

These reactions fall into three groups: reduction, formation of hetero-substituted diazo compounds, and coordination through the ω-nitrogen.

Diazoalkanes are reduced by a variety of reagents. Although they may be reduced to the hydrocarbon, careful catalytic hydrogenation yields the hydrazone [Eq. (78)] (*180*). Less severe reducing agents, such as sodium

$$R_2CN_2 + H_2 \xrightarrow{\text{Pd}} R_2CH_2 \quad \text{or} \quad R_2C{=}NNH_2 \tag{78}$$

amalgam (*138*, *180*, *196*), ammonium sulfide (*196*), hydrogen sulfide (*181*), or lithium aluminum hydride (*74*), may be used to obtain hydrazones, hydrazines, or amines.

Diazoalkanes which contain an α-proton may react with bases to form substituted diazo compounds [Eq. (79) and Section II,B].

$$MX_n + RCHN_2 \rightarrow M(CRN_2)_n + nHX \tag{79}$$

$$MX_n = HgO,\ Ag_2O,\ LiMe,\ R'_3SnNR''_2, \text{ and } (R'_3Sn)_2Sn(NR''_2)_2$$

Diazoalkanes may coordinate through the ω-nitrogen: in the case of tertiary phosphines, phosphazines are formed, which may be hydrolyzed to phosphine oxides [Eq. (80)] (*182*).

$$R_2CN_2 + R'_3P \longrightarrow R'_3P{=}NN{=}CR_2 \xrightarrow{H_2O} R'_3P{=}O + H_2NN{=}CR_2 \tag{80}$$

If the hydrolysis is carried out using a small amount of water, tetrazines may be formed [Eq. (81)] (*71*, *182*, *183*). In the presence of copper, phos-

$$2R_3P{=}NN{=}CR'_2 + H_2O \longrightarrow R'_2C\begin{matrix}N{=}N\\NH{-}NH\end{matrix}CR'_2 + 2\ R_3P{=}O \tag{81}$$

phorus ylids may result [Eq. (82)] (*192*). This provides a route for the conversion of a ketone to an alkene, via the ylid [e.g., Eq. (83)] (*192*).

$$Ph_3P + CH_2N_2 \xrightarrow{Cu} Ph_3P{=}CH_2 + N_2 \tag{82}$$

$$Ph_2C{=}O + CH_2N_2 \xrightarrow{Ph_3P/Cu} Ph_2C{=}CH_2 + Ph_3P{=}O \tag{83}$$

With triisopropyl phosphite and diphenyldiazomethane, rearrangement takes place at 180°C to give an azine [Eq. (84)] (*146*).

$$(i\text{-}PrO)_3PO + Ph_2CN_2 \xrightarrow{180^\circ C} Ph_2C{=}N{-}N{=}CPh_2 + (i\text{-}PrO)_2P(O){-}NHN{=}CPh_2 + MeCH{=}CH_2 \tag{84}$$

Grignard reagents attack diazoalkanes forming substituted hydrazones after hydrolysis [Eq. (85)] (*27*, *210*). In the case of diazomethane with an alkyl Grignard, reduction may take place to form a methylhydrazine [Eq. (86)] (*27*). If a large excess of Grignard is taken, further substitution may then occur [Eq. (87)] (*27*).

$$R_2CN_2 + R'MgX \longrightarrow R_2C{=}NN(MgX)R' \xrightarrow{H_2O} R_2C{=}NNHR \tag{85}$$

$$(\text{Alkyl})MgX + CH_2N_2 \xrightarrow{H_2O} CH_3NHNH(\text{Alkyl}) \tag{86}$$

$$2\ PhMgBr + CH_2N_2 \xrightarrow{H_2O} H_2C(Ph)NHNHPh \tag{87}$$

Two iron complexes have been identified, resulting from the reaction of diphenyldiazomethane and $Fe_3(CO)_{12}$ or, by irradiation, with $Fe(CO)_5$. One is black and has been shown by X-ray methods to be a trinuclear iron complex (XIX) (*9*), while the other is an orange binuclear iron complex (XX (*8*). Analogous reactions were also carried out using di-*p*-tolyldiazomethane.

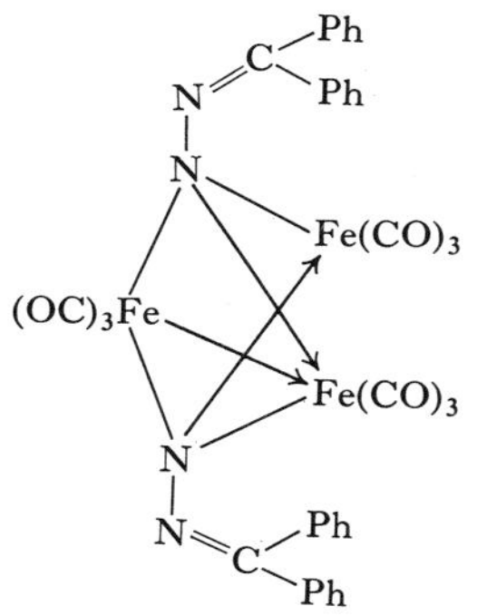

(XIX)

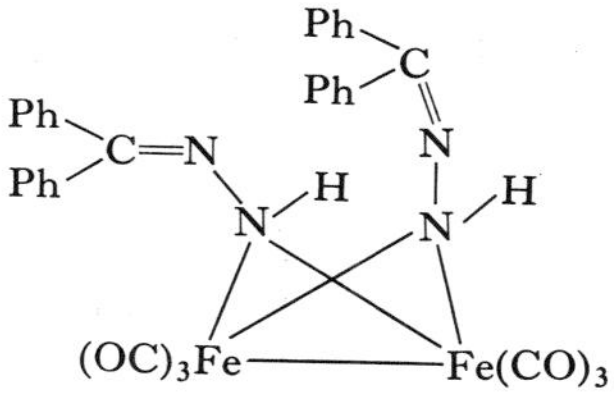

(XX)

IV

TABULAR SURVEY

A list of the known α-hetero-substituted diazoalkanes, together with appropriate references, is presented in Table I (see pp. 406–409). This is intended to be complete up to the end of September 1969. For each compound, also shown when available are (i) the preparative route, (ii) the b.p. or m.p., (iii) the position of the CN_2 asymmetric stretching vibration, and (iv) for compounds of type (I), the ^1H NMR chemical shift of the α-proton.

Compounds are arranged according to periodic groups of the hetero-element. Abbreviations used are Me for methyl, Et for ethyl, Pr for propyl, Bu for butyl, All for allyl, Ph for phenyl and Cp for π-cyclopentadienyl.

Table II (see pp. 416–420) provides a survey of the reactions of diazoalkanes and α-heterodiazoalkanes with compounds of metals and metalloids.

Tables I and II clearly refer to Sections II and III, respectively.

References

1. Almashi, L., Felmeri, I., and Gants, A., *Dokl. Akad. Nauk SSSR* **118**, 1121 (1958); *Chem. Abstr.* **52**, 12753 (1958).
2. Anselme, J. P., *J. Chem. Educ.* p. 596 (1966).
3. Applequist, D. E., and Babad, H., *J. Org. Chem.* **27**, 288 (1962).
4. Armstrong, R. K., *J. Org. Chem.* **31**, 618 (1966).
5. Arndt, F., *Angew. Chem.* **64**, 592 (1952).
6. Arndt, F., and Scholz, H., *Chem. Ber.* **66**, 1012 (1933).
7. Ashley-Smith, J., Clemens, J., Green, M., and Stone, F. G. A., *J. Organometal. Chem. (Amsterdam)* **17**, P23 (1969).

8. Bagga, M. M., Baikie, P. E., Mills, O. S., and Pauson, P. L., *Chem. Commun.* p. 1106 (1967).
9. Baikie, P. E., and Mills, O. S., *Chem. Commun.* p. 1228 (1967).
10. Bamford, W. R., and Stevens, T. S., *J. Chem. Soc.* p. 4735 (1952).
11. Bawn, C. E. H., and Ledwith, A., *Chem. & Ind.* (*London*) p. 1180 (1957).
12. Bawn, C. E. H., and Ledwith, A., *Chem. & Ind.* (*London*) p. 1329 (1958).
13. Bawn, C. E. H., and Ledwith, A., *Progr. Boron Chem.* **1**, 345 (1964).
14. Bawn, C. E. H., Ledwith, A., and Matthies, P., *J. Polymer. Sci.* **34**, 93 (1959).
15. Bawn, C. E. H., and Rhodes, T. B., *Trans. Faraday Soc.* **50**, 934 (1954).
16. Bestmann, H. J., Buckschewski, H., and Leube, H., *Chem. Ber.* **92**, 1345 (1959).
17. Bestmann, H. J., Klein, O., Göthlich, L., and Buckschewski, H., *Chem. Ber.* **96**, 2259 (1963).
18. Beutler, R., Zeeh, B., and Müller, E., *Chem. Ber.* **102**, 2636 (1969).
18a. Bogdanovic, B., Kroner, M., and Wilke, G., *Ann. Chem.* **699**, 1 (1966).
19. Braz, G. I., and Yakubovich, A. Y., *J. Gen. Chem.* (*USSR*) (*English Transl.*) **11**, 41 (1941); *Chem. Abstr.* **35**, 5459 (1941).
20. Brook, A. G., and Jones, P. F., *Can. J. Chem.* **47**, 4353 (1969); and unpublished observations (1970).
21. Brook, A. G., and Jones, P. F., *Chem. Commun.* p. 1324 (1969).
22. Buchner, E., *Chem. Ber.* **28**, 215 (1895).
23. Buchner, E., *Chem. Ber.* **28**, 218 (1895).
24. Buckley, G. D., Cross, L. H., and Ray, N. H., *J. Chem. Soc.* p. 2714 (1950).
25. Buckley, G. D., and Ray, N. H., *J. Chem. Soc.* p. 3701 (1952).
25a. Callot, H. J., and Johnson, A. W., *Chem. Commun.* p. 749 (1969).
25b. Caronna, G., and Sansone, B., *Atti 10th Congr. Intern. Chim., Rome, 1938* **3**, p. 77. Fac. Chim. Ind. Univ., Citta. Univ., Rome, 1939; *Chem. Abstr.* **34**, 980 (1940).
25c. Cardin, D. J., Cetinkaya, B., and Lappert, M. F., unpublished observations (1970).
26. Closs, G. L., and Coyle, J. J., *J. Am. Chem. Soc.* **87**, 4270 (1965).
27. Coleman, G. H., Gilman, H., Adams, C. E., and Pratt, P. E., *J. Org. Chem.* **3**, 99 (1938).
28. Cooke, J., Cullen, W. R., Green, M., and Stone, F. G. A., *Chem. Commun.* p. 170 (1968); *J. Chem. Soc., A* p. 1872 (1969).
29. Cookson, G. H., and Mann, F. G., *J. Chem. Soc.* p. 2895 (1949).
30. Cowell, G. W., and Ledwith, A., *Quart. Rev.* **24**, 119 (1970).
31. Davies, A. G., Hare, D. G., Khan, O. R., and Sikora, J., *Proc. Chem. Soc.* p. 172 (1961); *J. Chem. Soc.* p. 4461 (1963).
32. Diekmann, J., *J. Org. Chem.* **28**, 2933 (1963); **30**, 2272 (1965).
33. DoMinh, T., Font, J., and Strausz, O. P., *J. Am. Chem. Soc.* **90**, 1930 (1968).
34. DoMinh, T., Gunning, H. E., and Strausz, O. P., *J. Am. Chem. Soc.* **89**, 6785 (1967).
35. DoMinh, T., Strausz, O. P., and Gunning, H. E., *Tetrahedron Letters* p. 5237 (1968).
36. Dorion, G. H., Polchlopek, S. E., and Sheers, E. H., *Angew. Chem. Intern. Ed. Engl.* **3**, 447 (1964).
37. Dyakonov, I. A., and Vitenberg, A. G., *Proc. Acad. Sci.* (*USSR*), *Chem. Sect.* (*English Transl.*) **175**, 694 (1967); *J. Org. Chem. USSR* **3**, 1115 (1967).
38. Ebel, F., Brunner, R., and Mangelli, P., *Helv. Chim. Acta* **12**, 19 (1929).
39. Engberts, J. B. F. N., *Rec. Trav. Chim.* **97**, 992 (1968).
40. Engberts, J. B. F. N., and Strating, J., *Rec. Trav. Chim.* **83**, 733 (1964) and **84**, 942 (1965).
41. Engberts, J. B. F. N., Zuidema, G., Zwanenburg, B., and Strating, J., *Rec. Trav. Chim.* **88**, 641 (1969).

42. Engberts, J. B. F. N., and Zwanenburg, B., *Tetrahedron Letters* p. 831 (1967).
43. Engberts, J. B. F. N., and Zwanenburg, B., *Tetrahedron* **24**, 1737 (1968).
44. Fahr, E., *Ann. Chem.* **617**, 11 (1958); **638**, 1 (1961).
45. Farnum, D. G., *J. Org. Chem.* **28**, 870 (1963).
46. Feltzin, J., Restaino, A. J., and Mesrobian, R. B., *J. Am. Chem. Soc.* **77**, 206 (1955).
47. Fischer, E. O., *Angew. Chem.* **67**, 475 (1955).
48. Fischer, E. O., Hafner, W., and Stahl, H. O., *Z. Anorg. Allgem. Chem.* **282**, 47 (1956).
49. Freidlina, R. Kh., Nesmeyanov, A. N., and Tokarewa, F. A., *Chem. Ber.* **69**, 2019 (1936).
50. Gerhart, F., Schöllkopf, U., and Schumacher, H., *Angew. Chem. Intern. Ed. Engl.* **6**, 74 (1967).
51. Goh, S. H., Closs, L. E., and Closs, G. L., *J. Org. Chem.* **34**, 25 (1969).
52. Golodnikon, G. V., and Repinskaya, I. B., *J. Org. Chem. USSR* **1**, 210 (1965).
53. Goubeau, J., and Rohwedder, K. H., *Ann. Chem.* **604**, 168 (1957).
54. Green, M. L. H., Pratt, L., and Wilkinson, G., *J. Chem. Soc.* p. 3916 (1958).
55. Green, M. L. H., and Sanders, J. R., *Chem. Commun.* p. 956 (1967).
56. Grundmann, C., *Ann. Chem.* **536**, 29 (1938).
57. Hartzler, H. D., *Abstr. 155th Meeting Am. Chem. Soc., San Francisco, 1968* p. P205.
58. Hellerman, L., and Newman, M. D., *J. Am. Chem. Soc.* **54**, 2859 (1932).
59. Hieber, W., and Wagner, G., *Ann. Chem.* **618**, 24 (1958).
60. Hoberg, H., *Angew. Chem.* **73**, 114 (1961).
61. Hoberg, H., *Ann. Chem.* **656**, 1 (1962).
62. Hoberg, H., *Angew. Chem. Intern. Ed. Engl.* **4**, 1088 (1965).
63. Hoberg, H., *Ann. Chem.* **695**, 1 (1966).
64. Hodson, D., Holt, G., and Wall, D. K., *J. Chem. Soc., C* p. 2201 (1968).
65. Holter, D. J., and Stenberg, V. I., *Proc. N. Dakota Acad. Sci.* **17**, 31 (1963); *Chem. Abstr.* **60**, 5533 (1964).
66. Hooz, J., and Gunn, D. M., *Chem. Commun.* p. 139 (1969).
67. Hooz, J., and Gunn, D. M., *Tetrahedron Letters* p. 3455 (1969).
68. Hooz, J., and Gunn, D. M., *J. Am. Chem. Soc.* **91**, 6195 (1969).
69. Hooz, J., and Linke, S., *J. Am. Chem. Soc.* **90**, 5936 (1968).
70. Hooz, J., and Linke, S., *J. Am. Chem. Soc.* **90**, 6891 (1968).
70a. Hooz, J., and Morrison, G. F., *Can. J. Chem.* **48**, 868 (1970).
71. Horner, L., and Hoffmann, H., *Angew. Chem.* **68**, 473 (1956).
72. Horner, L., Hoffmann, H., Ertel, H., and Klahre, G., *Tetrahedron Letters* p. 9 (1961).
73. House, H. O., Grubbs, E. J., and Gannon, W. F., *J. Am. Chem. Soc.* **82**, 4099 (1960).
74. Huisgen, R., *Angew. Chem.* **67**, 439 (1955).
75. Huisgen, R., *Angew. Chem. Intern. Ed. Engl.* **2**, 565 (1963).
75a. Johnson, A. W., and Mahendran, M., unpublished observations (1970); Johnson, A. W., *Pure Appl. Chem.* (*London*), in press (1971).
76. Johnson, W. S., Neeman, M., and Birkeland, S. P., *Tetrahedron Letters* p. 1 (1960).
77. Johnson, W. S., Neeman, M., Birkeland, S. P., and Fedoruk, N. A., *J. Am. Chem. Soc.* **84**, 989 (1962).
77a. Jugelt, W., and Drahn, K., *Tetrahedron* **25**, 5585 (1969).
77b. Jugelt, W., and Schmidt, D., *Tetrahedron* **25**, 5569 (1969).
78. Kabachnik, M. I., and Gilyarov, V. A., *Dokl. Akad. Nauk SSSR* **106**, 473 (1956); *Chem. Abstr.* **50**, 13723 (1956).
79. Kantor, S. W., and Osthoff, R. C., *J. Am. Chem. Soc.* **75**, 931 (1953).
80. Kaufmann, K. D., Auräth, B., Träger, P., and Rühlmann, K., *Tetrahedron Letters* p. 4973 (1968).

81. Kaufmann, K. D., and Rühlmann, K., *Z. Chem.* **8**, 262 (1968).
82. Kirmse, W., and Horn, K., *Chem. Ber.* **100**, 2698 (1967).
83. Kirmse, W., Kapps, M., and Hager, R. B., *Chem. Ber.* **99**, 2855 (1966).
84. Klages, F., and Bott, K., *Chem. Ber.* **97**, 735 (1964).
85. Klages, F., Bott, K., and Hegenberg, P., *Angew. Chem. Intern. Ed. Engl.* **1**, 603 (1962).
86. Knox, R. J., *Chem. Soc. Autumn Meetimg, Keele, 1968* p. A32.
87. Kopecky, K. R., Hammond, G. S., and Leermakers, P. A., *J. Am. Chem. Soc.* **83**, 2397 (1961); **84**, 1015 (1962).
88. Kramer, K. A. W., and Wright, A. N., *Angew. Chem.* **74**, 468 (1962); *Tetrahedron Letters* p. 1095 (1962).
89. Kramer, K. A. W., and Wright, A. N., *J. Chem. Soc.* p. 3604 (1963).
90. Kramer, K. A. W., and Wright, A. N., *Chem. Ber.* **96**, 1877 (1963).
91. Kreutzkamp, N., Schmidt-Samoa, E., and Herberg, A. K., *Angew. Chem. Intern. Ed. Engl.* **4**, 1078 (1965).
92. Lappert, M. F., and Lorberth, J., *Chem. Commun.* p. 836, (1967).
93. Lappert, M. F., Lorberth, J., and Poland, J. S. *J. Chem. Soc. A* 2954 (1970).
94. Lappert, M. F., and Poland, J. S., *Chem. Commun.* p. 156 (1969).
95. Lappert, M. F., and Poland, J. S., *Chem. Commun.* p. 1061 (1969).
96. Lappert, M. F., and Poland, J. S., unpublished observations (1969).
97. Ledwith, A., *Chem. & Ind.* (*London*) p. 1310 (1956).
98. Ledwith, A., and Friedrich, E. C., *J. Chem. Soc.* p. 504 (1964).
99. Ledwith, A., and Phillips, L., *J. Chem. Soc.* p. 5969 (1965).
100. Leitch, L. C., Gagnon, P. E., and Cambron, A., *Can. J. Res.* **28B**, 256 (1950); *Chem. Abstr.* **45**, 2415 (1951).
101. Lesbre, M., and Buisson, R., *Bull. Soc. Chim. France* p. 1204 (1957).
102. Leusen, A. M. van, Mulder, R. J., and Strating, J., *Rec. Trav. Chim.* **86**, 225 (1967); *Tetrahedron Letters* p. 543 (1964).
103. Leusen, A. M. van, Mulder, R. J., and Strating, J., *Tetrahedron Letters* p. 3057 (1967).
104. Leusen, A. M. van, Smid, P. M., and Strating, J., *Tetrahedron Letters* p. 337 (1965).
105. Leusen, A. M. van, and Strating, J., *Rec. Trav. Chim.* **84**, 140 (1965).
106. Leusen, A. M. van, and Strating, J., *Rec. Trav. Chim.* **84**, 151 (1965).
107. Loose, A., *J. Prakt. Chem.* **79**, 507 (1909).
108. Lorberth, J., *J. Organometal. Chem.* (*Amsterdam*) **15**, 251 (1968).
109. Mango, F. D., and Dvoretzky, I., *J. Am. Chem. Soc.* **88**, 1654 (1966).
110. Matsumoto, K., Odaira, Y., and Tsutsumi, S., *Chem. Commun.* p. 832 (1968).
111. Mazac, C. J., and Simons, J. W., *J. Am. Chem. Soc.* **90**, 2484 (1968); *J. Phys. Chem.* **72**, 749 (1968).
112. Meerwein, H., *Angew. Chem.* **60**, 78 (1948).
113. Meerwein, H., and Hinz, G., *Ann. Chem.* **484**, 1 (1930).
113a. Moritani, I., Yamamoto, Y., and Konishi, H., *Chem. Commun.* p. 1457 (1969).
114. Moser, W. R., *J. Am. Chem. Soc.* **91**, 1135 and 1141 (1969).
115. Müller, E., Bauer, M., and Rundel, W., *Tetrahedron Letters* p. 30 (1960).
116. Müller, E., Beutler, R., and Zeeh, B., *Ann. Chem.* **719**, 72 (1968).
117. Müller, E., and Disselhoff, H., *Naturwissenschaften* **21**, 661 (1933); *Ann. Chem.* **512**, 250 (1934).
118. Müller, E., and Fricke, H., *Ann. Chem.* **661**, 38 (1963).
119. Müller, E., and Huber-Emden, H., *Ann. Chem.* **649**, 70 (1961).
120. Müller, E., Huber-Emden, H., and Rundel, W., *Ann. Chem.* **623**, 34 (1959).
121. Müller, E., Kästner, P., Beutler, R., Rundel, W., Suhr, H., and Zeeh, B., *Ann. Chem.* **713**, 87 (1968).

122. Müller, E., and Kreutzmann, W., *Ann. Chem.* **512**, 264 (1934).
123. Müller, E., and Ludsteck, D., *Chem. Ber.* **87**, 1887 (1954).
124. Müller, E., and Ludsteck, D., *Chem. Ber.* **88**, 921 (1955).
125. Müller, E., and Rundel, W., *Chem. Ber.* **88**, 917 (1955).
126. Müller, E., and Rundel, W., *Chem. Ber.* **89**, 1065 (1956).
127. Müller, E., and Rundel, W., *Chem. Ber.* **90**, 1299 and 1302 (1957).
128. Müller, E., and Rundel, W., *Chem. Ber.* **90**, 2673 (1957); **91**, 466 (1958).
129. Müller, E., and Rundel, W., *Angew. Chem.* **70**, 105 (1958).
129a. Nasini, A. G., and Trossarelli, L., *J. Polymer Sci. C. Polymer Symp.* **4**, 167 (1964).
130. Nasini, A. G., Trossarelli, L., and Saini, G., *Makromol. Chem.* **44**, 550 (1961).
131. Neeman, M., Caserio, M. C., Roberts, J. D., and Johnson, W. S., *Tetrahedron* **6**, 36 (1959).
132. Nesmeyanov, A. N., and Powch, G. S., *Chem. Ber.* **67**, 971 (1934).
133. Nesmeyanov, A. N., and Reutov, O. A., *Uch. Zap., Mosk. Gos. Univ., Org. Khim.* **175**, 55 (1956); *Chem. Abstr.* **51**, 9670 (1957).
134. Nesmeyanov, A. N., and Segalevich, A. E., *Bull. Acad. Sci. URSS, Classe Sci. Chim.* p. 8 (1942); *Chem. Abstr.* **37**, 3055 (1943).
135. Newman, M. S., and Beal, P. F., *J. Am. Chem. Soc.* **72**, 5161 (1950).
136. Nozaki, H., Moriuti, S., Yamabe, M., and Noyori, R., *Tetrahedron Letters* p. 59 (1966).
137. Nozaki, H., Takaya, H., Moriuti, S., and Noyori, R., *Tetrahedron* **24**, 3655 (1968).
137a. Pasto, D. J., and Wojtkowski, P. W., *Tetrahedron Letters*, p. 215 (1970).
138. Pechmann, H. von, *Chem. Ber.* **28**, 855 (1895).
139. Petrov, K. A., Sokolskii, G. A., and Neimysheva, A. A., *J. Gen. Chem. USSR* (*English Transl.*) **27**, 855 (1957); *Chem. Abstr.* **51**, 16334 (1957).
140. Petzold, G., and Henning, H. G., *Naturwissenschaften* **54**, 469 (1967).
141. Pfeiffer, P., and Jäger, H., *Chem. Ber.* **80**, 1 (1947).
142. Pfeiffer, P., Schulze-Bentrop, R., La Roche, K. H., and Schmitz, E., *Chem. Ber.* **85**, 232 (1952).
143. Phillips, D. D., *J. Am. Chem. Soc.* **76**, 5385 (1954).
144. Piper, T. S., and Wilkinson, G., *Naturwissenschaften* **42**, 625 (1955); *J. Inorg. & Nucl. Chem.* **3**, 104 (1956).
145. Plets, V. M., *J. Gen. Chem. USSR* (*English Transl.*) **7**, 270 (1937); *Chem. Abstr.* **31**, 4965 (1937).
146. Poshkus, A. C., and Herweh, J. E., *J. Org. Chem.* **27**, 2700 (1962).
147. Regitz, M., *Chem. Ber.* **98**, 36 (1965).
148. Regitz, M., *Angew. Chem. Intern. Ed. Engl.* **6**, 733 (1967).
149. Regitz, M., and Anschütz, W., *Chem. Ber.* **102**, 2216 (1969).
150. Regitz, M., Anschütz, W., Bartz, W., and Liedhegener, A., *Tetrahedron Letters* p. 3171 (1968).
151. Regitz, M., Anschütz, W., and Liedhegener, A., *Chem. Ber.* **101**, 3734 (1968).
152. Regitz, M., and Geelhaar, H. J., *Chem. Ber.* **102**, 1743 (1969).
152a. Regitz, M., Scherer, H., and Anschütz, W., *Tetrahedron Letters*, p. 753 (1970).
153. Rüchardt, C., and Schrauzer, G. N., *Chem. Ber.* **93**, 1840 (1960).
154. Rundel, W., and Kästner, P., *Ann. Chem.* **686**, 88 (1965).
154a. Saegusa, T., Ito, Y., Kobayashi, S., Hirota, K., and Shimizu, T., *Tetrahedron Letters* p. 6131 (1966).
154b. Saegusa, T., Ito, Y., Kobayashi, S., Hirota, K., and Shimizu, T., *J. Org. Chem.* **33**, 544 (1968).
154c. Saegusa, T., Ito, Y., Shimizu, T., and Kobayashi, S., *Bull. Chem. Soc. Japan* **42**, 3535 (1969).

155. Saegusa, T., Tomita, S., and Ueshima, T., *Bull. Chem. Soc. Japan* **41**, 1005 (1968).
156. Saini, G., and Nasini, A. G., *Gazz. Chim. Ital.* **87**, 342 (1957); *Chim. Ind.* (*Milan*) **40**, 467 (1958).
157. Saunders, B. C., Stacey, G. J., Wild, F., and Wilding, I. G. E., *J. Chem. Soc.* 699 (1948).
157a. Scherer, O. J., and Schmidt, M., *Z. Naturforsch.* **20b**, 1009 (1965).
157b. Schöllkopf, U., and Frasnelli, H., *Angew. Chem. Int. Ed. Engl.* **9**, 301 (1970).
158. Schöllkopf, U., Gerhart, F., Reetz, M., Frasnelli, H., and Schumacher, H., *Ann. Chem.* **716**, 204 (1968).
158a. Schöllkopf, U., Hoppe, D., Rieber, N., and Jacobi, V., *Ann. Chem.* **730**, 1 (1970).
159. Schöllkopf, U., and Markusch, P., *Tetrahedron Letters* p. 6199 (1966).
160. Schöllkpf, U., and Markusch, P., *Angew. Chem. Intern. Ed. Engl.* **8**, 612 (1969).
161. Schöllkopf, U., and Rieber, N., *Angew. Chem. Intern. Ed. Engl.* **6**, 261 (1967).
162. Schöllkopf, U., and Rieber, N., *Angew. Chem. Intern. Ed. Engl.* **6**, 884 (1967).
163. Schöllkopf, U., and Rieber, N., *Chem. Ber.* **102**, 488 (1969).
164. Schöllkopf, U., and Schäfer, H., *Angew. Chem. Intern. Ed. Engl.* **4**, 358 (1965).
165. Schöllkopf, U., Tonne, P., Schäfer, H., and Markusch, P., *Ann. Chem.* **722**, 45 (1969).
166. Schöllkopf, U., and Wiskott, E., *Ann. Chem.* **694**, 44 (1966).
167. Schönberg, A., Schutz, O., and Peter, J., *Chem. Ber.* **62**, 1663 (1929).
168. Schönberg, A., and Stolpp, T., *Chem. Ber.* **63**, 3102 (1930).
169. Seyferth, D., *Chem. Rev.* **55**, 1155 (1955).
170. Seyferth, D., and Cross, R. J., unpublished results cited by R. J. Cross, *Organometal. Chem. Rev.* **2**, 97 (1967).
171. Seyferth, D., Dow, A. W., Menzel, H., and Flood, T. C., *J. Am. Chem. Soc.* **90**, 1080 (1968).
172. Seyferth, D., and Hetflejš, J., *J. Organometal. Chem.* (*Amsterdam*) **11**, 253 (1968).
173. Seyferth, D., Hilbert, P., and Marmor, R. S., *J. Am. Chem. Soc.* **18**, 4811 (1967).
174. Seyferth, D., and Rochow, E. G., *J. Am. Chem. Soc.* **77**, 907 (1955).
175. Seyferth, D., and Rochow, E. G., *J. Am. Chem. Soc.* **77**, 1302 (1955).
176. Shaw, R. A., *J. Chem. Soc.* p. 2831 (1957).
177. Simons, J. W., and Mazac, C. J., *Can. J. Chem.* **45**, 1717 (1967).
178. Smith, P. A. S., "Open Chain Nitrogen Compounds," Vol. 2. Benjamin, New York, 1966.
179. Staudinger, H., Anthes, E., and Pfenninger, F., *Chem. Ber.* **49**, 1928 (1916).
180. Staudinger, H., Gaule, A., and Siegwart, J., *Helv. Chim. Acta* **4**, 212 (1921).
181. Staudinger, H., Hammet, L., and Siegwart, J., *Helv. Chim. Acta* **4**, 228 (1921).
182. Staudinger, H., and Luscher, G., *Helv. Chim. Acta* **5**, 75 (1922).
183. Staudinger, H., and Meyer, J., *Helv. Chim. Acta* **2**, 619 (1919).
184. Staudinger, H., and Pfenninger, F., *Chem. Ber.* **49**, 1941 (1916).
185. Strating, J., and van Leusen, A. M., *Rec. Trav. Chim.* **81**, 966 (1962).
186. Strating, J., and Reitsema, J., *Rec. Trav. Chim.* **85**, 421 (1966).
187. Takebayashi, M., Ibata, T., Kohara, H., and Kim, B. H., *Bull. Chem. Soc. Japan* **40**, 2392 (1967).
188. Thiele, J., and Meyer, C., *Chem. Ber.* **29**, 961 (1896).
189. Turner, H. S., *Chem. & Ind.* (*London*) p. 1405 (1958).
190. Werner, H., and Richards, J. H., *J. Am. Chem. Soc.* **90**, 4976 (1968).
191. Witenburg, A., Dyakonov, I. A., and Zindel, A., *J. Org. Chem. USSR* **2**, 1516 (1966).
192. Wittig, G., and Schlosser, M., *Tetrahedron* **18**, 1023 (1962).
193. Wittig, G., and Schwarzenbach, K., *Angew. Chem.* **71**, 652 (1959).

194. Wittig, G., and Schwarzenbach, K., *Ann. Chem.* **650**, 1 (1961).
195. Wittig, G., and Wingler, F., *Chem. Ber.* **97**, 2146 (1964).
196. Wolfrom, M. L., and Miller, J. B., *J. Am. Chem. Soc.* **80**, 1678 (1958).
197. Wright, A. N., Kramer, K. A. W., and Steel, G., *Nature* **199**, 903 (1963).
198. Yakubovich, A. Y., and Ginsburg, V. A., *Dokl. Akad. Nauk SSSR* **73**, 957 (1950); *Chem. Abstr.* **45**, 2857 (1951).
199. Yakubovich, A. Y., and Ginsburg, V. A., *Usp. Khim.* **20**, 734 (1951).
200. Yakubovich, A. Y., and Ginsburg, V. A., *J. Gen. Chem. USSR* (*English Transl.*) **22**, 1575 (1952); *Chem. Abstr.* **47**, 9254 (1953).
201. Yakubovich, A. Y., and Ginsburg, V. A., *J. Gen. Chem. USSR* (*E[illegible]lish Transl.*) **22**, 1821 (1952); *Chem. Abstr.* **47**, 9256 (1953).
202. Yakubovich, A. Y., Ginsburg, V. A., and Makarov, S. P., *Dokl. Akad. Nauk SSSR* **71**, 303 (1950); *Chem. Abstr.* **44**, 8320 (1950).
203. Yakubovich, A. Y., and Makarov, S. P., *J. Gen. Chem. USSR* (*English Transl.*) **22**, 1569 (1952); *Chem. Abstr.* **47**, 8010 (1953).
204. Yakubovich, A. Y., Makarov, S. P., and Gavrilov, G. I., *J. Gen. Chem. USSR* (*English Transl.*) **22**, 1827 (1952); *Chem. Abstr.* **47**, 9257 (1953).
205. Yakubovich, A. Y., Makarov, S. P., Ginsburg, V. A., Gavrilov, G. I., and Merkulova, E. N., *Dokl. Akad. Nauk SSSR* **72**, 69 (1950); *Chem. Abstr.* **45**, 2856 (1951).
206. Yakubovich, A. Y., Merkulova, E. N., Makarov, S. P., and Gavrilov, G. I., *J. Gen. Chem. USSR* (*English Transl.*) **22**, 2115 (1952); *Chem. Abstr.* **47**, 9257 (1953).
207. Yates, P., *J. Am. Chem. Soc.* **74**, 5376 (1952).
208. Yates, P., and Garneau, F. X., *Tetrahedron Letters* p. 71 (1967).
209. Yates, P., Shapiro, B. L., Yoda, N., and Fugger, J., *J. Am. Chem. Soc.* **79**, 5756 (1957).
210. Zerner, E., *Monatsh. Chem.* **34**, 1609 and 1631 (1914).
211. Zollinger, H., "Azo and Diazo Chemistry," Wiley (Interscience), New York, 1961.
212. Zwanenburg, B., and Engberts, J. B. F. N., *Rec. Trav. Chim.* **84**, 165 (1965).
213. Zwanenburg, B., Engberts, J. B. F. N., and Strating, J., *Tetrahedron Letters* p. 547 (1964).

Author Index

Numbers in parentheses are reference numbers and indicate that an author's work is referred to although his name is not cited in the text. Numbers in italic show the page on which the complete reference is listed.

A

C

D

E

G

L

Q

R

S

T

Y

Subject Index

Note: In general, for reference to organometallic compounds, *see* heading "Organo-*element* compounds."

G

H

I

L

M

P

U

V

W

Y

Z

Cumulative List of Contributors

Cumulative List of Titles